PELICAN BOOKS

A310

THE ETRUSCANS

M. PALLOTTINO

# THE ETRUSCANS

BY M. PALLOTTINO

*Professor of Etruscology
and Italic Archaeology in the
University of Rome*

TRANSLATED FROM THE ITALIAN BY

J. CREMONA

900
PA

PENGUIN BOOKS

Penguin Books Ltd, Harmondsworth, Middlesex
U.S.A: Penguin Books Inc., 3300 Clipper Mill Road, Baltimore 11, Md
CANADA: Penguin Books (Canada) Ltd, 178 Norseman Street,
Toronto 18, Ontario
AUSTRALIA: Penguin Books Pty Ltd, 762 Whitehorse Road,
Mitcham, Victoria
SOUTH AFRICA: Penguin Books (S.A.) Pty Ltd, Gibraltar House,
Regent Road, Sea Point, Cape Town

—

First Italian edition, 1942
Second Italian edition, 1947
Third Italian edition, 1954
Published by Penguin Books 1955
Reprinted 1956

Made and printed in Great Britain
by Hunt, Barnard & Co, Ltd, Aylesbury
Collogravure plates by Harrison & Sons

# CONTENTS

## PART ONE

*The Etruscans and their place in the History of Italy
and of the Mediterranean*

## PART TWO

*Aspects of the Civilization of Etruria*

# LIST OF TEXT FIGURES

# LIST OF PLATES

Photographs originating from commercial sources and from the British Museum are duly acknowledged in the list below. The remaining plates have been obtained from the photographic archives of the Institute of Archaeology in the University of Rome, the Museo Nazionale di Villa Giulia in Rome, the Musei di Roma (Sezione Antica), the Sopraintendenza alle Antichità di Bologna and from the author. Though the majority of the photographs in the Italian third edition have been incorporated here, it has not been possible to include them all; on the other hand, a substantial number of photographs of objects kept in the British Museum have been added as it was felt that they may be of especial interest to British readers. I should like to take this opportunity to express my warmest thanks to Mr D. E. L. Haynes of the Department of Greek and Roman Antiquities, British Museum, for his help and advice in choosing a representative selection.

THE TRANSLATOR

1 (A) Tumulus in the necropolis of Caere (Cerveteri). See *Studi Etruschi* I, 1927, pp. 157 ff. (*Phot. Alinari*).

(B) Gate of Etruscan type set in the third century B.C. walls of the town of Falerii Novi, now S. Maria di Fàlleri (*Phot. Alinari*).

2 (A) Sepulchral urn and lid in the form of a temple, from Chiusi: a winged goddess is seated in front and two panthers may be seen perched on the ridge of the roof (*Phot. British Museum*).

(B) Figure of deceased woman on the lid of the Gualandi Canopic ossuary (*Chiusi, Museo Civico*). This ossuary, belonging to c. 600 B.C., is a good example of the earliest phase of Etruscan plastic art.

3 (A) Bi-conical cinerary urn in dark terracotta with geometrical decorative pattern and a single handle, covered with a crested bronze helmet: a typical product of the 'Villanovan' culture (eighth century B.C.). This urn was found in Tarquinia and is now in the Museo Archeologico, Florence. See *Notizie degli Scavi*, 1907, p. 63.

(B) Naval battle scene decorating an Etruscan vase of the first half of the sixth century B.C. found at Cerveteri. The scene may have been inspired by contemporary events and may serve to illustrate the contests between Greeks, Etruscans, and

Carthaginians for the supremacy of the Western seas (*Paris, Louvre*). See E. POTTIER, *Vases antiques du Louvre*, 1897, D 150, p. 40, plate 34.

4 (A) Lid of a small terracotta urn representing the dead man and a female figure, possibly his wife. This group is a good illustration of the original tendencies towards expressivity in Etruscan art (*Volterra, Museo Guarnacci*).

(B) Lid of urn from Volterra, with the figure of the deceased man. The man may be seen wearing a plaited wreath and holding a *phiale omphalos* in his left hand and in his right, a drinking horn ending in the fore-part of a caparisoned horse. (*Phot. British Museum.*)

5 A master-piece of Ionic Etruscan art: detail from the Apollo of Veii (*c.* 500 B.C.), now in the Museum of Villa Giulia in Rome. See M. PALLOTTINO, *La scuola di Vulca*, 1945, and in *Archeologia Classica*, II, 1950, pp. 163 ff.

6 (A) Lid of sarcophagus from Tarquinia (Tomb of the Triclinium), belonging to the early fifth century B.C. (*Phot. British Museum*).

(B) Alabaster statue of woman holding a bronze gilded dove in her left hand; Vulci (Polledrara Tomb), first quarter of the sixth century B.C. (*Phot. British Museum*).

7 Two yoked winged horses in painted terracotta from the pediment of the 'Ara della Regina' at Tarquinia (fourth-third century B.C.), a sample of Etrusco-Italic art under classical influence (*Tarquinia, Museo Nazionale*). See P. ROMANELLI in *Le Arti* I, 1938-9, p. 436, plates CXXXI ff. and in *Notizie degli Scavi*, 1948, pp. 254 ff. (*Phot. Anderson*).

8 (A) Terracotta statuette of a woman seated on a block, found at Cerveteri (*Phot. British Museum*).

(B) Archaic female mask, taken from an antefix, Cerveteri (*Phot. British Museum*).

9 (A) Young woman's head in terracotta, showing Hellenistic influence (*Vatican, Museo Etrusco Gregoriano*).

(B) Daemon's mask in terracotta (*Orvieto, Faina Collection*).

10 Sepulchral urn in the form of a standing man of life-size. The body is hollowed to receive the ashes, the head and neck serve as stopper; from Chianciano, near Chiusi (*Phot. British Museum*).

11 (A) Two antefixes mounted on the cornice of a roof (restored from fragments); from Lanuvio (Civita Lavinia) (*Phot. British Museum*).

# FOREWORD

In spite of the wealth of means of study at our disposal, the sharp weapon of scientific method and the intelligent toil of research workers, far too many problems still remain unsolved concerning the history and culture of ancient peoples.

What in fact do we know of the ethnic origins of those builders of pyramids, the ancient Egyptians, and what is the true chronology of the oldest landmarks in their history? How and whence was the Phoenician alphabet born, mother of all modern writing? Up to what point are the poems of Homer the work of a single artist and the mirror of true historical figures and events? When and why did the ancient inhabitants of Malta raise the prodigious piles of their many megalithic 'temples'?

Great questions, chosen at random from among a great number – some of them going back many a long year. There is no need to conceal the fact that modern science has not yet been able to provide final answers to these questions, answers that would be accepted unanimously by all scholars.

Why is it then that so much interest, both expert and lay, focuses with ever-renewed vigour upon the problems of the origins and the language of the ancient Etruscans, almost as if they were the most fascinating 'mystery', the 'sphinx' *par excellence* of all ancient history?

One of the reasons is the following: the Etruscan 'mystery' is not merely one of science's curiosities, or the appeal of a world that is far from our own, both in time and spirit. It is the mystery of the budding of a civilization that was the first to flourish on Italian soil, at the very roots of the history of Rome and, hence, of western civilization. At the very time when love for research on the primitive life of peoples appears to be so profoundly active, we see in the Etruscan 'mystery' a key to the question of Italic origins and the foundation stone on which to base the difficult reconstruction of Italy's most distant past.

This lively and deep-felt interest of the public for the history and civilization of the Etruscans deserves the scholar's attention. Naturally, neither analytical research nor the slow and painstaking reconstructions found in scientific essays can satisfy the widespread and impatient desire to know and understand. But, at the same time, most works of vulgarization, by generalizing and simplifying the complex structures built by science, fail to satisfy the demands of those – by far the most numerous – who do not care to be left at the temple's door but wish to be led inside to the very centre of the problem, to the heated and troubled terrain of scientific controversy.

It is for them especially that this book is meant: for its author has striven to keep close both to matter and method and has even, in a few cases, put forward what he hopes may be new contributions to the problems under discussion. It attempts to be neither a work or analysis nor a rigid and impartial exposition; differing in this respect from such well-known monographs as K. O. Müller and W. Deecke's *Die Etrusker* (1877), P. Ducati's *Etruria antica* (1927), or B. Nogara's *Gli Etruschi e la loro civiltà* (1934), it seeks to give an up-to-date interpretation of the people and of the chief problems concerning them, an interpretation striving towards serenity and sound documentation but none the less personal and vivid. A number of obscure aspects of the civilization of Etruria and firm convictions which, till now, have only cautiously been put forward by the author in other works will here be brought into the full light of day and weighed and defended with tenacity and wealth of argument.

Amongst these, first and foremost comes the thesis of the autochtony of the Etruscans: a nation which, as a historical entity, became formed and defined in Italy, between the banks of the Tiber and Arno, even though many ethnic and cultural contributions may have reached it from near or far off regions, especially during the earliest stages of its development. This thesis is now set upon a scientific footing and its acceptance no longer requires an act of faith, though the whole problem has too often been obscured by that anxious search for relationships and provenances that contributes little to the study of the dawn of Italian history. It is a thesis that stands out particularly against the over-simplified myth of a migration from the east, bag and baggage, of the first

Etruscans: a myth born out of the comparison of ancient literary testimonies with archaeological clues made before more recent researches and excavations had taken place, but, unfortunately, a myth still widely spread – as undisputed and acquired fact – beyond the confines of etruscology, even to the pages of school books.

The bibliographical references will be found in notes gathered at the end of each chapter and are limited to the scope of this volume. They are not systematic in character if we except works of a general nature embracing the whole of our discipline or its major sections. For the remainder, references try to furnish material for discussion and the checking of more controversial data, concentrating especially upon little known or very recent works not included in the etruscological manuals of Ducati or Nogara. This policy, of proved utility not only to the more serious reader and the student, but also to workers in allied fields, has been further stressed in this third edition of the work, a considerably expanded version of its two predecessors.

MASSIMO PALLOTTINO

## Note to the English Translation

A CERTAIN difficulty was experienced in rendering into English many of the place-names of Etruria. We have generally referred to Etruscan towns by their Latin name, usually the best known in this country (e.g. Caere, Vulci, Veii, etc.); the modern Italian name of the site is often added in brackets for reference if necessary. At the risk of being taxed with inconsistency, we have used modern Italian names for those Etruscan centres whose light never dwindled in the past two millennia and whose Italian names are therefore more familiar to the English reader (e.g. Perugia, Fiesole, Volterra, etc.). Reference to the map on p. 107 (where both names are given in every case) should settle any difficulty that may arise.

J. CREMONA

# PART ONE

*The Etruscans and their place in the history
of Italy and of the Mediterranean*

# CHAPTER ONE

# ITALY AT THE DAWN OF HISTORY

### The Myth of the Northern Invasions

WHEN dealing with the legends of antiquity on the foundation of Rome, Theodore Mommsen, the father of historical
philology, wrote, 'History must first make a clean sweep of
these fables which, though purporting to be history, are
nothing more than somewhat simple improvisations.'[1]
Little did he dream that the cumbersome archaeological and
linguistic elaborations of modern science were soon to build
up, in attempting to explain the origin of the Italic peoples,
a whole series of reconstructions and hypotheses no less
fabulous or fantastic than those originating in ancient pious
traditions or in the fertile imaginations of mythographers,
even though they were buttressed by the would-be excellence of method and authority of undisputed scholars.

Much blame has been laid upon antiquity for inventing
such founder-heroes as Romulus and Remus, for creating
out of sheer fancy such peoples as the Aborigines or the
Pelasgians. What ought we to say then of a modern science
that created the Villanovans on the mere basis that certain
primitive peoples in Italy had in common a certain type of
cinerary urn, discovered for the first time at Villanova in
Aemilia? or of a science that believed for a long time in the
existence of an original Italic language because of certain
features Latin had in common with Umbrian and Oscan,
whereas the unity of Italic peoples was in point of fact only
realized as the result of the cohabitation of Indo-Europeans
in Italy and of the spread of Latin? or, again, of a science
that literally invented an Indo-European civilization in

Italy, whereas the concept of Indo-Europeanism is a purely linguistic one, in no way reflected (as far as we can say at the present moment) by manifestations or changes of culture? All these theories, however sketchy or absurd they may appear in the light of the latest advances of Etruscan studies, have nevertheless been current for many decades and exhibited a dogmatism verging at times on intolerance. They have left so deep a mark on research that even to-day, when bringing forward new concepts to replace the old, we unconsciously tend to use the terms and expressions which they created.

Is the fact that nineteenth-century science substituted its own 'myths' for the myths of antiquity a sufficient reason for too severe a judgement on our part? The youthful ardour of research-workers in a completely new field, where the last mists of eighteenth-century baroque learning were fast melting away; the possession of a new weapon – method – believed to be infallible; their faith in progress and their contempt for the intellectual activities of the past; all these causes explain, if they do not justify, the complacent attachment felt for the first results obtained and a certain intolerance in their attitude. Nor must we forget that, from many points of view, everything had still to be sorted, to be classified. It would be ungracious to complain of the makeshift plank that first enabled us to cross the river, though now we can, and must, build a far stronger and better bridge.

When a clean sweep had been made of the complicated ethnographic legends about primitive Italy inherited from classical times, historians and archaeologists of the end of the last century were faced with the following problems: when, and how, did the Indo-European peoples come to Italy? by what ethnic changes can the successive cultures revealed by Italian prehistory be explained?

As was only natural, the answers to these questions soon

led to an attempt to reconcile linguistic and archaeological facts within a single, all-embracing synthesis. It is worth recalling that, in linguistics, the concept of Indo-European unity, heroically fought for and consolidated during the nineteenth century, implied an original close relationship of peoples dispersed in historical times, such as the Celtic, Germanic, Italic, Greek, Slav, Armenian, Iranian, and Indian peoples. This in its turn implied an original point of departure and a particular moment of arrival in the various regions they are known to have inhabited in historic times. The arrival of a language could only signify the arrival of a people. Hence the idea of vast prehistoric migrations on the lines of the barbarian migrations at the time of the decline of the Roman Empire (with this important difference, that the Germanic peoples that spread over Europe and the Mediterranean world did in fact impose their language only in the British Isles and in a few marginal territories of the Empire). Hence again the concept of an 'Italic' invasion of prehistoric Italy.

On the other hand, prehistoric archaeology had at the same time made sufficient progress to recognize the existence of successive phases of culture. These came to be known as the palaeolithic (or chipped stone) age, the neolithic (or polished stone) age, the bronze age, and the iron age, the latter immediately preceding historical times. The then current method of chronological classification was of a typological and evolutionary nature, according to which the internal development of types of objects such as instruments, vases, weapons, and metal *fibulae* reflects a regular succession of periods common to the whole cultural area under consideration. A Swedish scholar, Oscar Montelius, after studying prehistoric remains of all kinds and particularly material found in tombs, succeeded in classifying the most recent phase of Italian prehistory into a 'bronze age' comprising four periods and an 'iron age' comprising six![2]

The first appearance of a bronze culture in Italy (occurring at the end of the neolithic stage when copper weapons and instruments were already in use, and hence labelled 'aeneolithic', 'cuprolithic', or 'chalcolithic') was assigned to the beginning of the second millennium B.C. and took the form of the Po valley *terremare* – prehistoric settlements built on palisades and surrounded by an embankment and a ditch to protect them from flood-waters. A connexion was seen between the *terremare* and a few rather meagre tombs that showed evidence of cremation as a funeral rite. The fact that the *terremare* were an isolated phenomenon, limited to northern Italy, and related structurally to the pile-dwelling system adopted by the prehistoric inhabitants of the Alpine lakes, the appearance of the cremation rite in neolithic tombs across the Alps (in France and Germany), the affinities between the *terramara* and the bronze cultures of Central Europe, all favoured the hypothesis that the bronze culture was introduced into Italy from over the Alps. This hypothesis appeared to be an historical and cultural reality of fundamental importance in the development of Italian prehistory, and it seemed obviously to indicate to scholars such as Gaetano Chierici, Wolfgang Helbig, and Luigi Pigorini, that the Indo-Europeans, i.e. the invading 'Italic' tribes, arrived in the peninsula as an already constituted people.[3]

This thesis, labelled 'Pigorinian', after its keenest and most famous exponent, acted as a keystone for the interpretation of the linguistic and archaeological facts of prehistoric Italy. It assumed in effect that the beginnings of Italy's cultural development were the result of a decisive ethnical impulse of transalpine origin. Whether this change was held to be solely due to the *terramara* wave, or whether it was thought that other invasions from the Danube basin followed it (thus giving rise to the iron civilizations of Italy, as others have believed), the civilizing wave always seemed to proceed from north to south. Rome itself was said to be linked in its earliest days to the northern *terremare;* and the square city, the Roman system of building its streets in chessboard pattern pointing towards the four directions of the compass, the very name of Palatine, all seemed to favour the theory according to which descendants of the inhabitants of the *terremare* founded the Eternal City. Thus the myth of the *terramaricoli* was substituted, in the name of science, for the myth of Romulus and Remus![4]

## Position of Contemporary Criticism

Voices were already being raised however in opposition to the Pigorinian theory; they belonged to Edoardo Brizio, to Giuseppe Sergi the anthropologist, and to the archaeologist Giovanni Patroni, and warned against over-estimating the importance of the *terramara* civilization. The discoveries of Paolo Orsi in Sicily and Calabria, those of Giuseppe Angelo Colini and Ugo Rellini in central Italy, have revealed during the last fifty years the existence of a very flourishing bronze civilization that blossomed out without any break in continuity on the oldest aeneolithic sites. This civilization was entirely independent of transalpine influences: the funeral rite, for example, was the primitive rite of burial. If anything, it received the cultural waves that spread with greater and greater frequency from the Mediterranean islands and the East, where for centuries already civilizations of a superior type had been thriving: the Egyptian, the Mesopotamian, the Anatolian, the Minoan-Mycenaean. It was particularly as a result of Rellini's intense research and of his conclusions that this bronze civilization (known at first by the still controversial name of 'extraterramara', and now more appropriately renamed Apenninic) was shown to have played a preponderant role in the material and intellectual development of primitive Italy and was taken as a likely external pointer to the formation of the Italic *ethnos*. Upon it in fact were grafted the later iron cultures which already existed by the first millennium B.C. and are proper to the Italic peoples at the threshold of their history. It was observed that the Italic peoples in their most ancient and secluded settlements still preserved burial, proper to the Apenninic culture, as their funerary rite. The Pigorinian equation: Italic peoples=cremation peoples, was thus seriously invalidated.[5]

Owing to the presence as far as northern Italy of the Apenninic bronze culture and of inhumation rites, the *terramara* culture – limited to parts of Aemilia and lower Lombardy – appeared to be, and in fact was, no more than an episode of purely local importance, and essentially due to the peculiar geographical conditions of an alluvial region covered by a network of large rivers. Doubt was even cast on whether the cinerary urns should be attributed to the inhabitants of the *terremare:* for scholars tend to date the latter even earlier than the beginning of the actual bronze age. The original formulation of the problem was thus reversed, and Pigorini's theory was overthrown by the facts.

Once more, therefore, the need to answer the following questions arises: When did the Indo-Europeans come to Italy? How can the cultures of prehistoric Italy be explained? What was the origin of the Italic peoples?

As we proceed along the path of science we cannot help noticing the extreme complexity of phenomena which at one time appeared to be simple and clear-cut. The very simplicity, relatively speaking, of Pigorini's explanation is a clear indication of its insufficiency. Any attempt to marshal the facts of such a remote and obscure past into a straightforward and coherent pattern, with clear and precise statements, leads inevitably to the dangers of oversimplification, to the premature statement of general conclusions without sufficient knowledge of factual data.

In attempting to reach not a reconstructive synthesis (this is not possible for the moment, and perhaps never will be) but a guiding principle that would conform as far as possible to factual reality, we must begin by separating and analysing singly, without bias or haste, the data provided by linguistics and archaeology.[6]

## Linguistic Outline of Primitive Italy

The present state of our knowledge provides us with the following linguistic outline of pre- and proto-historic Italy.[7] At the time of the spreading of the art of writing, i.e. between the sixth and fifth centuries B.C. the north of Italy and the greater part of the Alpine region seem to have been inhabited by peoples whose dialects are not yet properly classified but are usually referred to as 'Ligurian', for they roughly coincide with the area occupied by the Ligurians of history. In these dialects Indo-European elements seem to be superimposed on a pre-Indo-European substratum.[8] Along the whole of the valley of the Adige, in north-east Italy, there are traces of a 'Raetic' language belonging to a pre-Indo-European stock and possessing certain affinities with Etruscan.[9] Over the middle and lower Po plain, the slow spreading of Etruscan was taking place. In Venetia, Istria, and Carniola, a dialect was spoken that was certainly Indo-European: Venetic. Tyrrhenian (western) central Italy constituted the original area of diffusion of Etruscan, an essentially non-Indo-European language with Aegean and Asian affinities. In Latium, there was Latin, to which were probably related the primitive dialects of Tyrrhenian southern Italy, from Campania to Calabria. Along the backbone of the Apennines, stretching from Umbria to Lucania and spreading unevenly towards either shore, were scattered those linguistically related, pre-eminently 'Italic' peoples that spoke Umbrian and the Sabellic dialects, from which there derived, after the conquest of Campania at the hands of the Samnites, the Oscan language.[10] Along the Adriatic shore, in the region of Picenum, there are traces of

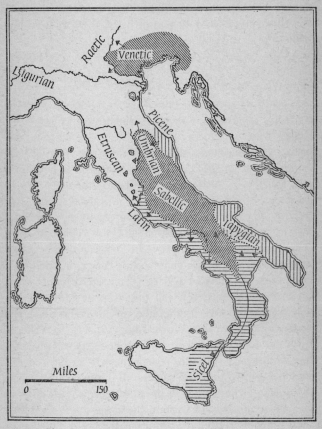

Figure I – THE LANGUAGES OF ANCIENT ITALY

Areas speaking a non-Indo-European language are left in white. Horizontal hatching indicates western dialects (Latin and Sicel); oblique hatching, falling to the left, dialects of the Umbro-Sabellic group; oblique hatching, falling to the right, Venetic; vertical hatching, other Adriatic dialects.

at least two very little known dialects, probably with Indo-European elements, but of uncertain origin. In Apulia, Iapygian (or Messapic) was also of Indo-European stock and possessed certain affinities with Illyrian. In eastern Sicily, an Indo-European dialect was spoken that possessed certain similarities with Umbro-Sabellic, but also significant affinities with Latin.[11] In the western half of the island, in Sardinia and in Corsica, languages were spoken which (though we have no direct supporting evidence) may be considered as non-Indo-European; they were probably related, even though indirectly, to African, Iberian, and Ligurian idioms.[12] We should finally mention the languages of colonization: Doric and Ionic Greek dialects in southern Italy and Sicily, Punic in the Carthaginian settlements of western Sicily and Sardinia, and finally Etruscan itself on the coasts of Campania and Corsica.

Thus, the linguistic picture is one of extreme complexity. We are a long way from the over-simple 'Italic' unity of certain scholars of the past; and we are a long way too from the conditions reigning in other countries, such as contemporary Greece, with its linguistic evenness broken only by dialect variations, quite negligible in most cases and soon destined to be smoothed by the literary κοινή of Attic culture.

In attempting to bring a little order into this intricate state of affairs, we must first distinguish those dialects that certainly belonged to the Indo-European stock from those foreign to it or that appear to have been influenced by it only in a limited way. The latter ('Ligurian', 'Raetic', Etruscan, and in all probability the island idioms) belong to the west, whereas the Indo-European dialects occupy the eastern areas of continental and peninsular Italy. The boundary dividing the two groups follows an imaginary line that roughly corresponds to the twelfth meridian, from the Trentine Alps to the mouths of the Tiber; the line is then carried over to Sicily, dividing the island into two. The linguistic, geographic, and historical importance of this fact cannot escape anyone: for if we suppose, as everything leads us to suppose, that the non-Indo-European linguistic area is older than the Indo-European area, the latter's position shows very clearly that Indo-Europeanism must have advanced from east to west rather than from north to south.

Within the sphere of the Indo-European dialects themselves a classification is both possible and useful.[13] The independence of Latin and of the Osco-Umbrian group has been definitely demonstrated. All the known Indo-European idioms of Italy can be thus divided into three fundamental groups:

(1) Latin, probably the dialects of the Tyrrhenian zone of southern Italy, and, perhaps, Sicel;

(2) Umbrian, the Sabellic dialects, Oscan;

(3) Venetic, partly (perhaps) the Picene dialects, Iapygian.

The geographic position of these three groups is significant: the first occupies the extreme western or Tyrrhenian regions and is in contact with the non-Indo-European area; the second is spread along the centre of the peninsula following the crest of the Apennines; the third, or eastern group, borders on the Adriatic. The affinities which have been found to exist between Venetic and Latin could be explained by the peculiar position of the former: for although it belongs to the Eastern or Adriatic group, it is, like Latin, in direct contact along its western border with the non-Indo-European linguistic area.[14] The Adriatic dialect-areas are not contiguous, and, as far as we are able to tell, do not constitute a single linguistic whole. Toponymic data, and tradition, refer us to the coasts of Illyria and to the Illyrians, though there is as yet no full agreement amongst scholars on the exact meaning to be attached to the word

'Illyrian', especially since present-day Albanian dialects, believed to be its surviving descendants, do not possess any affinities with ancient Venetic or Iapygian. It is probable that ethnic and linguistic influences from the opposite Adriatic shore also exerted themselves on Picenum, where we encounter little-known dialects and where there lived a people which the Umbrian text of the Iguvine Tablets designates by the name of *Iapuzci*, cognate with the *Iapodi* of Istria and the *Iapygi* of Apulia.

The area covered by the three Indo-European linguistic groups in Italy makes, in our opinion, the history of their original diffusion sufficiently clear. They are spread on three bands of territory that divide the Italian peninsula longitudinally, thus giving the impression of three successive waves. Since the eastern band is contiguous with the Indo-European zones of the Balkan peninsula and the western band borders on the non-Indo-European zone, it is self-evident that the linguistic waves must have spread from east to west and that the oldest must have been the one to which Latin belongs ('proto-Latin' according to Devoto's terminology). This in fact concurs with what is known of some of the marginal (and therefore archaic) characteristics of Latin when compared with other Indo-European languages. The Umbro-Sabellic wave that followed afterwards must have pushed these peoples back to the extreme margins of the peninsula and of Sicily, placing them in close contact with the surviving non-Indo-European areas and influencing their original languages, as is perhaps the case with Sicel. The oldest Umbro-Sabellic occupation zone was in the southern central Apennines and it is from this area that, in proto-historic and historical times only, speakers of these dialects spread northwards towards Romagna, westwards in the direction of Latium and Campania, and southwards to the extremity of the peninsula. Contrary to common opinion (established on the strength of the Pigorinian theory and still held to-day by some scholars) there is no certain trace of the presence of Umbro-Sabellic peoples in northern Italy before the Umbrian invasions of historical times. We have therefore no concrete proof of their having immigrated over the Alps. The hypothesis that makes them cross the Adriatic from the Balkan peninsula is far more likely to be true. That this was possible is proved by the third linguistic wave which our linguistic outline has caught, so to speak, in the act of crossing the Adriatic, having already established bridgeheads on the Italian shores (Apulia, Venetia and, perhaps, Picenum) while its bases are still on the Illyrian shore opposite.

The problem of the classification and the diffusion of the Indo-European languages of Italy may be further complicated by the recently examined likelihood of yet other Indo-European linguistic currents finding their way (in presumably very ancient times) to the peninsula.[15] This eventuality should be considered in connexion with the concept of 'Proto-Italics' put forward by Devoto, though it is a cultural rather than a linguistic concept. At any rate it is important to bear in mind that the structure of these languages and dialectal variations of historical times (Latin, Oscan, Umbrian, etc.) cannot without great difficulties be referred back to prehistoric times, i.e. to times when the Indo-European linguistic prototypes were introduced into Italy. It is likely that the historical idioms attested through inscriptions are only the culmination of a long and complicated process of concentration and specialization on the part of linguistic currents only approximately identifiable, of which, for various reasons, some may have developed in vigorous fashion, others may have been considerably mingled and altered, while yet others may have completely disappeared. This supposition is strengthened by analogy with events occurring in historical times, when we see the Oscan idioms impose themselves over southern Italy only to be submerged, together with their neighbours, by their sister Latin.

The arrival in Italy of the various Indo-European linguistic waves obviously presupposes an earlier non-Indo-European phase. But since the latter is a good deal older than the adoption of writing, we can only form an idea of it from the languages (i.e. Etruscan) of the western zone (though these are hardly better known), and from toponymy, i.e. the study of place names, which often stubbornly resist linguistic change and evolution. This type of research is of course extremely difficult; it is impossible to be too cautious, and results are always uncertain and subject to revision. The latest researches however seem to arrive at the recognition in the Mediterranean linguistic substrata of the Italian region of three sufficiently well-defined types: a Libyco-Iberian group in the islands, a 'Ligurian' group in northern Italy, and a third, 'Tyrrhenian' or 'Raeto-Tyrrhenian' in the eastern Alps, in the lower Po valley and over the rest of the peninsula.[16] The latter type is thought to be mainly related to the non-Indo-European languages of the Aegean basin and of Asia Minor, whereas the first two groups ought probably to be connected with the primitive idioms of Europe and western Africa. The arrival on the scene of the Indo-European languages from the East would then have pushed the older languages (Ligurian in the north-west and 'Tyrrhenian' in Tuscany) towards the western edge of the Italian peninsula. It is also possible however that the east-to-west movement of the 'Tyrrhenian' linguistic wave might be due to causes analogous to those that brought about the great speed of the Indo-European languages in Italy.[17]

### Bronze and Iron Cultures in Italy

Such is the broad outline of the linguistic prehistory of Italy sketched on the basis of reliable factual data. It gives us no

indication however as to when or how the Indo-Europeanization of Italy took place; the process, that is, by which the
peoples of historic Italy were first formed. It only provides
us with a relative chronology of events, and not with the
absolute chronology we need in order to localize them in
history; nor does it explain the actual mechanism of linguistic transformation: whether it was due to large migrations, to a slow infiltration, or to cultural or political
influences.[18]

We should therefore also examine the question of the
Italian prehistoric cultures, freed from the preconceptions
of the Pigorinian reconstruction. But let us first of all note
the birth of a new method in ethnological and palethno-
logical research in opposition to the old evolutionary and
typological method: we refer to the historico-cultural
method first introduced by F. Gräbner and by Father W.
Schmidt. Cultural facts are no longer studied on the basis
of an *a priori* supposition that a general and continuous
evolution took place from simple to complex forms. The
new basis assumes that every centre of culture created its
own peculiar conditions of life, and that the genius of single
individuals may have achieved in certain places conquests
and inventions that later became general, while in other
places very ancient or even primitive forms of life may have
survived for a long time. Once this is assumed, it is certainly not a given type of object that will furnish any precise idea of the age to which it belonged. An ordered classi-
ficatory system such as the one elaborated by Montelius
must of necessity be invalidated by the possibility that cultures of a more archaic type may survive other more progressive types. Instead of a general and continuous development, a new concept has been evolved, based on present-
day observations, especially amongst primitive peoples:
that of centres of development spreading their innovations
and civilizing influence in surrounding areas to a greater or

lesser degree. Instead of the idea of transitional cultures linking one phase to the next, we now have that of cultures uniting elements that originated in several different centres, or successive irradiations from the same centres.[19]

It is obvious that once the problem is set in this way we can no longer speak of a regular succession: stone age, bronze age, iron age, except on the broadest lines of time and space. Whereas the East (Egypt and Mesopotamia) rapidly developed an early civilization that from the beginning of the third millennium B.C. transformed its ancient stone and aeneolithic cultures into an advanced bronze culture that included cities, religious monuments, complex political organizations, writing, scientific, and artistic documents, etc., the majority of the inhabitants of Europe were to live for a long time yet at the stone age level, with rare influxes from the East and only a very limited use of copper weapons and instruments. In Italy the actual bronze culture spread slowly, perhaps only as a result of the effulgence of the Aegean civilization which had as its first and most resplendent centre the island of Crete. One can only speak of a true bronze age in Italy during the second half of the second millennium B.C., and it is possible that aeneolithic cultural traditions thrived on in secluded areas up to the end of the bronze age. Similarly, in an isolated territory such as the island of Sardinia, the iron age was not even able to establish itself, so that the Sardinians lived at the bronze culture level till they were conquered by the Romans, during the third century B.C.

Aeneolithic culture itself varied greatly from region to region, whereas the 'Apenninic' bronze culture possesses a relatively uniform character in central and southern Italy: it appears to have been especially vigorous in the Adriatic regions. Its ramifications are found in the direction of northern Italy, Umbria, Tuscany, and Campania, whereas on the Apulian coast, in Sicily and in the Lipari islands the direct influence of Mycenaean culture can be detected. The latest phase of the bronze culture, following its Apenninic flowering, appears to be represented in southern Italy (and in the Lipari islands) by a cultural phase that has received the name of 'Ausonian'.[20] The Po valley displays the phenomenon of the *terremare* which, as stated before, appears to have been geographically rather circumscribed: it is probably also late in character and is related on the one hand to forms of life belonging to the Alpine lake-village system (Polada culture) and on the other with the late Apenninic and 'Ausonian' cultures.

But the different regions of Italy present notable variants only with the appearance of iron culture, characterized by the spread of the use of the new metal alongside bronze, in the fashioning of arms and tools and by the use of geometrical decorative patterns with a preference for the straight line. It corresponds to a phase of history that followed the end of the Mycenaean civilization of Greece (the so-called geometric period), and represents the beginning of the cultures of the Italian peoples of historical times.[21] In Italy, as also in central and western Europe, its establishment took time in becoming effective; its progressive penetration amongst the late bronze cultures varied from place to place.[22] The principal regional varieties of the Italian iron culture are: (i) the northern cultures of Golasecca (Liguria, Piedmont, and Lombardy) and of Este (Venetia), (ii) the 'Villanovan' culture of Etruria and Aemilia, (iii) the Latian culture, (iv) the 'eastern' culture of Umbria, Picenum and Samnium and the Apulian culture, (v) the 'southern' culture of Campania and Calabria, (vi) the Sicel culture.

The question of funerary rites is of particular interest to the study of this period. Until then in Italy the dead were buried in little grottoes or in graves. Towards the end of the bronze age, corresponding with the last phases of the *terramara* and 'Ausonian' cultures, there began to appear

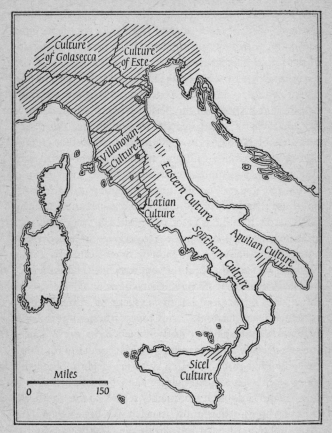

Figure 2 – THE CULTURES OF PROTO-HISTORIC ITALY
The cross-hatched areas are those where cremation rites prevailed;
areas left in white correspond to inhumatory customs.

groups of tombs with terracotta urns containing the ashes
of the cremated dead. They are not only met in the Po
valley, but also in the extreme south of Italy (Torre Castelluccia, in Apulia), and their presence proves the coexistence
of a cremation 'current' of continental origin related to the

Urn-fields of Europe and of another no less ancient current that reached the shores of Italy from the sea and that has left its traces from about the end of the bronze age to the beginning of the iron age in various coastal areas of the peninsula (Pianello della Genga in the Marches, Timmari in Apulia, Milazzo in Sicily, together with some traces in Latium and Etruria). In the period when the iron cultures reached their full development, we find an area where the two rites of cremation and inhumation coexisted, cremation predominating. This area included the northern, the 'Villanovan', and the Latian cultures, that is the whole of north-west Italy. Another area, including the 'eastern', 'southern', and Sicel cultures remained faithful to the inhumation rite; here cases of cremation were rare. An intermediary strip between the two areas stretched from north to south along a line running from Romagna, across Umbria, to reach the sea at the southern end of Latium.

The 'Villanovan' culture, characterized by the use as ossuaries of terracotta vases in the shape of a double cone, presented other analogies with the northern cultures; the latter seem to have been greatly influenced by the 'Villanovans' (especially by their more evolved aspects), and so may be considered in a general way as being chronologically more recent. The Latian culture had strong affinities with the 'Villanovan', but it was mainly related to the 'southern' culture whose northernmost branch it was, notwithstanding their different funeral rites. Both the 'southern' and the Sicel cultures developed when Hellenic influences first made their appearance, either at the same time as, or immediately preceding the earliest colonizations of southern Italy and Sicily. Finally, the 'eastern' culture, the most widespread of all, presented a great many similarities to the Apenninic bronze culture that preceded it; it occupied most of its territory and in certain aspects represented a local development. It was prolonged to the south into the Apulian culture which, however, possesses characteristics of its own and appears to be related to cultural manifestations on the opposite shore of the Adriatic. 'Oriental' cultural influences may also be found on the Tyrrhenian shore, especially in the area where the 'Villanovan' culture met that of Latium (Tolfa)[23]; the Apulian culture on the other hand, with its characteristic painted pottery, tended to expand towards the Tyrrhenian coasts of Lucania (e.g. Palinuro).

The transformation of the iron cultures into the full civilization of historical times was accompanied by a process of internal development which stood out most clearly in Etruria. For it was here that a great flowering of civilization occurred, ushered in by favourable economic and social conditions and by the influence of the highly-evolved societies of the eastern Mediterranean. In southern Italy and in Sicily the mature civilization of Greek colonists superimposed itself on the native one without however destroying it, but transforming it little by little. Elsewhere and especially in northern Italy, in the Apennines and on the shores of the Adriatic, iron age cultural conditions persisted for a long time, with few innovations, right up to the time of the Roman conquest during the fourth and third centuries B.C.

### The Problem of Chronology

Closely related to the review of archaeological data belonging to Italian protohistory is the problem of chronology. Except in the case of the more recent facts, chronology can only utilize, owing to the lack of written documents, elements provided by the comparison of types of objects and patterns belonging to other civilizations to which an approximate date at least can be given, i.e. the Egyptian and Aegean civilizations of the eastern Mediterranean. There are in fact many cases of isolated influences, even at times of direct importation of objects from the East; and during the later phases of the iron age culture these influences became more and more frequent till they produced the characteristic 'orientalizing' civilization, that spread from southern Etruria.

According to calculations that are still generally accepted (based for the older period on the chronology of the Aegean civilization and for the more recent one on that of archaic Greece), the first stages of the bronze age in Italy have been assigned to the beginning of the second millennium B.C., those of the iron age to about the year 1000, and the establishment of the orientalizing civilization in Etruria to about the year 700 B.C. The latest studies and investigations have proved that the flowering of the Apenninic and Sicel bronze cultures coincided with the later phases of the Mycenaean civilization in Greece.[24] This probably means that the aeneolithic culture lasted in many parts of Italy till the second half of the second millennium and that the full establishment and final phases of the bronze culture should be assigned to the centuries immediately preceding and following the year 1000 B.C. The appearance of the iron cultures in central and southern Italy may be placed between the end of the ninth and the beginning of the eighth century; their eastern and northern diffusion probably took place during the eighth and seventh centuries. The first evidence of cremation as a funeral rite in Italy is also attributed to the beginning of the first millennium. And by the seventh and sixth centuries appeared the first inscriptions; these bear certain witness to the presence of the peoples of ancient Italy in those centres they occupied in historical times.[25]

## Formation of Historical Peoples

We have now examined in the light of the newest discoveries and criteria the linguistic and archaeological data of the problem that confronts us, and we can without more

ado establish a certain number of points. There is first of all
no possibility of identifying the Italic peoples with northern
invaders introducing cremation as a funeral rite. In Italy the
Indo-Europeanization movement travelled from east to
west and its beginnings must have been, without a shadow
of doubt, older than the diffusion of the new rite. But of far
greater import is the singular and incontrovertible fact that
*the two linguistic and cultural maps of proto-historic Italy* (cf.
p. 26 and p. 35) *do roughly coincide along the longitudinal line
that divides the peninsula into two, from Romagna to Latium,
leaving to the east an Indo-European linguistic area with
inhumation as its prevalent funeral rite, and to the west a non-
Indo-European linguistic area where it was cremation that prevailed.* This fact radically invalidates the equation Italic
peoples=cremation peoples. It is harder to explain why the
new rite should have been adopted mainly in a region
inhabited by peoples belonging to the oldest linguistic
stock. This may have been due to peculiar social and
religious conditions or crises, to external influences or
internal migrations. In any case the problem very closely
concerns the question of the origin of the Etruscans, to be
dealt with in the next chapter.

If the peoples of Italy may be considered as already established in their historical centres at the time of the spreading
of the iron age cultures (as is proved by inscriptions belonging to a slightly later date), it is obvious that the Indo-
Europeanization of Italy belongs to a very remote age. Now
it is worth noting that the areas in which the Italic Indo-
European languages first established themselves (i.e. south-
eastern Italy) possessed a distinctive cultural unity not only
during the iron age, with its 'eastern' culture and the inhumation rite, but even in the bronze age, with the Apenninic culture whose most important centres were in the
heart of the peninsula and on its Adriatic slopes, and the
succeeding 'Ausonian' culture dominant in the south. The

picture of an Apenninic bronze culture slowly conquering Italy and spreading its influence towards the Tyrrhenian shores coincides remarkably well with the picture we may draw of the east-to-west advance of Indo-European speakers. Everything leads us to believe with the latest supporters of the anti-Pigorinian reaction, that the Apenninic culture mirrors, in the domain of external historical manifestations, the formation of an Italic *ethnos*.

But at this point to identify the cultural phenomena with the linguistic phenomena in question (i.e. to believe that the manifestations of the Apenninic culture mark the appearance of Indo-Europeans in Italy) would mean repeating the mistake made by the old theorists, though in a different direction. It has been proved that in certain sites such as the great prehistoric centre of Matera in Lucania the development from aeneolithic to bronze culture was uninterrupted. On the other hand Sicily showed a cultural dichotomy between its eastern and western halves (the two areas inhabited in historical times by – probably – non-Indo-European Sicans and by Indo-European Sicels) while still at the aeneolithic stage. It is likely that the diffusion of the oldest ('proto-Latin') Indo-European wave took place before the appearance of the bronze culture in Italy: it may even go back to before the beginning of the second millennium B.C. Towards the end of the bronze age, the region occupied by these peoples coincides fairly exactly with that of the so-called 'Ausonian' culture. The Umbro-Sabellic wave established itself most probably within the compass of the Apenninic culture.

This complex interweaving of linguistic and cultural phenomena and the long duration of the processes of penetration and establishment of the Indo-European languages on Italian territory are in a way sufficient to show that the obscure phenomenon of the Indo-Europeanization of Italy was substantially different from the rather over-simplified concept of a migration on the part of one or more peoples, so dear to the hearts of scholars of past generations. To come nearer to the truth, we have to imagine extremely varied, slow and complex changes, to whose final phases (the expansion of the Umbro-Sabellians) history is a witness. A reconstruction based on the analogy of such final phases may then perhaps be attempted: it should take into account the effect of various other possible factors such as conquests, partial displacements, cultural influences, etc., upon the broad picture presented by the attraction exerted by culturally more evolved territories upon more warlike and ruder peoples.

In any case the individuality of the various peoples of Italy was already evident in the main at the time of the diffusion of the iron cultures. The cultures of the Tyrrhenian coastal strips (Latian, 'southern', Sicel) doubtless belonged to the Latin-Sicel peoples.[26] The 'eastern' culture is proper to the Umbro-Sabellians, and its western ramifications correspond to the Umbro-Sabellic linguistic influences in Latium and in Campania, culminating later in historical times with the ethnic migrations of the Volsci, the Aequi and the Samnites towards the Tyrrhenian shores. The 'Villanovan' culture coincides broadly with the area inhabited by the Etruscans in historical times. The Golasecca culture was inherited by the Ligurians; that of Este, by the Veneti. To this period in fact may already be attributed the first settlements of speakers of Adriatic Indo-European dialects on the eastern shores of Italy; to the very flourishing culture of the Marches there corresponded the Picenes, while the Apulian culture together with its variants belonged to the Iapygi (Daunians, Peucetians, and Messapians).

## NOTES

1. *Römische Geschichte*, 7th edition, 1881, pp. 44 ff.

2. *Die vorklassische Chronologie Italiens*, 1912.

3. For more details see especially W. Helbig, *Die Italiker in der Po-Ebene*, 1879.

4. To mention only more recent works, cf.: E. Täubler, *Terremare und Rom*, 1926; V. Basanoff, *Pomerium palatinum* (in *Memorie della R. Accademia dei Lincei*, 1939). The theory is exhaustively criticized by P. Barocelli in *Bullettino della Commissione Archeol. comunale*, LXX, 1942, pp. 131 ff.

5. On this subject as a whole, see U. Rellini, *Le origini della civiltà italica*, 1929; *Recenti studi sulla civiltà enea in Italia* (*XXVIII Riunione della S.I.P.S.*, vol. IV, pp. 343 ff.); M. Pallottino, *L'origine degli Etruschi*, 1947, pp. 108 ff.; G. Patroni, *La preistoria* (*Storia politica d'Italia*), 2nd ed., 1951, pp. 612 ff. On the subject of the *terremare* and their chronology, see G. Säflund, *Le terremare delle provincie di Modena, Reggio Emilio, Parma, Piacenza* (*Acta Instit. Rom. Regni Sueciae*, VII, 1939): his conclusions however are not wholly acceptable: cf. U. Rellini in *Bullettino di Paletnologia*, new series, III, 1939, pp. 114 ff.

6. On the ancient peoples of Italy, see J. Whatmough, *The Foundations of Roman Italy*, 1937; A. Furumark, *Det äldsta Italien*, 1947; M. Pallottino, *Popolazioni storiche dell' Italia antica*, in *Guida allo studio della civiltà romana antica*, 1952, pp. 71–90; L. Pareti, *Storia di Roma e del mondo romano*, 1952, pp. 63 ff.

7. The elements for such a reconstruction are now gathered in V. Pisani, *Le lingue dell' Italia antica oltre il latino*, 1953; the reader is referred to the bibliography of this work for both ancient and recent publications on the single languages, with the exception of a few additions which will be found in our notes.

8. Cf. P. Kretschmer, in *Glotta*, XXX, 1943, pp. 203 ff.; on the Lugurians in general, both as to their language and history, and their relations with the other ancient peoples of Italy, see also M. Pallottino, *Il problema dei liguri nella formazione dell' ethnos italico*, in *Atti del I Congresso Intern. di Studi Liguri*, 1952, pp. 83 ff.

9. V. Pisani and P. Kretschmer consider Raetic to be a pre-Indo-European language distinct from Etruscan though related to it. On the other hand C. Battisti (in *Studi Etruschi*, XVIII, 1944, pp. 199 ff.; XIX, 1946–7, pp. 249 ff.) tends to see in it the direct and late influence of historical Etruscan, thus following tradition as stated in Livy V,

33 (Livy's quotation is given in Chapter IV). Other authorities (cf. E. Vetter, in *Glotta*, XXX, 1943, pp. 75 ff.) attempt to include Raetic within the Indo-European framework.

10. E. Vetter, *Handbuch der Italischen Dialekte*, I, 1953.

11. V. Pisani, in *Sulla lingua dei Siculi*, in *Bollett. del Centro Studi Filol. e Linguistici Siciliani*, I, 1953, pp. 5 ff., now confirms the doubts already expressed elsewhere on a specific Siculo-Latin relationship commonly accepted by scholars.

12. For Sardinia, see M. Pallottino, *La Sardegna nuragica*, 1950, pp. 22 ff., and bibliography, p. 28.

13. In addition to the works mentioned on p. 42, notes 6 and 7, see especially, G. Devoto, *Gli antichi Italici*, 2nd ed., 1951, pp. 41 ff., with bibliography on pp. 62 ff.

14. F. Altheim presupposes the existence of a primitive Latin substratum that extended from the Euganean region to the Val Camonica; this would later have been covered by the Venetic stratum of Illyrian origin (*Römische Geschichte*, I, 1951, pp. 14 ff., where references to previous studies will be found). This hypothesis rests upon no serious foundations.

15. See G. Devoto in *Studi Etruschi*, XIX, 1946–7, pp. 296 ff., and *Gli antichi Italici*, 2nd ed., pp. 51 ff., and pp. 65 ff.

16. Cf. G. Devoto, *Storia della lingua di Roma*, 1940, pp. 37 ff.; B. Gerola, *Substrato mediterraneo e latino* (in *Studi Etruschi*, XVI, 1942, pp. 345 ff.); P. Kretschmer, *Glotta*, XXVIII, 1940, pp. 231 ff.; XXX, 1943, pp. 84 ff.

17. Whether it be considered as a penetration by way of land routes from the Danubian region (P. Kretschmer, *Glotta*, XXX, 1943, pp. 104, 199, 168 ff., 213 ff.), or whether it be admitted as a coastal infiltration from the Eastern Mediterranean basin, in which case it would partly link up with the tradition and belief of an Aegeo-Asiatic origin of the Tyrrhenians and the Pelasgians, a theory that will be found discussed on pp. 53–63.

18. The hypothesis of a slow cultural infiltration (of 'linguistic ferments', as its author designates them, contrary to the old theory of invasion) is mainly due to G. Patroni (*Espansioni e migrazioni*, in *Archivio Glottologico Italiano*, XXXII, 1940, pp. 21 ff.). A critical examination of this hypothesis may be found in G. Devoto, *Studi Etruschi*, XVI, 1942, pp. 409 ff., and in *Gli antichi Italici*, 2nd ed., pp. 67 ff. The idea of a political influence on the other hand has been elaborated on the basis of C. Jullian's theories by L. Homo, in his work *L'Italie primitive et les débuts de l'impérialisme romain*, 1925, pp. 58 ff. The traditional 'invasion' theory is substantially restated by

F. Matz in *Neue Jahrbücher für Antike und deutsche Bildung*, I, 1938, pp. 367 ff., II, 1939, pp. 32 ff., and *Klio*, XXXV, 1942, pp. 299 ff.; by H. Krahe, *Die Indogermanisierung Griechenlands und Italiens*, 1949; by F. Altheim, *Römische Geschichte*, I, pp. 13 ff. and by other, but especially German, scholars.

19. On the historico-cultural method, cf. G. Montandon, *Traité d'ethnologie culturelle*, 1934, pp. 26 ff.; W. Schmidt, *Handbuch der Methode der kulturhistorischen Ethnologie*, 1937. On its applications in the field of pre- and proto-history, see P. Laviosa Zambotti, *Origini e diffusione della civiltà*, 1947; B. Pace, *Dubbi metodologici e ipotesi di lavoro per la cronologia delle civiltà protostoriche*, in *Atti del I Congresso Intern. di Preistoria e Protostoria Mediterranea*, 1952, pp. 265 ff. On Italy in particular, see B. Pace, *Arte e civiltà della Sicilia antica*, I, 1935, pp. 142 ff.; M. Pallottino, *Sulle facies culturali arcaiche dell' Etruria*, in *Studi Etruschi*, XIII, 1939, pp. 85 ff.

20. L. Bernabò Brea, *Civiltà preistoriche delle isole eolie*, in *Archivo di Preistoria Levantina*, III, 1952, pp. 69 ff.

21. On the manifestations of the iron cultures of Italy, cf. F. v. Duhn, F. Messerschmidt, *Italische Gräberkunde*, I, 1924; II, 1939. Cf. also F. Messerschmidt, *Bronzezeit und frühe Eisenzeit in Italien*, 1935, and U. Rellini and G. Säflund in *Studi Etruschi*, XII, 1939, pp. 9 ff.

22. We are still a long way from a definite settlement of the chronological relations between the first manifestations of the iron cultures of Italy and the northern and north-eastern civilization areas of the late bronze age (a so-called transitional phase: Lausitz, *Urnenfelder*) or of the iron age (Hallstadt, Danubian cultures, etc.). Many scholars, the Germans in particular, believe in the derivation of the culture of the Italian cremation peoples from transalpine cultures. In fact, however, we possess no definite evidence by which to determine the absolute chronology of transalpine cultures and thereby establish definite priority over the Italian parallels. The recentness of Hallstadt is now universally accepted (N. Åberg, *Bronzezeitliche und Früheisenzeitliche Chronologie: Italien*, 1930). In southern Gaul, the 'transitional' manifestations of the *Urnenfelder* (urn fields) culture now appear to be contemporary with the beginnings of Ionic colonization (sixth century B.C.): cf. *Gallia*, I, 1943, pp. 5 ff. For European and Italian cultures of the late bronze age and early iron age and their inter-relations, cf. E. Dunareanu-Vulpe, *L'espansione delle civiltà italiche verso l'oriente danubiano nella prima età del ferro* (in *Ephemeris Dacoromana*, III, 1925, pp. 58 ff.) as well as Åberg's work referred to above; G. von Merhart, *Donauländische Beziehungen der früheisenzeitlichen Kulturen Mittelitaliens*, in *Bonner Jahrbücher*, 147,

1942, pp. 1 ff.; C. F. C. Hawkes, *From Bronze Age to Iron Age: Middle Europe, Italy and the North and West*, in *Proceedings of the Prehistoric Society for 1948*, pp. 196 ff.; G. Kossack, *Problemi cronologici della prima età del ferro in Italia e nell' Europa Centrale*, in *Atti del I Congr. Intern. di Preistoria e Protostoria Mediterranea*, 1952, pp. 368 ff. (with divergent views on the subject).

23. Such cultural influences, which often possess an archaic flavour, have been considered (most probably in error) as manifestations of a chronological 'transition' from bronze to iron age: cf M. Pallottino, *Sulle facies culturali arcaiche dell' Etruria*, in *Studi Etruschi*, XIII, pp. 85 ff.

24. B. Pace, *Arte e civiltà della Sicilia antica*, I, 1935, pp. 142 ff.; G. Buchner, *Nota preliminare sulle ricerche preistoriche nell'isola di Ischia*, in *Bulletino di Paletnologia*, 1936–7, pp. 78 ff.).

25. For the chronology of the beginnings of the iron age in Italy, see (in addition to the studies quoted on p. 44, notes 21 and 22): Å. Åkerström, *Der geometrische Stil in Italien*, 1943; M. Pallottino, *Nuovi orientamenti sulla cronologia dell' Etruria protostorica*, in *Rendic. della Pontificia Accad. di Archeologia*, XXII, 1946–7, pp. 31 ff.; C. F. C. Hawkes, *Chronology of the Bronze and Early Iron Ages, Greek, Italian and Transalpine*, in *Atti del I Congr. Intern. di Preistoria e Protostoria Mediterranea*, 1952, pp. 256 ff.

26. Cf. M. Pallottino, *Appunti di protostoria latina ed etrusca* in *Studi Etruschi*, XIV, 1940, pp. 27 ff.; G. Devoto, *Protolatini e Tirreni*, in *Studi Etruschi*, XVI, 1942, pp. 409 ff.

# CHAPTER TWO

# THE PROBLEM OF ETRUSCAN ORIGINS

## The Present State of the Question

THE problem of the origin of the Etruscans was first formulated by Dionysius of Halicarnassus, a Greek historian of the Augustan age, who devoted six chapters (xxv–xxx) of the first book of his *Early History of Rome* to a treatment of the question. With the critical means at his disposal he refuted the theories that identified the Etruscans with the Pelasgians or with the Lydians and declared himself favourable to the hypothesis that they were a people 'who had not come from outside, but were indigenous', and whose name was supposed to be Rasenna.

Before him, opinions current as to the origin of the Etruscans did not, so it seems, possess a scientific basis. Like all views on the origins of peoples and cities of the classical world they were on the border-line between history and myth, for the most part seeking their justification in etymological and onomastic similarities: thus the origins of Rome and of the Latins were taken back to the Trojans by way of Aeneas' wanderings. In the case of the Tyrrhenians (i.e. the Etruscans), there had been talk of an eastern origin – Lydia, in Asia Minor – and of an oversea migration led by Tyrrhenus, the son of King Atys of Lydia, to the Italic territory of the Umbrians (Herodotus, 1, 94); they had also been identified with those mysterious nomads the Pelasgians (Hellanicus, in Dionysius, 1, 28); or again there had been the theory of a migration of Tyrrhenus with the Pelasgians, who had already colonized the Aegean islands of Lemnos and Imbros (Anticleides in Strabo v, 2, 4). The Lydian origin of the Etruscans was accepted without difficulty, and became a common motif in classical literature: Virgil speaks indiscriminately of Lydians or Etruscans. Dionysius of Halicarnassus also stated that some authorities suspected them of being indigenous to Italy. But only Dionysius gathered the various opinions together, sifted them, and sought to prove that the Etruscans were autochthonous, basing his contention on their extreme antiquity and on their cultural and linguistic isolation amongst the various peoples of whom he had knowledge.

The problem has been taken up again in modern times with particular sharpness and polemic vigour, degenerating at times into sterile debates on preconceived theses. At first only classical texts were used as a basis for discussion; later, archaeological and linguistic data were also enlisted.[1] The first stage of the discussion occupied the whole of the eighteenth and the first half of the nineteenth century and was led by N. Fréret, B. G. Niebuhr, and K. O. Müller, who supported Dionysius of Halicarnassus' theory against the Asiatic origin tradition transmitted by Herodotus. But whereas Dionysius had given positive arguments in support of his theory, modern scholars particularly stressed the negative aspect of his criticism and, basing themselves on the analogy of the name Rasenna (which Dionysius had attributed to the Etruscans) with that of the Alpine Raetians, imagined the Etruscans to have originally descended from the Alps. It is interesting to note that right from this moment the problem of Etruscan origins was considered as being one of *provenance*, and not of *ethnic formation* as is usual when nations belonging to historical times are being studied. This polarization of the problem weighed heavily (except in a few rare cases) upon the whole future development of the discussion.

The success of comparative linguistics in establishing the relationship of a group of languages which it called Indo-

European; the discussions on whether Etruscan did or did not belong to the Indo-European group and, more particularly, to its Italic sub-group; the attempts to relate Etruscan with the non-Indo-European languages of the Caucasus and of Asia Minor; the discovery on the island of Lemnos of an inscription written in a dialect remarkably close to Etruscan; the identification (based chiefly upon toponymic data) of a Mediterranean linguistic substratum over which the Indo-European languages are thought to have spread, leaving here and there linguistic islands belonging to older stocks: these were the stages of linguistic research that added gradually more and more weight now to one now to the other thesis that sought to explain the origin of the Etruscans.

The same may be said for the data provided by archaeological discoveries. At first, these were largely fortuitous, but after the first half of the nineteenth century they were the result of excavations conducted with increasing enthusiasm in the territory of Etruria and in neighbouring areas. They revealed the existence of an Etruscan civilization, ethnically defined by inscriptions in Etruscan, that began to appear in the seventh century B.C. and lasted up to the beginning of the Roman Empire. Its area included Etruria itself (northern Latium and Tuscany), Campania, and the eastern half of the Po valley. The oldest phase of this civilization, characterized by a strong influx of oriental elements and known as a result as the 'orientalizing' period, merged at first with the 'Villanovan' iron culture. We have already described in Chapter One the manifestations in Italy of the iron age and of the preceding bronze age. As for the funerary rite in Etruria, the prehistoric period (aeneolithic and bronze cultures) is exclusively inhumatory, the subsequent 'Villanovan' iron culture predominantly crematory, and the orientalizing phase that followed in southern and coastal Etruria again inhumatory. The subsequent stages of the Etruscan civilization saw the coexistence of both rites, but inhumation predominated in the south and cremation in the north. It is worth recalling that in Rome too both rites lived side by side, strongly linked to family traditions: the great prevalence of cremation at the end of the republic and during the first century of the empire was followed in the second century A.D. by the general adoption of inhumation, though no ethnic transformation accompanied this change.

On the basis of the data provided by literary tradition, linguistic comparison, and the interpretation of archaeological discoveries, a great many theories have been put forward since the end of the last century. These may be grouped within three main systems: the first takes up and develops the traditional thesis of antiquity and ascribes an eastern origin to the Etruscans; the second follows the teachings of Niebuhr and Müller and believes the Etruscans to have descended from the north; and the third, the most recent, attempts to uphold Dionysius of Halicarnassus' theory on Etruscan autochthony by seeking their origin amongst the oldest ethnic substrata of Italy.

Of the three theses – which we shall respectively label oriental, northern, and autochthonous – the best known and most accepted is undoubtedly the first. It has been especially dear to those numerous archaeologists who have devoted themselves to the study of the antiquities of proto-historic Italy. These scholars have been greatly struck by the coincidence of traditional data with the orientalizing phase of the Etruscan civilization that appeared on the Tyrrhenian shores between the eighth and seventh centuries B.C. as a sudden flowering of civilized life in great contrast with the apparently backward manifestations of the preceding 'Villanovan' iron culture. They were also struck by similarities in religious rites, such as the change-over from cremation to inhumation. Edoardo Brizio in

1885 was the first to formulate this theory on a scientific basis: he identified the Etruscan invaders with the importers into Tuscany and Aemilia of the orientalizing and later of the Hellenistic civilization, and recognized in the 'Villanovan' cremation peoples the Umbrians of Herodotus, i.e. the Indo-European Italic peoples. Amongst the most important followers of Brizio's thesis were O. Montelius, B. Modestov, G. Körte, G. Ghirardini, L. Mariani, A. della Seta, P. Ducati, G. Patroni. The oriental thesis also appealed to many non-specialists . . . (archaeologists and linguists) who were attracted by the authority of tradition, the simple explanation of certain 'oriental' characteristics of the Etruscan civilization, the remarkable onomastic similarities between Etruscan and the languages of Asia Minor (first noticed by G. Herbig), and by the still plainer linguistic relationship linking Etruscan with the pre-Hellenic language of Lemnos. Slightly different theories were put forward by E. Pottier, who believed in the arrival of the Etruscans by sea, but by way of the Adriatic instead of the Tyrrhenian; and by F. Weege, who though also of the opinion that the Etruscans had reached Italy via the Adriatic dated their arrival during the second millennium B.C. F. Schachermeyer and E. Bulanda held that the Etruscan invasion from the East did not correspond exactly to the orientalizing period but took place in several waves, the oldest of which they ascribed to about the year 1000 B.C. The thesis of a Tyrrheno-Pelasgian migration to Italy during the bronze age (and of a partial return by sea towards the Aegean) has been recently taken up by J. Berard.[2] A confirmation of these oriental connexions might be the identification of the Etruscans or Tyrrhenians with the *Trš.w* mentioned in Egyptian hieroglyphs, i.e. with one of the seafaring peoples who attempted an invasion of Egypt under the Pharaohs Amejnoptah and Rameses III, between the years 1230 and 1170 B.C.

The 'northern' theory, though continuing Niebuhr's and Müller's hypothesis, based itself principally upon the archaeological discoveries that brought to light the bronze age *terramara* culture, linking it to the cremation cemeteries of northern Italy and to other iron cultures with cremation rites in central Italy. As we have already seen, they suggested to the archaeologist W. Helbig and to the Italian palethnologist L. Pigorini the idea of peoples descending from the north and of their subsequent historical development in central Italy. These tribes were thought to have included both the Italic and the Etruscan peoples, for no clear ethnic or linguistic distinction had yet been made between them. This theory was further strengthened by the fact that authoritative linguists such as W. Corssen and E. Lattes were convinced supporters of the Italic nature of the Etruscan language. Helbig thought there was a direct continuity, with no important breaks, from the *terramara* culture to the Etruscan civilization of historical times, via the 'Villanovan' and the 'orientalizing' phases.

The 'northern' theory greatly appealed to many archaeologists and historians, some of whom however (e.g. F. von Duhn and G. Körte) later went over to the 'oriental' theory. But the profound ethnic and linguistic differences between the Italic and the Etruscan peoples could no longer be ignored. This led the historian Gaetano De Sanctis to modify Helbig's thesis: he saw in the Etruscans the new northerners that had brought over with them the cremation rite, and in the Italic peoples the aeneolithic groups that had already settled in the centre of the peninsula. Luigi Pareti on the other hand distinguished an early Indo-European wave (the native aeneolithic inhabitants of Italy), a late Indo-European wave (the iron age cremation peoples other than the 'Villanovans', i.e. those possessing the 'eastern' Italic and the Latian cultures, which Pareti connects with the culture of Pianello della Genga), and finally the ethnic nucleus of the Etruscans (the actual 'Villanovans' who derived their culture from that of the *terramara* and the pile-dwellings of northern Italy). On the linguistic plane, an examination of the 'northern' theory should also take account of P. Kretschmer's hypothesis that the Etruscans belonged to an ethnico-linguistic 'Raeto-Tyrrhenic' or 'Raeto-Pelasgic' group that originally spread from the Danubian region of the Balkans towards Greece and Italy.[3]

The third, or 'autochtonous' theory, foreseen by the historian E. Meyer, was elaborated in the field of archaeology by Ugo Antonielli; during the last decades it has been especially well received by linguists as eminent as Alfredo Trombetti and Giacomo Devoto, who expounded it in detail in the first edition of his book *Gli antichi Italici* (1931). It does in fact rest upon a linguistic concept of the Etruscan nation: the links that connect Etruscan with the pre-Indo-European languages of the Mediterranean tend to make it appear rather as a relic, as an ethnic island of very ancient peoples isolated by the flood of Indo-European speakers, just as the present-day Basques of the Iberian peninsula represent the last-surviving remnants of primitive Hispanic populations in a sea of Romance speakers. And in fact, as we have seen in our preceding chapter, the toponymy of our area seems to bear evidence to the existence in the peninsula of a linguistic stratum older than the Italic dialects and akin to Etruscan and to the languages of Asia Minor, a stratum conventionally defined as 'Tyrrhenian'. The Etruscans would then have been a western concentration, under the pressure of Italic invaders, of elements belonging to this primitive layer. They would also naturally have received important racial and linguistic Indo-European contributions. From the archaeological (i.e. cultural) point of view, the earliest ethnic layer would have been that of the aeneolithic inhumators; these would then have been submerged by the Italic or proto-Italic cremation peoples, giving rise to the Etruscan nation of historical times, i.e. the consolidation of the original elements of the primitive stock under the cultural influx of the East.

## The Theory of Oriental Provenance

Each of the theories outlined above seeks to explain satisfactorily the data obtained from tradition, from linguistic research, and from archaeological discoveries, so as to reconstruct the sequence of events that led to the establishment and development of the Etruscan people. They are in fact ingenious combinations of the various known elements, but satisfy only partially the requirements that a full critical evaluation of these elements demands. Each one of the three systems and their variants leaves something unexplained, comes up against well-established facts, without however helping in any way the other two reconstructions. Had this not been so, the discussion would have ended long ago with a working agreement amongst scholars; the debate would not have arrived at a dead end.

Let us consider the 'oriental' theory first: it rests upon the correspondence of traditional data (that agree in stating that the Etruscans came from the Aegean East, whether they be Pelasgians, Lydians, or inhabitants of Lemnos) with archaeological data (i.e. the presence of an orientalizing cultural phase). Moreover, there is the close resemblance of Etruscan with Lemnian, as well as the relationship that is thought to exist between Etruscan and languages in Asia Minor (Hittite, Lycian, Lydian, etc.). Let us try first of all to establish the actual value of each of these elements taken separately.

Concerning the migrations and ethnic relationships which tradition, in the mouths of Greek poets and logographers, has passed on to us, modern criticism is either definitely sceptical or extremely cautious. We are all well aware of the legendary nature of the tradition concerning the arrival of Aeneas in Latium, and hence the descent of the Romans from the Trojans, a legend that formed such an important part of the mythico-historical inheritance of late republican and imperial Rome. Equally baseless historically for the most part is the whole series of traditions concerning the Pelasgians, a people of Thessaly who were thought to have emigrated in post-Homeric times to various regions of the Aegean and even to Italy on the grounds of certain similarities in the form of place-names in Thessaly and in the countries that were thought to have been the goal of these migrations. Thus all those areas where the name Larissa appeared were called Pelasgic, because of Larissa in Thessaly: e.g. Attica, Argolis, Achaia, Crete, Lesbos, Troas, Lydia, southern Italy. The same may be said of names resembling that of the Thessalian city of Gyrton, such as Gortyna in Crete, Gortynia in Macedonia, Gortys in Arcadia, Croton in southern Italy, and Cortona in Etruria. That Hellanicus' identification of the Tyrrhenians of Italy, i.e. the Etruscans, with the Pelasgians was largely a learned hypothesis based on toponymic similarities and due to the mania for looking everywhere in the world around Greece for traces of the Pelasgians, is proved by the fact that other writers did speak of a Pelasgian occupation of Etruria, but earlier than, or, in any case, distinct from that of the Tyrrhenians, and that geographers vaguely refer to a land of the Pelasgians somewhere in Italy close to the land of the Etruscans.[4] This does not exclude, however, the possibility that ancient tradition, recorded by Herodotus himself (I, 57), as to the presence in Italy (at Cortona?) and in the Aegean (Hellespont) of Pelasgians speaking the same tongue, cannot be based upon observed affinities between the pre-Hellenic ethnic substrata of the two areas in question.[5]

Of a more complex nature is the problem concerning the migrations of the Tyrrhenians from Asia Minor or from the Aegean isles. It is very probable that, according to Pareti's criticism, Herodotus' well-known relation of the arrival of the Lydians in Italy under the leadership of Tyrrhenus should also be relegated amongst the learned fables of Ionic logographers, attracted by the similarity of the name Tyrrhenian (*Tyrrhenòi, Tyrsenòi*) with that of the cities of Tyrrha or Torrhebus in Lydia. Tradition knew of peoples bearing the name of Tyrrhenians in the east as well. But it is unlikely that ancient writers had notice of other Tyrrhenians, besides those of the west (i.e. the Etruscans), before the fifth century B.C., for otherwise the silence of Herodotus and Hellanicus on the matter would be difficult to explain. It is possible that the localization of Tyrrhenians at Lemnos, in the Aegean and in Asia Minor (frequent among later writers) followed on learned elaborations of the Ionian historians: i.e. of the identification of the Tyrrhenians with the Pelasgians (well known as the primitive inhabitants of Lemnos) and with the Lydians.

The question of the *Trš.w*, mentioned in Egyptian monuments as a people that came from the sea, does not vitally affect the Etruscan problem, though it has often been brought into the field especially in support of the 'oriental' theory. The first difficulty arises in reading the word, which in the hieroglyphic inscriptions is literally rendered as *Twrwš.w* (with the variants *Twrjš.w, Twjrš.w*). The spelling is a syllabic one adopted for foreign names, where the semi-vowels *w* and *j* may represent vowel sounds (the pronounciation would thus be *Toorooshah, Tooreeshah,* or *Toorshah*). Amongst the various assailants of Egypt there are also mentioned the *Rk.w* (or Lookah, Lookoo), the *Jqjwšw.* (or Aqajwahshah), the *Drdnj.w* (or Dardnooey), the *Prst.w* (or Pooloosaht), the *Šrdn.w* (or Shardeenah, Shardahnah), the *Šqrš.w* (or Shahqahlooshah), respectively identified with the Lycians, the Achaeans, the Dardanians, the Philistines, the Sardinians, the Sicels. Some of these identifications (such as the Achaeans and the Philistines) are by now undisputed; others, like the Sardinians and the Sicels, are still weak and uncertain. In equating the *Trš.w* with the Tyrrhenians, scholars had in mind the ancestors of the Etruscans while still in the Aegean or wandering over the seas in search of new lands. The thematic identity of *Trš.w* with *Tyrsenòi* is possible and even probable. But the frequency of analogous forms attested in ancient Mediterranean proper names deprives the comparison of any specific value it may have. We are therefore unable to demonstrate for the moment the identity of the Mediterranean people mentioned by the Egyptian monuments of the end of the second millennium B.C. with the Etruscans, called Tyrrhenians by the Greeks and whose national life developed in Italy during the first millennium. Similarly we cannot definitely exclude the possibility that the *Trš.w* that attacked Egypt were a people who came from the West.[6]

Let us now consider the archaeological aspect of the problem. We should point out straightaway that the manifestation of the Etruscan orientalizing civilization did not take place in such a way as to justify the hypothesis of the landing of a foreign people bringing their own culture with them; whereas unmistakable manifestations accompanied the arrival of Greek colonists in Sicily and southern Italy and of Carthaginian colonists in Sicily and Sardinia. In the more evolved phases of the 'Villanovan' iron culture there began to appear noticeable changes in the form and decoration of monuments (e.g. tombs) and objects (e.g. vases, weapons, etc.). These changes anticipated the splendour of the subsequent orientalizing phase: the use of iron became general, precious metals (gold and silver) were more frequent and at the same time there was a greater number of objects and patterns of foreign extraction (scarabs and amulets from Egypt, imitations of Greek painted pottery, etc.). But these exotic features were not exclusively and specifically the essential elements of the orientalizing civilization. The great architectonic tombs, black *bucchero* and *impasto* pottery, vases and weapons in laminated bronze, the shape of jewels and especially of *fibulae*, were well within the scope of the indigenous culture, even though activated by external ferments and the stimulus of economic prosperity. Other Mediterranean cultures of the same period offer only vague parallels to these manifestations. There was as already stated no lack of objects imported from the Syro-Egyptian and Greek worlds, but they were relatively limited in number; on the other hand there was a characteristic type of decoration where Egyptian, Mesopotamian, Syriac, and Aegeo-Asiatic motifs mingled at times in hybrid compositions; its original inspiration has been sought in the cities and ports of mixed culture such as those of Phoenicia and Cyprus, but its spread and elaboration was largely due to the Greeks themselves in the course of the seventh century B.C.[7] The main impression gained when considering Etruscan tombs of the orientalizing period, and their sumptuous fittings, is that their structure and the essential forms of the culture they represent were a development of local tendencies, whilst the spirit and characteristics of the decorative elements were external and acquired, and may be attributed to the oriental 'fashion'. If we ignore for the moment the composite character – indigenous and exotic – of this orientalizing civilization, and examine only its exotic elements, it becomes clear that they are no longer exclusive to Etruria, but appear in approximately the same forms in many contemporary Mediterranean lands, as in Punic Sardinia, southern Italy, the sanctuaries of the Greek world, Crete, etc., in those places in fact where no Tyrrhenian immigration could possibly be suspected.[8]

During the two centuries that followed the orientalizing fashion of the seventh to sixth century B.C., Etruria received in large measure cultural and artistic influences from Greece (Ionia at first and later Attica). A much more decisive alteration of the old indigenous culture took place under this influx: it even affected religion and everyday customs, as is clearly shown by the Hellenic deities and myths that penetrated Etruria. No one of course would dare put forward the historical absurdity of a sixth-century Greek colonization of Etruria, although we have actual proof of the presence of Greek trading colonies in Etruscan ports. Though the value of this argument is only indirect and analogical, it may help to reject the hypothesis that would make the Etruscan orientalizing civilization coincide with a presumed arrival of the Etruscans from the East.

As for the funeral rite, we should bear in mind that though it is true that cremation tombs were predominant during the 'Villanovan' phase whereas inhumation tombs were more numerous during the succeeding orientalizing period, the fact is of extremely limited value. We find iron age cremation cemeteries spread along the coast, backed by a compact area of inhumation peoples in the centre of Italy. These coastal cemeteries are seldom entirely devoted to cremation, for they are often found scattered with inhumation tombs. The latter, consisting mostly of poorly furnished graves, are difficult to date; but when it is possible to demonstrate that the funeral deposits are contemporary (as in the later phase of the 'Villanovan' culture and especially in southern Etruria: Tarquinii, Caere, Veii), we are immediately struck by the fact that the frequency of burial graves is as great as, if not greater than that of incineration tombs. There is no sudden change from one rite to the other. It is probable that in lower Etruria, already predominantly given to inhumation and exposed to the most direct cultural influences from central Italy, inhumation triumphed as easily as the seventh century B.C.; in inner northern Etruria however (e.g. Clusium), the advent of the orientalizing civilization was marked by no change in the cremation rite, which continued uninterruptedly up to the days of Imperial Rome. Now Clusium was just as Etruscan as Tarquinii and Caere. Should an explanation for this phenomenon be sought, it will be found only in the progressive reconquest on the part of inhumation of the originally much greater area where cremation was practised, and not in the advent of a new rite introduced by a new people.

In spite of objections to the contrary made by Lattes, Pareti, and other scholars,[9] a close relationship unites Etruscan with the dialect spoken at Lemnos before the Athenian conquest of the island at the hand of Miltiades in the second half of the sixth century B.C.

There are precise agreements in flexional endings (-*z*, -*eiz*, -*zi*, -*ai*, -*aiθ*, -*ale*, -*ial*, etc. in Lemnian, and -*s*, -*eis*, -*si*, -*ai*, -*aiθ*, -*ale*, -*ial* in Etruscan inscriptions); in roots and in words (*naφoθ*, *ziazi*, *maraz* and *marazm*, *aviz*, *zivai*, *zeronai* and *zeronaiθ*, *morinail*, *haralio*, *arai*, etc. in Lemnian, and *napti* or *nefts*, *zia*, *mar* and *maru*, *avils*, *zivas*, *zeri*, *murinasie*, *harc*, *are* and *aras* in Etruscan inscriptions); and even in whole expressions (*holaiezi φokiasiale* and *larθiale hulχniesi; aviz sialχviz* and *avils . . . sealχlsc*). These agreements are all the more remarkable since we are only able to utilize a single Lemnian document of some importance, the funerary stele found at Kaminia.[10] This does not mean however that Lemnian and Etruscan were the same language, or even two dialects of the same language. Many words and forms have no equivalent in the opposite language, and the concordances so far observed have not helped to explain definitely the lexical and grammatical forms of the Lemnian inscriptions. As for Lydian and the other hitherto known languages of Asia Minor, their relationship with Etruscan within the compass of the pre-Indo-European Mediterranean linguistic units appears to be still more remote. Further, the onomastic agreements between Etruscan and the Asian languages carry no great weight (as Miss Fiesel correctly pointed out) when we consider that they are based upon material collected from Asian languages of great diversity, and that the onomastic agreements linking Etruscan with the Italic languages, for example, do not prove any common relationship between the two.[11] In the case of Lydian, these facts definitely exclude the possibility that the Etruscans, according to the letter of Herodotus' relation, were an ethnic group that had split from the main body of the Lydian nation.

Let us now examine arguments in support of the oriental hypothesis, not in isolation, but in the light of their reciprocal geographical and chronological relations. Classical sources agree in placing the original home of the Etruscans within the Aegean or on the Asiatic coast, and the linguistic analogies with Lemnian and the Asian languages partly concur with them. But those foreign elements that went to make up the orientalizing civilization lead us to a south-eastern cultural area, i.e. to Syria and Egypt, and not to the Aegeo-Asiatic area as would be expected if the Etruscans had brought these elements over from their presumed home. The principal vehicle for the orientalizing influx must therefore have been the Phoenician and Greek navigators: they influenced in much the same way various other regions of the Mediterranean basin. The counter-proof to these statements is obtained from an examination of the Asian culture of the eighth century B.C., i.e. of the period when the migration is said to have taken place; and this despite the small number of protohistoric excavations made on the Aegean coast of Asia Minor.

The discoveries made in Lemnos, at Smyrna (Bayrakli) and at other coastal points of Ionia and Asiatic Aeolis, at Sardis and in the interior of Anatolia (Alishar, Pozarli, etc.) have not brought to light any elements common to the orientalizing civilization of Etruria (if we except those of a rather vague and generic nature, such as tumuli, rock tombs, etc.) for the period termed 'Phrygian' in Asia Minor (eleventh to seventh century) and 'Tyrrhenian', but improperly, at Lemnos ('Pelasgian' would be a better term, on the basis of the oldest and most authoritative historical tradition).[12] Pottery continues to feature Anatolian geometric patterns or Mycenaean elements in its painted decorations, and the vases differ in shape from traditional and typical Etrusco-Italic ware. No derivations, in either direction, need be postulated between the black and grey ceramic of Anatolia and the characteristic *bucchero* of Etruria. The typical Asiatic *fibula*, extremely common everywhere, consisted of a semicircular rigid bow with pearl ornamentations, or was shaped like a magnet. It seems impossible that it should not have accompanied the migrations of an Asiatic people, and it is remarkable that it did not spread westwards, not even by way of commerce. And yet only one typical specimen has so far been found in central Italy: in the Riserva del Truglio, in Latium,[13] i.e. outside Etruria proper! The relations between Asia Minor and Etruria appear on the other hand to have become more and more close as we pass on to historical times, culminating in the preponderant Ionian influences in Italy during the sixth century. But this has nothing to do with the question of Etruscan origins as presented by supporters of the 'oriental' theory.

The identification of the orientalizing civilization with a presumed Etruscan immigration also appears to be invalidated for chronological reasons. The beginnings of the Etruscan orientalizing phase cannot be taken further back than the beginning of the seventh century B.C., i.e. the period during which Greek colonists were already firmly established on the coasts of Sicily and southern Italy. But Herodotus' relation on the Lydian migration should not on the other hand be detached arbitrarily from his chronological system that places it during the reign of King Atys of Lydia, i.e. (according to traditional mythical chronology) shortly after the Trojan war, between the thirteenth and twelfth century B.C. Such an important event occurring at the dawn of history and parallel with Greek colonization (and also competing with it) would not have been silently passed over by ancient historians nor transfigured, as in Herodotus, into a mythical event occurring half a millennium earlier. On the other hand as authoritative a source as the Greek historian Ephorus (quoted by Strabo, VI, 2, 2), when speaking of the founding in Sicily of Naxos – the oldest Chalcidian colony – during the eighth century, stated that before that time the Greeks would not venture on the western seas for fear of the Tyrrhenians. He therefore implicitly admits the presence of Tyrrhenians on the Italian shores.[14]

After breaking the link that was thought to unite the orientalizing civilization of Etruria with a possible Etruscan immigration, there is still the possibility that the latter might have occurred at an earlier period (as held by Bérard). In this case however no archaeological evidence can any longer be adduced in support of the theory, since there are no traces of eastern influences during the bronze age and the beginning of the iron age in Etruria (there is not even so far any evidence of relations with the Mycenaean world, so very plain in the south of the peninsula!). We should therefore have to limit ourselves to the data obtained from tradition with all their uncertainty and all their weakness. However, the linguistic evidence still remains: the similarities between Etruscan and Lemnian are certainly remarkable when considered in the light of the legends that give Lemnos as the original home of the Etruscans. This is the only argument in favour of the oriental theory that carries a certain weight, though the problem is rendered extremely intricate by it, and we are left without the possibility of defining either the character or the time of the relations between Lemnos and Etruria. These may find their place within the pre-Indo-European Aegeo-Tyrrhenian linguistic unit mentioned in the preceding chapter. Etruscan, forced to the extreme west by the Indo-European advance, and Lemnian, relegated to an island, would then represent conservative and marginal relics of such a unit, bound by certain similarities, in the sense of the Pelasgic ethno-linguistic 'islands' presupposed by the passage of Herodotus, I, 57, as outlined above. At any rate the known Lemnian inscriptions belong to the seventh or sixth century, that is to a period when the Etruscan nation was already formed in Italy. Moreover to isolate Etruscan from its geographical setting – as the supposition of a recent colonization of the Etrurian coast on the part of Lemnians would lead us to do – would mean going against the evidence of the presence of an ancient 'Tyrrhenian' toponymy in the regions of Italy that were later occupied by Indo-European-speaking peoples, and against the undoubted affinities that exist between Etruscan and other very ancient Italian dialects such as 'Raetic'.[15]

### The Theories of Northern Provenance and of Autochthony

Let us now pass on to a review of the 'northern' theory. The old comparison of the name of Rasenna with that of the Raetians is puerile: the inscriptions found in the region of Trento and the upper valley of the Adige were written at a comparatively recent date (after the fourth century B.C.) and if they reveal very ancient ties or more recent relationships with Etruscan, they are quite valueless for the purpose of ascribing an Alpine origin to the Etruscans as a fully constituted people. From the archaeological point of view, the criticism already made of Pigorini's and Helbig's theories seriously invalidates the 'northern' hypothesis. The

Etruscan character of the Po valley was the result of a historically well defined conquest that took place between the end of the sixth and the beginning of the fifth century, as is proved by the nature of its culture and its inscriptions; here we may agree with Brizio and Ducati, though denying that the 'Villanovans' of the earlier Bologna phases were Italic Umbrians, whose appearance on the eastern slopes of the Apennines is more recent still.

Linguistic science has now definitely discarded any possibilities of a relationship between Etruscan and the Italic languages, so that even from this point of view Helbig's and Pigorini's theses of a single descent on the part of Etruscan and Italic peoples has lost all meaning. This explains the reaction of De Sanctis and Pareti who tend to identify the Etruscans with the 'Villanovan' cremation peoples, and the Italic peoples with the inhumators of the old aeneolithic stock (or, as we would say now, with the central Italian peoples possessing the Apenninic bronze culture). This identification is the only one that satisfies the correspondence we have already noted between the inhumation and cremation areas on the one hand and the Indo-European and non-Indo-European linguistic areas on the other.

The value of De Sanctis' and Pareti's observations is however mainly of a general order: they should not be taken as an identification of particular peoples. There is no proof of the existence of a 'Villanovan' ethnic unit, still less of its descent from the North. The simpler and more archaic 'Villanovan' cemeteries of Aemilia and Romagna do not attest a chronological priority in the strictest sense: they may equally well be explained as marginal or late manifestations. In any case these primitive atypical monuments suggest an Adriatic area of diffusion (Lozzo near Este, Pianello della Genga in the Marches) rather than a northern origin.[16] On the other hand, the fact that the Latins cremated their dead whereas the Umbro-Sabellians practised inhumation cannot be explained by supposing with Pareti that the Latin immigration took place later than the Umbro-Sabellian (thus contrasting with the linguistic data). The explanation lies rather in the fact that the Latins during the protohistoric period lived close to the cremation area, whereas the peoples of southern Italy and Sicily, thought to be more closely related to the Latins from the linguistic point of view, belonged culturally to the inhumating civilizations.

A further argument disproving the northern theory is the nature of Etruscan itself, a Mediterranean language more or less closely related to the pre-Hellenic languages of the Aegean. In order to admit that it belonged to a continental rather than a southern ethnic group, we would have to imagine a migration originating from the East and proceeding across the Balkans; but we would still have to explain those elements in the 'Tyrrhenian' toponymy of peninsular Italy seemingly related to Etruscan. These reservations do not however exclude the presence in Etruscan of linguistic elements belonging to the north-western branches of the pre-Indo-European substratum (such as 'Ligurian' or 'Raetic') or even to the Indo-European stock. If anything, this points to a widespread mingling in the area of elements of different origins due to the complex superposition of linguistic strata.

The autochthonous theory is also open to justified attacks. The linguistic conception of Trombetti, Devoto, Ribezzo, etc., who saw in the foundations of Etruscan the relic of a greater pre-Indo-European linguistic unit, is, methodologically speaking, indisputable. It rests upon the Mediterranean affinities of Etruscan and the presence throughout most of Italy of a 'Tyrrhenian' underlayer as revealed by toponymy. *Vice versa* the archaeological reconstruction attempted by Antonielli and Devoto comes up against very serious objections. It presupposes a clear ethnic opposition of aeneolithic inhumators to 'Villanovan' cremation peoples descended from the North, and identifies the former with the primitive 'Tyrrhenian' stratum, the latter with the Italic Indo-European invaders. Once again however the almost exact correspondence of the cremation and inhumation areas with those of non-Indo-European and of Indo-European dialects respectively is obviously opposed to this 'autochthonous' reconstruction. Can it be that Etruria, where the cremation peoples (or, according to the old Pigorinian conception, the Italic peoples descended from the North) were most typical and most numerous, and where the preceding cultures (aeneolithic and bronze) were of a rather secondary and marginal character – can it be that Etruria was the very corner of Italy where the primitive language had preserved its main features down to the fullness of historical times? Whereas the Italic languages should have triumphed in the eastern areas of the peninsula where only sporadic and insignificant traces exist of the passage of the presumed Italic cremation peoples! It is clear that linguistic autochthony cannot be constrained within the absurd limits imposed by archaeological reconstructions in which the mark of the old Pigorinian prejudice is still so very patent. At any rate a purely autochthonic origin reveals itself *a priori* as an abstract, unhistoric theory; it also clashes with the evidence of cultural developments that reveal European and eastern influences and also with the presence of deep-seated Indo-European elements in the Etruscan language.

### Towards a Solution of the Problem

None of the three fundamental theories concerning the origin of the Etruscans may this be invoked towards a definite solution of our problem. But in the review of each of these theories, there stand out, together with negative elements, several positive specific aspects that fit without difficulty all the factual data we possess, and which therefore may be used in our discussion; they are:

(i) the establishment of a certain link between the Etruscans of historical times and the inhabitants of pre-Hellenic Lemnos;

(ii) the identification of the cremation peoples of western Italy and particularly of the peoples of the 'Villanovan' culture with the ethnic stock of the Etruscans;

(iii) the definition of Etruscan in its fundamental nucleus as a linguistic relic of a vaster pre-Indo-European 'Tyrrhenian' unit that once occupied the peninsula, in a zone where south-eastern ('Tyrrhenian') and northern ('Ligurian' and 'Raetic') substratum areas met and were superimposed.

Having set down these data, we shall now use them as starting-points in attempting a satisfactory explanation of our problem. But first it is necessary that the problem should be correctly formulated. In the various theories that have been advanced so far, the complexity of a phenomenon as great and many-sided as that of the origin of an historical nation has been reduced to schematic, and at times oversimplified, formulae. The Etruscan people have been considered as a unit, a block, right from their inscrutable prehistory; and to explain their appearance in Italy it was necessary to have recourse to the external and over-simple concept of *provenance:* in a positive sense, by accepting the idea of an actual arrival from foreign lands (eastern or northern) and thereby merely shifting the problem in space without actually solving it; and in a negative sense, by excluding an actual arrival and identifying the Etruscans with the ancient inhabitants of the peninsula, and thereby shifting the problem back in time. Even when the idea of a mingling of peoples has been put forward (e.g. that of a mingling of Tyrrhenians from Asia with indigenous

Umbrians, or of Mediterranean aeneolithic peoples with Italic cremation peoples) the predominance given to one of the formative elements has had the effect of attributing to it by anticipation the name and characteristics of the Etruscan nation.

Now the methodological basis of our discussion must be as follows: we must consider the concept 'Etruscan' as well defined, limited, and attached to a controllable historical reality: that of a nation that flourished in Etruria between the eighth and first century B.C., possessing its own language and its own customs. Various ethnic, linguistic, political, and cultural elements contributed to the formation of this historical reality. We may discuss the origin and provenance of each of these elements; but a more appropriate concept for the comprehensive phenomenon determined by them, would be that of *formation*. So as to make our meaning clearer we would like to point out that no one would dream of asking where Italians or Frenchmen came from originally, it is the formation of the Italian and French nations that we study. We may however speak of the origin of the Celts, of their Roman conquerors, of the Franks that were later to invade Gaul: ethnical elements that all went to the formation of the French nation. The same may be said concerning its linguistic and cultural elements. An essential factor in the formation of a nation is the geographical: the actual territory of a nation is that in which its formative process has taken place.

The inadequacy of the theories on Etruscan origins is due to the fact that the problem has been considered as one of provenance, whereas there merely existed one of ethnic formation. There have been discussions on whether they came from the east, the north, or on whether they were actually autochthonous, whereas the Etruscans formed a complex of eastern, European, and Italian elements which must be isolated, weighed, and compared one with the other.

It is naturally far from easy to attempt a reconstruction of the facts and tendencies that determined the birth of historical Etruria; but we are meanwhile able to state without fear of going wrong that the formative process of the nation *can only have taken place on the territory of Etruria proper;* and we are able to witness the final stages of this process thanks to the rich archaeological documentation we possess for the period from the eighth to the sixth century. This point of view has recently also been adopted by the historian F. Altheim, who, though he postulates a fusion of eastern immigrants with indigenous peoples, identifies the origins of the Etruscan nation with the formation of a political and cultural κοινή of those peoples inhabiting Etruscan territory.

The linguistic elements point to eastern affinities within the compass of the pre-Indo-European 'Tyrrhenian' unit. But the theories of oriental origin and of autochthony end by merging if we suppose a Tyrrhenian east-to-west movement in prehistoric times; Etruscan would then have been the westernmost outpost of such a movement as well as its last surviving remnant in the Italian peninsula. Naturally this explanation would be different if direct historical contacts were supposed between Etruria and, say, Lemnos; we have however no archaeological evidence and insufficient historical documents concerning such contacts.

We have already seen how absurd it was to wish to dissociate the 'Villanovan' cremation peoples from the Etruscan *ethnos*. Their appearance is in fact marked by a remarkable progress in the cultural development of Etruria which until then had displayed quite primitive manifestations linked in their essentials to aeneolithic culture and only partly influenced by the Apenninic bronze civilization.

With the 'Villanovan' culture we begin to see the growth of considerable centres of population in those sites which were to become the great historical centres of Etruria: Veii, Caere, Tarquinii, Vulci, Vetulonia, Populonia, etc. From the beginning of the 'Villanovan' culture till the fullness of historical times, this civilization develops without any break or sudden transformation. This cultural horizon clearly represents the external aspect of the Etruscan people during their formation; this statement however does not imply its reciprocal, i.e. that the appearance of the 'Villanovan' culture marks the appearance of the Etruscans.

In the present state of our knowledge, we are faced with a very arduous problem when trying to explain the origin of the 'Villanovan' culture of Etruria. Its characteristics, quite revolutionary when compared with the cultural level preceding it, would justify the classical hypothesis of an immigration of peoples. But this does not mean that it had to appear suddenly; it is even probable that its formative process may have been quite long and complex. Certain factors – e.g. the very rite of cremation, with ossuaries made of rough pottery, spheroidal or with a tendency to be biconical – should be considered as imported from regions outside our area, perhaps even by way of more or less substantial migrations. One may postulate infiltrations from the continent by way of the land route, as a reflection of the spread of the 'urn-fields' of central Europe and connected with the cremation cemeteries that make their appearance in northern Italy towards the end of the late bronze age. But infiltrations may also have taken place from the south by coastal or sea routes, if account is taken of certain very archaic cemeteries, traces of which have recently been discovered in Etruria not far from the Tyrrhenian coast (in the neighbourhood of Ischia di Castro and at Sticciano, near Grosseto [17]) and of a number of the more primitive cremation tombs of the Villanovan cemeteries belonging to the great southern Etruscan cities. In both cases there are unusual affinities with the culture of those isolated centres of cremation peoples who, as has already been seen, make their first appearance between the end of the bronze age and the beginning of the iron age in Apulia (Torre Castelluccia, Timmari) and on the coasts of Sicily (Milazzo).

But the true 'Villanovan' civilization, considered as a whole, is an original phenomenon, wrought locally upon Apenninic bronze-culture foundations, some of whose characteristic elements it absorbs (e.g. the shape of the great biconical *hydria* of dark *impasto* with wave patterns on the necks[18]). It is unnecessary, therefore, to postulate a deep ethnic transformation at the beginning of the 'Villanovan' period; but rather an impulse, a determining ferment which would have brought about the crystallization of 'Tyrrhenian' ethnic elements into an Etruscan nation in those territories that lie north of the Tiber. Thus the 'Villanovan' culture of Etruria proper would already mirror in the main the dawning of an Etruscan *ethnos*, the 'eastern' iron culture would indicate the formation of Umbro-Sabellic Italic elements, and the southern and Latian cultures that of the Latins and kindred peoples.[19]

This picture of the formation of the Etruscan nation is not complete without the inclusion of the elements that accompanied its first historical stages. The intellectual and artistic contacts with the East and with Greece played a preponderant role: they occurred through oversea trade, but probably also through direct intercourse or contacts with commercial colonies on Etruscan territory. The impression received by the still fresh, primitive, malleable Etruscan mind from the mature oversea civilizations was probably such as to orientate decisively the spiritual bent of the nation and to justify the feeling of strong ethnic affinities with the eastern world, a feeling which perhaps the ancients themselves did not eschew. This does not mean however that the civilization of ancient Etruria grew entirely from foreign seeds;

even less does it mean that the Etruscan national entity should be estranged from the racial, linguistic, and cultural background of ancient Italy.

## NOTES

1. A history of the problem will be found in P. Ducati, *Le problème étrusque*, 1938. The whole problem of Etruscan origins is also tackled in the monographs of L. Pareti, *Le origini etrusche*, 1926, and of F. Schachermeyer, *Etruskische Frühgeschichte*, 1929; their conclusions however do not agree. Cf. also M. Pallottino, *La origine degli Etruschi*, 1947; F. Altheim, *Der Ursprung der Etrusker*, 1950; where full bibliographical data will be found.

2. *Revue des Études Anciennes*, LI, 1949, pp. 201 ff.

3. *Glotta*, XXX, 1943, pp. 213 ff.

4. M. Pallottino, *Tradizione etnica e realtà culturale dell' Etruria, Umbria e Romagna prima della unificazione augustea* (in *Relazioni della XXVIII Riunione della Società Italiana per il Progresso delle Scienze*, V, 1940, pp. 81 ff.). See also note 1 on p. 82.

5. Cf. M. Pallottino, *Erodoto autoctonista?* in *Studi Etruschi*, XX, 1948–9, pp. 11 ff.

6. On the sources and problem of the *Tršw*, cf. F. W. von Bissing, *Die Überlieferung über die Turuscha* (in *Wiener Zeitschrift für die Kunde des Morgenlandes*, XXXV, 1928, pp. 177 ff.).

7. Cf. L. Pareti, *La tomba Regolini-Galassi e la civiltà dell' Italia centrale nel sec. VII av. Cr.*, 1947, pp. 520 ff. It should be remembered, however, that the Greeks responsible for the spread of the orientalizing civilization were unlikely to be Phocaeans, as thought by Pareti, but rather Chalcidians and Dorians: cf. *Studi Etruschi*, XX, 1948–9, pp. 335 ff.

8. F. Poulsen, *Der Orient und die frühgriechische Kunst*, 1912.

9. C. Pauli, *Eine vorgriechische Inschrift von Lemnos* (*Altitalischen Forschungen*, 1886, 1894); E. Nachmanson, *Die vorgriechische Inschriften von Lemnos* and G. Karo, *Die 'Tyrsenische' Stele von Lemnos* in *Atenische Mitteilungen*, XXXIII, 1908, pp. 47 ff.; L. Pareti, *Le origini etrusche*, pp. 89 ff.; S. P. Cortsen, *Die lemnische Inschrift*, in *Glotta*, XVIII, 1929–30, pp. 101 ff.; J. Friedrich, *Kleinasiatische Sprachdenkmäler*, 1932, pp. 143 ff.; B. Hrozny, *Die Inschrift von Lemnos*, in *Studi Etruschi*, IX, 1935, pp. 127 ff.; S. P. Cortsen, *L'inscription de Lemnos*, in *Latomus*, Brussels, II, 1938, pp. 3 ff.; P. Kretschmer, *Die*

*tyrrhenischen Inschriften der Stele von Lemnos*, in *Glotta*, XXIX, 1941, pp. 89 ff.

10. The other known inscriptions are only very brief and scratched on fragments of vases; they are practically useless from the linguistic point of view: cf. A. della Seta, in *Scritti in onore di B. Nogara*, 1937, pp. 119 ff.

11. A. Trombetti, *La lingua etrusca*, 1928; E. Fiesel, *Etruskisch*, 1931, p. 63. P. Meriggi (in *Osservazioni sull'Etrusco*, in *Studi Etruschi*, XI, 1937, pp. 129 ff.), re-examined the close relationship between Etruscan and Lydian but with negative results as far as the interpretation of Etruscan is concerned.

12. On Lemnos D. Mustilli, *La necropoli tirrenica di Efestia*, in *Annuario Scuola Ital. d'Atene*, XV, XVI, 1938. For Asia Minor, cf. H. Th. Bossert, *Altanatolien*, 1942; K. Bittel, *Grundzüge der Vor- und Frühgeschichte Kleinasiens*, 2nd ed., 1950, with relevant bibliography.

13. U. Antonielli, in *Bullettino di Paletnologia*, L–LI, 1930–1, pp. 191 ff.

14. Cf. E. Fiesel, *Etruskisch*, 1931, pp. 65 ff., who also quotes U. Wilamowitz' authoritative opinion on the subject.

15. G. Devoto, *Storia della lingua di Roma*, pp. 17 ff.

16. Cf. G. Patroni, *La preistoria*, 2nd ed., pp. 733 ff.

17. For Sticciano, cf. *Studi Etruschi*, XXI, 1950–1, pp. 297 ff.; for Ischia di Castro, see F. Rittatore, in *Rivista di Scienze Preistoriche*, VI, 1951, pp. 167 ff.

18. See M. Pallottino, *L'origine degli Etruschi*, pp. 113 ff.

19. Cf. note 26 on p. 45.

# CHAPTER THREE

## THE ETRUSCANS AND THE SEA

### *The Etruscan 'Thalassocracy'*

THESE frequently sterile and interminable discussions on the origin of the Etruscans have generally led etruscologists and students of ancient history to lose sight of problems much more attractive and useful in the study of the ancient civilizations of Italy.

It has been said, for instance, that it was Carthage that taught the Romans navigation and how to be masters of the sea: just as Greece had been their teacher in the realms of art and poetry. There is a part of truth in both assertions, in the sense that on the high and universal level of Hellenistic culture the teachings of both Carthage and Greece played a decisive role in the growth of the civilization and might of Rome. But it would be a very serious mistake to imagine that republican Rome, like the Rome of the kings before it, was no more than a city of shepherds and semi-barbarous peasants, when she lived on the borders of, and greatly profited by the advanced civilization of Etruria. To the refined generations of Cicero and Augustus, the Roman of one or two centuries before could well have seemed *'ferus victor'*, *'arte rudis'*. But when we think that already towards the end of the sixth or the beginning of the fifth century such superb and mature works of art as the Capitoline she-wolf or the Ficoroni cist were being produced in Rome, we cannot help realizing the absurdity of a definition that many moderns have unfortunately accepted uncritically from the hands of ancient authors.

It was Etruria that first gave the Italic peoples the urge to conquer and dominate the sea. We cannot overlook the unanimous testimonies given by historical tradition: they all speak of a far-reaching domination of the sea on the part of the Tyrrhenians or Etruscans. Greek historians referred to this domination by the traditional name of 'thalassocracy'. From relatively ancient times Greek tradition took pleasure in representing the supremacy of the Etruscans both in eastern and in western seas as dreadful and unceasing piracy. In the 'Homeric' hymn to Dionysus, for example, the god is ravished by Tyrrhenian pirates whom he later succeeds in metamorphosing into dolphins. Under the name of Pelasgians, they were also held responsible for the stealing of Hera's statue on the isle of Samos (Athenaeus, xv, 12), for the rape of Brauron's wives in Attica and the conquest and sack of Athens (Plutarch, *de mul. virt.*, 8; *Aetia gr.*, 21; Eustathius, *Comm. Dion*, 591; Philochorus, 5).[1] The control and ceaseless threatening of the western seas, especially the Tyrrhenian, the Ionian, and the coasts of Sicily, were also attributed to the Tyrrhenians (Palaephatus, *Epist.*, xx; Strabo, vi, 2, 2; etc.). To this list should be added references to an Etruscan colonization of Corsica (Diodorus Siculus, v, 13), of Sardinia (Strabo, v, 2, 7), of the Balearic Isles and even of the coasts of Spain (Stephen of Byzantium, s.v. *Banaurides;* Ausonius, *Epist.*, xxxi, 326),[2] and the story of the conflict between Etruscans and Carthaginians for the possession of an Atlantic island (Diodorus Siculus, v, 19 ff.). Etruscan achievements in naval technique, first mentioned by Dionysius (i, 25), are confirmed by the mythological tradition concerning the Tyrrhenian origin of the *rostri* (Pliny, *Nat. Hist.*, vii, 56, 209).

As far as may be inferred from external remains, archaeology supports historical tradition as to the maritime power of the ancient Etruscans. Even without taking into consideration the very large, almost incalculable, number of foreign objects and motifs (Eastern, Sardinian, Punic,

Hellenic) that have been found in archaic Etruscan tombs, denoting intense maritime activity that cannot wholly be due to Phoenician and Greek shipping, there is no lack of evidence pointing to the spread of the Etruscan civilization along the shores of Italy, Sardinia, Corsica, North Africa, as well as in Greece, southern France, and Iberia.[3] This consists of *bucchero* vases, of wrought bronzes, and even of inscriptions in Etruscan (e.g. an ivory tablet bearing the effigy of a lion found at Carthage).[4] From the name of the Etruscan people and that of an Etruscan port, Adria, are derived the names of the two great seas surrounding Italy: the Tyrrhenian and the Adriatic.

When and how did the Etruscan supremacy on the seas become established? How should we interpret the data provided by classical and archaeological sources? It is obvious that such an ample, varied, but in the main unanimous historical documentation as that referring to Etruscan 'thalassocracy' and piracy cannot have been born from nothing and must have largely been due to a widespread feeling of admiration and fear on the part of the Greek world, though it too was much devoted to daring sea and colonizing ventures. A clear indication of such feelings is the core of legends on Tyrrhenian piracy, legends unknown to epic literature but which arose in time to be introduced in the last stages of the elaboration of Greek myths, between the sixth and fifth century B.C. They were obviously embroidered around the core of fearful tales told of these freebooters of antiquity in the coastal towns of Hellas and its colonies. The historical basis of tradition becomes more evident in those western sea areas that were the scene of the adventures of the Tyrrhenian pirates: we are told of the difficulties the Greeks had to face on the seas around Sicily and of the contests between Greeks and Tyrrhenians for the possession of the Lipari islands.

This picture of the Tyrrhenians as fearful and ferocious

bands of privateers fits in well with the tendency to over-simplify ethnic characteristics, both good and evil, that was so dear to classical antiquity; even we moderns cannot wholly free ourselves from it. Its origins must doubtless be sought in the sharp commercial and territorial competition between Etruscan navigators and Greek colonists around the coasts of Italy. Piracy is the most obvious facet of a keen maritime war; and since both the legendary and the histori-cal sources in our possession are Greek, we can easily under-stand the bad name given to the Tyrrhenians by ancient literature. And the great conflict between Greeks and Etruscans in historical times was to be the cause of other preconceived judgements on the moral character of the Etruscans: accusations as to their lasciviousness, sensuality, and refined cruelty were far from uncommon.

The fact that Homer is silent on the subject of Tyrrhenian piracy, whilst the later 'Homeric' hymns on the Dionysus myth refer to it, enables us to place the period of greatest development of Etruscan naval supremacy between the eighth and sixth centuries B.C. Archaeological evidence confirms this. If the passage ascribed to the historian Ephorus (probably derived from one of the Siceliot historians) and included in Strabo's *Geography* (VI, 2, 2) is trustworthy, we are able to state that in the eighth century, when the Greeks were beginning to establish their first trading outposts on the eastern shores of Sicily, the seas surrounding the island were already being ploughed by Etruscan ships. Now the eighth century offers us an apparently primitive picture of the cultural development of Etruria, for it corresponds to the development of the 'Villanovan' culture. But towards the end of this period oriental objects were already beginning to appear, and also the first scratched or painted reproductions of ships (see plate 3B). [5] It is not actually possible to have a clear idea of the capabilities and activities of a people merely from the examination of their tombs, even when the latter show them to be archaic: we only need think of the very daring navigational exploits of the Polynesians, whose culture is of a neolithic type and relatively less advanced than that of the iron age inhabitants of Italy. We cannot exclude therefore that the first seafaring activities of the Etruscans went back as far as the eighth century and that they did come across the oldest Greek colonists.

The Etrurian coastline, jagged and rich in islands, with alternate promontories and flat stretches of coast, must have favoured an early development of coastal navigation for fishing and barter. It is worth noticing that facing Etruria there lay not only Elba with its iron deposits and other small islands near it, but also the great lands of Sardinia and Corsica; the former of the two being the seat of ancient cultures and of a well-developed social organization.

In considering the earliest stages of the civilization and seafaring activities of the Etruscans, we are faced with the problem concerning the relations of Etruria and Sardinia.[6] The legend concerning the foundation of Populonia by the Corsicans (Servius, *ad Aen.* x, 172) is evidence of the presence on the coasts of Etruria of inhabitants from the islands facing it. Strabo (v, 2, 7) explicitly refers to incursions on the coasts of Tuscany by Sardinian pirates, and also attributes a Tyrrhenian origin to the Sardinians. We have much evidence of the commercial relations between the Etruscans of the mining areas and the Sardinians: some objects, including a little bronze ship with animal figurines, found in eighth- and seventh-century tombs at Vetulonia, seem to be incontestably Sardinian. Here and there we also find elements recalling characteristic types of the civilization of the *nuraghi* (those Sardinian prehistoric monuments built without mortar in the shape of a truncated cone): as, for instance, long-necked vases whose occurrence at such an early phase seems to be limited to the Vetulonia necropolis.

There is also the question of whether the technique used in building the typical pseudo-cupola constructions of the northern Etrurian coast is connected with that of the *nuraghi*. In Sardinia too, there are traces of Etruscan influence: these may include the name *Aesaronenses* belonging to one of the peoples inhabiting the eastern coast (cf. the Etruscan word *aisar*, 'gods'), the presence of *bucchero* vases, certain early Sardinian bronze statuettes of Etruscan type, etc. Similarly, a few rock-hewn tombs in the necropolis of S. Andrea Priu or at Fordongianus imitate architectural details found in the Etruscan sepulchres of Cerveteri.

It is interesting to note that the Etruscan area most closely linked with Sardinia is the northern one. This is due to geographical reasons: for even in the Middle Ages and in modern times sea-traffic between Sardinia and the peninsula followed the coasts of Corsica and the Elban archipelago in the direction of Pisa. But the mineral resources of the Populonia and Vetulonia regions must also be taken into account, for this most important factor closely unites Etruria and Sardinia and the characteristics of the two peoples, both equally skilled craftsmen in bronze. This mineral region is the only one in Etruria or, for that matter, in the whole of Italy. Though we would not overstress the economic factor in history, we should remember that, except for the Sardinian mines, the only great iron, copper, and argentiferous lead mines in the central Mediterranean were those of Etruria. From the moment when they first began to be worked (during the iron age, roughly corresponding with the beginnings of the Etruscan civilization), they must have been a centre of especial attraction to the seafaring nations on the shores of the great sea.

Amongst the most characteristic cultural phenomena of primitive Etruria is the passage from the simple iron age 'Villanovan' culture to the orientalizing civilization; as we have seen, this change has been explained by believers in the oversea origin of the Etruscans as a sign of the ethnic change resulting from the establishment of oversea colonists on the coasts of Italy. As far as we are concerned for the moment however, the important aspect of this phenomenon is the great display of wealth that accompanied it: a rapid rise in living standards and a great increase in purchasing power are both attested by large quantities of costly articles from far-off lands, and of precious imported raw materials such as gold, silver, and ivory. The following phase (occupying the sixth and the beginning of the fifth century) also displayed this feature, at least as far as the presence in Etruria of Greek wares is concerned: the cemeteries of the coastal towns of Vulci, Tarquinii, and Caere especially have restored them by the thousand; as a result of this, the present-day study of Attic pottery seems to be based almost exclusively on material extracted from Etruscan sites. It is also clear that in the commercial exchanges between Etruria and the East, Etruria played on the whole a buyer's role: the quantities of Etruscan articles found in other lands, especially in Greece,[7] cannot be compared with that of foreign articles found in Etruria. We are thus faced with a new problem: what was the nature of Etruria's purchasing power? Or, better, what products were exchanged for goods imported from Greece and the Orient? Everything leads us to believe that these products were crude and wrought metals from the Etruscan mines; we already know that a proportion of these metals was sent to Campania (Diodorus Siculus, v, 13), and that metal goods were prominent amongst the Etruscan products known in Greece.

The above statements appear to be obvious and they are in fact admitted by the majority of scholars. They are confirmed by the presence of Greek merchant colonies in the Etruscan ports of Caere and of Spina on the Adriatic. An important objection could however be raised against this over-simplified reconstruction of the facts: namely that those cities that were richest and most rapidly transformed by eastern ideas were in southern Etruria, not in the mining area at all. The answer to this might be that, at first, the exploitation of the great natural wealth of the Etruscan soil largely benefited centres that specialized in brokerage, centres of early political and cultural attainments, in direct contact with the great Mediterranean trade lanes, such cities in fact as Caere or Tarquinii; whereas it was only later that the cities that grew in the neighbourhood of the mining area seized the initiative in the commercial field. This explanation may agree with the late entry of Populonia into the alliance of the twelve Etruscan states (Servius, *ad Aen*, x, 172), and with the fact that in the archaic culture of Vetulonia we find a great abundance of bronze objects, but no imported Greek products such as painted vases. It is certain however that throughout the centuries the mining area represented a constant goal for the Greeks, who during the fifth and fourth centuries sent naval expeditions in an attempt to conquer Elba, without however being able to set foot on the coast of Etruria. The lasting importance of the southern towns as markets for the exchange of Etruscan raw materials for manufactured articles from abroad is shown by the fact that Dionysius of Syracuse's expedition against the Etruscan mining territory began before Caere, with the capture and sack of the port of Pyrgos (Santa Severa) in 384 B.C.

Not only Greek and Phoenician, but Etruscan seamen too must have participated from the very beginning in this great commercial exploitation of the western Mediterranean. Hence the development of Etruscan shipping culminating in its dominance of the Tyrrhenian sea. The Greek colonization of the southern Italian and Sicilian coasts formed an obstacle to the free expansion of Etruscan naval and commercial activities; it gave rise to those conflicts whose echo has reached us by way of the historians of antiquity: Corsica (Herodotus, I, 166), the Lipari islands (Strabo, VI, 2, 10), Cumae (Diodorus Siculus, XI, 51); an explicit reference to an Etruscan naval expedition to Sicily is found in the *elogium* to a personage of ancient Tarquinii preserved in a Latin fragmentary inscription.[8]

The second stage of the Etruscan 'thalassocracy' was in fact characterized by this naval conflict with the Greeks, by the race for the possession of bases on the Tyrrhenian coast (as in Campania and Corsica), and finally by that policy of compromise typified by the alliance with Carthage against the Greek world, an alliance that was so close and so significant that Aristotle in his *Politics* (III, 9, 128a, 36) states that Etruscans and Carthaginians were as citizens of a single state. As a consequence the Etruscan naval sphere of action gradually became restricted during the sixth century, and during the fifth there developed the threat of an economic crisis that was going to hit central Italy with very serious repercussions. The most obvious and characteristic sign of this crisis was the sudden interruption of large-scale importations of Greek vases in the cities of southern Etruria. After this time, the Etruscan dominion of the seas was to be little more than a glorious memory, and the states of Etruria gradually assumed the character of small inland powers waiting to be absorbed by the political hegemony of Rome. When the latter prepared to fight her tremendous naval duel with Carthage, in the third century, not a trace remained of the Etruscan navy, and the allied cities of Etruria did no more than help provide materials for the construction of the Roman fleet.[9]

## NOTES

1. The traditions concerning the adventures of the Tyrrheno-Pelasgians and the possibility of their being historically founded will be found discussed by J. Berard in *Revue des Études Anciennes*, LI,

1949, pp. 224 ff., and in *Studies Presented to D. M. Robinson*, 1951, pp. 135 ff.

2. The demonstration of a proto-Etruscan colonization of Spain attempted by A. Schulten (*Los Tirsenos en España*, in *Ampurias*, ii, 1940; *Tartessos*, 1945) on the basis of toponymy, has however no reliable foundation. These hypothetical linguistic relationships and the analogies found between place-names in Lusitanian inscriptions and in the Tyrrheno-Pelasgic world (cf. *Glotta*, xviii, 1930, pp. 106; *Klio*, xxxiii, 1940, pp. 83 ff.; *Glotta*, xxix, 1941, pp. 90 ff.) may, if need be, be explained by referring back to older, prehistoric contacts (cf. my review of O. F. A. Menghin, *Migrationes Mediterraneae*, in *Doxa*, iii, 1950, pp. 266 ff.).

3. For Greece, see G. Karo, *Etruskisches in Griechenland*, in *Archaiologike Ephemeris*, 1937, pp. 316 ff.; for Spain and Gaul: M. Almagro, *Los hallazgos de bucchero etrusco hacia occidente y su significación*, in *Boletín Arqueol. de la Sociedad Arqueol. Tarraconense*, xlix, 1949, pp. 1 ff., with bibliography of previous studies; M. Pallottino, in *Archeologia Classica*, i, 1949, pp. 80 ff.; H. Rolland, in *Revue des Etudes Anciennes*, li, 1949, pp. 90 ff.

4. E. Benveniste, *Notes étrusques*, in *Studi Etruschi*, vii, 1933, pp. 245 ff.

5. R. Vighi, *La più antica rappresentazione di nave etrusco-italica in un vaso della necropoli veiente* (in *Rendiconti della R. Accademia dei Lincei*, vi, viii, 1932, pp. 367 ff.).

6. Cf. A. Taramelli, *Sardi ed Etruschi*, in *Studi Etruschi*, iii, 1929, pp. 43 ff.; G. Lilliu, in *Studi Sardi*, viii, 1948, pp. 19 ff.; M. Pallottino, *La Sardegna nuragica*, 1950, pp. 37 ff.

7. See note 3 above.

8. Discovered at Tarquinia, near the temple of the 'Queen's altar', and published recently with other historically interesting fragments in M. Pallottino, *Uno spiraglio di luce sulla storia etrusca: gli 'Elogia Tarquiniensia'*, in *Studi Etruschi*, xxi, 1950–1, pp. 147 ff.

9. For the historical problems concerning Etruscan maritime expansion and the relations with the Greek colonies and with Carthage, cf. M. Pallottino, *Gli Etruschi*, 1940, pp. 73 ff.

# CHAPTER FOUR

## THE ETRUSCANS AND ITALY

### *The Etruscan Expansion in Italy and its Starting Point*

*In Tuscorum iure pene omnis Italia fuerat:* in the words of
Cato (Servius, *ad Aen.*, XI, 576), nearly the whole of Italy
had been under Etruscan domination. And Livy (I, 2; V, 33)
stresses the power, the wealth, the renown which the
Etruscans had acquired on land and sea, from the Alps to
the Straits of Messina: a clear proof that the Etruscans did
not merely hold the seas but had also extended their power
over the lands of the peninsula. We are sufficiently well
informed to-day as to which lands lay under Etruscan rule,
and which were only indirectly subjected to its influence.
But Cato's and Livy's statements are of real value, especially when we consider that before the domination of Rome,
the only power able to effect a partial ethnico-political and
a wider cultural unification of Italy was Etruria. In spite of
the loose political system that seems to have dominated
much of its history. Etruscan expansion, relying no doubt
upon the effective union of individual energies, must have
been so powerful (at least for the period that stretched from
the seventh to the sixth century B.C.) that it was able to
achieve a political, territorial, and linguistic unity, in the
Etruscan sense, over most of northern and central and part
of southern Italy as well as over the islands lying off its
Tyrrhenian shores. And there is no doubt that the cultural
mark left on Italy by the Etruscans went far beyond the
geographical and temporal boundaries of their national
life; their civilization radiated over the whole of the peninsula and even over northern lands beyond the barrier of the

Alps,[1] whilst it penetrated at the same time deep into the traditions and customs of Rome so as to survive the death of Etruria as a racially and linguistically distinct nation.

The stretch of land that may be considered as the original territory of the Etruscans lies between the Tyrrhenian and the rivers Tiber and Arno: this is Etruria proper or Tyrrhenian Etruria. To it belong the twelve cities which, according to tradition, make up the Etruscan nation; and here, from a very early age, Etruscan is written and, therefore, spoken. When presented with this rather simplified picture of an Etruscan national territory where the stock had its roots, it is only natural one should suspect the critical validity of the original Etruscan character of this region as a whole. According to the theory that ascribes an oversea origin to the Etruscans, for instance, the Tyrrhenian colonists would first have settled on the coastal strip, and this would have been the starting point for the gradual occupation of the territory. This view seems to be borne out by the difference in the funeral rites – mainly inhumatory in southern Etruria and crematory in northern Etruria: a sign of the predominance of Tyrrhenian immigrants in those regions nearest their landing points, and of pre-Etruscan (i.e. Umbrian) populations in the interior. This idea of an Italic substratum subjugated by a small number of Etruscan conquerors occasionally re-emerges on the margin of discussions or in the study of certain isolated phenomena: as, for example, in the study of the personal names of the Caere inscriptions. These appear to be strongly influenced by Italic elements; according to R. Mengarelli, who was in charge of the excavations, this proves the original 'Italicity' of the population.[2] These inscriptions are comparatively recent, however, for they belong for the most part to the period of direct Roman domination over the Etruscan city, when it actually was the Etruscan element that was disappearing. Just as fanciful, the hypothesis of an Italic origin of Veii has been thoroughly disproved by the discovery in a Veii sanctuary of an abundant crop of archaic Etruscan inscriptions, and by G. Q. Giglioli's studies on the subject.[3]

We cannot however exclude that within geographically Etruscan territory (i.e. on the right bank of the Tiber) there existed important groups of non-Etruscan speakers: the Faliscans for instance, who occupied the area within the curve formed by the Tiber between Orte and the territory of Rome. Though they had been politically and culturally dominated by the Etruscans, they always kept their ethnic and linguistic Italic individuality. The archaic culture of Visentium (Bisenzio) too is remarkably close to that of Latium, whilst 'eastern' cultural elements occur in the oldest manifestations of the Tolfa region. The whole of Etruria, not merely Caere, abounds in onomastic and toponymic elements of Italic origin that betray deep and ancient penetrations of peoples with Indo-European tongues. The fact that the growth of the population and the urban development in coastal southern Etruria occurred earlier and were more vigorous than in the vast inland areas, leads to the conclusion that the formative processes of the Etruscan nation did not occur simultaneously over the whole of Etruria proper, but only after a long struggle with Italic elements, especially in the inland areas of southern Etruria, and they must have ended in the ethnic assimilation or political conquest of such elements.[4]

The lack of authentic historical sources prevents us from attempting the reconstruction, even along the broadest of outlines, of the political and military position of the various Etruscan cities and of their reciprocal relations. The most vivid aspect of history – names of kings and rulers, revolutions, wars, alliances, dates, all those things, that is, that we know with a fair degree of certainty for archaic and classical Greece – remains steeped in darkness for us. We can only just make out an organization based upon city-states more or less independent of each other, but united (at least at the time of the Roman conquest) in a kind of confederation, and perceive their development from monarchical to republican institutions; a process that will be treated in more detail in Chapter VI. The only concrete events of which we have notice are those connected with foreign policy and recorded in Greek and Roman sources. We may even go so far as to presume, on the basis of archaeological data and certain evidence of a literary nature (of Graeco-Roman origin in every case), that the cities of coastal Etruria, and especially Caere, Tarquinii, and Vulci, did go through a phase of particular splendour (both on the seas and, perhaps, on land) during the seventh and sixth centuries. The text of one of the Latin *elogia* recently recovered at Tarquinii, though unfortunately in a fragmentary state, would tend to prove the breadth of Tarquinian interests in archaic times, for it refers on the one hand to some unknown political action with regard to Caere and on the other to a war fought on the territory of Arezzo.[5] Towards the end of the sixth century Clusium probably became dominant (as reflected by the legendary traditions concerning King Porsenna), and this hegemony coincided probably with the beginning of the decadence of the coastal towns. Once again archaeological evidence comes to our support, for it shows a gradual increase in the importance of central and northern centres (Chiusi and Orvieto at first, and later Arezzo, Cortona, Perugia, Volterra, etc.) as the Etruscan civilization drew on to its final phase (from the fifth to the first century B.C.).

The 'Etruscanization' of Italy followed two main directions: to the south, along the Tyrrhenian coast, over Latium and Campania; to the north across the Apennines and over the lower Po valley. As a result Etruscan ethnic and political continuity was established from the Gulf of Salerno to the Tridentine Alps. Outside it to the west we have western Lombardy, Piedmont, and Liguria (all occupied by peoples of Ligurian stock);[6] to the east, Venetia, the whole of the eastern half of Italy (inhabited by Picenians, Umbrians, and Sabellians), and, finally, the southern extremity of the peninsula. It is interesting to note that Etruscan expansion seems to have been most vigorous in those areas inhabited during the iron age by predominantly non-Indo-European peoples or by peoples who practised the cremation rite, areas where ethnic individualities were least marked and where a new amalgamation was therefore less difficult to attain under the compulsion of a strong political force. We may even go so far as to imagine an ethnico-linguistic substratum fitted to receive the Etruscan stamp; as far as the Po valley is concerned, believers in the northern origin of the Etruscans also believed that its primitive inhabitants were Etruscans. The lack of written documents relegates all this to the realms of pure hypothesis. We should not however exclude the possibility of remote links uniting the Ligurians, the Raeto-Euganeans and perhaps even the inhabitants of northern Picenum with the earliest inhabitants of Tyrrhenian Etruria on whose stock the nucleus of the Etruscan nation of historical times was later to form. These links would explain on the one hand the affinities between the 'Villanovan' civilizations of Aemilia and Etruria and on the other the later contrast, in Aemilia itself, between 'Villanovan' and Etruscan civilizations, the latter having been introduced in historical times, towards the end of the sixth century B.C.

The overland expansion of the Etruscans towards the south (i.e. Campania) must have taken place at a very early date. It should be considered in relation to the question of Etruscan predominance over the southern Tyrrhenian and of the opposition they met on the part of the Greek colonies. As early as the eighth century colonists from Chalcis had occupied outposts on the Campanian coast and founded

Cumae, a long way from their bases. Capua, the centre of Etruscan rule in Campania, was built in direct opposition to Cumae, and it seems that frequent attempts were made to eliminate this dangerous Hellenic competitor but with no success.[7] And in this connexion it is interesting to remember that the same wave of Italic peoples from the hills of Samnium who during the second half of the fifth century overwhelmed the Etruscan cities of Campania, also succeeded in dislodging the Greeks from the coast of Campania by occupying Cumae.

Many problems are presented by the Etruscan southward expansion. In the first place, whether the Etruscans had ever in fact been in Campania; some doubts had been cast on this point, soon dispelled however by the discovery of the inscribed tile of Capua and by J. Beloch's arguments.[8] Secondly there is the question of the route: according to some authorities the sea route was used, according to others the land route. A few supporters of the latter alternative believe that the Etruscans followed the valley of the Liri. This presupposes an Etruscan predominance over Latium, which brings us to the problem of the Etruscans in Rome. The existence of an Etruscan phase in the history of Rome is admitted even by those who, like De Sanctis, are little disposed to admit the truth of the Etrusco-Roman legends on the kings of Rome and who refute the Etruscan origin of the Tarquin dynasty.[9] Two recent discoveries have brought this question to the fore, confirming more or less directly the veracity of tradition. Ancient writers speak of two Etruscan brothers, Aulus and Caelius Vibenna, who lived during the last years of the Rome of the kings, and of a certain Mastarna reputed to have been their friend and ally and later identified with the king Servius Tullius of Roman tradition (Varro, *de ling. lat.*, v, 46; Servius, *ad Aen.*, v, 560; Festus 31/44, s.v. *Caelius mons;* Dionysius of Halicarnassus, II, 36, 2 ff.; Claudius, in *C.I.L.*, XIII, 1668;

Tacitus, *Ann.*, IV, 65). In the François tomb at Vulci there is a painting of a battle scene: one camp is composed of a group of fighters amongst whom we find Aule and Cele Vipina (the two brothers Vibenna) and Macstrna (Mastarna); the other, of warriors amongst whom is a Cneve Tarchunies Rumach, who is undoubtedly Gnaeus Tarquinius Romanus, a member therefore of the Tarquin dynasty. These paintings, though probably belonging to the end of the second or beginning of the first century B.C., are accompanied by Etruscan inscriptions and represent the Etruscan version of the tradition.[10] Again in the course of the excavation of a Veii sanctuary, a fragment of a *bucchero* vase has recently come to light; it bears an Etruscan votive inscription, the dedicator being one Avile Vipiiennas, an archaic Etruscan form of Aulus Vivenna or Aule Vipina (see plate 29B). The inscription has been dated around the second half of the sixth century B.C., just at the time of the monarchy in Rome and of the Tarquins. It is therefore a contemporary and original document of the historical period referred to by the above-mentioned legend. It is probable that Aulus and Caelius Vibenna were real historical personages, Etruscan leaders who participated in a political struggle whose object was the domination of Rome, and that one of them made a votive offering at the sanctuary at Veii, so very near Rome. That close relations united Veii and Rome at this time is borne out by the tradition concerning works of art fashioned by Vulca and other Veii artists for the sanctuary dedicated to Jupiter, Juno, and Minerva on the Capitol (Varro in Pliny, *Nat. Hist.*, XXXV, 157; Plutarch, *Public.*, 13). Even if the two Auli were not the same person, we would still have proof of the existence during the sixth century of a Vibenna family in southern Etruria.[11] Two other discoveries are perhaps more important: they consist in the finding of two Etruscan inscriptions on *bucchero* vases on the slopes of the Capitoline hill and on the top of the Palatine (see plate 29A).[12] They confirm the presence of Etruscan speakers in Rome during the sixth century and, in contrast with archaic Latin inscriptions (such as that of the famous *cippus* under the *Lapis Niger*, the Duenos vase, etc.), place the city within the bilingual Etrusco-Italic zone, to which the Faliscan territory was also known to have belonged.

The Etruscan domination of Latium and Campania at first comprised a phase of expansion that may go back as far as the seventh century and ended with a fairly intensive colonization of Campania, where it gave rise to Etruscan cities such as Capua, Nola, Acerrae (Acerra), Nuceria (Nocera), and others as yet unidentified but whose names are known to us through coins (i.e. Uri or Urina, Velcha, Velsu, Irnthi).[13] Whether the Etruscans ever reached or even occupied Pompeii, as stated by Strabo (v, 4, 8), has been a long-debated question; it has now been resolved by the discovery of fragments of *bucchero* vases bearing inscriptions that are certainly in Etruscan.[14]

## Political Domination and Colonization of Campania and the Po Valley

We know that the Campanian dominion was governed in the same way as the cities of the mother country: it was divided into twelve small allied states, probably under the rule of Capua. As for Latium, we probably ought not to speak of colonization in a demographic sense: Etruria, as likely as not, merely dominated the political scene with a view to controlling the trade routes to the South, and maintaining territorial continuity with its Campanian dominion. Rome must have been particularly important in this respect because of its controlling position over the Tiber fords.

The second phase of Etruscan political activity in the South is chiefly marked by the struggle against local nationalisms, against the arch-enemy of Etruria, the Greeks, and especially against the threat represented by the expansion of bellicose Italic tribes from the Apennines, the Umbro-Sabellians, who at that period began to spread over the plains of the Tyrrhenian shore. We are now at the end of the sixth and the beginning of the fifth century, and the threat of the great economic crisis that was to follow already loomed large over Etruria's maritime and commercial interests. An alliance between the Latins and the Greeks from Cumae (Livy, II, 14; Dionysius of Halicarnassus, VII, 5 and 6) resulted in the collapse of Etruscan hegemony over Latium. Within this series of events we must no doubt place the liberation of Rome from Etruscan rule and the traditions concerning the end of the Tarquin monarchy and the institution of the republic. Events are complicated by the descent over the greater part of Latium of Italic mountain peoples, the Volsci and the Aequi: an event also known to us from the accounts of Roman historians. For a few decades the Etruscan dominion of Campania survived the territorial separation from the mother country, but it too finally succumbed around the year 430 B.C., before the descending wave of the Italic Samnites (Diodorus Siculus, XII, 31, 1; Livy, IV, 37, 1).

Etruscan expansion towards the north occurred later than the southern expansion. Its points of departure were the cities of inner northern Etruria: Perugia, whence, according to a traditional legend, an Etruscan chief by the name of Aucno or Ocno moved to the conquest of the Po valley and founded Felsina (Bologna) and Mantua (*Interpr. Verg.; Servius, ad Aen.*, X, 198). In reality the oldest Etruscan tombs in Bologna (distinguished by the cremation rite, the presence of imported Greek vases and funerary inscriptions in Etruscan), only go back to the very last years of the sixth or the beginning of the fifth century. Thus we may not attribute the founding of Bologna to the Etruscans, for it had been an important centre before their arrival, probably a market for the exchange of products from Etruria and the south with goods from central Europe (e.g. amber [15]). In the direction of the Adriatic, the Etruscans founded and occupied the cities of Caesena (Cesena), Ravenna, Ariminum (Rimini), and Spina. The latter became an important emporium for trade with Greece, as the recently discovered tombs of its rich necropolis testify. Inland, there were the cities of Parma, Placentia (Piacenza), Mutina (Modena), and Melpum, perhaps in the vicinity of Milan; near the village of Marzabotto, in the valley of the upper Reno (near Bologna), an Etruscan centre has been discovered which is particularly important for its characteristic chess-board pattern (the 'gridiron' system), with straight streets rigorously laid at right angles to one another in the direction of the four cardinal points, thus following the rules for the planning of Etruscan cities later handed down to the Romans.

In northern Italy, Etruscan expansion was held up by the Veneti to the east and the Ligurians to the west. It lasted little more than a century, for towards the end of the fifth and the beginning of the fourth century Gaulish hordes swept down upon Italy, spread over the whole of the Po valley as far as Etruria proper and even succeeded in sacking Rome. It would be interesting to study which local Etruscan ethnic groups survived these Gallic invaders. The latter's tombs may be distinguished by the fact that they were more poorly furnished with objects belonging to the backward iron culture of the Gauls known as 'La Tène'. Town-dwellers were very likely mainly Etruscan and their position with respect to the Gauls was probably much the same as that of the Romans of late Imperial times with respect to the Germanic peoples. It is probable for instance that Mantua preserved its Etruscan traditions until conquered by Rome.

As for the Etruscan inhabitants of the Adige valley, the late 'Etruscoid' inscriptions that have been found in the locality may have belonged to ethnic groups that became severed from the main body of the Etruscan world and mixed with Alpine peoples. The following well-known passage in Livy (v, 33) is the main basis of this theory: *Alpinis quoque ea gentibus haud dubie origo est, maxime Raetis: quos loca ipsa efferarunt, ne quid ex antiquo, praeter sonum linguae, nec eum incorruptum, retinerent.* (The Alpine peoples too, especially the Raetians, have undoubtedly the same origin (i.e. Etruscan); but the very nature of their surroundings caused them to grow so wild that the only memory they preserved of their past was the sound of their language and it too not uncorrupted). A more likely explanation may be that the above inscriptions belonged to indigenous speakers of a pre-Indo-European dialect presenting certain affinities with Etruscan.[16] In any case it is impossible to demonstrate that these peoples were remnants of an earlier Etruscan migration, as supporters of the theory of northern origin believed.

A final word on the question of Etruscan influence in Liguria. Ancient tradition speaks of an Etruscan domination along the Ligurian coast as far as the Val di Magra and of the founding by the Etruscans of Luna (Luni). Archaeology on the other hand reveals the Ligurian cultural horizon as extending as far south as the northern bank of the Arno, and the presence of Etruscan works of art in Luna only at a very late period. These regions were probably the object of violent struggles between the Etruscans and the fierce Ligurian tribes; Etruscan rule had probably a transitory character till Rome appeared upon the scene and finally established herself in the area.[17]

### The Spread of Etruscan Culture and the Growth of the Etrusco-Italic Civilization

If the political rule and direct colonization of the Etruscans only extended over part of continental Italy, their commercial activities and their cultural influence reached much further afield. Situated at the centre of the peninsula, Etruria was in fact the only beacon to radiate its civilization from early times upon generally backward peoples. Its only rivals were the Greek cities of Sicily and southern Italy, though the latter's influence was scarcely felt at first. As for the influence of Carthage, its cultural importance was only secondary and limited in range to western Sicily and to Sardinia. When speaking of a pre-Roman Etrusco-Italic civilization we are involuntarily led to place upon equal historical and chronological footings the various peoples of ancient Italy: Etruscans, Ligurians, Veneti, Latins, Umbro-Sabellians, etc., whereas a careful study of the archaeological documents in our possession is sufficient to persuade us that both the predominant role and absolute chronological priority in the formation of the civilization of ancient Italy belong to Etruria. During the sixth century, at the time of the great expansion and of the greatest flowering of the Etruscan civilization, the peoples of Aemilia, of Venetia, and of Liguria were still living within the scope of a backward iron age; the Picenians and the Umbrians were elaborating ways of life in which barbaric orientalizing elements were to predominate for a long time, elements which Etruria had discarded long ago, or alternately were more or less directly affected by Etruscan influences; Latium and Campania revolved within the orbit of Etruria and Greece; the Samnites showed, and went on showing for many decades, late features of the eastern iron culture. In all these peripheral regions, with the only exception of the extreme south colonized by the Greeks, there mainly subsisted a rather archaic *village* culture; its definite transformation into an *urban* culture, into a true and proper civilization, was at first due to the political predominance and cultural radiance of Etruria, and, later, to the unification of the peninsula achieved by Rome, the bearer of civilized forms of life which themselves owed much to Etruria.

That close links united the religion and ritual of Etruria, Umbria, and Latium is clearly shown by the texts of the Iguvine Tablets and by the sacred Latin formulas given by Cato in his *De re rustica*. They reveal a close analogy with what we are able to make out of Etruscan religious literature, e.g. in votive formulas and prayers, the names of deities and liturgical expressions.[18] It is worth recalling that many Etruscan deities are identical with Latin and Italic gods, even to their names: *Uni* – Juno, *Menerva* – Minerva, *Neθun* – Neptune, *Selvan* – Silvan, *Satre* – Saturn, *Velχan* – Vulcan, *Maris* – Mars, *Vesuna* – Vesona. Even if there existed common elements going back to an earlier prehistoric cultural unity, there is little doubt that these close analogies developed as a result of the cultural and political hegemony of Etruria in central Italy.

The same may be said for personal names. The Etruscans, the Latins and the Umbro-Sabellians were the only peoples of antiquity possessing a dual system: the *praenomen*, or personal name, and the name of the *gens*, or family. The system has no parallel amongst other Indo-European-speaking peoples and must have been formed within the Etrusco-Italic world. It had already appeared in Etruria by the seventh century B.C., whereas there is ground for believing that in Latium at that same period the use of a single name predominated.[19] Together with the social system, the Etruscan political system was also adopted in varying degrees by the peoples of Latium and of its hinterland. The Umbrians adopted the Etruscan magistrature of the *maru*, while the Roman monarchy, even in its external symbols (the golden crown, the throne, the *fasces*, the *toga palmata*, etc.) was explicitly stated by Latin writers to have been of Etruscan origin.

The diffusion of writing is one more important aspect of Etruscan cultural influence on the Italian peninsula. It spread in two directions. To the south the same Greek alphabet adopted by the Etruscans was also used at an early stage by the Faliscans and the Latins (although naturally including variants determined by the presence of different sounds, such as *o* and the voiced consonants, lacking in Etruscan). The form of the alphabet is still the same in the seventh and sixth centuries. Traces of a direct Etruscan influence are common: e.g. the Latin use of the digamma symbol to indicate, as in Etruscan, the unvoiced velar consonant *k* instead of the voiced *g*. The Umbrians and the Oscans on the other hand, directly adopted the Etruscan alphabet with the same inevitable modifications: this occurred at a later period, i.e. not earlier than the fifth to fourth centuries B.C. The other direction in which the Etruscan alphabet spread was to the north: the alphabets of the Veneti, the Raetians, the Lepontians and of the other Alpine peoples were linked to the so-called northern Etruscan alphabet adopted in the Po valley during the fifth century. To-day there is a growing tendency to believe that the runic alphabets of central and northern Europe were also derived, at least in part, from the northern Etruscan alphabet. [20]

Let us finally consider the realms of art and culture. Objects found in the culturally advanced Umbrian cities of Vettona (Bettona) and Tuder (Todi) reveal a very marked Etruscan influence: in some cases we may even speak of articles imported from Etruria. Etruscan elements belonging to the orientalizing period are also present in Picenum. The whole civilization of Latium and Campania from the seventh to the sixth century B.C. was frankly Etruscan: we only need think of the type and form of the temple, and of its decorations in painted terracotta as seen at Falerii, Rome, Satricum, Aletrium (Alatri), and Capua. Painted tombs similar to those of Etruria have been discovered at Rome, Capua, and Paestum: they were adopted by the Samnite invaders of Campania who also took over other Etruscan customs, e.g. the gladiatorial combats which from Capua later spread to Rome. Similarly, material elements of the Etruscan civilization spread over northern Italy: the Venetic culture of Ateste (Este) seems deeply impregnated with Etruscan elements which at first reached it via 'Villanovan' Bologna, and later through direct contacts with the Etruscan Po valley; the same may be said of coastal and inland Liguria.

Thus, despite the persistence of backward and archaic forms right up to the threshold of the Roman conquest, especially in the peripheral areas, despite the lingering regional characteristics of some of its cultures, a certain unity was arrived at in Italy well before the unification achieved by Rome. This unity was mainly due to the political dominance and cultural prestige of the Etruscans. These forces were exerted longitudinally along the whole peninsula from the Po to the southern Tyrrhenian. At the centre, a more clearly defined Etrusco-Italic cultural block grew up after the seventh and sixth centuries B.C.: the regions of Etruria proper, Latium and Campania. It became one of the two great historical poles of ancient Italy, in opposition to the Hellenic block of Sicily and Magna Graecia. The meeting of these two spheres was to form the basis of an Italian civilization under the imperial domination of Rome, and the starting-point for the development of ways of life destined to triumph in Western Europe.

## NOTES

1. Cf. E. Genthe, *Über den etruskischen Tauschhandel nach dem Norden*, 1874; J. Gy. Szilágyi, *Zur Frage des etruskischen Handels nach dem Norden*, in *Acta Antiqua Hungariae*, I, 1953, 3–4, pp. 419 ff.

2. *Cere all' epoca della sua annessione a Roma*, etc. (in *Atti del II Congresso di Studi Romani*, 1931, pp. 411 ff.); L. Pareti, *La tomba Regolini-Galassi*, pp. 8 ff.

3. In *Notizie degli Scavi*, 1930, pp. 335 ff.

4. The ethnic unification of Etruria considered as the assimilation and incorporation of peoples belonging to different linguistic stocks is a fundamental concept of F. Altheim's synthesis *Der Ursprung der Etrusker:* cf. p. 72, note 1, and p. 69.

5. Cf. note 8 on p. 83. This is a different *elogium* from the one quoted there, and refers to a different personage. The mention of a 'king of Caere' ( (*C*)*aeritum regem*) makes it almost certain that the personage lived in archaic times. For the possible hegemony of Tarquinia during the oldest phase of Etruscan history, see M. Pallottino, *Tarquinia* (*Monumenti Antichi dell'Accademia dei Lincei,* XXXVI, 1937), cols. 245 ff. and 367 ff.

6. The presence of Etruscan inscriptions in Piedmont (cf. M. Buffa, *Iscrizioni etrusche nel territorio del popolo ligure* in *Memorie dell'Accademia Lunigianese,* XV, 1934) has raised the question of an Etruscan colonization of the valleys of the Tanaro and of the Stura as far as the outskirts of Cuneo. On the frontier between Etruscans and Ligurians, cf. also N. Lamboglia, in *Studi Etruschi,* X, 1936, pp. 137 ff.

7. We should mention here the great expedition against Cumae of 524 B.C. mentioned by Dionysius of Halicarnassus, VII, 3 ff. The Etruscan army, reinforced with Umbrian and Daunian contingents, was defeated under the city walls.

8. *Campanien,* 1879.

9. G. De Sanctis, *Storia dei Romani,* I, 1906, pp. 371 ff.

10. The most recent discussions on the subject may be found in L. Pareti, *Studi Etruschi,* V, 1931, pp. 147 ff.; A. Momigliano, *L'opera dell'Imperatore Claudio,* 1932, pp. 30 ff.; M. Pallottino, *Studi Etruschi,* XIII, 1939, pp. 456 ff. and in *Gli Etruschi,* pp. 108 ff., p. 270; S. Mazzarino, *Dalla monarchia allo stato repubblicano: ricerche di storia romana arcaica,* 1945, pp. 184 ff.; in the above works the reader will find full bibliographical data. On the date of the François tomb, see M. Pallottino, *La peinture étrusque,* 1952, pp. 123 ff.

11. *Studi Etruschi,* XIII, 1939, pp. 455 ff.

12. M. Pallottino, *La iscrizione arcaica su vaso di bucchero rinvenuta ai piedi del Campidoglio* (in *Bullettino Archeol. Comunale,* LXIX, 1941; *Rivista di epigrafia etrusca,* in *Studi Etruschi,* XXII, 1952–3, pp. 309 ff. An Etruscan inscription had already been found at Satricum, in Latium (*Studi Etruschi,* XIII, 1939, p. 427 ff.).

13. On the subject of the Etruscan domination of Campania and particularly of Capua, cf. J. Heurgon, *Recherches sur l'histoire, la religion et la civilisation de Capoue pré-romaine,* 1942. The city of Uri is probably to be identified with Nola.

14. The find was made under the temple of Apollo near the Forum at Pompeii (cf. A. Maiuri, *Greci e Etruschi a Pompei*, in *Memorie della R. Accademia d'Italia – Classe scienze morali e storiche*, IV, 1943, pp. 121 ff.). On the question of the Etruscans in Pompeii, cf. A. Sogliano, *Pompei nel suo sviluppo storico*, I, 1927; A. Boëthius, *Gli Etruschi in Pompei* (in *Symbola Philologica O. A. Danielsson dicata*, Uppsala, 1932); G. Patroni, in *Studi Etruschi*, XV, 1941, pp. 109 ff.

15. On the question of amber in Italy and the doubts now entertained as to its northern origins, see *Studi Etruschi*, XVII, 1943, pp. 31 ff., 419 ff.

16. Cf. p. 42, note 9.

17. For more details see the recent and competent studies of L. Banti in *Studi Etruschi*, V, 1931, pp. 163 ff. and *Luni*, 1937.

18. Cf. K. Olzscha, *Interpretation der Agramer Mumienbinde*, 1939, pp. 3 ff.; M. Pallottino, *Sulla lettura e sul contenuto della grande iscrizione di Capua*, in *Studi Etruschi*, XX, 1948–9, pp. 159 ff.

19. In the inscription of the Palestrina *fibula*, only the two single names *Manios* and *Numasios* occur, but the latter may be the name of a divinity.

20. Cf. D. Diringer, *The Alphabet*, 1947, p. 516; F. Altheim, E. Trautmann, *Vom Ursprung der Runen*, 1939 (to be consulted with caution); J. G. Février, *Histoire de l'écriture*, 1948, pp. 513 ff.

# PART TWO

*Aspects of the Civilization of Etruria*

# CHAPTER FIVE

## CITIES AND CEMETERIES OF ETRURIA

*The Resurrection of Etruria*

THE history of etruscology is closely linked to the story of the resurrection of the dead cities of Etruria. For almost two centuries now, investigators of all kinds, impelled at first by greed for treasure or local pride and later by thirst for knowledge, have relentlessly worked at the remains of the great Etruscan cities and their cemeteries. Even so the immense field of excavations is to-day a long way from being exhausted, though a very great number of monuments of prime importance to art, history, and epigraphy have seen the light of day these last two hundred years. Those familiar with the terrain of Etruscan cities know well that only a tiny fraction of the sites likely to yield interesting remains has so far been touched by modern excavators: the majority of documents needed for the reconstruction of the civilization of ancient Etruria still lie below ground awaiting the pickaxe.

The tale of the resurrection of Etruria is varied, stimulating, at times dramatic. At first, oblivion and silence lay over these ancient cities, whether it was the fresh sap of medieval and Renaissance life and art that had extinguished all memory of Etruscan monuments in towns like Volterra, Arezzo, Cortona, Chiusi, and Orvieto (whose life has continued uninterruptedly since Etruscan days), or that the wild Mediterranean scrub had covered all traces of the abandoned cities:

> *Ricordi tu le vedove piagge del mar toscano*
> *Ove china su'l nubilo inseminato piano*
> *La torre feudal*

*Con lunga ombra di tedio dai colli arsicci e foschi*
*Veglia de le rasenie cittadi in mezzo ai boschi*
*Il sonno sepolcral . . . ?*
(CARDUCCI, *Avanti, Avanti!*)

(Do you remember the widowed shores of the Tuscan
sea, where the feudal tower bends over the virgin fallow
plain with long and dreary shadow and watches from
the dark, burnt hills over the sepulchral sleep of the
Rasenna cities buried deep amidst the woods . . . ?)

The very name of many a famous city has been lost.
Over the ruins of Tarquinii, near Corneto (now re-christened
Tarquinia), fabulous stories were told of a city by the name
of Corythus. The site of Veii was the subject of much discussion during the eighteenth century; in the nineteenth
that of Vetulonia. To-day, important centres whose cemeteries were unearthed near Marsiliana d'Albegna and Massa
Marittima, and the Etruscan city of Orvieto itself, still
remain hidden and nameless to us.

Little by little, from the darkness of the past, some of the
features of the civilization of ancient Etruria begin to emerge.
At first it was the peasant and the passer-by, marvelling at
the weapons and jewels the earth had unexpectedly brought
forth, or wondering at the strange paintings and unde-
cipherable inscriptions on the walls of mysterious and
intricate underground chambers. It was finds such as these
that inspired the humanist Lucius Vitellius to sing of the
palace of Corythus buried close to the walls of Corneto in
a delicate poem to Philelphus, and that prompted Michel-
angelo to draw the head of Aita, king of the Etruscan underworld. Then, at the height of the *cinquecento*, at the golden
age of Renaissance sculpture, came the unearthing of superb
Etruscan bronzes, the pride of the Florence Archaeological
Museum: the Chimaera and the Minerva of Arezzo, the
Trasimene 'orator' (see plates 16A and 17). Finally, when
interest in ancient Etruria had wakened and reached a

climax through the work of Dempster, Buonarroti, Gori, and Passeri, there followed in ever-quickening succession the discoveries of Etruscan tombs at Siena, Corneto, Volterra, Cortona, till the day when, parallel with the creation of an Etruscan Academy at Cortona, began the first systematic search for Etruscan remains.

The second phase in the resurrection of the dead cities of Etruria began with the nineteenth century. On the initiative of private individuals and of institutes, the great Etrurian cemeteries, particularly those lying near the sea, were intensively explored. We cannot yet speak of strictly scientific activity; nevertheless the greater part of the material we possess came to light during this period of enthusiasm. Excavations that had begun in the eighteenth century around the centres of northern Etruria were now mainly concentrated upon the cities of coastal Etruria, especially Caere, Tarquinii, and Vulci. For years and years the immense necropolis that surrounded the latter city became (chiefly through the enterprise of Lucien Bonaparte, Prince of Canino) an inexhaustible quarry of Greek and Etruscan vases that now enrich the museums of the principal cities of Europe. The interest of local authorities and landowners was joined by that of the newly founded Institute of Archaeological Correspondence and, within the borders of the Papal States, that of the Camerlingate on whose account excavations were undertaken.

The second half of the nineteenth century generally brought a pause in the resurrection of Etruscan cities. A greater interest in prehistorical studies resulted in a series of discoveries that served to illustrate and to locate the very first Etruscan sites. Thus, at first in Aemilia (Bologna, Villanova, etc.), and later in Etruria proper (Tarquinii, Chiusi, Volterra, Vetulonia), iron age sepulchres of a distant culture were revealed that received the label 'Villanovan'. During this period the Italian government began to take an active interest in the search and excavations of ancient remains, but it was only during the first decades of this century, with the creation of a *Direzione Generale delle Antichità e Belle Arti* and of its dependent organizations in Tuscany and Latium, that a new and intensive campaign of exploration began that has greatly enriched Italy's national and local museums. To-day, the exploratory phase has reached its peak, with large-scale excavations at Veii, Caere, Tarquinii, and Populonia. We should also note that most recent researches no longer tend merely to increase the stocks of our museums by the easy and less costly excavation of tombs (generally well supplied with funerary objects); they are directed at the exploration of city sites and especially of those where favourable circumstances have left them unencumbered by later constructions. This change of emphasis is due to the rigidly scientific criterium of filling the gaps in our knowledge of certain aspects of the Etruscan civilization and to the hope of meeting with non-funerary inscriptions of a certain length or even perhaps with a bilingual Etrusco-Latin text.

## Cities of Southern Etruria

Let us now cast a rapid glance at the principal centres of Etruscan life, tell the story of their discovery and describe their most obvious characteristics.[1] Geographical and historical factors first require a fundamental distinction to be made between the cities of southern and those of northern Etruria. The approximate line of demarcation between the two regions is marked by the rivers Fiora, that flows into the Tyrrhenian sea, and Paglia, a tributary of the Tiber; it is substantially the modern frontier between Tuscany and Latium. Southern or Latian Etruria consists of volcanic or alluvial terrains and belongs to the volcanic hill and lake system of Latium; northern Etruria, larger in area, lies over

Figure 3 – THE CITIES OF ETRURIA PROPER

The modern Italian names are given in brackets after the
Latin names.

the foothills of the Apennines, rich in rivers and vegetation.
From the historical, and monumental, point of view the
two regions are fairly clearly differentiated. The south
developed far earlier, and comprises great and ancient
cities, especially near the sea, and at a relatively short distance from one another: Veii, Caere, Tarquinii, Vulci;
their decadence, in the final phase of the Etruscan civiliza-

tion and under the Roman empire, was correspondingly quick, and was hastened by the spread of malaria in the Maremma region. The limited development of this area in medieval and modern times has done much to preserve its ruins in a wild and primitive landscape. The cities that stood along the Tyrrhenian shore to the north of the Fiora and of Monte Argentario (such as Rusellae (Roselle), Vetulonia, and Populonia), present much the same characteristics: the same precocious development and just as precocious decadence, the same Maremman landscape, etc. Altogether different is the case of the cities of inland northern Etruria: Clusium (Chiusi), Cortona, Perusia (Perugia), Arretium (Arezzo), Faesulae (Fiesole), Volaterrae (Volterra); these stood at a certain distance from one another and developed more tardily as compared with the cities of the south: they flourished during the final phase of the Etruscan civilization and in Roman times. Even more important however is the fact that they continued to live without a break through the Middle Ages; we should not speak of them as of dead cities, and it is in them that we should seek the links that unite the ancient Etruscan nation with the spirit of the Tuscan civilization of the Renaissance.

An ordered survey of the cities of Etruria should begin with Rome, the Etruscan form of whose name was *Ruma-*.[2] It is quite certain that for a period during the sixth century B.C. Rome was the centre of an Etruscan monarchy, with monuments, works of art, a constitution, and a religion under Etruscan influence. The people were of Latin and, partly, of Sabine stock; but the already mentioned recent finds of Etruscan inscriptions on vases within the area of the city testify to the presence of Etruscan inhabitants, according to tradition (Varro, *de ling. lat.*, v, 46; Livy, II, 14, 9; Dionysius of Halicarnassus, v, 36; Festus, 536/355, s.v. *Tuscum vicum*), in the Velabrum quarter, near the Vicus Tuscus. The political contingencies that led to the downfall of Etruscan supremacy in Latium, to the sweeping down of the Italic peoples, to the isolation of the city and, finally, to its spectacular political and military recovery, were such as to cause the future metropolis of the Mediterranean world to develop outside the orbit of the Etruscan nation if not actually of the Etruscan civilization. Thus it is that we have so very little left of the external, monumental features of the Rome of the sixth century. Only the excavation of the city's sacred sites (as for instance the three-cell Capitoline temple built according to the Etruscan manner and with the help of Etruscan artists, or the recently discovered sacred site of Sant'Omobono in the Forum Boarium) and the exploration of those few square feet of archaic cemeteries that escaped the upheavals of thousands of years of building activity, allow us to imagine the life of the city under Etruscan rule.

Within a few miles from Rome, on the right bank of the Tiber and at the confluence of the two branches of the Cremera, there stood upon a high and rocky spur the city of Veii. Veii was the only great city of Etruria that ceased to be such with the decline of the archaic period. This occurred as the result of a well-determined historical fact: the implacable life and death struggle with Rome, towards the end of the fifth and the beginning of the fourth century B.C. It ended with the capture and destruction of Veii in 396. We ought not to think however of total and instantaneous obliteration: at the time of the Gallic invasion, Camillus found refuge in the city and after the burning of Rome, the possibility of transferring the seat of government to Veii was seriously considered; there are also traces of monuments belonging to the republican and imperial age. That a great city should survive and grow at such small distance from the capital was clearly unthinkable; and at the beginning of the Empire, Propertius was able to write (IV, x, 27):

Heu Veii veteres! et vos tum regna fuistis
 et vestro positast aurea sella foro.
Nunc intra nuros pastoris bucina lenti
 cantat, et in vestris ossibus arva metunt.


(Veii, thou hadst a royal crown of old,
And in thy forum stood a throne of gold! –
Thy walls now echo but the shepherd's horn,
And o'er thine ashes waves the summer corn.)[3]


 The Augustan poet perhaps romantically overstressed the desolation of the ancient city; but it is significant that his description corresponds perfectly to the impression received by the modern sightseer. There is nothing to show that life continued there during the Middle Ages, and the growth of a little hamlet round the castle of Isola Farnese that dominates the Veii plateau is comparatively recent. The site of the city was discovered only at the beginning of the last century: it was thought at first to have been at Civita Castellana. The first great discovery was of a painted tomb named, after its finder, Campana, in 1842. After that time excavations were sporadically conducted in the necropolis, but with no great results. It was only during the second decade of our century that a systematic exploration of the sacred zone of Portonaccio (where the famous Apollo of Veii came to light – see plate 5) was undertaken. Much, however, remains to be done.

 To the unsuspecting sightseer, Veii appears as one of the most suggestive spots in the neighbourhood of Rome: a picturesque tumble of rocks, torrents, cascades, and thick brushwood meets the traveller quite unexpectedly as he crosses the volcanic and rather monotonous plateau traversed by the Via Cassia. The millennial neglect of the site heightens the charm of its setting: here nature is once more the mistress of a landscape that long ago teemed with life.

From the hamlet of Isola Farnese, beyond the confines of the old Etruscan city, the visitor descends to the foot of the rocky cliff and crosses the foaming Cremera at the little bridge of La Mola set between two cascades; then up again, along a stretch of the old Roman road, till he reaches the level ground of Portonaccio, where the temple once stood. Excavations have revealed this area to be a complex sacred enclosure, an Etruscan sanctuary clearly connected with the cult of the health-giving waters emerging from the hillside. There stood the temple, of which only the foundations remain, built in tufo stone according to the Etruscan plan with three cells (or one cell and two wings) and a wide forecourt. Along one of the temple's sides there is a pool, in whose healing waters the pilgrims probably bathed. At a certain distance before the temple a rectangular altar has been found, with a square opening in the centre and traces of sacrificial burnings. The whole surrounding ground has yielded fragments of the painted terra-cotta decorations of the upper portion of the temple, and of other sacred buildings, as well as votive objects, statues, fragments of vases with Etruscan inscriptions, etc. The most important discovery, made in 1916, consisted of fragments of a series of large painted terra-cotta statues of archaic style, the most complete of which is one of Apollo. More recently, the greater part of a statue of a goddess (Latona?) bearing a child in her arms has been discovered: its technique and style are the same as those of the Apollo. These statues were *acroteria* placed upon the roof of the rich temple, and reveal the hand of an artist with a most original style who worked towards the end of the sixth and the beginning of the fifth century B.C. In other areas within the city, and especially in the locality known as Campetti, large quantities of votive objects have come to light, particularly terra-cotta statuettes. All this material is generally believed to be earlier than the fourth century B.C., and the same may be said of the objects found in the tombs. The rock-hewn 'Campana' tomb, painted with figured scenes and ornamental patterns, is attributed to the beginning of the sixth century.[4]

Upon one of the hillocks of the tufo plateau that lies between the Lake of Bracciano and the sea, stand the remains of another great and famous Etruscan metropolis: Caere (the Etruscan form of which was probably χaire). The little town of Cerveteri (i.e. old Caere) is its impoverished descendant. The city or rather the immense necropolis that surrounds it began to be excavated during the first half of the nineteenth century, when the famous discovery of an intact and wealthy tomb belonging to the orientalizing period was made. The material belonging to this tomb, named 'Regolini-Galassi' after its excavators, is of unique importance and may be seen at the Gregorian Etruscan Museum in the Vatican (see plate 28). The systematic excavation of the sepulchres of Caere and of a few monuments in the city, and the careful restoration of the grandiose tumuli are however quite recent. To this work we owe the precious material (vases in particular) that so enrich the collection of the Museum of Villa Giulia (the 'Museo di papa Giulio') in Rome. To-day, the Cerveteri necropolis is one of the most suggestive groups of monuments not only of Italy but of the whole Mediterranean world. Within the restored area may be seen a series of tumuli heaped on rock or stone plinths, whose diameter may reach the truly impressive figure of one hundred feet (see plate 1A). Carved out of the tufo at the base of the tumuli one or more groups of tombs may be found; these imitate the interiors of houses and consist of several rooms, with doors, windows, columns, and pilasters outlined on the walls, beamed or coffered ceilings, and including furniture, armchairs, funerary couches, etc. The impression one receives in some of these tombs is quite uncanny. One of the most recent, a hypog eum deep below ground level, possesses walls and pilasters decorated with painted stucco reliefs reproducing objects supposed to be hanging on them (see plates 30 and 31). These stuccoes provide us with an extraordinary vivid picture of weapons and tools used in domestic life. The material found in the Cerveteri tombs covers without any interruptions a period that runs from the iron age to Roman times. Amongst the most characteristic objects found there are archaic terra-cotta sarcophagi with lids in the shape of reclining figures and painted panels that originally covered the walls of sacred or public buildings and tombs. A special type of painted vase – the so-called *hydria* of Caere – the probable local production of Ionic artists, has only been found in the Cerveteri necropolis. The city itself was protected by rocky cliffs and, in the more accessible places, by walls of square stone blocks and a wide ditch; within the city, temples abounding in votive objects have been excavated.5

The great quantity of objects of foreign manufacture brought over by sea from the East and from Greece show Caere to have been an important coastal city though actually a few miles distant from the sea. Its ports were Alsium (near Palo), Pyrgis (Santa Severa), and Punicum (corresponding perhaps to Santa Marinella). The period of Caere's greatest prosperity coincides with the seventh and sixth century B.C.; during this time, unless we are being misled by the nature and quantity of the tombs, it must have been an extraordinarily rich and populous centre, perhaps one of the most splendid of the world as then known. And in spite of the long struggles with the Greeks and, later, its submission to the Romans, life at Caere continued to be fairly prosperous up to imperial times.

Between the Cerveteri and the Tarquinia area stand the trachytic hills of La Tolfa, on the slopes and at the foot of which were many small Etruscan villages that deserve careful exploration; the whole of this area is as yet practically untouched by the archaeologist's pickaxe.[6]

The story of Tarquinii (in Etruscan: *Tarχ(u)na-*) is quite different: it lived on throughout the Middle Ages and up to modern times as the town of Corneto, one of the most sizeable of Latian Tuscia and of the whole Patrimony of Saint Peter. The heated controversy on the exact location of Etruscan Tarquinii (some scholars believed it to be on the hill of Corneto, next to the necropolis) may now be considered definitely solved in favour of another hill, parallel to it, the *colle della Civita*, abounding in ancient remains. Nevertheless Corneto may be considered as the modern descendant of ancient Tarquinii, and, as a result, its name has now been changed to Tarquinia. Already in the eighteenth century, but especially in the first half of the nineteenth, the site was famous owing to the discovery of painted tombs. Local authorities, private individuals, and, later, the Italian State, conducted excavations on the site of the necropolis huddled on the hill of Corneto. Objects found in the tombs went to build up the two rich collections of the Counts Bruschi-Falgari and of the local Commune; they are now gathered together in the Museo Nazionale Tarquiniense housed in the Palazzo Vitelleschi. Within recent years the systematic excavation of the ancient city site has begun with very promising results: not only has the grandiose wall of squared stone blocks dating back to the fourth century B.C. been brought to light, but the foundations of a majestic Etruscan temple as well, the so-called *Ara della Regina* (the Queen's altar), to which belong two terracotta winged horses which may be considered as among the greatest masterpieces of Etruscan art (see plate 7).

Instead of the tumuli and the rock-hewn tombs of Caere, carved to represent the interiors of houses, the Tarquinii cemetery is famous for its painted underground chambers.

These are generally small and scattered throughout the hill of the necropolis. Of the very great number of which we have some knowledge, only twenty or so are still open, accessible, and in a good state of preservation: in recent years, the paintings of two of the most famous tombs (the Tomb of the Chariots and the Tomb of the Triclinium), in serious danger of being irreparably damaged, have been detached and remounted in the Museo Tarquiniense.[7] This unique collection of monuments is as interesting to the art historian as it is to the archaeologist. The life which the Etruscans led at the most felicitous period in their history (the majority of tombs date back to the end of the sixth and the beginning of the fifth century B.C.) vividly unfolds itself before our eyes in realistic scenes: banquets, dancing, and musical scenes; hunting, fishing; circus games with their accompanying crowds of spectators; all partly connected with funeral ceremonies. In the most recent tombs however (from the fourth to the second century) the paintings tend more and more to deal with the underworld, with its gods and its mythical dwellers, and especially the frightening demons that symbolize death wrenching the souls of the dead from the joys of existence and the love of dear persons, to direct them towards the dark and hopeless kingdom of the nether regions. Amongst the most characteristic monuments found in the Tarquinii necropolis, we should mention archaic stone reliefs roughly decorated in oriental styles, and sarcophagi belonging to a later period in stone or in terracotta with the reclining figures of the dead reproduced on the lids, and figured reliefs sculptured on the sides. There is also a remarkable number of inscriptions painted on the walls of tombs or carved on the sarcophagi; some of these are of substantial length and are important to the study of Etruscan epigraphy.

About twelve miles to the north-west of Tarquinii, on the banks of the Fiora, there stood another great city of

southern Etruria: Vulci (in Etruscan, *Veiχ-*). The ruins of
this city and of its boundless cemeteries stretch along a vast
uninhabited area between the two small villages of Mon-
talto di Castro and Canino, in one of the most picturesque
districts of the whole of central Italy. As we have already
seen, the golden period of the Vulci excavations occurred
during the first half of the nineteenth century, and was
mainly due to the interest shown by the Prince of Canino.
During the second half of the century the necropolis was
again intensively explored on the initiative of Prince
Torlonia, who owned much of the site. Objects discovered
during the initial excavations may mostly be found scattered in the Vatican, the Louvre, and the Munich and
British Museums, etc.; those that came to light in the
course of the Torlonia excavations are still for the most part
in private collections. A few tentative excavations have
been sporadically undertaken by the state or under its control during the last few decades: these later findings are
preserved in the Museum of Villa Giulia in Rome. The
tumuli and hypogea of Vulci do not differ much from those
of Caere or of Tarquinii: amongst the most remarkable is
the 'François' tomb, named after its discoverer: its mural
frescoes have been detached and are kept at the Torlonia
Museum in Rome. They probably belong to the last phase
of Etruscan artistic production (second to first century B.C.)
and feature a number of portraits and mythical and historical scenes, the latter referring to events that occurred during
the earliest phases of Etruscan history (the exploits of the
Vipina brothers and of Macstrna). Amongst the outstand-
ing monuments of the Vulci necropolis, there is a grandiose
tumulus comprising an intricate network of underground
chambers and passages, termed *la cuccumella* (the little coffee-
pot). Vulci was an important centre for the marketing of
bronze products: its cemeteries have in fact returned many
bronze articles: weapons, tools, tripods, etc. But even more

remarkable are the large quantities of painted vases that have been found, mainly imported from Greece. There are also many samples of curious sculptures.[8] This city too appears to have reached its highest peak of prosperity during the second half of the sixth century B.C.

So far we have dealt with the cities of coastal southern Etruria. The inland towns are, generally speaking, smaller and of minor historical importance; this fact has naturally caused them to have been rather neglected by archaeologists. Many areas in the vicinity of the lakes of Bracciano, Vico, and Bolsena may thus be considered to be still virtually unexplored.

Within Faliscan territory (the country between the Sabatine and Cimine mountains and the Tiber), finds of a certain importance have been made. This fraction of Etruscan land was mainly inhabited by Italic peoples or, more precisely, by peoples speaking a Latin influenced by Sabine. It appears however to have been linked to Etruria by strong political and cultural ties.[9] Its principal centre was Falerii (now Civita Castellana) in a well-protected and picturesque setting, with its many sanctuaries (rich in figured terracottas) and a vast necropolis. The Romans, who finally subdued the city in 241 B.C., wished to transfer it to another, at a short distance from it: Falerii Novi (Santa Maria di Fálleri), whose imposing crown of walls is still standing. Other minor Faliscan towns stood on the sites of the modern Narce, Vignanello, and Corchiano.

Amongst the more truly Etruscan centres of the interior, we should record Nepete (Nepi); Sutrium (Sutri, in Etruscan, *Suθri*-), a bone of contention between the Etruscans and the Romans during the fourth century, with imposing city walls and rock-tombs belonging to a late period; Horta (Orte), on a high and dominating site in the valley of the Tiber, on the borders of Faliscan and Sabine territory; Polimartium (Bomarzo). Of greater importance are the monuments found in a band of territory in the hinterland of Tarquinii and Vulci: this comprises a number of small cities each surrounded by a characteristic necropolis whose principal feature consists of tombs hewn out of the rock face and sculptured so as to imitate the façades of houses or temples (San Giuliano, Blera (Bieda), Norchia, Castel d'Asso and, further north, Sovana, the Suana of old).[10] A few other centres in this same band of territory appear to have flourished particularly during the archaic period, between the eighth and sixth centuries B.C., as far as can be surmised from their cemeteries: e.g. Vetralla, near the lake of Vico; Visentium, now Bisenzio, near Capodimonte, on the southern shores of the lake of Bolsena; they appear to cluster especially thickly along the higher course of the Fiora, north of Vulci: Ischia di Castro, Farnese, Poggio Buco (probably corresponding to Statonia),[11] Pitigliano. Tuscania, on the other hand, appears to have developed late; its chief feature is a number of sculptured sarcophagi of the Tarquinian type.

Within this inner zone of southern Etruria, there rose one of the most important Etruscan cities, considered by the ancients to be the spiritual centre of the whole nation: this is Volsinii (In Etruscan, *Velzna-*). In its neighbourhood, in fact, there stood the famous sanctuary of Voltumna (the *Fanum Voltumnae*), where the yearly gathering of the twelve Etruscan *populi* took place, accompanied by feasts and celebrations. Recent excavations have definitely proved that Volsinii corresponds to modern Bolsena, as the latter name implies (an earlier hypothesis connected it with Orvieto).[12] A powerful girdle of city-walls crowned the acropolis dominating the lake, upon which the remains of a three-celled temple have been found. The site of the Sanctuary is still unknown; it has been variously located at Orvieto, Montefiascone, etc., but it may well have stood in the immediate vicinity of the city.

And so we come to Orvieto, upon its mighty pedestal of red tufo stone, watching over the valley of the middle Tiber, about eight miles, as the crow flies, north-east of Bolsena. Its Etruscan origins have been confirmed by an imposing series of discoveries of sacred buildings and depositories made within the city enclosure, as also by the cemeteries that surround it, that include tombs both of the chamber and of the painted varieties (Sette Camini, Porrano). It appears that this great centre flourished especially between the sixth and the fourth centuries B.C. The first direct references to it, however, only go back to the Byzantine age (Procopius, *De bello Gothico*, II, 20), when the city is referred to as *Ourbibentos*, a name that may perhaps be related to *Urbs vetus* (whence Orvieto). Its true ancient name remains therefore a mystery, and Orvieto is the only city of Etruria of any size and importance whose ancient name is still unknown to us. For various reasons, carrying more or less weight, identifications with Etruscan Volsinii or with the Voltumna sanctuary must be rejected; for what it is worth, the hypothesis may be put forward of a connexion with the Salpinum mentioned by Livy, V, 31–2, as an autonomous and militarily powerful centre situated at not too great a distance from Volsinii.

### Cities of Northern Etruria, Campania, and the Po Region

In passing from southern to northern Etruria, we should begin by mentioning those coastal sites that continue to the north of Vulci the constellation of cities dotted along the Tyrrhenian shore. At a short distance from the Lake of Orbetello, there rise the ruins of Cosa, with its famous girdle of polygonal walls, its temples, its public buildings, a town wholly built by the Romans as a military colony in the year 273 B.C.:[13] its Etruscan origins are as yet uncertain. Beyond Monte Argentario lies the small sea town of Telamon (Talamone) where remains of a temple and a collection of votive objects have been found: they may be connected with the battle fought in this area by Romans and Gauls in the year 225 B.C. Further inland, in the neighbourhood of Marsiliana d'Albegna, a large archaic necropolis was discovered and excavated: it has been hypothetically related to Caletra, whose site is unknown.[14] Other Etruscan cities in the same region with some remains of interest to archaeology include Heba (the Magliano of to-day) and Saturnia.[15] In the Grosseto area there are the ruins of a city that was one of the greatest in Etruria: Rusellae (Roselle). Here too, traces of a city wall, of a temple and of a few tombs have been found, but the site awaits large-scale systematic excavations.[16]

Still within the Grosseto area but nearer to the sea stood Vetulonia (or Vetulonii, the Etruscan name of which was *Vetluna, Vatluna*). The site of this famous city was sought all along the Etruscan coastal belt, and was, till the last few decades, the object of heated arguments between scholars who placed it at Poggio Colonna and others who identified it with Poggio Castiglioni near Massa Marittima. There can no longer be any doubt that the first is the correct site: there, in fact, remains of city walls and of houses have been found. But the importance of the city is mainly revealed to us by the vast necropolis that surrounds it. A systematic excavation of the site was conducted with ample means towards the end of the last century: the abundant material found there became the nucleus of the collections now at the Museo Archeologico in Florence. The most important tombs are marked by stone circles or are in the shape of tumuli, and the funerary furnishings, consisting for the most part of bronze objects, have been attributed to the period stretching from the eighth to the sixth century B.C. After this period, as far as we can tell from archaeological data, the city must have fallen into rapid and complete decline, for there remain no traces of life after the beginning of the Roman age.[17]

Further to the north there stood Populonia (or Populonium, the Etruscan form of which was *Pupluna, Fufluna*) on the site of Porto Baratti, near Piombino. It is the only important Etruscan city built right on the sea shore. Its discovery is quite recent. Great excavations have been conducted in its necropolis since the beginning of this century under the direction of the *Soprintendenza dell' Etruria*, and are still continuing. The most characteristic sepulchres of Populonia are great tumuli comprising chambers with false cupolas or vaulted ceilings; within these chambers objects have been found dating from the archaic period up to the late sixth century.[18] An important feature of the site is the presence round the city of vast fields of iron slag, the result of the smelting of iron ores extracted from the Elba mines in Etruscan and Roman times. For Populonia was one of the most important iron centres of the ancient world. The earliest tombs were found under the slag: this is now being removed and made to undergo a new industrial process of extraction with excellent results. More traces of Etruscan mining activity may be seen on the slopes of the metal-bearing hills nearby, where numerous ancient shafts have been discovered.

Let us now examine the inland cities, found scattered mainly along the banks of large rivers. Here, we should first mention Clusium (Chiusi; the Etruscan name was in all probability *Clevsin-*, but the town also appears under the name of *Camars*). This city, famous for its part in the history of both Etruria and Rome, never ceased to be an important centre throughout the Middle Ages and up to modern times. This fact explains the almost complete disappearance of all Etruscan buildings on the one hand, and on the other, the early and frequent discoveries made in the vicinity. A characteristic feature of Clusium and of the surrounding region is the presence of a large number of cemeteries distributed near the city and neighbouring towns (Pania, Poggio Gaiella, Poggio Renzo, Dolciano, Sarteano, Chianciano, Città della Pieve, Montepulciano). All these small towns possessed a substantially similar type of civilization: their presence shows that the territory was occupied by a number of small inhabited centres under the aegis of the metropolis. Excavations, made at varying times according to the site, have brought to light much material now mostly kept at the Museo Archeologico of Florence and the Museo Civico of Chiusi (a small number of objects, belonging to the late Casuccini Collection, may be seen in the Palermo museum). The earliest cultural phase of Clusium is characterized by cremation tombs and the presence of so-called 'canopics', i.e. ossuaries with a lid in the shape of a human head and roughly imitating the human form. A few chamber tombs in the environs of Chiusi have painted scenes from daily life, as in Tarquinii, and largely belong to the fifth century B.C. Stone cippi and cinerary urns decorated with reliefs of banquets, games, funerals, etc. are typical of the phase that stretched from the end of the sixth to the end of the fifth century B.C. This artistic production is representative of the most flourishing period in the history of the town, a period that coincides with the beginning of the decadence of the coastal cities. We may remember, in fact, that tradition ascribes to the end of the sixth century the reign of King Porsenna, the attacker and, according to some sources, the conqueror of Rome, indicating a period of expansion in the history of Clusium. Later, the end of the fifth century and the beginning of the fourth witnessed the production in and around Clusium of sarcophagi and funerary statues; to the Hellenistic period, on the other hand, there belongs a rich collection of small cinerary urns of painted terracotta, with the dead person's image on the lid and mythological reliefs on the front.[19]

Perusia (Perugia) was one more great centre of ancient Etruria destined to acquire an ever-growing importance through the centuries of the Roman Empire, the Middle Ages, and the modern era. This continuity of life was not sufficient however to erase all traces of the most glorious period in the life of the Etruscan city, a period that lasted from the third to the first century B.C., and thus coincided with the final phase of the Etruscan civilization. The many remains include long tracts of the city wall built with large squared blocks of travertine, the grandiose arched gateway that came to be named after Augustus, and the handsomely sculptured design of the Porta Marzia, adorned with sculptured deities which, with humanistic foresight, the Renaissance architect Sangallo succeeded in incorporating into one of the bastions of his Rocca Paolina. As the main centre of etruscological studies during the nineteenth century, Perugia was the subject of intense research on its urban and suburban monuments; occasional discoveries led to the creation of the valuable Etruscan collection in its Museo Civico. So far however, there has been no organic plan for the exploration of its foundations and its cemeteries. A monument particularly worthy of notice is the Volumni Hypogeum in the Palazzone necropolis, quite near the town: a tomb hewn out of the rock and consisting of several chambers containing reliefs and cinerary urns with figured decorations and Etruscan and Latin inscriptions belonging to the first century B.C. Typical of Perugia and its surrounding area are the small travertine and terracotta urns decorated in relief. Amongst the numerous inscriptions which may be seen in the Perugia Museum, there is a cippus, perhaps a boundary-stone, inscribed with the longest Etruscan epigraphic text on stone in our possession.[20]

The role of Perugia as a centre of research on ancient Etruria during the nineteenth century was previously filled in the eighteenth century by Cortona (in Etruscan, *Curtun-*).

Here isolated discoveries and excavations were made in the neighbourhood of the town. Of the old city there remain a few traces of its walls; of the cemeteries surrounding the town, isolated tumuli (locally known as 'melons') and a circular mausoleum of later date, known as '*la Tanella di Pitagora*' (Pythagoras' little den). In the Museo dell' Accademia Cortonese is preserved a famous bronze candelabrum with rich figured decorations (see plate 19A).[21] At Arretium (Arezzo) sections of the famous brick wall protecting the city have been unearthed, and a part of the old Etruscan city level may still be recognized; here, during the sixteenth century, were found the Chimaera (see plate 16A) and a bronze statue of Minerva. We should also mention the figured terracottas in Hellenistic style discovered in the course of the exploration of the city walls and now kept at the Archaeological Museum in Florence. Another important Etruscan centre was situated on the hill of Faesulae (Fiesole) dominating the valley of the Arno and the Florentine plain. The excavation of this vast archaeological site has brought to light the foundations of a three-cell temple and of an altar in front of it, together with a fine stretch of city wall. Typical of Fiesole are stone funerary steles in the shape of a horseshoe with figured reliefs, many of which are kept at the local Museo Civico.[22] The Florence site, though already inhabited in archaic times (as shown by some iron age graves discovered in the heart of the city) only re-emerged as a centre of life during the Roman period.

We should finally mention the city of Volaterrae (Volterra, in Etruscan *Velaθri*) that stands upon a high hill dominating the valley of the Cecina. Like the other centres of northern Etruria it survived the end of the ancient world, though in medieval and modern times the city has occupied a far more reduced area than the one indicated by its powerful girdle of Etruscan walls. Of the old city's monuments, the gate known as the *Porta dell' Arco*, embellished with sculptured heads of Etruscan deities, is perhaps the most remarkable. Like Cortona, Volterra was a centre of etruscological research during the eighteenth century, when excavations of its tombs were begun, excavations that have often been taken up again in brief and successful campaigns. The greater part of the archaic necropolis of the city was destroyed in the huge landslide of the *Balze*. Volterra's most characteristic yield belongs to the later phases of the Etruscan civilization; it consists of alabaster cinerary urns with decorations in high-relief, a large number of which may be seen in the local Museo Civico Guarnacci.[23]

To this review of the principal characteristics of the cities of Etruria proper should be added a mention, however brief, of the Etruscan centres in Campania and the Po valley. The capital of the Etruscan dominion in Campania was Capua (known also as Volturnum) which later became one of the greatest and most populous cities of both the Italic and the Roman worlds. It stood upon the present site of Santa Maria di Capua Vetere. Amongst the most characteristic Etruscan remains found at Capua are the architectural terracottas and votive statues now gathered together in the local Museo Campano.[24] One of the most important finds was a terracotta tile bearing a lengthy Etruscan inscription, now in Berlin. Other Etruscan centres in Campania were Nola (in Oscan *Núvla* and in Etruscan *Nula*), Acerrae (Acerra), Pompeii (Pompei), and Salernum (Salerno).

The capital of northern Etruria was in all likelihood Bononia (Bologna, in Etruscan *Felsina*), a city founded in archaic times during the period of the 'Villanovan' iron culture, and conquered by the Etruscans towards the end of the sixth century. The very abundant material found in its Etruscan tombs (amongst which are some typical sculptured steles) is kept at the town's Museo Civico.[25] An interesting Etruscan city in the vicinity of Bologna was discovered in the valley of the upper Reno near the modern village of Marzabotto (its ancient name was probably Misa); it was built in chess-board pattern with paved streets and a fairly evolved water system; on the acropolis, the foundations of a number of sacred buildings may still be seen. Its excavation has yielded large quantities of material dating back to the fifth and fourth century B.C. and kept in the local Museo Aria, though the collection was much mutilated during the 1939 war.[26] The sea town of Spina was also important; its necropolis, rich in Greek vases, has been identified and excavated within the last decades: the funerary furnishings of its tombs have been used to create the new Archaeological Museum of Ferrara.[27] Other Etruscan cities to the north of the Apennines were Ariminum (Rimini, probably from an Etruscan *Arimna*-), Caesena (Cesena, probably cognate to the Etruscan *Keisna*, a family name found in Bologna), Mantua (Mantova, in Etruscan *Manθva*-?), Mutina (Modena), Parma and the city which the Romans rechristened Placentia (Piacenza); these towns all present merely sporadic evidence of Etruscan occupation, for they were early overrun by Celtic invaders.

## NOTES

1. As a work of reference on the topography, history, and archaeology of the cities and sites of Etruria, G. Dennis' *Cities and Cemeteries of Etruria*,[3] 1883, would be difficult to replace, for its descriptions, its erudition and its considerable literary merits. See also A. Neppi Modona, *A guide to Etruscan Antiquities*, Florence, 1954; H. Nissen, *Italische Landeskunde*, 1883–1902; A. Solari, *Topografia Storica della Etruria*, I–IV, 1915–20, and the short introductory chapters to the collections, divided according to cities and territories, of inscriptions in the *Corpus Inscriptionum Etruscarum*.

2. On the Rome of the Etruscan period, with special reference to the archaeological data, see I. Scott Ryberg, *An Archaeological Record of Rome from the Seventh to the Second Century B.C.*, 1940.

3. The translation is from G. Dennis' *Cities and Cemeteries of Etruria*, 1883, I, p. 16.

4. There is no comprehensive work on Veii; particulars may be had in *Notizie degli Scavi*, 1919, pp. 8 ff.; 1929, pp. 325 ff.; *Le Arti*, I (XXVII), pp. 402 ff.; II (XVIII), pp. 17 ff.; *Monumenti Antichi della Accademia d' Italia*, XI, 1944, col. 177 ff.; *Bollettino d'Arte*, 1952, pp. 147 ff. Cf. also M. Pallottino, *La scuola di Vulca*, 1945.

5. On Caere, cf. R. Mengarelli, in *Studi Etruschi*, I, 1927, pp. 145 ff.; IX, 1935, pp. 83 ff.; X, 1936, pp. 77 ff.; XI, 1937, pp. 77 ff.; M. Pallottino, *La necropoli di Cerveteri (Itinerari dei Musei e Monumenti d'Italia)*[2], 1950. A series of accounts of Mengarelli's excavations are in course of publication in *Monumenti Antichi dei Lincei*.

. 6. Cf. S. Bastianelli, *Il territorio tolfetano nell'antichità*, in *Studi Etruschi*, XVI, 1942, pp. 229 ff.

7. M. Pallottino, *Tarquinia (Monumenti Antichi della Accademia dei Lincei)*, 1937; P. Romanelli, *Tarquinia. La Necropoli e il Museo (Itinerari dei Musei e Monumenti d'Italia*, 1940). For the most recent discoveries, see *Bollettino d'Arte*,1 948, pp. 54 ff.; *Notizie degli Scavi*, 1948, pp. 133 ff.

8. S. Gsell, *Fouilles de Voulci*, 1891; F. Messerschmidt, *Die Necropolen von Vulci*, 1930.

9. On the Faliscans: W. Deecke, *Die Falisker*, 1888; V. Pisani, *Le Lingue dell'Italia antica oltre il latino*, 1953, pp. 316 ff. For archaeological remains belonging to Faliscan territory (mostly kept at the Villa Giulia Museum in Rome), see especially A. Della Seta, *Museo di Villa Giulia*, 1918, pp. 37 ff.

10. G. Rosi, *Sepulchral Architecture as Illustrated by the Rock Façades of Central Etruria*, in *Journal of Roman Studies*, XV, 1925, p. 1 ff.; XVII, 1927, pp. 59 ff.; H. Koch, E. v. Mercklin, C. Weickert, *Bieda*, in *Mitteil. des deutschen Arch. Instituts Rom*, XXX, 1915, pp. 161 ff.; A. Gargana, *La necropoli rupestre di S. Giuliano (Monumenti Antichi dell' Accademia dei Lincei*, 1929); R. Bianchi Bandinelli, *Sovana*, 1929.

11. G. Matteucci, *Poggio Buco. The Necropolis of Statonia*, 1951.

12. R. Bloch, *Volsinies étrusque. Essai historique et topographique*, in *Mélanges de l'École Française de Rome*, 1947, pp. 99 ff.; *Volsinies étrusque et romaine. Nouvelles découvertes archéologique et épigraphique*, in *Mélanges*, etc., 1950, pp. 53 ff. For Orvieto: P. Perali, *Orvieto etrusca*, 1928; S. Puglisi, *Studi e ricerche su Orvieto etrusca*, 1934.

13. As shown by recent excavations undertaken by the American Academy in Rome: see F. E. Brown, *Cosa, I. History and Topography*, in *Memoirs of the American Academy in Rome*, XX, 1951.

14. A. Minto, *Marsigliana d'Albegna*, 1921.

15. A. Minto, *Per la topografia di Heba etrusca* in *Studi Etruschi*, IX, 1935, pp. 11 ff.; *Saturnia etrusca e romana* (*Monumenti Antichi dell' Accademia dei Lincei*, XXX, 1925).

16. R. Bianchi Bandinelli, *Roselle* (in *Atene e Roma*, VI, 1925, pp. 35 ff.).

17. I. Falchi, *Vetulonia*, 1891; *Studi Etruschi*, V, 1931, pp. 13 ff.; XXI, 1950-1, pp. 291 ff.

18. A. Minto, *Populonia. La necropoli arcaica*, 1922; *Populonia*, 1943.

19. R. Bianchi Bandinelli, *Clusium* (*Monumenti Antichi della R. Accademia dei Lincei*), 1925.

20. C. Shaw, *Etruscan Perugia*, 1939 (to be consulted with caution); A. M. Pierotti, M. Calzoni, *Ricerche su Perugia etrusca: la città e la necropoli urbana*, in *Studi Etruschi*, XXI, 1950-1, pp. 275 ff.; for the territory of Perugia, cf. L. Banti, in *Studi Etruschi*, X, 1936, pp. 97 ff.

21. A. Neppi Modona, *Cortona etrusca e romana*, 1925.

22. F. Magi, *Contributi alla conoscenza di Fiesole etrusca* (in *Atene e Roma*, X, 1930, pp. 83 ff.).

23. L. Consortini, *Volterra nell'antichità*, 1940 (to be consulted with caution).

24. J. Heurgon, *Recherches sur l'histoire, la religion et la civilisation de Capoue préromaine*, 1942.

25. A. Grenier, *Bologne villanovienne et étrusque*, 1912; P. Ducati, *Storia di Bologna, I tempi antichi*, 1928.

26. E. Brizio, *Guida alle antichità della villa e del Museo di Marzabotto*, 1886, reprinted in 1928; P. E. Arias, *Considerazioni sulla città etrusca a Pian di Misano (Marzabotto)*, in *Atti e Memorie della Deput. di Storia Patria per le Provincie di Romagna*, III, 1953.

27. S. Aurigemma, *Il R. Museo di Spina*, 1935.

(A) Tumulus in the necropolis of Caere. *Cerveteri*

(B) Gate of Etruscan type at Falerii Novi. *S. Maria di Fàlleri*

I

(A) *Above:* Sepulchral urn in the form of a temple with winged
goddess and panthers; from Chiusi. *British Museum*

(B) *Right:* Female figure on the lid of a Canopic ossuary;
*c.* 600 B.C. *Chiusi, Museo Civico*

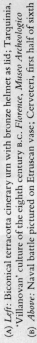

(A) *Left*: Biconical terracotta cinerary urn with bronze helmet as lid; Tarquinia, 'Villanovan' culture of the eighth century B.C. *Florence, Museo Archeologico*

(B) *Above*: Naval battle pictured on Etruscan vase; Cerveteri, first half of sixth century B.C. *Paris, Louvre*

3

(A) Aged married couple portrayed on the lid of a small terracotta urn.
*Volterra. Museo Guarnacci*

(B) Lid of urn from Volterra with figure of the deceased man. *British Museum*

Head of the Apollo of Veii: Ionic–Etruscan art of the fifth century B.C.
*Rome, Villa Giulia*

(A) Lid of sarcophagus from Tarquinia
*British Museum*

(B) Alabaster statue of woman holding a bronze gilded dove; Vulci, first quarter of the sixth century B.C.
*British Museum*

6

Yoked winged horses in terracotta, part of the frontal decoration of a temple; fourth-third century B.C. *Tarquinia, Museo Nazionale*

(A) *Left*: Terracotta statuette of seated woman; from Cerveteri. *British Museum*

(B) *Above*: Archaic mask, from an antefix at Cerveteri. *British Museum*

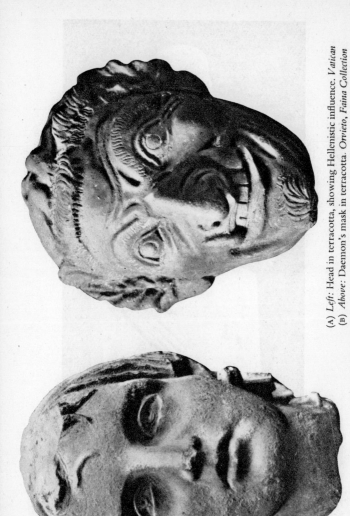

(A) *Left*: Head in terracotta, showing Hellenistic influence. *Vatican*

(B) *Above*: Daemon's mask in terracotta. *Orvieto, Faina Collection*

9

Sepulchral urn in the form of a man (life-size);
from Chianciano. *British Museum*

(A) Two antefixes mounted on cornice of roof; from Lanuvio. *British Museum*

(B) Dancing scene; low relief on an urn from Chiusi. *British Museum*

Bronze statue of Mars found at Todi; fourth century B.C. *Vatican*

Terracotta fragment of the statue of a young god (the 'Apollo' of Falerii).
*Rome, Villa Giulia*

(A) Wedding scene; relief on a small urn. *Chiusi, Museo Civico*

(B) Funeral scene; relief on a cippus from Chiusi.
*Munich, Museum Antiker.Kleinkunst*

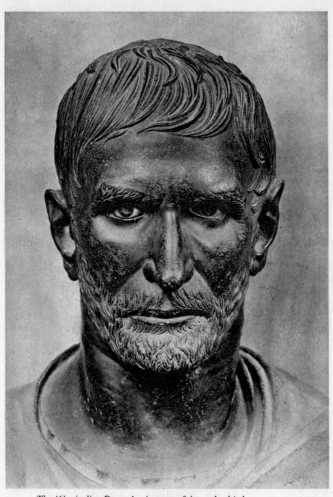

The 'Capitoline Brutus', a bronze of the early third century B.C.
*Rome, Palazzo dei Conservatori*

(A) The Chimaera of Arezzo. *Florence, Museo Archeologico*

(B) Reclining man; bronze of the archaic period. *British Museum*

16

Bronze statue of Aule Meteli, known as the 'Orator'.
*Florence, Museo Archeologico*

(A) *Left:* Warrior with cuirass; bronze statuette of the fifth century B.C. *British Museum*

(B) *Above:* Bronze statuette of haruspex. *Vatican*

(C) *Right:* Bronze statuette of a war-god. *Florence, Museo Archeologico*

(A) *Above:* Bronze lamp. *Cortona, Museo dell' Accademia Etrusca*
(B) *Right:* Bronze situla from the Certosa. *Bologna, Museo Civico*

19

Nobleman seated before the statue of a goddess; painted plaque from Cerveteri.
*Paris, Louvre*

Mythological scene; painted plaque from Cerveteri, sixth century B.C.
*Paris, Louvre*

Circus scenes: detail of a mural painting in the Tomb of the Monkey at Chiusi

22

Jugglers and musicians: detail of a mural painting in the Tomb of the Monkey at Chiusi

(B) Piper: detail of mural painting in the Tomb of the Triclinium at Tarquinia. *Tarquinia, Museo Nazionale*

(A) The daemon Tuchulcha: detail of a mural painting in the Tomba dell'Orco at Tarquinia

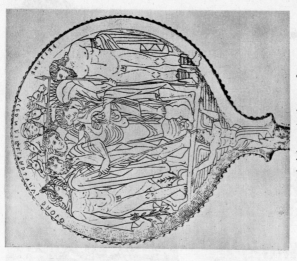

(A) Uni (Juno) giving suck to Hercle (Hercules): an
Etruscan myth illustrated on a mirror found at Volterra.
*Florence, Museo Archeologico*

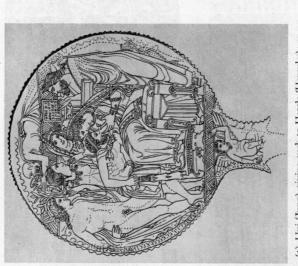

(B) A lesson in the art of
divination, from a mirror found at Tuscania.
*Florence, Museo Archeologico*

(A) *Top:* Large gold fibula from Vulci.
*British Museum*
(B) *Left:* A gold bracelet from Tarquinia.
*British Museum*
(C) *Right:* Ornamental gold disc.
*British Museum*

26

(A), (B), (C) Portions of three gold necklaces. *British Museum*

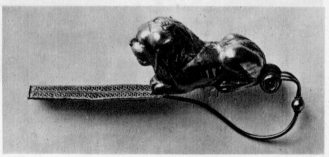

(D) Gold fibula with lion. *British Museum*

Large gold fibula of the 'orientalizing' period (seventh century B.C.), found at Cerveteri. *Vatican*

(A) Bucchero dish with Etruscan inscription found on the slopes of the
Capitoline Hill in Rome. *Rome, Musei Capitolini*
(B) Fragment of a sixth century B.C. bucchero cup found at Veii.
*Rome, Villa Giulia*

Cerveteri, Tomb of the Stucchi: interior showing alcoves and pillars

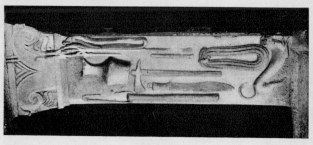

(A), (B), (C) Cerveteri, Tomb of the Stucchi: pillars with painted stucco representations of household objects, etc.

The Vetulonia fascis, with two-bladed axe and iron rods.
*Florence, Museo Archeologico*

# THE POLITICAL AND SOCIAL ORGANIZATION OF ETRURIA

### *The Etruscan Constitution*

THUS the cities of old Etruria give us the picture of a rich and interesting life, whether they show no more than a few limestone blocks above the surface of the ground, the dark mouths of their sepulchral caves well hidden in the wild Mediterranean scrub; or whether they have been unearthed and made accessible to the modern tourist. It is a picture that may reach grandiose proportions, worthy of being placed on the same level as the most famous ruins of the East, Greece, and Rome. And the question that immediately comes to the mind of the sightseer the first time he visits these monuments or of the scholar trained in the examination and investigation of ancient buildings, is the same: how can we become a little more intimately acquainted with the way of life and the civilization of the builders of these monuments and tombs?

There are ruins in the world that have come to light as if they were expected, as if carrying a passport: they are the monumental confirmation of events in the history of past civilizations already known through the songs of poets or the accounts of historians. We need only think of the grandiose buildings of Mycenae, first brought to light by Schliemann's eager pickaxe, when all around him spoke of Atreus, of Agamemnon, Clytaemnestra, and Aegisthus; even though the figures of these Homeric heroes had been relegated by official science, often unjustifiably, as we are now beginning to see, amongst the shades of small deities made human, or to the realms of poetic fantasy; even though the protagonists of the Trojan war were to be considered as no more than late and barbarized descendants of magnificent kings buried deep amongst the treasures and splendours of Cretan art in their Mycenaean tombs! When faced with such almost familiar ruins, the confident scholar does not hesitate to put forward hypotheses and utter names of places and persons. Only quite recently have the ruins of a palace with vases and tablets of inscribed terracotta been found at Koryphasion in western Peloponnesus in the area of ancient Pylos: and there was naturally no hesitation in referring to it as 'Nestor's palace', on Homer's authority.

At other times, however, as in the case of the *nuraghi* of Sardinia or the megalithic temples of prehistoric Malta, the ruins appear obscure and mysterious. Tradition, both poetical and historical, has been interrupted; it is practically useless to question stones on which no written word exists. The monuments of ancient Etruria, despite their relatively recent age and the thousand bonds that unite them to the contemporary civilizations of Greece and republican Rome, are closer to this second class of archaeological remains than to the first. This is perhaps why they exert such a strong fascination and such a desire to probe further, if only in the imagination, into the various aspects of the public and private life of their builders.

The problems concerning the political and social life of the Etruscans are many, controversial, and often still unresolved.[1] The only information we have on the subject we owe almost exclusively to indirect references in ancient writers and to the recording of events in which the Etruscans came into contact with the Romans. With the help of these data, scholars are generally agreed on a picture of Etruria in which (in historical times at least) political sovereignty coincided with the city and its surrounding territory, as it did in the Greek πόλις or in the medieval commune. It also appears that the city states were united permanently in a kind of league or federation with a common centre, and a predominantly religious and economic, perhaps even political, character, but without affecting the independence of each individual state. As for the internal political and social organization of the various cities, it is known that the aristocratic class was mainly concerned in government and that there was a gradual evolution from the monarchy of historical times to the republican oligarchy of Hellenistic times. These fundamental data are naturally accompanied by many more elements but their interpretation is a good deal less easy.

It is only quite recently that answers to some of these questions have been sought in monuments: their principal features (as for instance the characteristics of tombs), their figured decorations, their inscriptions, all help to integrate the fragmentary data provided by tradition. Naturally the inscriptions would be of decisive importance to our knowledge of Etruscan political institutions were we able to interpret them wholly and convincingly. Nevertheless the present state of our knowledge of the Etruscan language (an outline of which will be found in the latter part of this volume) allows inscriptions, and particularly funerary inscriptions, to play a most important role in the reconstruction of Etruscan political and social life.[2] It is only natural that many difficult problems arise from the study and comparison of literary evidence and monumental sources and it is to these problems that we shall devote most of the following pages, since they form the most interesting part of our subject.

## The League

First and foremost, what exactly do we know of the Etruscan 'league'? The term is a modern one; ancient writers

speak of the *duodecim populi*, of the *duodecim populi Etruriae*'
of δώδεχα ἡγεμονίαι (Dionysius, VI, 75) or more simply
of *Etruria*, or *omnis Etruria*. The fact that the great cities of
Etruria proper were twelve in number (to which corresponded a like number in northern Etruria and in Campania),
has in all probability a ritual significance: if we take account
of the close cultural relations existing between Etruria and
Asiatic Ionia during the sixth century, the possibility comes
to mind that the Etruscan league had as a model the league
of the twelve cities of Ionia.[3] That it was a real and political
institution as well as an ideal unit may be deduced from the
study of the references to the twelve Etruscan states found
in ancient authors (see especially Livy, IV, 23; V, 1; X, 16,
etc.); reference is made, for example, to consultative meetings held by the Etruscan states and their heads (*principes*) at
the *Fanum Voltumnae*. Pareti very justly pointed out that
such evidence is not sufficient to prove the continuity or the
strong suprastatal power of the presumed Etruscan federal
union. If we admit the existence of annual pan-Etruscan
festivals and games at the sanctuary of Voltumna (similar to
the Pan-Hellenic games at Ephesus, Olympia, Delphi, and
Corinth) it would be perfectly justifiable to suppose that
only exceptional political circumstances such as the threat
of Rome would have induced the representatives of the
various Etruscan states to meet in consultation at the
national shrine and even form a political and military
coalition.[4]

There are also references that seem to point to a certain
continuity in this institution and to a formal dependence on
it of the various single states: e.g. a passage in Servius (*ad
Aen.*, VIII, 475), which states that Etruria had twelve *lucumones*, or kings, one of whom was at the head of the others;
and from Livy's references (I, 8, 2; V, 1) to the election of a
lictor for the *fasces*, and to the election of a *sacerdos* at the
*Fanum Voltumnae* on the occasion of the meetings of the

Etruscan states. Our assessment of the Etruscan league wholly depends upon the reliability of the above statements. It is interesting to notice that in two of the passages the word king is mentioned; they must therefore refer, as far as we can tell, to a period earlier than the fifth century B.C. On the other hand the two passages in Livy mention an elected head of the alliance of Etruscan states, a personage who at the end of the fifth century (i.e. at the time of the conflict between Veii and Rome) was designated by the title of *sacerdos*, and therefore invested with eminently religious powers.

A few Latin inscriptions of the imperial age (during which ancient Etruscan institutions and titles still formally subsisted) give us the title *praetor Etruriae* accompanied at times by the name of a city in the locative case (*Tarquiniis, Pisis*). This title also appears in the form *praetor XV populorum*, i.e. of the Etruscan national community which in Roman times seems to have been increased by three cities. This is however a collegiate magistrature[5] and it is doubtful therefore whether it can be identified with the supreme head of the league. We should rather think of it as designating the representatives of each state to the federal councils, or the magistrates connected to the league itself, rather like the *principes* and the *lictores* recalled in the above-mentioned passages in Livy.

Amongst the various offices filled by Etruscan personages and recorded in Etruscan inscriptions, we know of the following:

(i) *zilaθ amce meχl rasnal* (*C.I.E.* 5360 – Tarquinii);
(ii) *zilaθ . . . rasnas* (*C.I.E.* 5472 – Tarquinii);
(iii) *meχlum rasneas clevsinsl . . . zilaχnve* (*C.I.E.* 5093 – Orvieto).

These expressions are substantially identical, as the nominal formula *zilaθ amce* 'he was "zilath" ' corresponds to the

verbal one *zilaχnve* 'he filled the office of "zilath"'. Thanks
to the celebrated passage in Dionysius (I, 30, 3), where the
Etruscans are designated by their national name of *Rasenna*,
we know that *rasna* signifies 'Etruscan, Etruria'. On the
other hand, the magistrature designated by the word *zilaθ*,
apparently the highest office in the Etruscan republics, corresponds very probably with the praetorship of the Romans.
Thus there appears to be an obvious correspondence between the title *zilaθ meχl rasnal* and *praetor Etruriae;* a
correspondence that probably extends also to the name of
the city in which or on behalf of which the office was filled,
as in the case of inscription *C.I.E.* 5093, where the word
*clevsinsl.* may perhaps stand for Chiusi and would be the
equivalent of the expressions *Tarquiniis, Pisis* of the Latin
inscriptions mentioned above.[6]

The word *meχl, meχlum* still remains to be explained; it
has often been connected with the *meθlum* that appears in
other Etruscan texts and variously interpreted as 'league' or
'people'. In the Etruscan manuscript of the Zagreb mummy,
*meθlum* is found next to the word *spur*, which seems to
indicate 'city', in a passage which lists the institutions for
the benefit of which the religious ceremonies were performed, just as in the Umbrian text of the Gubbio Tablets.
We should also notice the fact that several names of offices
are accompanied by the terms *spureni, spurana* indicating
that the office was a city magistracy. It is probable therefore
that *spur* was the technical term for the single city-states
and that it is exactly rendered by the Latin *populus;* whereas
*meθlum* or *meχl* concerns a larger entity, perhaps the Etruscan league or nation. It should perhaps be equated with
*nomen*, in the Latin or Umbrian sense of this word, i.e.
the race or spiritual entity of the nation.

In conclusion, the various data in our possession are not
sufficient to allow us to form an exact notion of what the
Etruscan league was, or to outline, however briefly, its

history. If the accounts of the supremacy of one of the ancient sovereign states over the others are not wholly baseless, we may think of a close alliance of the southern Etrurian centres that flourished in archaic times under the hegemony of one or other of their number; the important role played by Tarquinii in the primitive legends of Etruria may lead us to infer a period of Tarquinian hegemony. Later, this ancient unity may have assumed the character of a religious confederation, with games and national gatherings at the sanctuary of Voltumna, near Volsinii. The election of an annual supreme magistrate is perhaps a survival of the supreme sovereignty of one head over the others. We know from Livy that in the fifth century the future king of Veii was a candidate for the election (thus implicitly confirming the importance of the national magistracy); he was however defeated. This institution may be compared – though the comparison is wholly hypothetical – to the growth of the Germanic Empire from the feudal sovereignty of the German kings during the high Middle Ages to the autonomy of the regional electorates of modern times.

## The Peoples

At the time of Etruria's contacts with Rome, despite the concept of national unity and the actual existence of federal institutions, the political structure of the Etruscan nation consisted chiefly of a system of small regional states having at their head whichever city dominated them by its size and wealth. We do not know what conditions reigned during the archaic period, but the coexistence of various centres of great importance at short distances from each other (e.g. Veii, Caere, Tarquinii, Vulci), with their own sovereigns, their own characteristics and customs, remind us of the fragmentary nature that characterized the political system of the archaic Greek πόλις. As time went on the single sovereign cities must have gradually increased their territory, subjugating and incorporating rival cities perhaps, as was the case in the early history of Rome. As a result a system of small regional states was arrived at, until the Romans came to impose their hegemony and, finally, political unity from the outside.

The Etruscan regional state was dependent in all its essentials on its central city; the latter represented something more than a mere capital: state and city were one both in name and in structure. *Populus*, the probable equivalent of the Etruscan *spur*, [7] was synonymous in some of its meanings at least with *urbs* and πόλις. The names of the *populi* were the same as those of the inhabitants of the city: thus we have Veians, Tarquinians, Caeretans, Clusians, etc. It is quite possible that in the course of the formation of regional states, certain conquered cities may have preserved an appearance of autonomy or may have contracted alliances with their conquerors: this may be the case of certain important towns like Sutrium or Nepete with respect to Veii, in whose sphere of influence they were at the time of the Roman conquest. There is also the possibility that the colonies may have retained some form of dependence on their city of origin, as in the Etruscan expansion towards Campania and the north. As far as we are aware however, the principle of autonomy and division must also have prevailed in the political constitutions of the Etruscan dominions in southern and northern Italy.

The great cities whose magnificent ruins still remain for us to see must therefore have been the centres of political and cultural life in Etruria. Tradition tells us that they were twelve in number; it is not until the days of Rome that we hear of fifteen peoples. Which were these cities? At the time of the Roman conquest the following were certainly counted amongst them: Caere (Cerveteri), Tarquinii (Tarquinia-Corneto), Vulci, Rusellae (Roselle), Vetulonia,

Populonia, Volsinii (Bolsena), Clusium (Chiusi), Arretium (Arezzo), Perusia (Perugia), Volaterrae (Volterra). To these may perhaps be added Faesulae (Fiesole), Cortona, or Salpinum. Veii had already been conquered and annexed by Rome at the beginning of the fourth century B.C. It is quite possible that a few minor centres were still autonomous during the fourth and third century B.C., as the existence of coins bearing the names of Peithesa, Echetia, and other unidentified cities seems to indicate. Centres that flourished in archaic times, as for instance Visentium (Bisenzio), Marsigliana d'Albegna (Caletra?), and Vetulonia itself, soon fell into decadence, while other cities developed only towards the end of the Etruscan civilization, when Etruria was under Roman domination: e.g. Siena, Pisa, Florence, and Luni.

There is no evidence of the stage that preceded the organization into cities, and we are thus unable to ascertain what political system originally existed in the prehistoric settlements of Etruria. Indirect references in ancient authors and the analogy of the primitive constitution of Rome lead us to the conclusion that the cities were divided into tribes, probably three in number, which in their turn were each divided into four *curiae* (Servius, *ad Aen.*, x, 202). Apart from these few surmises we are left in utter darkness as to the organization of the cities and of their dependent territories.

### The Primitive Monarchy

The conditions reigning in Etruscan cities during the Roman age, on the eve of the great social upheavals that marked the political life of Italy during the first century B.C., influenced to a certain extent the judgement ancient authors had formed on Etruscan society, as recorded in their writings. The cities seem to have been governed by aristocratic oligarchies, and these were only sporadically and temporarily replaced by other classes of society. The oligarchies governed through magistrates designated at times by the name of *principes*. This tradition is for the most part confirmed by the existence of large and wealthy family tombs enclosing numerous bodies, with inscriptions referring to members of a few closely related families, in particular epitaphs listing the titles of various temporary and collegiate offices, according to a system proper to oligarchic republics.

Such a state of affairs cannot however have existed in Etruria during the earlier centuries of its history. Many sources refer to the existence of kings in Etruscan cities. The term *lucumo* (Lat. *lucumo, lucmo;* Gk. Λοχόμων, Λουχούμων; Etruscan, probably *lauχume, lauχme, luχume*) at times forms part of the name of Etruscan personages, as in the case of the King of Rome, Tarquinius Priscus; but it is generally used as a common name to designate the Etruscan chiefs. Virgil's commentator, Servius, on one occasion names lucumones the magistrates in charge of the *curiae* of the city of Mantua (*ad Aen.,* x, 202); on other occasions he identifies them explicitly with the kings of the cities (*ad Aen.,* II, 278; VIII, 65, 475). Basing himself on the aristocratic conception of the Etruscan state, K. O. Müller assumed that the lucumones must have been the eldest sons of noble families and many scholars have echoed his assumption. But there is nothing to warrant the assumption that early conditions in Etruria were mirrored in those current during the Roman era, nor is there anything to preclude that the term lucumo did refer to the Etruscan kings of the archaic period, according to the several and explicit statements made by Servius on this matter. It is thus unnecessary to seek, like S. P. Cortsen, the Etruscan word for 'king' in the root *purt* – and in the title *\*pursna, \*purtsna, purθne,* that may have been taken for a proper name in the case of Porsenna, king of Clusium.[8] We are, on the other hand, most probably faced here with a parallel to what occurred in Greece and in Rome (for the titles βασιλεύς and *rex*), where the office filled by the ancient monarchs was not abolished when the state changed from a monarchy to an aristocratic republic; it was substantially emptied of its political content and preserved, alongside the new republican magistracies, as a religious institution. Nothing can be so misleading as the anticipation of phenomena characteristic of modern times when attempting to assess those of the ancient world. Such an error would be committed in assuming that the abolition of the monarchy must necessarily have been accompanied by the abolition of the figure of the monarch. In an inscription referring to a Tarquinian priest of the second century B.C. (*C.I.E.* 5430), we find amongst the verbs denoting the offices filled by the priest the verb *lucairce*, whose root is connected with that of the word *lucumo*. In the sacred text of the Zagreb mummy, mention is made of ceremonies celebrated *lauχumneti*, i.e. 'in the *lauχumna*', probably the residence of the *lauχume*, the lucumo (cf. the Roman *Regia*), the official residence of the *Pontifices* in Rome. Finally, the elective head of the *Fanum Voltumnae*, whom Livy designated as a priest, was originally probably no other than the king elected by the twelve peoples and the chief lucumo mentioned by Servius, even though the importance of his functions may have been substantially reduced and transformed by the passage of time and the change in political ideas.

What was the nature of the primitive Etruscan monarchy? Our knowledge is unfortunately insufficient to answer the question, and all we may do is put forward certain suppositions based on analogy with what little is known with historical certainty of the Roman monarchy. The king must have held supreme judiciary power, which he exercised, according to Macrobius (*Saturn*, I, 15, 13) once a week in public audiences. He must have been the military and religious head of the state. We are a little better informed on certain external symbols relating to the monarchy, for these were inherited by Rome and considered by ancient writers to have had a specifically Etruscan origin. Amongst these were the golden crown, the sceptre, the *toga palmata*, the throne (*sella curulis*), the *fasces*, and other symbols of power, as well as the ceremony of the triumph where the king was identified with the supreme deity.

The problem of the origin of the lictor's *fasces* is particularly interesting.[9] Writers of the imperial age such as Silius Italicus (*Punica*, VIII, 483 ff.) and Florus (I, 1, 5) believe them to be of Etruscan origin. We have already referred to the passage in Livy in which there is a mention of the lictors sent by each Etruscan city to escort the elective head of the union. The earliest representation of the *fasces* without the axe occurs in a fifth-century Chiusi relief kept in the Palermo Museum. This destroys the hypothesis that the lictors and *fasces* in the escort of the Etruscan magistrates of the federated cities (as shown on sarcophagi from Tarquinii) were an imitation of a Roman custom.

In 1898, during the excavation of an archaic tomb in the Vetulonia necropolis, there came to light an object made up of many parts of oxidized iron. This was thought by I. Falchi to be a *fascis* consisting of small hollow rods and a double-bladed axe. The object disintegrated when it was moved, but was put together again in the Florence Archaeological Museum where it may still be seen (see plate 32). Some doubts have been expressed as to the original shape of the object and its interpretation as a *fascis;* but a careful examination of various fragments is even more conclusive than Falchi's report and interpretation. There is no doubt that the object is a *fascis*, or rather the reproduction of a *fascis*, wholly made of non-perishable materials and probably reduced in size, for funerary purposes. It is the oldest *fascis* known to us and differs from later specimens in that its axe has two blades. The use in Vetulonia of a double-edged axe for fighting or ceremonial purposes at a time roughly contemporary to that of the tomb mentioned above (seventh to sixth century B.C.) is attested by a funerary stele

Figure 4 – STELE OF AVELE FELUSKE
Sepulchral Stele of an Etruscan Warrior
armed with a two-bladed axe found at
Vetulonia (*Florence,
Museo Archeologico*)

bearing the name of Avele Feluske, where it appears in the hand of an armed warrior. But the strangest coincidence of all is the fact that Silius Italicus attributes the invention of the *fascis* to the very inhabitants of Vetulonia. Should this be true we are faced once again with a fortunate instance of the correspondence between literary traditions and archaeological discoveries.

What significance was attached to the *fascis* at the beginnings of the Etruscan civilization? The axe is well known as a political and religious symbol of the Eastern civilizations and the Mediterranean world. Ceremonial axes are quite well known in ethnology: e.g. the Polynesian axes of the Cook Islanders with carved wooden handles, connected with ancestor worship; the axes of the Basongi tribes in the Belgian Congo, etc. But it is especially in the civilization of Crete that the two- or even four-bladed axe takes on a religious character, as a symbol of divinity. The two-bladed axe of nuragic Sardinia was also probably endowed if not with religious, at least with ritual significance. Archaic Etruria, standing as it did at the confluence of various Mediterranean cultural currents, undoubtedly made use of the hatchet as a chieftain's weapon, as well as a tool and an instrument of war; this may be seen in the reliefs of the bronze *situla* of the *Certosa* at Bologna (see plate 19B) or on the figured steles of Larth Ninie or Avele Feluske found respectively at Fiesole and Vetulonia. The Vetulonia example is unusual in that it reproduces a double-edged axe, which may also in fact have been a symbol of authority. So that on the one hand there was the axe, the ceremonial weapon of the king, and on the other, the wooden rods for corporal punishment carried by the sovereign's escort when he was acting in his judicial capacity; it is quite possible that the two became united in a single object symbolizing sovereignty in its fundamental aspects: the judicial, the military, and perhaps even the religious. It is also probable that only one *fascis* was used at first and that the increase in the number of lictors was due to the extension of the sovereign's authority over a larger number of cities.

The material symbol of the *fascis* corresponded to a

political and religious authority which the Romans designated by the name of *imperium*. For further confirmation that the axe symbolized sovereign power, there is the fact that only the *imperium maius* and certain special circumstances gave the Roman magistrate the right to carry the *fascis* with the axe. The *imperium*, distinct from a more general *potestas*, represented the full judiciary and military power: it is in fact the sovereignty of the old kings of Rome passed on to the republican magistrates. The concept of *imperium*, with its religious undertones, was doubtless derived from the Etruscan monarchy.[10] A gloss of the late lexicographer Hesychius even provides us (though in a Greek form) with the Etruscan word for the Greek ἀρχή, 'power', probably corresponding to the Latin *imperium:* this is θρούνα, that probably went back to an Etruscan *\*truna*, *\*θruna*, a cognate perhaps of the pre-Hellenic root τύραννος and of the root of the Etruscan name for Venus, *Turan* (lady? mistress?).

## The Republican Magistracies

When studying the transition from monarchy to republic that took place in Etruria between the sixth and the fifth century B.C., the widespread occurrence of this political phenomenon in the Mediterranean has perhaps not been sufficiently taken into account. It is found to have taken place along substantially similar lines in the constitutional histories of at least four ancient racial stocks: the Greek, the Latin, the Etruscan, and the Semitic. Analogies such as these clearly demonstrate the profound unity underlying the Mediterranean civilization, as far as certain important aspects of its public life are concerned, even before Greek and Roman times. Primitive monarchies with their religious basis gave way to oligarchic states with temporary collegiate and elective magistracies; this process is at times paralleled or followed by the seizure of power on the part of individuals (tyrannies) or by solutions of a democratic nature. In many Greek cities, this transformation was already taking place in proto-historic times, at the end of the Mycenaean age, whereas other cities, e.g. Sparta, preserve in form at least the institution of monarchy till they cease to exist as historical entities. The new solutions arrived at by the western Greek world seem to be of a precocious nature. In Rome and in Etruria the change occurs after the second half of the sixth century. The Phoenician cities of Syria and Africa too, though with outcomes that varied with time and place, tend to change their monarchies into republican oligarchies from about the eighth to the fifth century B.C.

Once this point is established, the causes of the constitutional changes in Rome and Etruria need no longer be sought only in local conditions; there was a general tendency towards the differentiation of classes in society, towards the consolidation of genealogical and religious traditions in the aristocracy and towards the ousting of primitive monarchical institutions. At the most we may ask ourselves whether archaic monarchies in Italy ever fulfilled the political needs of local tendencies: they may have merely masked a power limited originally by the authority of heads of families or of assemblies, under the influence of purely external Eastern forms. In this case the changes of government we are considering may be no more than a return to original and genuine political forms. The question ought to be discussed mainly in conjunction with the question of the primitive Roman *gentes* and their place in the monarchical state: a thorny problem indeed.[11]

The political crisis of the end of the sixth century is in any case the sign of a decisive change of direction in the development of the constitutional system of Etruria as well as that of the Italic states generally. The many theories that have been put forward to account for the passage from primitive monarchies to republican magistracies either tend to explain it as a continuous and necessary evolution, or as a sudden innovation, possibly due to the imitation of foreign (and especially Greek) institutions.[12] Whatever might be the origin of the Roman consulship, for instance, it is possible, if not probable, that the first days of the Etrusco-Roman republic saw the triumph of a strong military authority (that of the *magister populi* or of the *dictator*), replacing the archaic sovereign, perhaps as a result of the influence of Greek tyrannies (a contemporary example of which was Cumae under Aristodemus). The Etruscan figure of *Macstrna* (Maṣtarna) or rather of the *macstrna* (since in the François tomb of Vulci the name of the hero is not preceded by a first name and thus seems to have actually been a title), the ally of the Vulci adventurers Caile and Avle Vipina against the kings of Rome and of other cities of inner Etruria, embodies this constitutional transformation which must have originated in the large and more evolved cities of the coastal belt and gradually spread to the more secluded and backward inland regions. The title *macstrna* is no more than the Etruscan form of the Latin *magister*, with the addition of an apparently unstable suffix-*na* (cf. the case of *φersu=persona*, a mask). It reappears at a later date amongst the titles of Etruscan magistrates in the form *macstrevc* (Fabretti, *C.I.I.*, 2100). Significantly enough, Roman tradition identified Mastarna with Servius Tullius, the beneficent king who broke the dynastic series of the Tarquins and to whom the reform of the centuries was attributed; a figure therefore who does not coincide with our idea (and with that of the ancients) of the primitive monarch ruling by divine right.

But even if a period of military dictatorships occurred between the archaic monarchy and the republic of full historical times, the collegiate nature of the offices (of equal authority, as in Rome, or unequal as amongst the Oscans), their temporary nature and the authority of the aristocratic senate were soon to bring a further change in the direction of the oligarchic republic. We may reconstruct the way in which this change took place in Etruria with the help of our knowledge of the Roman republic before the great wars of conquest: a senate composed of the heads of the *gentes*; a popular assembly, most probably; a supreme, temporary, and collegiate magistracy; and other collegiate magistracies of a political and religious nature. There was in any case a general tendency to parcel out power, to decrease it and to place it under constant reciprocal control, so as to prevent the rise of a tyrant. This stiffening of oligarchic institutions was accompanied by a hatred for monarchy of which we possess few but eloquent testimonies: we need only think of the opposition of the Etruscan cities to the threatened city of Veii, owing to the fact that she was governed by a king (Livy, v, 1); Etruria seems to have carried this tendency further than Rome. Differences also appear with regard to the claims for a more active part in government made by the lower classes: for in Etruria the latter were generally bereft of any possibility of becoming included more or less peacefully in the constitution, with the result that Volsinii, Arretium, and, perhaps, Volaterrae went through short periods of popular anarchy. It was only with the crumbling of the traditional Etruscan political system and the granting of Roman citizenship (a consequence of the *lex Iulia* of the beginning of the first century B.C.) that the popular classes generally managed to assert themselves over the impoverished and archaic ruling classes.[13]

The titles of the Etruscan magistracies, in their original forms, are known to us through the *cursus honorum* of the funerary inscriptions, some of which must have been written in the form of actual poetical *elogia* to the dead man, as in the case of the Roman inscriptions of the Scipio family. It is however far from easy to establish the nature of the various offices, their inter-relations, the differences between them and their correspondence with the magistracies of the Latin and Italic worlds.

The most frequent title is one drawn from the root *zil-*, whose origin is still obscure, in the forms *zil, zili, zilc* or *zilχ, zilci* and *zilaθ*. To these nominal forms there corresponds a verb *zilχ-* or *zilaχ-* with the meaning of 'to be *zilc* or *zilaθ*'. We already know that *zilaθ* corresponds in some cases to the Roman title 'praetor'. It is quite certainly a high office, perhaps the highest in the land; but the title is often accompanied by determinants *zilaθ* or *zilχ parχis; zilaθ eterau* and *zil eteraias; zilc marunuχva; zilχ ceχaneri*) which may indicate the specialization of the office (cf. the Latin *praetor peregrinus*) or the head of a particular college (*zilc marunuχva*=head of the college of *marunu*?). Thus the title may well have possessed both a specific and a generic acceptation, just as in the case of the Latin *praetor*.

Another office of great importance, more important in the eyes of some scholars than that of the *zilaθ*, is designated by terms built on the root *purθ*, which has been connected with the title πρύτανις the origin of which is probably pre-Hellenic. It appears under the forms *purθ, purθne, purtśvana, eprθne, eprθni, eprθnevc*, etc.

Yet another title frequently found in inscriptions is *maru, marniu, marunuχ*: its religious connotations are made evident by its connexion with the priestly title *cepen*, and with determinants of the type *maru paχaθuras caθsc* or *marunuχ paχanati*, which contain the names of the gods *Paχa* (Bacchus) and *Caθa*. It also appears in Umbria as the college of *marones*. It has been thought to correspond to the Latin *aedilis*. Other administrative or military offices are designated by the terms *camθi, mactrevc*, etc.

To indicate the urban character of the magistracies and to differentiate them perhaps from magistracies connected with the league, the terms *spurana*, *spureni*, *spureθi*, etc. are added in inscriptions. Though cases of magistracies for life (*svalas*, *svalasi*="διὰ βίου"?) are not unknown, in most cases there is a numeral next to the title to show the number of times the office was held and to bear witness to its temporary nature.

## Etruscan Society

The oligarchic state presupposes a social organization based on gentilitial lines. Only the most obvious characteristics of the latter, as revealed in inscriptions and on monuments, are known to us. The Etruscan personal name system was identical with the Latin and the Italic, and quite distinct from that of other Indo-European and non-Indo-European speaking peoples, from that of the Greeks or Semites for instance, amongst whom the simple name accompanied by a patronymic (Apollonius of Nestor, Joseph son of Jacob) does not express very clearly the idea of family continuity. The system current in ancient Italy was based essentially upon two elements, the personal name proper and the name of the family or *gens*. Thus it is the only personal name system of the ancient world to foreshadow a custom that was to become general, for social, cultural, and political reasons, in the civilization of the modern world. Next to the two principal elements, the patronymic and the matronymic were often used and even at times the names of the grandparents. A third element may be found added to the name of the *gens*, the Latin *cognomen*, which may have had a personal origin, though it was generally used to designate a particular branch of the *gens*.

The Etruscans probably created the 'gentilitial' name system at the beginning of their history, which tends to prove a keen feeling for the family unit and for its continuity. The most ancient of the two elements is certainly the personal, or individual, as its very simplicity clearly shows (*Vel, Laris, Arnθ*, etc.). The gentilitial names are always derivatives and take adjectival forms: they are based on personal names (*Velna*), on the names of gods (*Velθina*), on place names (*Suθrina*), etc. The number of known *gentes* is very large indeed: an interesting fact, for it excludes the hypothesis of an original opposition between a narrow oligarchy composed of the members of the *gentes* and of a population outside the gentilitial system. Here the question becomes particularly delicate and complex especially when considered in conjunction with the gentilitial system of primitive Rome as generally reconstructed by specialists in social and constitutional history.

Indeed one has the impression that originally the whole Etruscan people was included in the framework of the gentilitial system: not in few and very large family groupings, but rather belonging to numerous separate family trees each of which was distinguished by a gentilitial name, perhaps along similar lines to those of the modern world at the end of the Middle Ages when family names began to be used and everyone, from the highest to the lowest, ended by adopting a single onomastic system. It is possible of course, although no proof has yet been given, that there existed patrician and plebeian *gentes* in archaic Etruria as in republican Rome. But the impression received is that originally there were no great differences of social levels. The only real lower class was composed of servants, acrobats, and strangers who in monuments appear distinguished by a personal name only and who are therefore outside the gentilitial system.

If a society of freemen, subdivided into numerous small family units, can be reconciled with a monarchical constitution of an archaic type (like the one dominant in Etruria up to the end of the sixth century B.C.) the same cannot be said for the later oligarchic state as it is revealed to us through passages in ancient writers referring to the public life of the Etruscans. A great many families belonging to this late period are now known to us through inscriptions in each of the cities of Etruria and are of apparent equality in social standing. But it is also possible to make out the beginnings of larger family units, with a common gentilitial name but numerous ramifications spreading at times outside the territory of the city of origin. It was the formation of the *gens* in the Roman sense of the word, and in many cases a surname (*cognomen*) was added to the name of the *gens* so as to distinguish the various branches of the family. The small archaic tombs, each of which belonged strictly to one family, were replaced by grandiose gentilitial hypogea providing for the burial of a much larger number of persons. Marriages between members of certain *gentes* became more and more frequent, those very same *gentes* whose members most often held political or priestly office. It is not easy to provide a clear explanation of these facts; certain *gentes* may have gradually predominated over others belonging to the same original social system, and formed the new oligarchy. This phenomenon was especially characteristic of some northern towns of Etruria proper: Volaterrae, for instance, where the *gens* Ceicna (Cecina) with its numerous ramifications predominated, or Arretium, where the Cilnii, the ancestors of Maecenas, seem to have ruled for a certain length of time.

Even more difficult to establish is the position of the lesser or plebeian *gentes* within the framework of the oligarchic state, and the characteristic features of the proletarian and serving classes. Funerary inscriptions belonging to personages generally designated by a single person name (i.e. outside the gentilitial system) followed by the terms *lautni*, *etera*, or *lautneteri*, occur fairly frequently, especially in northern Etruria. The word *lautni* is derived from *lautn* 'family' and literally stands for 'familiar, of the family', though its use corresponds to that of the Latin *libertus*. As for *etera*, the precise meaning of the word is unknown; some translate it as 'slave' (the interpretation of *etera* as 'of noble birth' or 'noble on the mother's side' is wholly unfounded). There were particular magistracies connected with the *etera*: the *zil eteraias*, the *zilaθ eterav*, and the *camθi eterau*. The use of the name *leθe* or *leθi*, frequently borne by slaves, is also worthy of note: it was probably also used as a common appellative term.[14] A social and political rising of the lower classes took place in Arretium and Volsinii during the third century B.C.: as historical tradition tells us, it took the form of an actual proletarian revolution with the seizure of power and the temporary abolition of caste differentiations between the lower and the aristocratic classes (e.g. the abolition of the ban on intermarriage).[15] We still do not know however whether such a revolt should be interpreted as a clash between families of a higher and of a lower rank but still within the gentilitial system and similar to the struggle between patricians and plebeians of republican Rome, or whether it should be interpreted as a rising of those elements outside the *gentes*.

As we have been dealing with the family and the personal name system of the Etruscans, we should end by a passing reference to the so-called Etruscan 'matriarchy'. This is no more than a learned legend, born from the comparison of the customs of Etruria and of Asia Minor reported by Herodotus (I, 173), and supported by the references of ancient authors to the freedom of the Etruscan woman. The fact that Lydian children were called by their mother's name instead of their father's was compared to the Etruscan use of the matronymic as revealed by inscriptions. It is the patronymic element however that predominates in Etruscan inscriptions, even though many epitaphs bear the name of the *gens* and at times that of the mother.[16] There is no doubt that in Etruria (and later, in Rome) the woman's place in society was particularly high and quite different in any case from that of the Greek woman. The fact that both men and women took part in banquets, far from being a sign of dissolution as maliciously stated by many Greek writers astonished and scandalized at a custom quite foreign to the Greeks, is a clear indication of social equality and yet another link between the civilization of ancient Etruria and the customs of the modern Western world.

## NOTES

1. Cf. especially A. Solari, *La vita pubblica e privata degli Etruschi*, 1928.

2. They have been utilized in the reconstruction of the Etruscan constitution especially in the following works: A. Rosenberg, *Der Staat der alten Italiker*, 1913; S. P. Cortsen, *Die Etruskischen Standes- und Beamtentitel, durch die Inschriften beleuchtet*, 1925; F. Leifer, *Studien zum antiken Ämterwesen*, I, *Zur Vorgeschichte des Römischen Führeramts*, 1931; S. Mazzarino, *Dalla monarchia allo stato repubblicano: ricerche di storia romana arcaica*, 1945.

3. F. Altheim, *Der Ursprung der Etrusker*, pp. 61 ff.

4. Cf. L. Pareti, *La disunione politica degli Etruschi e i suoi riflessi storici e archeologici* (in *Rendiconti Pont. Accademia di Archeologia*, VII, 1929–31, pp. 89 ff.).

5. Cf. the inscription *C.I.L.*, XI, 2115.

6. Cf. M. Pallottino, *Tarquinia*, col. 553.

7. Though *populus* itself may be of Etruscan or 'Tyrrhenian' origin: see Devoto in *Studi Etruschi*, VI, 1932, pp. 243 ff.

8. S. P. Cortsen, *Die etruskischen Standes- und Beamtentitel*, 1925, p. 126.

9. See A. M. Colini, *Il fascio littorio*, 1932, pp. 5 ff.

10. For the distinction between the primitive religious concept of sovereignty (*auctoritas*) and the later and essentially military power (*imperium*), see S. Mazzarino, *Dalla monarchia allo stato repubblicano*, pp. 208 ff., 216 ff.

11. Cf. De Sanctis, *Storia dei Romani*, I, 1907, pp. 224 ff.; E. Pais, *Storia di Roma dalle origini all' inizio delle guerre puniche*, II, 1926, p. 296 ff.

12. For a critical account of these theories and of the whole question, see S. Mazzarino's *Dalla monarchia allo stato repubblicano* to which we have already referred.

13. Cf. M. Pallottino, *Gli Etruschi*, pp. 208 ff.

14. Cf. E. Vetter, in *Jahreshefte der Österr. Archäol. Inst.*, XXXVII 1948, pp. 60 ff.

15. For the sources, see K. O. Müller, W. Deecke, *Die Etrusker*, I, pp. 120, 351 ff.

16. See on the subject F. Slotty, *Zur Frage des Mutterrechtes bei den Etruskern*, in *Archiv. Orientálni*, XVIII, 1950 (*Symbolae F. Hrozný dicatae*, V), pp. 262 ff.

# CHAPTER SEVEN

# THE RELIGION OF THE ETRUSCANS

## Problems and Documents

SINCE the aim of the present work is not so much to pile detail upon detail on the various aspects of the Etruscan civilization, but to interpret these data and to discuss certain fundamental problems as yet unsolved, there would be little point in repeating what has already been described elsewhere on the religion of the Etruscans, whether considered as a whole or in its several aspects: on the deities, the forms of worship, the interpretation of divine will, funerary customs, etc. Religion is in point of fact the best known facet of the Etruscan civilization; this is hardly surprising owing to the relative abundance of sources of a literary nature, and especially the great number of archaeological monuments that, in one way or another, throw some light upon the subject.[1] This does not mean however that everything has been said that can be said, or that the data in our possession – especially archaeological – have been so worked that no further research or results may be expected. Clemen's comparatively recent work on the subject (*Die Religion der Etrusker*, 1936) is a case in point: here, the various problems have been attacked from a most original angle, with an intelligent and modern critical approach. This book, together with the more recent and no less praiseworthy essays of Giglioli and Grenier,[2] confirms our opinion of the need for a vast future survey that would re-examine all useful sources and make use of all the various results arrived at so far to paint a single, comprehensive picture of the whole.

The reputation the Etruscans had of being a most religious race is one of those frequent literary commonplaces continually to be found in the works of ancient writers. Livy (v, 1, 6) describes them as *gens ante omnes alias eo magis dedita religionibus, quod excelleret arte colendi eas* (a people who above all others were distinguished by their devotion to religious practices, because they excelled in their knowledge and conduct of them). Arnobius (*Adv. gentes*, VII, 26) proclaimed Etruria to be *genetrix et mater superstitionum*. There is even an ingenuous folk-etymology that would derive Tusci from δυσιάζειν 'to sacrifice' (Isidore, *Etym.*, IX, 2, 86; cf. also Dionysius of Halicarnassus, I, 30, 3). Modern scholars too seem prone to give credit to this unusual reputation the Etruscans enjoyed amongst ancient peoples. In actual fact, the *quantitative* assessment of religiosity on the part of different peoples runs the risk of losing all reality unless we take into account the historical reasons prompting it. Etruscan traditions were of very great importance to the Romans of the imperial age, not only because Etruria gave the first and most important contribution to the definition of those Italic religious forms amongst which the religion of Rome developed from its very beginnings, but also because religion was that portion of the Etruscan inheritance acknowledged with the least reserve by Rome and most vigorous in its resistance to the overwhelming impact of Hellenic culture. But more important are the *qualitative* differences that existed between the religion of Etruria on the one hand and that of Greece and Rome on the other. In the former are evident a scrupulous attention to ritual, to conformity and to the will of the gods, the continual dread of dark and overwhelming forces, of time limits that could not be deferred. There was in Etruria a feeling of the nonentity of man before the divine will, unknown to the Greeks even in the anguish the latter felt before the all-powerful Fates, and which the Romans tended to resolve in a prevalently juridical conception of the relationship between man and god – both a concrete and practical solution. For both in the religion and the religious art of the Graeco-Roman world, man played in spite of all the role of the protagonist; in Etruria on the other hand, the deity appears to dominate to the exclusion of man, as if reciting an eternal monologue in which the only role left to man was that of a cautious and timorous commentator. Once this qualitative point of view is accepted, the result of the comparison becomes obvious and the statements of ancient writers on the deep and exceptional religiosity of the Etruscans are shown to be fully justified.

In attempting to reconstruct a picture of that particular combination of spiritual attitudes, tendencies, and practices that constituted the religious world of the Etruscans, the question of sources becomes all-important. These are of two kinds: direct, such as original Etruscan texts, the majority of which are still obscure: i.e. the ritual texts of the *liber linteus* (linen book) of the Zagreb mummy or those of the Capua tile; a number of inscribed objects (e.g. the famous bronze model of a liver found at Piacenza); figured monuments (paintings, sculptures, and especially scenes engraved on the back of mirrors); the ruins of temples, tombs, etc.; or indirect, such as the accounts by Latin and Greek authors of imperial and post-classical times. This second class of documents must naturally be made to undergo a thorough critical examination before being utilized towards a reconstruction of the religion of the Etruscans, for in matters as delicate as religious beliefs and ritual, there are bound to occur many alterations, misunderstandings, and contaminations of the original elements. Owing to the relative resemblance of certain spiritual attitudes of Etruria and Rome, the correspondence of certain deities and the parallelism of various ritual forms, it is hardly surprising that Etruscan traditions as transmitted by Roman writers on religious matters or as included in the treatises of Christian apologists (e.g. Arnobius) should have reached us in somewhat distorted versions. Typical in this respect is the tradition referring to the creation of the world: the Etruscans believed, according to the medieval encyclopaedist known as Suidas, that this took six millennia to accomplish – an obvious reminiscence of biblical cosmogony. In this particular case the explanation probably lies in the contamination of Etruscan and Christian elements within the literary elaborations of the late Roman age.

To conclude, the elements that can be used towards a reconstruction of Etruscan beliefs and ritual are both limited and of uncertain interpretation. The loss of original Etruscan religious literature is irreparable: how small in fact our knowledge of the spirit, the dogmas, the rites of Christianity would be, if all we had to go by were a few sacred images and liturgical objects, and the ruins of churches.[3]

## The Etruscan Conception of the Divine

But even if we did possess a greater number of documents it would not be easy to obtain a true picture of the Etruscan religion and of its original and most genuine forms. The influence exerted by the civilization of Greece upon the Etruscans was too powerful and too ancient in character, especially in mythological and artistic inspiration, not to have left a considerable mark upon Etruscan religious attitudes and manifestations. This is particularly evident in the Etruscan conception of both the individuality and the form of the divinity. Clemen has attempted to find in certain aspects of Etruscan religious conceptions the survival of fetishist forms such as the worship of weapons, trees, waters, etc. It is doubtful however whether the worship of weapons or trees was ever a genuine manifestation even amongst the earlier Mediterranean civilizations: it may have been no more than a religious symbol whereby the personality of the god, even if not conceived anthropomorphically, was represented by its chief attribute. Similarly, it is difficult to connect Etruscan animism with animism understood as the worship of ancestors. [4] There is, however, no doubt that in the most genuine aspects of the Etruscan religious expression – genuine both because they had been recorded by the ancients and because of their continued survival despite the contrast they offered with the more widespread and familiar forms belonging to the classical world – their conception of supernatural beings was permeated by a certain vagueness as to number, attributes, and appearance. This vagueness seems to point towards an original belief in some divine entity dominating the world through a number of varied manifestations which later became personified into gods, or groups of gods and spirits. This outlook is responsible for the concept of the *genius* as a vital and life-giving force which is, or may be, a single divinity or the prototype of a great number of male or female spirits (the *lasae*) [5] mingling with men and gods and inhabiting the underworld; or which may actually manifest itself in non-anthropomorphic sexual symbols. The Roman *genius*, reflecting and accompanying both human and divine beings, was originally mainly an Etruscan conception.

Thus one is naturally led to the conclusion that the great individual deities were solely due to foreign, or to be more specific, Greek influences, playing upon this vague and amorphous religiosity of the Etruscans. Such a conclusion is unlikely to be true, however, especially when it is considered that the formation of the Etruscan civilization occurred rather late in the Mediterranean world and was preceded by centuries, not to say millennia, of cultural minglings and elaborations. The concept of a supreme being, with eminently celestial attributes, manifesting his will by means of the thunderbolt, may in no way be considered to have been a late *motif* or one imitated from outside. The same may be said of the concept of the goddess of Love, Turan (whose name probably meant originally 'the lady'), which certainly crystallized within the compass of the primitive religious elaborations of the Mediterranean world. At most we may speak of a typical archaic or primitive flavour of Etruscan religious conceptions, of lingering themes and beliefs that had already been discarded, or very nearly, by their Mediterranean neighbours; this will become more apparent in the light of the following considerations.

It is true on the other hand that the influence of Greece may have assisted and favoured the individualization and the humanization of the Etruscan deities, multiplying and defining as a result the various aspects of the major deities, promoting local spirits and heroes to the rank of national gods, fusing groups of beings with analogous characteristics into one. A typical case is that of Veltha or Veltune or Voltumna (*Vertumnus* in its Latin form): a god with strange and contrasting attributes, represented at times as a maleficent monster, at others as a god of vegetation of uncertain sex or as a great war god. We have here a typical example of the process of the individualization and the transformation of a local earth spirit, pertaining to a territory of southern Etruria, into a superior divinity, or rather into the national god *par excellence*, the *deus Etruriae princeps* (Varro, *de ling. lat.*, v, 46). [6] In the same way, the protecting spirits of war, represented as armed heroes, tend to coalesce into a single deity, the Etrusco-Roman Mars, on the model of the Greek god Ares.

We thus pass on to the second consequence of the Hellenic influence on the Etruscan religion: the giving of human forms to (or anthropomorphization of) the various deities, or, to be more precise, the external and formal moulding of divine figures on the patterns provided by

Greek anthropomorphism. The Etruscans must have possessed from the very beginning a certain anthropomorphic image of their own for their gods, though we are unable to tell how important the early influence of the mature civilizations of the East may have been on such popular representations. This must certainly have played a part in the case of the war gods mentioned above or in that of the celestial god *Tin*, which a coarse bronze statuette represents as a young man holding a thunderbolt in his right hand.[7] But Greek literature and art soon imposed – from the first half of the sixth century at least – its own representations of the great divinities as they gradually came to be elaborated in the various cities of the Hellenic world.

As a result of this process a whole series of Etruscan deities came into being, substantially parallel, if not identical, with those of Hellas: Tin, Tinia (Jupiter) corresponding to Zeus, Uni (Juno) to Hera, Menerva (Minerva) to Athene, Sethlans to Hephaistos, Turms (Mercury) to Hermes, Turan (Venus) to Aphrodite, Maris (Mars) to Ares, etc. A number of Greek divinities were also introduced directly into Etruria: Herakles who became the Hercle of the Etruscans and the Hercules of the Romans, Apollo who in Etruria became Apulu or Aplu, Artemis, known as Artumes or Aritimi. Characteristic specializations of gods, myths, and ritual also gradually came to be modelled upon corresponding Greek forms. Original Etruscan monuments and texts give evidence of such syncretisms and contaminations: the lead tablet found at Magliano, the Capua tile or the text of the wrappings of the Zagreb mummy all mention individual deities, as also the bronze model of a sheep's liver found at Piacenza, used by the haruspices to facilitate the reading and interpretation of the liver of sacrificed sheep – its surface is in fact divided into compartments, each enclosing the name of a particular deity.

Next to the major deities whose personalities and outer

forms became fixed under the influence of the Greek Olympian gods, there were a number of indigenous supernatural beings, colleges of obscure and mysterious divinities, whose number and whose very names were unknown (Varro, in Arnobius, III, 40). Ancient writers, recalling, though often none too clearly, native traditions, speak of *Dii Superiores* or *Involuti* (i.e. enveloped in the shadows of mystery), who counselled Jupiter on when to throw his most dreaded thunderbolt (Caecina, in Seneca, *Quaest. natur.*, II, 41); the *Dii Consentes* or *Complices*, also advisers to Jupiter, pitiless and anonymous, generally thought to be twelve in number (Varro and Caecina, in the passages referred to above); the *Penates*, divided into four classes: of the heavens, the waters, the earth, and the souls of men (Nigidius Figulus in Arnobius, III, 40); the 'nine gods' (*novensiles*), casters of lightning (Pliny, II, 52, 138; Arnobius, III, 38); the *Favores Opertanei* (Martianus Capella, *de nupt. Merc. Philol.*, I, 45); the *Lares*, the *Manes*, etc. The relationships between some of these deities are far from being clear: Varro, for example, identifies the *Consentes* with the *Penates*. Indirect references appear to indicate that many should be considered as gods of fate. Etruscan texts in their frequent mentioning of the word 'gods' (*aiser, eiser*), most probably refer to such divine colleges, i.e. the gods considered as a collective object of worship as against individual deities (Zagreb mummy, lead tablet of Magliano, various minor inscriptions).

There is also no lack of specific determinants, as in the case of *eiser śi-c-śeu-c* (Zagreb mummy), or *aiseraś θuflθicla* or, simply, *θuflθas, θuplθaś*, etc. (in the genitive case):[8] in the latter word there may be correspondence with the Latin *consentes, complices*, on the analogy of *tuśurθir=*'*consortes, coniuges*', if we accept the correspondence of the Etruscan root *θu-, tu-* with the numeral 'one': it would therefore also be equivalent to Latin *una*, 'together'.

Next to the colleges of twelve gods and to the enneads, the existence of triads has also been surmised on the basis of the shape of the three-cell temple and on the analogy of the religion of Rome. First and foremost, that of Jupiter, Juno, and Minerva, worshipped upon the Capitoline hill in Rome, and generally thought to be of Etruscan origin; the question however has recently been re-opened to discussion. [9] The existence of dyads is, on the other hand, more certain: each is composed of a male deity and of an accompanying goddess (e.g. the infernal pairs Aita and Phersipnai, Mantus and Mania), or of twins such as the *Dioscurides*, Castor and Pollux (*Tinas clenar*), or the *θuluter* of a terracotta from Bolsena (*C.I.E.* 5180).

But where the religiosity of the Etruscans most clearly manifested itself was in the so-called *discipline:* i.e. that collection of rules regulating the relations between men and gods.[10] Its main basis was the scrupulous questioning of the divine will by all available means; amongst these, the most important and traditional were the reading and interpretation of animal entrails (and especially the liver: *haruspicina*) and the interpretation of lightning. The antecedents of both these sciences may be traced back to the East, and particularly to Mesopotamia;[11] in Etruria, however, they assumed specific national characteristics which were to render them in certain ways both foreign and superficial to the religious customs of the Roman world though intimately tied in other respects to the Etruscan tradition. It is interesting to note that the Romans, on the other hand, like the Umbrians before them, used the method of divination based upon the observation of the flight of birds (*auspicium*). But was this latter method really of secondary importance in the Etruscan discipline of the *ostenta* (the interpretation of divine signs and prodigies)? We know a great deal on this subject, but very much more escapes us. Amongst the other aspects of the Etruscan discipline that ought to be mentioned here are the detailed rules governing the ritual of ceremonies and sacrifices, the doctrine of fixed time-limits for both men and states (a doctrine connected with the religious chronology of the 'centuries') and the beliefs and prescriptions concerning life after death.

Among the many gaps that exist in our knowledge of the Etruscan discipline, there is one question of fundamental importance that is as yet unanswered: what is the significance of this discipline taken in its entirety, what vision of the world, human and divine, was responsible for it? Both these worlds were intimately connected, according to a principle of mystical participation and indiscrimination that calls to mind the mentality of primitive people. As far as we are able to perceive from available sources, many aspects of the Etruscan spirituality that seem obscure when appraised by means of standards belonging to Graeco-Roman thought become clear when seen from the different viewpoint provided by classification under a different system of religious conceptions.[12] Heaven and earth, supernatural and natural reality, macrocosm and microcosm appear to echo each other down open or recondite channels within a preordained unitary system in which the orientation and the division of space assume fundamental importance. In this connexion the findings of modern scholarship (susceptible of further developments) are based on the one hand upon the comparison of the names of deities written in the various compartments into which the surface of the bronze liver found at Piacenza is divided and, on the other, the partition of the sky, with its divine inhabitants, according to Pliny (*Nat. Hist.*, II, 54, 143) and Martianus Capella (*de nuptiis Mercurii et Philologiae*, I, 45 ff.).[13]

This 'sacred' space, orientated and subdivided, corresponds to a concept which in Latin finds its expression in the word *templum*. It refers to the sky or to a consecrated area on earth (such as the enclosed space within a sanctuary, city, or acropolis, etc.) or even to a much smaller surface (e.g. the liver of an animal used in divination) as long as the orientation and the partition of the area according to the celestial model are followed. Orientation is determined by the four cardinal points, joined by two intersecting straight lines of which the north-south line was called *cardo* (a word of pre-Latin origin) and the east-west one *decumanus:* both these forms belong to the Roman town-planning and surveying vocabulary which we know was closely connected with the Etrusco-Italic doctrine. If the observer places himself at the cross-point of the two lines with his shoulders to the north, he will have behind him the space to the north of the *decumanus:* this half of the total space is in fact called the 'posterior part' (*pars postica*). The other half placed before him towards the south constitutes the 'anterior part' (*pars antica*). A similar partition of space also occurs along the *cardo* line: to the left of the observer, the eastern sector, of good omen (*pars sinistra* or *familiaris*); to the right, the western sector, of ill omen (*pars dextra* or *hostilis*).

The vault of heaven, thus quartered and orientated, was further subdivided into sixteen minor parts in which were placed the habitations of many divinities. This plan appears to be reflected in the outer ring of compartments of the liver of Piacenza (which are in fact sixteen in number) and in the inner compartments corresponding, though not very clearly, to them. There are unmistakable identities between the gods of the sixteen celestial regions, quoted by Martianus Capella, and the names of the divinities inscribed upon the liver, though the correspondence is by no means absolute since the original Etruscan tradition must have reached the writer of late Roman times in a much altered state, with a number of breaks in the sequence. Nevertheless it is possible to reconstruct an approximate picture of the relative cosmic stations of the gods according to the Etruscan

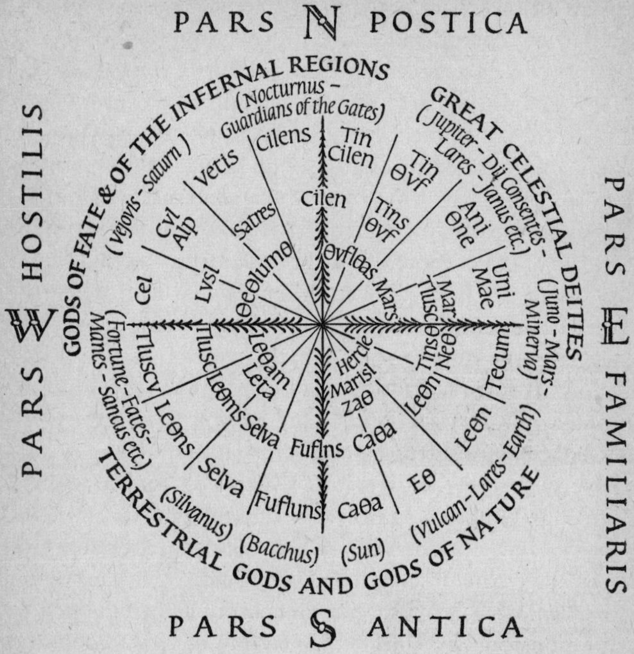

Figure 5 – THE SUBDIVISION OF THE 'SACRED' SPACE

doctrine. This shows us that the great superior deities, strongly individualized and generally favourable were placed in the eastern sectors of the sky, especially in the north-eastern; the gods of the earth and of nature were towards the south; the infernal deities and the gods of fate, inexorable and fearful, were supposed to inhabit the dread regions of the west, especially the north-west, considered to be the most inauspicious of all.

The position of signs manifested in the sky (thunderbolts, flights of birds, portents) indicates the god responsible for the message and whether it be of good or bad omen. Apart from its point of origin, a complicated casuistic body of information concerning the characteristics of the signal (e.g. the shape, colour, and effect of the lightning, etc.) helps to narrow down its meaning: whether it is a friendly message, for example, or an order, an incommutable pronouncement, etc. The same exhortative or prophetic messages may be communicated through the appearance of the liver of a sacrificed animal, which the *haruspex* interprets by making its various parts correspond to the sectors of the sky. Thus the art of the *fulguriator* and of the *haruspex*, the two typical forms of Etruscan divination, appear to be closely connected and it is not surprising to find them occasionally united in the same person – as in the case of L. Cafate, whose bilingual epitaph was found at Pesaro[14] and who was both *haruspex* (in Etruscan *netśvis*) and *fulguriator* (i.e. interpreter of lightning, in Etruscan *trutnvt frontac*). Similar rules must have governed the divinatory observation of the flight of birds, as Umbrian sources (the Iguvine tablets) and Latin ones make clear. In this respect special importance was attached to the observation area on land, i.e. to the augural *templum*, with its orientation and partitions, with which are almost certainly connected the lay-out of sacred enclosures generally and of the temple itself, i.e. the sacred edifice containing the divine image. This generally faces towards the south in Etruria, with a *pars antica*, probably corresponding to the façade and colonnade, and a *pars postica* represented by the cell or cells. And, similarly, the sacred rules of orientation were observed (ideally at least) in the lay-out of cities – a concrete representation of which is given by Marzabotto in Aemilia – and in the partition of fields.

In all these practices and conceptions, as in all Etruscan ritual manifestations generally, one receives the impression of surrender, almost of abdication, of all human spiritual activities before the divine will: this is shown by the twofold obsession to know and to put into effect the will of the gods. The deity, omnipresent and vague, is generally obscure, hermetic, incomprehensible: its very name, character, form, or sex is often unknown. The whole desperate effort of life was directed towards making it speak, forcing its secret and penetrating its mysteries; recourse was taken to the strangest of means at man's disposal, generally involved and ineffectual. Once the god's will was understood, or thought to be understood, it became necessary to make good any eventual lapse, involuntary though that might be, and execute its wishes so as not to incur the tragic consequences of divine vengeance dimly foreseen in the doctrine of fatal and peremptory time limits. Such a religion, pushing as it does to extremes well-known tendencies in the spiritual life of ancient peoples, with its blind fatality and its formal and juridical aspects, does not appear to have possessed ethical values, though certain scholars[15] have found parallels with Christianity. It is however possible that at least the more rigid aspects of such a conception only took shape during the final phase of the Etruscan civilization within the orbit of the priest class and the ritual and theological elaborations that found their expression in the sacred books. This tendency was probably, perhaps unconsciously, favoured by the desire of the priests to become the sole interpreters of the divine will and thus gather into their hands the reins controlling the spiritual life of the nation. What is certain is that, with the exception of mystery cults (which appear to have been somewhat widespread in Etruria), Greek religion, with gods made human and intelligible in all their aspects through myth, appears diametrically opposed to the Etruscan. And perhaps it is this clash that underlies the variety, confusion, and even contrasts to be observed from time to time within the complex of Etruscan religious phenomena and, in the realm of figurative art, the decorative superficiality given to the illustration of Greek myths – modified occasionally with local elements – and the few existing Etruscan myths.

Another aspect of this 'primitive' mentality of the Etruscans is illustrated by the illogical and mystical interpretation of natural phenomena which, persisting as it did till a fairly late period, contrasts strikingly with the scientific rationalism of the Greeks. Particularly significant and revealing in this respect is the following passage from Seneca (*Quaest. nat.*, II, 32, 2) on the subject of lightning: *Hoc inter nos et Tuscos . . . interest: nos putamus, quia nubes collisae sunt, fulmina emitti; ipsi existimant nubes collidi, ut fulmina emittantur (nam cum omnia ad deum referant, in ea opinione sunt, tamquam non, quia facta sunt, significent, sed quia significatura sunt, fiant) . . .* 'The difference between us [i.e. the Graeco-Roman world] and the Etruscans . . . is the following: that whereas we believe lightning to be released as a result of the collision of clouds, they believe that clouds collide so as to release lightning (for as they attribute all to the deity, they are led to believe not that things have a meaning in so far as they occur, but rather that they occur because they must have a meaning) . . .'

### Life After Death

The mystic unity between the celestial and the terrestrial world extended in all likelihood to the underworld as well, which, according to later Etruscan doctrines, was the abode of the dead.

Much of our knowledge of the civilization of ancient Etruria comes, as we know, from tombs: the very great majority of inscriptions are funerary in character and we owe our fundamental data on the development of artistic forms and on various aspects of everyday life to funerary paintings, sculptures, and furnishings. And it is natural that tombs should offer us, more or less directly, indications of the beliefs concerning the future destiny of man and the customs and rites connected with these beliefs. Nevertheless, we are still a long way from possessing a clear picture of Etruscan eschatology. Complex and contrasting themes point to different levels of religious attitudes and to heterogeneous influences: a source of many problems as yet unsolved but particularly alluring to the research worker.[16]

The very character of the tombs and of their furnishings, especially during the earliest phases, is an unmistakable pointer to the persistence of those primitive beliefs common to the whole Mediterranean world according to which the individuality of the dead man, in whichever way it was conceived, survived in some way linked to its mortal spoils, wherever the latter were laid. Hence the necessity on the part of the living to guarantee, protect, and prolong in a concrete way this survival not only as the sentimental tribute of loving piety, but also as a religious obligation where the element of fear played in all likelihood an important part. To this type of belief was owed the tendency in Etruria and elsewhere, especially in ancient Egypt, to give the tomb the shape and layout of a house, to provide it with furniture and household objects, to ornament it with decorations that must, originally at least, have carried a magical meaning; to surround the corpse with its clothes, jewels, or arms, to provide it with food and drink and an entourage of statuettes to represent the servants; and, finally, to reproduce the features of the dead man himself so as to provide an incorruptible 'seat' for the soul menaced by the decomposition of the body: whence the development of the funerary portrait in Etruria, reflecting what had earlier taken place in Egypt.

But what may have been the true and deeper nature of the religious ideas that break to the surface in such customs and how they might have been able to subsist and evolve by the side of other and contrasting beliefs are both matters that remain on the whole very obscure. At the beginning of the history of the Etruscan cities we see in fact the almost exclusive dominance of the funerary rite of cremation which, wherever it appears and in whichever way it spreads, cannot help reflecting beliefs incompatible to that of a material link between the body and the soul of the dead man. Indeed, cremation appears at times to carry the idea of a 'liberation' of the soul from the shackles of matter towards a celestial sphere.[17] It is all the more odd, therefore, that in Etruscan tombs of the 'Villanovan' and 'orientalizing' period, the ashes and bones of the cremated dead are sometimes contained in urns in the shape of houses or in vases attempting to reproduce the features of the dead person (the so-called *canopics* of Chiusi). This reveals, from the very earliest formative period of the Etruscan nation, a mingling of beliefs including perhaps the re-establishment of Mediterranean funerary traditions over crematory customs.

Nor is it possible categorically to state that belief in man's survival in the tomb excludes all belief in the transmigration of souls to a realm beyond the grave. It is certain, however, that in Etruria the latter belief became progressively more established and definite under the influence of Greek religion and mythology, with a consequent weakening of the original beliefs. This realm beyond the grave was conceived according to the Homeric Avernus and peopled with local divinities, the spirits of ancient heroes and the shades of the dead. Monuments as early as those of the fifth and fourth century, but especially those belonging to the Hellenistic period, represent death as a journey to the kingdom of the dead, the future subterranean abode of the soul: a sad, hopeless sojourn dominated at times by the fear inspired by the presence of monster demons or even by tortures inflicted upon the souls of the dead. It is, basically, the materialization of the fear of death in an atmosphere of true pessimism. And two infernal figures are the most symbolic of death: Vanth, the goddess with the great wings, representing, like her Greek counterpart Moira, implacable fate; and Charun the demon, a semibestial figure armed with a heavy hammer, who may be considered as a frightening deformation of the Greek Charon, whose name he assumes.[18] The Etruscan infernal demonology is both rich and picturesque: it includes a number of other personages partly inspired by Greek mythology (e.g. the Erinyes) as well as completely original ones such as the horrific Tuchulcha with the face of a vulture, the ears of a donkey, and armed with serpents (see plate 24A).

Even for this later period monumental sources are insufficient in their fragmentary and external aspects to provide a reliable or complete picture of contemporary beliefs concerning the underworld. If we are to go by funerary paintings and reliefs, the fate of the dead would appear to be inexorably mournful and equalitarian: the merciless law spared not even the most illustrious dignitary – his superiority is expressed only in the sumptuous clothing, the attributes of office and the retinue that accompanied him on his journey to the underworld. However, a number of references to consoling doctrines of salvation, more or less explicit in nature, exist in literary tradition (Arnobius, II, 62; Servius, *ad Aen.*, III, 168; Martianus Capella, II, 142): these mention the possibility of attaining a state of beatitude or even of deification, by means of certain rituals supposed to have been described by the Etruscans in their *Libri Acherontici*. A precious original document of such a ceremony of suffrage, with prescriptions as to offerings and sacrifices to deities (especially infernal deities), has been preserved in the Etruscan text of the Capua tile, that dates back to at least the fourth century B.C.[19] We do not know how much the development of these new eschatological beliefs owe to the diffusion in Etruria of Orphic or, still more, of Dionysiac doctrines (the cult of Bacchus is in fact widely attested in Etruria, even in connexion with the funerary world).[20] Nevertheless hopes of salvation appear to be tied mostly to the concept of magico-religious rituals proper to a primitive type of spiritual development, rather than to a superior ethical principle of recompense for the good done during life on earth.

## Forms of Worship

Monumental sources and documents written in Etruscan (as far as we are able to understand them) together with references in classical literature provide us with numerous data towards the reconstruction of the religious life and the forms of worship of the Etruscans. Traditional customs in this respect, at least as far as their material aspects are concerned (i.e. sacred places and temples, organization of priestly bodies, sacrifices, prayers, offerings of votive gifts, etc.) do not differ substantially from their counterparts in the Greek, Italic, and especially Roman worlds. This may be explained by taking into account on the one hand the common spiritual orientation of the Graeco-Italic civilization beginning with the archaic age; on the other, the very strong influence exerted by Etruria on Rome in matters of religion. A study of Etruscan religious antiquities should not therefore be considered apart from the much more detailed and complex picture given to us by Greece and Rome on the chapter of ritual, and, as a result, it becomes all the more difficult to estimate how much the development of rituals of worship owed to the religious mentality of Etruria.

In the first place we should attribute to the Etruscans that concrete and almost materialistic adherence to rules established *ab antiquo*, that scrupulous formalism of ritual and frequent demand for expiatory sacrifices that may be detected within the body of Roman religious traditions as elements foreign, as it were, to the simple and rustic religiosity of the earliest Latins and indicating the presence of a collateral factor that it is impossible not to identify with the ceremonial of an ancient and mature civilization such as, in fact, the civilization of Etruria. This *ars colendi religiones*, to quote the expression used by Livy in a passage to which we have already referred,[21] fully agrees with the feeling of subordination of man to the deity, which, as we have seen, was a predominating factor in the Etruscan religion, and presupposes faith in the magical virtue of ritual, a faith frequently met in more primitive mentalities.

This concrete quality is shown by precise determinations as to place, temple, persons, and formalities in which or by means of which the acts of invoking or placating the deity take place: proceedings which the Romans designated by the term *res divina* and the Etruscans (probably) *aisna* (i.e. 'divine' service, from *ais* 'god').

These proceedings take place within consecrated ground (the *templum*) of which mention has already been made: an enclosure with altars and sacred buildings containing images of the gods. Such buildings were often made to face the south.[22] The concept of consecration for worship of a particular piece of ground or building was perhaps expressed in Etruscan by the word *sacni* (whence the verb *sacniša*): this status could be extended, as in Greece and Rome, to a complex assemblage of enclosures and temples as on the acropolis of many cities (e.g. Marzabotto). Characteristics in some ways similar were shown by funerary enclosures, near which or within which sacrifices were offered and gifts deposited.

The regulations pertaining to the timing of feasts and ceremonies must also have been of especial importance in Etruria; these, together with the ceremonial surrounding acts of worship, constituted the subject-matter of the *Libri Rituales* mentioned by tradition. The longest ritual text in Etruscan in our possession, the manuscript on cloth preserved in the bindings of the Zagreb mummy, contains an actual liturgical calendar with indications as to the month and day on which the ceremonies described were to take place. It is probable that other documents were also drawn up, similar to the sacred calendars of the Romans: i.e. consecutive lists of days countermarked solely by the name of the feast or of the deity to be honoured. The Etruscan calendar was probably similar to the pre-Julian Roman calendar: we know the names of some of its months,[23] and it appears as if the 'ides' had, at least in name, an Etruscan origin; the numbering of the days of the month is, however, consecutive. Each sanctuary and each city must have had, as is to be expected, its own particular feasts: as in the case of the *sacni cilθ* – the sanctuary of a city which remains unidentifiable – referred to in the Zagreb ritual. On the other hand, the yearly celebrations at the sanctuary of Voltumna, near Volsinii, were national in character.

Even when we come to try and understand the nature and organization of the priestly bodies we are forced to have recourse to comparisons with the Italic and Roman worlds. There are at any rate grounds for believing that they were many and had specialized functions, closely connected with public magistracies and often grouped into colleges. The priestly title *cepen* (with variant *cipen* found in Campania), particularly frequent in Etruscan texts, is, for example, often followed by an attribute that determines its sphere of action or its specific functions; e.g. *cepen θaurχ*, a name that almost certainly indicates a funerary priest (from *θaura* 'tomb'). Other words connected with priestly offices, both general and specific in character, include *eisnevc* (connected with *aisna*, the sacrificial action), *celu*, *ceχasie*, and, perhaps, *tamera*, *santi*, etc.

There are moreover the priests with divinatory functions: the haruspices (*netśvis*), represented on Etruscan monuments in characteristic dress consisting of a pointed cap and a fringed mantle (see plate 18B), and the interpreters of lightning (*trutnvt frontac*). The title *maru, marum* was connected, as we know, with sacred functions as, for example, in the cult of Bacchus (*marunuχ paχanati, maru paχaθuras*). The double *cepen marunuχva* is worthy of note, combining as it probably did a priestly title with the functions pertaining to the *maru;* and also *zilχ ceχaneri* which must probably be understood as something approaching the Roman *curator sacris faciundis*. The collective *paχaθuras, alumnaθuras*, etc., probably refer to confraternities and should be compared as to their formal structure with such formations as *velθinaθuras*, i.e. members of the *Velθina* family. At Tarquinii there existed in Roman times an *ordo LX haruspicum* (*C.I.L.*, XI, 3382), of probable ancient origin. An attribute particular to the priest was the *lituus*, a stick curved at one end.

Worship could be directed either towards interrogating the will of the gods, according to the rules of divination, or invoking their help or pardon by means of an offering. It is probable that both these operations were closely connected one with the other, though literary sources distinguish between victims sacrificed for the consultation of entrails (*hostiae consultatoriae*) and victims destined to act as actual offerings in place of human beings (*hostiae animales*). The offerings of liquids and food appear to be similarly mixed in complex ceremonials with the blood-offerings of animals. These liturgies are minutely described in prescriptive tones by the great ritual of Zagreb and the funerary ritual of the Capua tile; unfortunately our knowledge of Etruscan is not sufficient to allow us to establish accurately the meaning of the terms used in the description of the rites and, consequently, prevents us from reconstructing the ceremonies. Prayer, music, and dance must all have played a large part in such ceremonials.

Votive gifts offered in sanctuaries for favours requested or received mainly consist of statuettes in bronze, stone, or terracotta, reproducing the features of the divinity or of the giver or even of animals, in substitution for victims and parts of the human body. These objects, kept together in coffers or deposits, often carry dedicatory inscriptions. They vary greatly in value, artistic and otherwise, but, for the greater part, consist of modest moulded terracotta figurines: a sign that deep and widespread popular religious feelings existed round the great centres of worship.

## NOTES

1. Here are the names of some of the scholars who have studied the problem: C. Thulin, G. Herbig, R. Pettazzoni, C. Clemen, G. Furlani, C. C. van Essen, H. M. R. Leopold, B. Nogara, G. Q. Giglioli, and A. Grenier.

2. G. Q. Giglioli, *La religione degli Etruschi*, in *Storia delle Religioni*, 4th ed., 1949, I, pp. 635 ff.; A. Grenier, *Les religions étrusque et romaine*, in '*Mana*', *Les religions de l'Europe ancienne*, 1948. Both works are easy to consult and contain all the preceding bibliography.

3. Cf. H. J. Rose, *On the relations between Etruscan and Roman religion*, in *Studi e materiali di Storia delle Religioni*, IV, 1928, pp. 161 ff.

4. The attempt to connect certain aspects of the Etruscan religion (divination, ecstasy, belief in the journey to the underworld, asexuality or bisexuality, bells, etc.) with Shamanistic ideas and practices (cf. W. Muster, *Der Schamanismus bei den Etruskern*, in *Frühgeschichte und Sprachwissenschaft*, herausg. von W. Brandenstein, 1948, pp. 60 ff.) rests upon very slender arguments when it is considered that such *motifs* are very widely spread throughout the world, and that it is doubtful whether some of these aspects were native to Etruria.

5. A mistaken attempt has recently been made to deny the existence of the *lasae* as minor deities and to substitute for them a single great goddess Lasa (cf. R. Enking, *Lasa*, in *Mitteilungen des Deutschen Arch. Int. Rom.*, LVII, 1942, pp. 1 ff.).

6. See R. Pettazzoni, *La divinità suprema della religione etrusca*, in *Studi e materiali di Storia delle Religioni*, IV, 1928, pp. 207 ff., where the hypothesis is advanced that the god was a local gentilitial form of the uranic god Tin (Jupiter). On the origin of the names *Vertumnus-Voltumnus*, see G. Devoto, in *Studi Etruschi*, XIV, 1490, pp. 275 ff.

7. At the *Museo di Villa Giulia*, in Rome: see G. Q. Giglioli, in *Archeologia Classica*, IV, 1952, pp. 189 ff.

8. See *Studi Etruschi*, XX, 1948–9, pp. 253 ff.

9. See L. Banti, *Il culto del cosidetto tempio 'dell'Apollo' a Veio e il problema delle triadi etrusco-italiche*, in *Studi Etruschi*, XVII, 1943, pp. 187 ff.

10. C. O. Thulin, *Die etruskische Disciplin*, in *Göteborgs Högskolas Årsskrift*, 1905, 1906, 1909.

11. R. Pettazzoni, in *Studi Etruschi*, I, 1927, pp. 195 ff.; G. Furlani, in *Studi e materiali di Storia delle Religioni*, IV, 1928, pp. 243 ff.; VI, 1930, pp. 9 ff.; *Studi Etruschi*, V, 1931; p. 203 ff.

12. See in this respect M. Pallottino, '*Partecipazione' e senso drammatico nel mondo figurato degli Etruschi*, in *Arti Figurative*, 1946, pp. 149 ff., and R. Enking, *Etruskische Geistigkeit*, 1947 (to be consulted with a certain amount of care).

13. C. Thulin, *Die Götter des Martianus Capella und der Bronzeleber von Piacenza*, in *Religionsgeschichtliche Versuche und Vorarbeiten*, III, 1, 1906, pp. 60 ff.; S. Weinstock, *Martianus Capella and the Cosmic System of the Etruscans*, in *Journal of Roman Studies*, XXXVI, 1946, pp. 101 ff.; A. Grenier, *Les religions étrusque et romaine*, op. cit., pp. 18 ff., 34 ff.

14. A. Fabretti, *Corpus Inscriptionum Italicarum*, 69.

15. E.g. T. Zielinski, *Studi e materiali di Storia delle Religioni*, IV, 1928, pp. 179 ff.

16. See F. Cumont, *Lux perpetua*, 1949.

17. Cf. A. Brelich, *Aspetti della morte nelle iscrizioni sepolcrali dell'Impero Romano* (*Dissertationes Pannonicae*, I, 7), 1937, pp. 80 ff.; F. Cumont, *Lux perpetua*, p. 390.

18. F. de Ruyt, *Charun, démon étrusque de la mort*, 1934.

19. See pp. 271 ff.

20. See A. Bruhl, *Liber Pater*, 1953, to which should be added the not inconsiderable direct epigraphic documentation (Capua tile, C.I.E., 5430, 5472, C.I.I. 2250, etc.).

21. See p. 155.

22. For the shape of the temples, see pp. 188 ff.

23. See pp. 279 ff.

# CHAPTER EIGHT

## LITERATURE AND THE ARTS

### *Literature*

WE have already noted the particular character of Etruscan monuments, that though they belong to full historical times, in some aspects they are regarded and studied almost as if they were prehistoric documents. There is not, in fact, the direct light thrown by a great literary tradition to allow us to penetrate deep into the thought, the feelings, and the ways of life of their creators as is possible with the other great peoples of the classical world. We owe much to the indirect information, whether contemporary or not, which Greek and Roman authors have left us, as also to actual documents written in Etruscan (consisting mostly of short inscriptions often of difficult interpretation): we have seen this when dealing with the political and social organization and the religion of Etruria. But neither can in any way make up for the lack of a national literature with poetical, historical, and scientific works.

Doubts may arise on whether a true literature ever existed among the Etruscans.[1] Its total loss, however, is no valid argument against its existence. We possess Greek and Latin literature almost entirely because it was passed down to us uninterruptedly from scribe to scribe, right through the centuries of the Middle Ages. Ancient texts on papyrus and epigraphic documents restored to light by archaeology are relatively insignificant in importance. But if the works of classical writers were copied and handed down to modern times, it was because they were written in a living language and constituted an essential foundation of European civilization. On the other hand, the original texts of ancient Italic peoples, including the Etruscans, had lost all interest right from imperial times: they were couched in languages no longer spoken and presumably incomprehensible to all, with the exception, perhaps, of a few isolated scholars. It is obvious that it would occur to no one to transcribe and preserve them for future generations.

A certain type of Etruscan literary activity, it is true, has been positively, though indirectly, attested by the notice it has received in Greek and Roman sources, consisting of fragmentary references chiefly to the existence of books with religious content known in translation or in compendia amongst priestly or scholarly circles in Rome. We know that they were classified into three fundamental groups under the names of *Libri Haruspicini*, *Libri Fulgurales*, and *Libri Rituales*.[2] The first dealt with divination by the examination of animal entrails and the second with divination from objects struck by lightning. As for the *Libri Rituales*, they seem to have dealt with a field much vaster and more complex: the rules of worship, the formalities governing the consecration of sanctuaries, the foundation of cities, the division of fields, civil and military organization, etc. Moreover they contained special texts on the division of time and the limits of the life of men and peoples (*Libri Fatales*), on life beyond the grave and the rituals of salvation (*Libri Acherontici*) and, finally, on the interpretation of miracles (*Ostentaria*).

Etruscan and Roman tradition tends to attribute to these works an extremely ancient and venerable origin, to the extent that a number of them were actually believed to go back to the teachings of the genius Tages (*Libri Tagetici*, corresponding, as far as we can tell, to the *Libri Haruspicini* and *Acherontici* – see plate 25B) or the nymph Vegoia or Begoë (*lasa Vecui*) to whom were assigned the *Libri Fulgurales* and the passages on mensuration contained in the *Libri*

*Rituales*. They were, in fact, believed to have been divinely inspired and to have originated in a kind of primordial 'revelation' identified with the very origins of the Etruscan civilization. And it is quite possible that the collection of sacred books as known during the last centuries of the Etruscan nation and as translated (in part at least) into Latin, did contain elements of great antiquity. But on the whole the essentially normative aspect of the texts appears rather to reflect an evolved and, perhaps, final phase in the spiritual and religious development of Etruscan society. It is quite possible that their final, and as it were, 'canonical' elaboration, may have taken place within narrow priestly circles such as the Order of the Sixty Haruspices which still flourished at Tarquinii in Roman times (see p. 175), a world to which doubtless belonged a certain Tarquitius Priscus (or Tuscus?) to whom Roman tradition attributed the composition, vulgarization, and translation into Latin of a number of sacred books.[3]

Let us now consider the nature of this religious literature. It was probably varied and heterogeneous, with sections in verse or at least metrically composed (*carmina*) and others minutely ritual and descriptive. We are able to form an idea of the latter by considering surviving original texts in Etruscan such as the manuscript of the Zagreb mummy or the Capua tile. Some scholars have in fact already pointed to an eventual connexion between the funerary ritual of the tile and the *Libri Acherontici*. Altogether, the corpus of sacred books must have possessed a fundamentally religious inspiration but, at the same time, a genuinely juridical character. It was a treatise of sacral doctrines and, at the same time, a constitution, a collection of laws, including profane ones. This is where its originality lies when compared to the body of Greek literary works and, perhaps, its analogy to the religious, juridical, and sapiential contents of certain eastern literatures and particularly that of the Hebrews.

There remains the question whether the Etruscans did pursue other forms of literary activity and up to what point these manifestations developed independently of sacred literature. The existence of annals or historical documents seems confirmed by the mention of *Tuscae Historiae* quoted by Varro (Censorinus, *de die nat.*, 17, 6). There is on the other hand a complete lack of references to epic or mythological narrative; and though we should not exclude the possibility that this *genre* may have been cultivated in Etruria, we should point out that the Etruscan mentality does not appear to have possessed to any great extent that mythographic inventiveness that flowed with such distinctive and productive force among the Greeks. With only a few exceptions, figured art imitates and re-elaborates only the sagas of gods and heroes received from the Greek world.

That convivial poems and Fescinnine satires (whose origins used to be traced back to the Faliscan town of Fescennia) had their parallels in Etruria is quite possible, but cannot be definitely proved. There are on the other hand a number of funerary inscriptions longer than average and with, perhaps, a metric or rhythmic structure that may point to the existence of *elogia*, or praises, sung in honour of important deceased personages. Dramatic poetry, as evidenced by the mention of a certain Volnius, author of tragedies in Etruscan (Varro, *de ling. lat.*, v, 55), was probably only a late phenomenon modelled upon Greek drama.

The presence has often been pointed out in Etruscan texts of regular groupings of words and syllables, repetitions, alliterations, rhymes, etc., that point to a marked disposition for the rhythmic form. But we have no reliable data on the existence of a quantitative metre comparable to that of Greek or Latin verse.[4] It is highly probable at any rate that votive inscriptions, particularly those belonging to the archaic period, and certain funerary inscriptions were in verse form, as was frequently the case among the Greeks and Romans. Sacred hymns and prayers, and perhaps profane songs as well, must also have possessed a metric form.

## Music and Dancing

Music, whether accompanied by song or not (and especially the latter) must have played a very important role in the ceremonies and the public and private life of the Etruscans if we are to judge from the evidence of both literary and monumental sources. [5] The instruments (and, consequently, the rhythms, harmonies, and melodic arrangements) are manifestly the same in Etruria as those met in the musical world of the Greeks; this identity cannot fail to surprise us, even if we take into account the many debts Etruscan cities owed to the civilization of Greece. Among the string instruments we should mention the zither, the lyre, and the *barbiton;* among the wind instruments, the double pipes (*tybiae pares*) and the straight trumpet (*salpinx, tuba*) or curved trumpet (*cornu*); among the percussion instruments, the castanets played by dancing women. As in Greece, duets consisting of a zither player (or a lyre or *barbiton* player) and a double pipe player were a common combination, as can be deduced from the frequency with which they are represented in tomb paintings.

And yet Etruria must have had its own individual tendencies and traditions of style and practice against this common musical background. We should not disregard the insistence with which ancient writers speak of the popularity of the double pipes amongst the Etruscans, almost as if it were a national instrument (see Athenaeus, IV, 154a) brought over from Lydia and transmitted by the Etruscans to the Romans: the pipe player was called *subulo* in Rome, a name derived from the Etruscan. Indeed the art of pipe playing was widely diffused in Greece, but it was attributed originally to the Phrygians and the Lydians: it reflects a taste for the pathetic and the orgiastic in music. In this case too, as with other manifestations of their artistic culture, the Etruscans appear to have adopted those elements of the complex artistic experience of the Greeks that were closest to their own sensibilities,[6] especially in the direction of those forms elaborated in the Graeco-Oriental cities of Asia Minor. We must logically suppose that Etruscan music preferred those modes defined by Greek theorists as Lydian, Hypo-Lydian, Phrygian, and Hypo-Phrygian, with their respective tonal systems, as against the grave and solemn Dorian music. On the other hand, Greek tradition agrees in attributing the trumpet or *salpinx* to the Etruscans (Aeschylus, *Eumen.*, 567 ff.; Sophocles, *Ajax* 17; Euripides, *Phoen.*, 1377 ff.; etc.). Though we need not take this to mean that the trumpet was actually invented in Etruria, nevertheless this ancient instrument must have played a characteristic part in Etruscan military and, perhaps, religious ceremonials and must eventually have been made and exported by Etruscan bronze manufacturers. Figured monuments, however, more commonly show a curved trumpet, or horn, or a straight trumpet curved at one end, like the *lituus.*

At any rate the great popularity of wind instruments corresponds to a notable development in the practice of music away from song. Music not only formed with dancing and mime part of the religious celebrations and stage performances of Etruria, but it also frequently accompanied, as an exciting rhythmic and melodic commentary, various moments of the ritual and of the public and private life of the Etruscans, i.e. games, hunting, the preparation of banquets, and even the scourging of slaves. This connexion of music with gesture rather than the spoken word finds its parallel in forms of stage performances peculiar to Etruria; these, our sources tell us (Livy, VII, 2, 4 ff.), were mimed by masked actor-dancers (*histriones* or *ludiones*), reminiscent at times of both farce and satire. This does not exclude the actual possibility of dialogued dramatic actions, which after the fourth century must certainly have been affected by the influence of Greek dramatic forms, as borne out by the many statuettes in Etruscan tombs representing masked comedy types.

Etruscan dancing is chiefly known to us through the funerary paintings of the sixth and fifth centuries. It generally appears to be performed by professional dancers: single dancing girls accompanied by a double pipe player or dancing pairs and especially troops of men and women. The latter advance separately with individual movements and are guided by musicians who perhaps filled the role of dance leaders, for they join in the steps of the dance. Occasionally – as for example in the paintings of the Tomb of the Inscriptions at Tarquinii – members of the gentilitial class to which the family of the dead man belonged may also be seen dancing. The jerky movements of the legs and the emphatic and presumably rapid gestures of the arms and head reveal a type of dance that must have been markedly rhythmical and animated if not actually orgiastic, probably inspired by the Greek *sikinnis* of Dionysiac origin. But the documents we possess, limited in time and range by funerary art, are not sufficient to prove that this was the only type of dance practised in Etruria, though it was attuned to the musical 'modes' we have assumed to be dominant in the Etruscan world (see plates 11B, 23, and 24B).

## Architectural Monuments

Of quite a different order is the wealth of direct evidence we possess on the architecture and figurative arts of ancient Etruria, for these are the very monuments and materials brought to light by archaeological discovery. In spite of the destruction of so many ancient works of art, whether buildings or objects, by the slow inexorable agency of time or the superimposing of new civilizations, these documents are sufficient to allow us a broad enough vision of the artistic activity of ancient Etruria both in its tendencies and in its developments. [7]

The buildings of Etruria cannot of course be evaluated on the same basis as those of Greece and Rome. Only in fortifications and tombs was stone employed to the exclusion of all other materials; in other constructions, such as temples or civic buildings, it was only used for the foundations: the remainder of the building was composed of lighter materials such as wood, rubble, baked or unbaked clay. This means that all that remains of such edifices is their layout and a few fragments of the decorations. Nevertheless it is possible to reconstruct their original aspect by using as a model the rock tombs and urns or small votive reproductions made to imitate them. [8]

Walled structures offer much variety in materials and techniques according to the time, place, and type of building. The commonest materials were limestone, travertine, sandstone, and tufo, all locally quarried; the absence of marble (so important in Greek architecture) is due to the fact that the exploitation of the Carrara quarries only began in Roman times. The style of masonry varies from large irregular roughly hewn blocks (as shown, for example, in the city walls of Vetulonia), to the fine revetments of small square blocks met with in the walls of southern Etruscan cities and other, though especially funerary, constructions. Generally speaking no evolution from a rougher and more primitive type of structure to more refined and elaborate styles may be detected: the square and regular type was known and employed from the earliest stages of the Etruscan civilization and differences in technique seem to be due to particular conditions such as materials at hand, available craftsmanship, urgency, etc. Contrary to opinion current among many archaeologists, the true polygonal style must be considered foreign to the building customs of the Etruscans and a late introduction on the part of the first Roman colonists in the case of the fortresses of Pyrgi, Cosa, and Saturnia.[9] The exceptional use of bricks in the late city walls of Arezzo constitutes, as far as we can tell, a local departure, even if it did derive from the brick constructions of Greek military architecture (though in the latter case the bricks were unbaked). Also widely diffused in Etruria was the system of pseudo-vault and pseudo-cupola revetments, formed by the gradual convergence of blocks laid in horizontal courses: a system widely spread throughout the Mediterranean.[10] Later, the technique of the perfect arch became established, evidenced by city gates (e.g. at Volterra, Perugia) and sepulchral monuments, a prelude to the dominant structures of the architecture of Rome. In this predilection for vault lining, Etruscan architecture carries over and perfects (though without innovations) ancient eastern forms which Greek classical architecture rejected as foreign to the rigorous rectilinear motif of its conceptions, based upon the architrave.

Among the more notable examples of military architecture we should mention the city walls of Tarquinii (and surviving sections of similar constructions at Veii, Caere, Vulci, Sutrium, etc.), of Volsinii (Bolsena), Vetulonia, Clusium (Chiusi), Cortona, Perusia (Perugia), Faesulae (Fiesole), Arretium (Arezzo). These works are generally attributed to between the sixth and the fourth centuries, with later additions and rebuilding, since they generally remained serviceable in Roman times and, in one or two cases, even later. In spite of the variety of styles, they are all continuous walls, originally uninterrupted by towers: projections and indentations only occur in connexion with gates. The latter may at first have been spanned by lintels; but the grandiose monuments of the *Porta dell' Arco* at Volterra and the *Porta Marzia* and *Porta 'di Augusto'* at Perugia feature the true arch together with architectural and figured decorations (though the *Porta 'di Augusto'* probably does not date further back than the third century B.C.; see also plate 1B). The ancient nature of city walls with battlements and arched gateways is also evidenced by figured urns and sarcophagi.

Funerary architecture is somewhat heterogeneous in character owing to the fact that it represents the occasional complement or development of sepulchral styles of varied origin and inspiration. The great majority of tombs, even those of a monumental type, were in fact hewn out of the living rock, whether they consist of underground chambers (ranging from the modest *pozzetti* and primitive pits to the grandiose and complex hypogea of a later age) or of external adaptations in the shape of circular tumuli and quadrilateral constructions covered over with earth or of façades sculptured on the cliff face. These works, though not architectural in character, are closely connected with architecture in so far as they often faithfully imitate down to the minutest detail the shapes of real buildings both in their exterior and their interior aspects. Walled structures, however, are frequently found, whether they are simply additions to the rock walls and ceilings or whether they make up the whole of the monument. Sepulchral chambers built during the earliest phase feature revetments with false vaults or, but exceptionally (as in the tomb of Casal Marittimo near Volterra), with false cupola structures. In later years, finely constructed barrel-vaulted chambers were built, e.g. the tomb of the Grand Duke at Chiusi, and the San Manno hypogeum near Perugia. The round tumulus type of monument (with drum hewn out of the rock as at Cerveteri – see plate 1A, or built upon it as at Populonia) became far less frequent after the fifth century B.C., but it evolved, owing perhaps to contacts with Hellenistic funerary architecture, towards the type of the great circular Roman mausoleum of imperial times such as those of Augustus or of Hadrian in Rome. There is also no lack of quadrilateral tombs shaped like small temples (e.g. at Populonia). Finally, mention should be made of a type of tomb built on a plinth and surmounted by large cippi, in the shape of truncated cones, or by obelisks: a type known chiefly through the reliefs of sepulchral urns, but directly attested, though outside Etruria, in the so-called Tomb of the Horatii and Curiatii near Albano in Latium. A fine monument of this type, with several obelisks adorned with bells, is mentioned by ancient sources as having existed at Chiusi and identified as the Tomb of King Porsenna. [11]

Domestic and religious architecture have common origins and characteristics. Mention will later be made of the various forms of Etruscan house (see p. 210). The temple, at first identified as in the palaeo-Hellenic world with the rectangular house with inclined roof but without portico (as evidenced by votive models and the remains of an edifice discovered on the Veii acropolis – see, for example, plate 2A) later assumed more complex forms, parallel in certain aspects to those of the Greek temple. The type attributed by Vitruvius to the Etruscans (*de archit.*, IV, 7) is characterized by a layout where the width is slightly less than the length, with the first half occupied by a colonnaded portico and the back consisting of three cells, each dedicated to a different deity, or by a single cell flanked by two *alae* or open ambulacra. Monumental remains at Veii, Orvieto, Bolsena, and Marzabotto show that this layout was in effect widely and lastingly used in Etruria from the archaic to the Hellenistic period: it is the one used for the Temple of Capitoline Jove in Rome, first built in the days of the Etruscan dynasty of the Tarquins. [12] It seems certain, however, that sacred edifices were also built with a layout more similar to that of the Greek temple: i.e. with a lengthened rectangular base and a columned façade (prostyle) or even with a continuous colonnade on all four sides (*peripteros*) as in the great temple of the 'Ara della Regina' at Tarquinia. The originality of Etruscan temples does not therefore reside so much in their layout as in the materials used for their construction, in the proportions and forms given to the rest of the building and in the types of decoration. We have already referred to the fact that, apart from the foundations, they were generally built entirely of light materials with wood for the framework of the building. This meant limited development as to height (as in effect was the case in the measurements of the 'Tuscanian' temple, according to Vitruvius), wide intercolumnar spaces and a broad roof with marked lateral projection of the eaves. Wooden beams require the protection of compact but light materials, whence the universal use of polychromic terracotta coverings; [13] these developed colourful geometric and figurative decorative patterns, with longitudinal or terminal facings for the beams and cornices, adorned with antefixes and acroteria (see plate 11A). Later (but not before the fifth or fourth century B.C.) was added the decoration of the pediment, which originally was left open so that the roof timbers could be seen from the front of the building.

All these characteristics of the Etruscan temple have undoubted counterparts in the primitive architecture of Greece and, as has been said, partial parallels with the archaic and classical Greek temple. The difference resides in the fact that the Greek temple tends to transform itself as early as the seventh century B.C. into an edifice almost entirely built of stone and evolving its own unmistakable architectonic forms, whereas in the Etruscan temple there is no departure from the tradition of using wood as a building material until full Hellenistic times; if anything, the decorative exuberance of the terracotta facings became more accentuated. These show (especially during the sixth

and fifth centuries) many variations in conception and
development: the longitudinal facings of the beams for
example may form a continuous frieze figured in relief, of
Graeco-Oriental inspiration (the so-called 'first' or 'Ionic'
phase) or they may simply feature painted ornamentations
accompanied by the stressing of the overlying and project-
ing cornice, as in the fictile decorative systems of Greece
proper and its colonies in southern Italy and Sicily. This
latter type of decoration became established after the end of
the sixth century and coincided with the period of greatest
wealth of the Etruscan temple, characterized by shell-shaped
antefixes and by large figured acroteria as shown by the
typical decorations of the temple at Veii ('second' or
'archaic' phase). This state of affairs was to remain substantially unchanged during the centuries that followed.
The only innovation worthy of note was the introduction
of a decorated pediment with figured compositions in high
relief, though still in terracotta: an imitation of the decoration of Greek pediments. Remnants of this 'third' or
'Hellenistic' phase have been found at Tarquinii, Telamon,
and Luna.[14] When treating of the forms and coverings of
the Etruscan temple we should not neglect to mention the
historically fundamental fact that these same characteristics
and developments are also met in the temples belonging to
Faliscan territory, Latium and also, though with a number
of differences, to Campania. Thus we may speak of an
architectural cultural link uniting all Tyrrhenian Italy
north of the area directly affected by Greek colonization.
On the other hand the establishment of the stone temple
during the Hellenistic age, under Greek influence but with
original characteristics, in place of the traditional wooden
temple, occurred earlier in Latium and only affected
Etruria as the result of its romanization.

The predominance even in works belonging to a comparatively recent period of elements of archaic inspiration

may moreover be observed in all motifs of Etruscan architectural decoration (whether in stone or in wood and terracotta buildings) as also in their innumerable reproductions
and imitations for funerary or votive purposes. Vitruvius
speaks of a 'Tuscanian' order, distinct from the Doric, Ionic,
and Corinthian orders of Greek architecture. It is characterized by a type of column that is in fact found employed
in Roman monuments and represents a variant of the Doric
column, with smooth shaft and footings. Its Etruscan origin
is proved by testimonies that go back as far as the archaic
age; it was, presumably, the shape of the majority of the
wooden columns in sacred and civic buildings. In reality, it
is a survival and an elaboration of the so-called 'proto-
Doric' type, with moulded plinth, a noticeably swollen
shaft devoid of channellings and capital with curved cushion.
In primitive Greece, it was very soon replaced by the true
Doric column. Together with it, there was also in Etruria
another widespread type of column and pilaster with
capitals adorned with flowered volutes, both simple and
composite, which owe their inspiration to eastern capitals
from Syria and Cyprus and to the so-called 'Aeolian'
capitals of eastern Greece that also disappeared from the
Greek world after the establishment of the Ionic capital.

## Figured Works of Art

The documents we possess on the figurative arts of Etruria
come to us almost exclusively from sanctuaries and tombs.
This is not merely due to the circumstances surrounding
their preservation and discovery. In Etruria more than elsewhere the religious and funerary inspiration of works of
art does in fact seem to prevail over the profane. There is at
any rate an almost complete lack of evidence of a monumental art aimed at exalting or commemorating historical
events or civic occasions such as are met in the Greek and

Roman worlds: in this respect, a parallel may be drawn with Etruscan literature. On the other hand, the solid ties binding art with religion and the generally concrete – we could almost say utilitarian – bent of the Etruscan mind must have obstructed the process that can be detected more or less clearly in the Greek world and which led to an autonomous conception of the artistic phenomenon as an activity that was not merely practical and ethical, but aesthetic as well. This incapacity of arriving at a conception of art for its own sake, an incapacity shared by all pre-classical civilizations, explains why the Etruscan figured arts generally present the characteristics of applied art and never reach, or very exceptionally, the level of what is usually termed 'great' art, i.e. the personal work of an artist aware of his creative capacity and socially appreciated because of it. In fact we have notice of only one Etruscan craftsman through ancient tradition (Varro, in Pliny, xxxv, 157): Vulca the modeller, of Veian origin but who also worked in Rome during the sixth century B.C.

A short review of the categories of surviving monuments according to their techniques may help to clarify these preliminary considerations. The plastic arts[15] are found represented by bronzes (other metals are less frequent), terracottas, and sculptures in stone: marble is absent for it was not available locally and only very rarely imported. Indirect sources allow us to presume that wood was also very widely used; moreover, small objects feature intaglioes in ivory, bone, and amber. Statuary belonging to holy places may be classified as follows: divine images as objects of worship, often mentioned in ancient authors (e.g. the famous painted terracotta statue of the Capitoline Jove in Rome, attributed to Vulca) but now generally lost; statues and votive groups representing deities or worshippers of which we possess copious examples, in particular small bronzes and terracottas from sanctuary deposits; parts of the architectural decoration of temples, such as the great acroteria to which the famous Apollo of Veii belonged. Within the funerary sphere should be mentioned the statuettes found in tombs, the Chiusi 'canopics', the great portrait-statues and the figures sculptured upon the lids of sarcophagi: it is especially with this latter genre that the development of the personal portrait or likeness is connected (see plate 4A). Apart from these sacral or funerary manifestations there may have been a type of statuary of an honorary character such as the statues erected to celebrate illustrious men, as was the custom in the Rome of republican times (Pliny, *Nat. Hist.*, xxxiv, 26). We should however be especially careful in attempting to identify this type of monument: until recently, for example, it was thought that the famous statue of the Orator in the Florence Archaeological Museum was an honorary statue; but since K. Olzscha interpreted the Etruscan word *flere* as 'god', the inscription accompanying the statue appears to be of a votive character and would therefore point to some religious purpose for this work of art (see plate 17).[16]

Among the architectural terracottas, figures in relief often alternate with figures in the round.[17] In the archaic acroteria and antefixes of southern Etruria and Faliscan territory, figures and groups are met standing free in space though modelled as if they were reliefs. Conversely, in pediments belonging to a late period, figures in high relief tend to detach themselves from the background as if they were statues. Both characteristics have their counterparts in the great ornamental sculpture decorating the Greek temple. True low relief is met in friezes found on beam facings. The mythological repertoire usually provided the craftsmen with their subjects. But reliefs appear to have become especially common in funerary art, as witnessed by the Tarquinii slabs ornamented with chequered patterns and friezes belonging traditionally to the 'orientalizing' repertoire; by the sepulchral steles of Volterra, Fiesole, and Bologna belonging to a period dating from the sixth to the beginning of the fourth century and picturing the dead person or his surroundings or his journey to the nether world; by the scenes on the *cippi* and archaic urns from Chiusi, with realistic subjects such as funerals, banquets, dances, and athletic games; by the mythological compositions sculptured on the walls of tombs but especially on the sides of stone sarcophagi (southern Etruria, Chiusi)[18] and of alabaster (Volterra), terracotta (Chiusi), or travertine (Perugia) cinerary urns produced between the fourth and first centuries B.C. Of especial importance is the working of laminated bronze with embossed decorations for the ornamentation of furniture, shields, chariots, vases, and candelabra; this was initiated during the orientalizing period and flourished in the course of the sixth century: an especially productive centre may be identified with Perugia, and we should not forget to mention in this respect the famous situla of the Bologna *Certosa* (see plate 19B). A similar technique, but for objects of smaller proportions, is met in precious metal vases and in goldwork. Mention should also be made of intaglios on ivory, bone, etc., and of the very rich collection of seals carved in hard stones. In all these more strictly decorative or 'applied' productions, figures and compositions derived from Greek mythology prevail.

Painting is represented by monuments of conspicuous importance, an exceptional state of affairs for the classical world before late Hellenistic times.[19] These Etruscan documents are of especial importance to us owing to the total or almost total loss of the original works of the great painters of Greece. The custom of painting the walls of subterranean tombs (generally with frescoes) was especially prevalent at Tarquinii, but it also occurs, though less intensely or sporadically, at Chiusi, Orvieto, Caere, Vulci, Veii, and elsewhere. Of those paintings that have come to light in the last few centuries, many have been lost or are irreparably damaged, others have kept in good condition; in certain cases they have been detached so as to preserve them from further deterioration.[20] Besides wall paintings we also possess a number of paintings on terracotta slabs which were originally fitted together to line and decorate the inner walls of sacred buildings (as is almost certainly the case with those found in the Portonaccio sanctuary at Veii) or even of tombs (such as the Caere groups – see plates 20 and 21). Finally, in a few isolated cases, the sides of sarcophagi and urns feature painted decorations instead of reliefs. The subject-matter was originally purely decorative (like those of orientalizing inspiration) or taken from Greek mythological themes. But the great funerary paintings of the archaic period and of the fifth century at Tarquinii and Chiusi reproduce funeral scenes with banquets, dancing, and circus games (see plates 22, 23, and 24B), or, more generally, scenes from everyday life (hunting, fishing, etc.). Later (i.e. after the fifth century), the prevailing subjects include journeys to the nether regions, infernal banquets, etc., together with mythological compositions (Orvieto, Tarquinii, Vulci); particular attention was given to the portrayal of the dead person's features.

Etruscan painted ceramics appear more or less faithfully to imitate Greek ceramics which were in any case very popular in Etruria, especially during the archaic period. But we should speak of designs rather than paintings, for only exceptionally were polychromous patterns employed.[21] Greek and Oriental craftsmen probably worked in the cities of Etruria during the sixth century and formed local schools: this occurred in the case of the production of the Caere *hydriae*, decorated with lively mythological themes. The activity of the ceramic workshops of the fourth century is also important. Draughtsmanship appears to be even more directly inspired by Greek models: it is manifested in engravings on the backs of mirrors and on bronze cists, and often exhibits a high degree of workmanship (see plate 25). Owing to their prevailingly antiquarian interest, bronzes, ceramics, and jewellery will be found more fully treated in the chapter dealing with aspects of Etruscan life (see pp. 212 ff.).

## The Problem of Etruscan Art

Having considered the various categories of artistic monuments we are now faced with the greater problem, the problem *par excellence* in fact: that of their aesthetic meaning. Many of the works in our possession cannot obviously be considered as original creations: they belong to the products of traditional craftsmanship and only distantly reflect the main trends in the history of art. There are however a number of monuments or groups of monuments where both subjective impressions and objective considerations allow us to detect more or less distinctly the hall-mark of a certain artistic personality. The problem consists in attempting to establish up to what point this possibility corresponds to reality, i.e. whether we are really faced in such cases with original creations, great or small as the case may be, or whether we are still dealing with simple imitations of objects now lost; and, if this be the case, where could we expect to find the originals.

The fact that immediately springs to our attention is that the very great majority of themes, types, and patterns of the artistic production of Etruria find their antecedents and their inspiration in Greek models. This dependence extended also, broadly speaking, to stylistic forms. As a result, the development of Etruscan art, from the beginnings of the archaic period down to late Hellenistic times, mainly re-echoed the various phases of development undergone by Greek art. But a number of differences occur: Etruria ignored certain Hellenic motifs while developing others which in Greece met with little popularity or which belonged to styles that had already been discarded. There are also indications of certain attitudes foreign, or even opposed, to the figurative conceptions of the Greek world.

We should ask ourselves up to what point Etruscan artists meant to react and did react with original solutions against the dominant formulae from Greece. We should then seek to establish whether in the realization of a personal artistic vision, conditions were laid for the formation of local traditions distinct from those of Greece, and how widely and for how long these traditions were able to impose themselves. On the other hand, if we accept the growth of autonomous trends in Etruscan art, it becomes necessary to decide on whether such trends were ephemeral and unrelated or whether a connexion existed between them; and also whether a hypothetical 'constant' in the tendencies of Etruscan taste down the centuries should be attributed to historical continuity or whether it corresponded rather to a deep-seated predisposition in the Etruscan mind for ways of expression different from those of the Greeks. All these questions may, all things considered, be gathered into the single one: how far and in what sense may we speak of 'Etruscan art'? [22]

Nineteenth-century critics, largely dominated by classicist or naturalistic preconceptions, tended on the whole to answer this question in the negative. For them, Etruscan art productions were to be considered as provincial manifestations of Greek art, composed of rough and artistically valueless works: all finds made in Etruria possessing a certain value were straightway attributed to Greek artists. But the new directions taken by art historians in the matter of aesthetic criticism at the beginning of the twentieth century, particularly as a result of studies made by A. Riegl, allowed full validity of expression to artistic experiences outside the classical orbit and opened the way to the comprehension of stylistic phenomena of the ancient world that hitherto had been misjudged, as did in fact occur with the artistic production of Etruria. From the analysis of recently discovered single works of art (such as the Apollo of Veii – see plate 5), or of works rediscovered in the light of a new aesthetic sensibility (such as the 'Capitoline Brutus' – see plate 15), there was put forward the more or less cautious affirmation of the originality and independence of Etruscan art with respect to that of Greece, based upon a different, unmistakable vision of form, evident even in imitations of Hellenic types and patterns. Mention was even made of a peculiar disposition of the Italic peoples (including therefore not only the Etruscans but also, though later, the Romans) to conceive reality according to an 'illusionistic', 'inorganic', immediate and strongly individualized picture as against the 'naturalistic', 'organic', 'typal' vision of Greek art; a disposition whose definition was attempted by G. Kaschnitz Weinberg in his concept of 'structure'. A number of justified criticisms have been made to these points of view. More recently, in fact, the statement was even made that there do not exist in Etruria true works of art except under the direct influence of Greek forms, and that the Etrusco-Italic 'originality' was no more than the occasional and ephemeral manifestation of a colourful popular craftsmanship incapable of quickening a truly artistic tradition (R. Bianchi Bandinelli).

The problem, therefore, remains for the most part unsolved. This is perhaps due to an unsatisfactory formulation of it by both sides. Etruscan art is in fact generally considered as a whole, ignoring the fact that it embraces many types of manifestations over a period of seven centuries at least, and that the transformations that took place in the course of such a long span of time (from protohistory to the beginnings of the Roman Empire) do not merely concern

Etruria and Greece but have decisive bearings over the whole development of ancient art. It is obvious that perspectives vary according to the times: it would therefore seem more logical, and closer to the concrete reality of history, to examine the problem of 'Etruscan art' by referring to the situation of each period rather than abstractly seeking a hypothetical and unitary solution.

Thus it may be that at first, between the eighth and the beginning of the seventh century, artistic activity in the cities of Etruria developed parallel to that of other Mediterranean countries, including Greece, in a complex interplay of themes of prehistoric origin (particularly evident in the lively realism displayed by the smaller products of the plastic arts) and of oriental influences which characterize that phase in the history of Etruscan decoration which we in fact call 'orientalizing'. It is obvious that for this period it would not be correct to speak of subordination to Greek art. It would be better to say that Etruria participated, in a western peripheral position, in one of the last elaborations of an ancient 'pre-Hellenic' Mediterranean artistic experience. But with the exception of a few traces of originality in the plastic funerary arts (as in the expressive heads of the Chiusi canopics) there is no sign of the burgeoning of local, or national, artistic traditions. This is in fact where the difference with Greece lies, a difference that was to have far-reaching repercussions, for at this crucial age, Greece with its vigorous creative spirit was to leave the formulas of the old world far behind and open a new chapter in the history of world art.

Unsupported by a tradition of its own, Etruria was fatally destined to be absorbed into the orbit of Greek artistic experience. For the latter's power of attraction did not only consist in the intrinsic superiority of its aesthetic values: it owed much to its very widespread implantations in the Greek colonies of Sicily and the Italian mainland. This took place effectively from the beginning of the sixth century, and it is most likely that the artistic influence of Greek archaism on Etruria (together with parallel influences in the fields of religion, institutions, music, dress, etc.) did not exert itself merely through the importation of objects and models, but also through the direct activity of Greek artificers in Etruscan cities. But it is just during this period (from the sixth to the first decades of the fifth century) that the artistic production of Etruria burst into a wonderful, and even, in certain aspects, unsurpassed, flowering, specially in temple architecture, in the plastic arts, in painting and in 'minor' decorated objects: a large number of works appear refined in technique, of high stylistic value and not without a certain peculiar 'character' that makes them often recognizable as Etruscan or of Etruscan inspiration. The original dilemma of dependence or independence now acquires overtones that render it all the more delicate as the facts seem to lead towards contradictory judgements (thus explaining the hesitancies of modern critics): these works of art, though 'Etruscan', do not in fact cease to be 'Greek' – a statement that may at first seem paradoxical, but which clearly is not, once we have freed ourselves of the notion of 'national art', inapplicable in this particular case.

We should also keep in mind the fact that Greek archaic art does not represent a rigidly unitarian or stylistically logical phenomenon; it is rather the result of the local elaborations of many and varied scattered centres with changing, lively, and multiform currents crossing and re-crossing each other in all directions. Within this essentially regional framework, partly Greek and even non-Greek territories found their place under the influence of the civilization of Hellas: e.g. Cyprus, Lycia, Caria, Lydia, and Phrygia in the east, Macedonia and Thrace in the north, Etruria in the west. These countries were not merely receptive 'provinces' in the elaboration of archaic art, passively submitting to the stamp of the Greek creative genius; they themselves participate as the 'regions' of a vast civilized community according to their own particular circumstances, requirements, and capabilities and, therefore, featuring characteristics of their own within the greater compass of a peri-Hellenic unity. In the case of Etruria, an outline of the 'regional artistic peculiarities of the archaic period may be traced in the following principal traits: (1) the existence of religious and funerary requirements predisposing the figurative arts towards a concrete, immediate, and actual representation of reality; [23] (2) a notable persistence of formal patterns, techniques, and traditions belonging to the earlier 'Mediterranean' and orientalizing phase; (3) direct and very close relations with the artistic experiences of the eastern Greek world, i.e. of the coastal and island centres of Aeolis and Ionia in western Asia Minor; these relations were close enough for many decades (from the middle of the sixth to the beginning of the fifth century) for the figurative arts of Etruria to follow much the same patterns as those of the eastern Greek world, so as to create what in fact has come to be known as Ionic-Etruscan art; (4) the local appearance of considerable schools and artistic personalities with a high standard of achievement (bronze-casters at Perugia, painters like the decorator of the Tomb of the Baron at Tarquinii, modellers in terracotta at Veii such as the creator of the 'Apollo' or his followers, etc.); it would be difficult to deny these artists an authentic, original and, at times, powerful creative genius.

A radical change occurred during the first half of the fifth century. Greece passed from archaic to classical art in a process of fundamental importance to the history of human civilization. But the activity of the great Greek masters tended to become more closely knit from a stylistic point of view and to acquire a more 'national' character, concentrating more and more around Athens and the Peloponnesian cities. At the same time, the peripheral regions declined for reasons of a political and economic order. Etruria was left isolated. The classical spirit, the result of an unrepeatable and inimitable moment, found no echo in Etruria, where, amongst other things, the historically favourable conditions that encouraged the artistic flowering of archaic times came to an end, bringing in their wake a long period of depression and decadence. Thus we witness for the whole of the fifth and well into the fourth century, the persistence of patterns and formulas belonging to the archaic tradition or inspired by Greek art of the 'severe' style, i.e. of that transient stage between archaism and classicism. The phenomenon of delayed action proper to marginal countries (as, for example, in the contemporary 'sub-archaic' art of Cyprus) [24] is most clearly manifested. The penetration of classical influences was slow and sporadic. In this atmosphere, deprived of a unitarian and respected tradition such as existed previously, artistic vitality only broke out in small, ephemeral bursts of expressive originality. The activity of bronze craftsmen continued, however, unabated.

Contact was re-established between the artistic worlds of Greece and Etruria after the fourth century B.C. and continued throughout the Hellenistic age, merging finally into the triumphal victory of Hellenism in Roman Italy at the end of the republic and the beginning of the empire. But the attitude of Etruscan artists towards the products of Greece does not this time appear to be the same as in archaic times: we can no longer speak of the elaboration, with original elements, of a common inheritance: it is rather the imitation of 'foreign' models, more or less faithfully and successfully reproduced. Not only are forms and single typological patterns taken over, but whole compositions for the decoration of buildings and objects, especially in the case of paintings. In this last phase, and in this type of

Hellenizing decorative production the concept expressed by certain modern critics, namely that of Etruria as a 'province' of the Greek world – i.e. the denial of all artistic originality – appears particularly justified.

Account however should be taken of another aspect, of quite different order and importance, of the figurative activity of the Etruscans during the Hellenistic age. In a number of isolated cases or in groups of monuments, especially funerary monuments, there appeared stylistic patterns and solutions that presented a clear contrast with classical taste: compact structures with geometric tendencies, 'unfinished' forms, disproportions, exasperation in the treatment of certain expressive details, etc. We may well ask how far these manifestations were to be explained as the handing down by craftsmen of remote archaic formulas, survivals favoured by the static quality of the Etruscan ritual, or as popular improvisations of no consequence or even as the effect of a falling-off in quality of manual techniques. But it is possible that they may have been the reflections, however indirect, of the activity of artists who by adopting age-old local conventions and reacting against Greek models according to their temperament, may have sought new forms of expression.

This hypothesis becomes transformed into certainty as far as the art of portraiture is concerned: for it offers us many authentic and original works of art (large bronzes, paintings, etc.) and innumerable secondary products (sarcophagus lids, terracottas) which witness in their turn the crystallization of a solid and lasting local tradition centred around the activity of the greatest masters of the craft. In contrast with the Greek portrait (its original inspiration in the fourth century), the Etruscan portrait tends to seek a maximum of expressive concreteness for the features and, in certain ways, for individual 'character', neglecting the organic coherence of natural forms but stressing essential elements by means of the simple, rough, discontinuous and, at times, violent use of lines and masses. We may well say that a new style was born, a new artistic tradition independent of the Greek world: a tradition which may be 'Etruscan' but which was also more generically 'Italic', for its seeds were carried on beyond the decline of Etruria as a nation, by the art of Roman Italy and of the Western world under the empire. Such an 'expressionistic' view of reality – particularly manifest in the portrait but also present in other art forms – was to live in popular art currents of the first centuries of the empire, spread to the provincial art of Europe, and break out impetuously as the great courtly art of the end of the second and the third century A.D.: it was destined to form one of the most significant contributions to the artistic inheritance of late imperial and medieval times.[25]

## NOTES

1. B. Nogara, *Gli Etruschi e la loro civiltà*, 1934, pp. 405 ff.

2. For a complete account and an interpretation of classical sources on the sacred literature of the Etruscans, see especially C. O. Thulin, *Die etruskische Disciplin*, in *Göteborgs Högskolas Årsskrift*, 1905, 1906, 1909.

3. See E. Bormann, in *Jahreshefte der österr. Archäol. Inst.*, II, 1899, pp. 219 ff.; M. Pallottino, *Tarquinia* (*Monumenti Antichi dell'Accademia dei Lincei*), XXXVI, 1937, col. 561 and in *Studi Etruschi*, XXI, 1950–1, pp. 167 ff.; J. Heurgon, in *Latomus*, XII, 1953, pp. 462 ff.

4. See in this connexion, B. Nogara, *Gli Etruschi e la loro civiltà*, 1934, pp. 425 ff.

5. No up-to-date or detailed analyses exist on this question, which has only been touched on in general works such as K. O. Müller and W. Deecke, *Die Etrusker*, 1877, II, pp. 200 ff.; P. Ducati, *Etruria antica*, 1927, pp. 167 ff. For a recent work on the music of the Greeks, see M. Wegner, *Das Musikleben der Griechen*, 1949.

6. For a connexion between pipe-laying and the 'primitive' spirituality of the Etruscans, see R. Enking, *Etruskische Geistigkeit*, 1947.

7. On the subject of Etruscan art, the following general works may be consulted: P. Ducati, *Storia dell'arte etrusca*, 1927; G. Q. Giglioli, *L'arte etrusca*, 1935; P. J. Rijs, *An Introduction to Etruscan Art*, 1953.

8. On the subject of Etruscan architecture, besides the works quoted above, see especially A. Andren, *Architectural Terracottas from Etrusco-Italic Temples* (*Acta Inst. Rom. Sueciae*, VI), 1939–40; G. Patroni, *Architettura preistorica generale ed italica. Architettura etrusca*, 1946; L. Polacco, *Tuscanicae dispositiones*, 1952 (to be consulted with care).

9. See F. E. Brown, in *Memoirs of the Amer. Acad. in Rome*, XX, 1951, pp. 102 ff.

10. A. Minto, *Pseudocupole e pseudovolte nell' architettura etrusca delle origini*, in *Palladio*, III, 1939, pp. 1 ff.

11. F. Messerschmidt, *Das Grabmal des Porsenna*, in *Das neue Bild der Antike*, pp. 53 ff.

12. An attempt to throw doubt upon the Etruscan origin of the three-celled temple and to attribute it to the Romans will be found in L. Polacco, *Tuscanicae dispositiones*, 1952. See also *Studi Etruschi*, XXII, 1952–3, pp. 458 ff.

13. Metal coverings (Vitruvius, III, 3, 5) must be considered to have been exceptional and limited to small and unusually rich buildings.

14. The chronological classification of Etruscan temple decorations into 'phases' is due to A. della Seta, *Museo di Villa Giulia*, 1918, pp. 120 ff. Further details will be found in A. Andrén, *op. cit.*, pp. CXXX ff., and M. Pallottino, in *Bullettino Archeol. Comunale*, LXVIII, 1940, p. 253.

15. Apart from the general works on Etruscan art already quoted, see also: P. Ducati, *La scultura etrusca*, 1935; G. Hanfmann, *Altetruskische Plastik*, 1936; L. Goldscheider, *Etruscan sculpture*, 1941 (Phaidon); P. J. Rijs, *Tyrrhenika. An Archaeological Study of Etruscan Sculpture in the Archaic and Classical Periods*, 1941.

16. See K. Olzscha, *Interpretation der Agramer Mumienbinde*, 1939, pp. 20 ff.

17. See A. Andrén, *op. cit.*, p. 241, note 1.

18. R. Herbig, *Die jüngeretruskischen Steinsarkophage*, 1952.

19. On the subject of Etruscan painting, see F. Weege, *Etruskische Malerei*, 1921; F. Poulsen, *Etruscan Tomb Paintings*, 1922; F. Messerschmidt, *Beiträge zur Chronologie der etruskischen Wandmalerei*, I, 1923; M. Pallottino, *La peinture étrusque* (*Etruscan painting*), 1952.

20. The friezes of the François Tomb at Vulci, the property of the

Torlonia family, had been detached as early as the last century; more recently, the removal and restoration took place of frescoes at Tarquinii (Tombs of the Chariots, of the Triclinium and of the Funerary Couch) and at Orvieto (see *Bollett. dell'Ist. Centr. del Restauro*, 2, 1950; 3–4, 1951; 5–6, 1951).

21. See J. D. Beazley, *Etruscan Vase Painting*, 1947.

22. For a comprehensive view of the problem, see J. Martha, *L'art étrusque*, 1889, p. 614; A. della Seta, *Antica arte etrusca*, in *Dedalo*, I, 1920–1, pp. 559 ff.; C. Anti, *Il problema dell'arte italica*, in *Studi Etruschi*, IV, 1930, pp. 151 ff.; G. Kaschnitz-Weinberg, *Bemerkungen zur Struktur der altitalischen Plastik*, in *Studi Etruschi*, VII, 1933, p. 135 ff.; R. Bianchi Bandinelli, *Storicità dell' arte classica*, 2nd ed., 1950, pp. 77 ff., pp. 93 ff.; pp. 115 ff. (see also the 1st ed., pp. 257 ff.); M. Pallottino, *Sul problema delle correlazioni artistiche fra Grecia ed Etruria*, in *La parola del passato*, fasc. XIII, 1950, pp. 5 ff.

23. See M. Pallottino, '*Partecipazione*' e senso drammatico nel mondo figurato degli Etruschi, in *Arti Figurative*, II, 1946, pp. 149 ff.

24. See *The Swedish Cyprus Expedition*, IV, 2; E. Gjerstad, *The Cypro-Geometric, Cypro-Archaic and Cypro-Classical Periods*, 1949, pp. 93 ff., 117 ff., 364 ff.

25. See G. Rodenwaldt, *Über den Stilwandel in der Antoninischen Kunst*, in *Abhandl. der Preuss. Akademie der Wissensch.*, *Phil-Hist. Klasse*, 1935, and *Römische Reliefs-Vorstufen zur Spätantike*, in *Jahrbuch des deutsch. archäol. Instituts*, LV, 1940, p. 12 ff.; M. Pallottino, *Civiltà romana, arte figurativa e ornamentale*, 1940, p. 81 ff.; R. Bianchi Bandinelli, *Tradizione ellenistica e gusto romano nella pittura pompeiana*, in *La critica d'arte*, IV, 1941, p. 3 ff.

# CHAPTER NINE

## LIFE AND CUSTOMS

### *Monuments as a Source of Information*

HOWEVER important our knowledge of the cultural life of a people as revealed by the manifestations of its religious feelings, of its thought, of its organizing abilities and artistic aptitudes, we shall never come fully close to it nor understand its most intimate psychology unless we are able to visualize and understand the various aspects and habits of its everyday life, to penetrate its homes, to catch it in its familiar surroundings and become fully conversant with its traditions and customs. [1]

There is no doubt that literature, especially in such forms as comedy, satire, letters, etc., is irreplaceable as a source of information on the private life and habits of ancient peoples. The complete loss of Etruscan literature (if we admit that there ever existed a literature with *bourgeois* or private themes, such as the Roman satire or epistle) deprives us of a means precious in the reconstruction of family life and customs of ancient Etruria.

But besides literary sources there also exist monumental, or archaeological, sources: on the one hand these consist of objects actually preserved in the interior of tombs, as well as the character, the peculiarities, the very arrangement of such tombs together with the very few remains we have from inhabited sites; on the other of figured works of art reproducing actual scenes taken from contemporary life. As far as this type of monument is concerned, Etruria finds itself in an exceptionally privileged position. We have already referred to the deep-rooted tradition of recreating

life-like surroundings for the entombed dead, surroundings
as authentic and as sumptuous as possible, with jewels,
weapons, instruments, household articles. To it we owe
that our excavations of Etruscan cemeteries have provided
us with such ample and direct sources of information on the
personal clothing, the weapons, the articles of everyday life,
and the shape of objects that furnished the home. Our only
limitation in this field, unfortunately a limitation of fundamental importance, is the almost total disappearance of
objects made of perishable materials such as cloth, leather,
wicker, or wood. The climate of Italy, as against the hot
dry North African climate, has not allowed in the great
majority of cases the preservation of such objects: hence the
gaps present in the 'ethnography' of ancient Etruria. Only
exceptionally, as in the case of the tombs of Visentium and
Vulci, have we been able to recover fragments of perishable
materials: a wooden tray, the handle of an axe, a razor
sheath, wicker baskets, pieces of leather ornaments, etc. We
have also been able to find a few small pieces of cloth or
traces of cloth on oxidized bronze. [2]

## The Home and its Furnishings

Figured monuments allow us to see what objects have survived as they were actually used in everyday life; they also
complete the picture of the furnished house by including
those that have perished. Such monuments, funerary paintings in particular, have a documentary value surpassing
that normally offered by artistic representations left to us
by the classical world, with the exception of a few 'popular'
Roman frescoes and reliefs, which however derive their
naïve realism and directness of expression from the tradition
of Etrusco-Italic art. In the Greek world, as far back as the
archaic period, man played a preponderant or even exclusive role, with a background reduced to a few necessary

elements strictly dependent on the human form and not infrequently rendered symbolically or by simple allusive touches. With the Etruscans however, as with Oriental peoples, artistic composition has a descriptive and narrative character and indulges in background detail. Thus funerary paintings and sculptures introduce us, plunge us so to speak, into the very heart of a past reality. And though to us these reproductions appear naïve and stylized both in form and technique, they are nevertheless faithful in the highest degree, almost photographically faithful, to the chosen subject. He who can read through the difficulties of formal language, and knows how to translate it (there is often no need for a translation) may, thanks to these monuments, witness the unfolding of banquet scenes, dances, games, etc., as if he were living two thousand five hundred years ago. Added to this general scenic faithfulness there is a close faithfulness to detail in furniture and dress. So that even though Etruria lacks literary sources, we possess the highly valuable evidence of figured monuments: it can even be stated that from a certain point of view the latter are more important still in the study of life and customs: narrative always requires a reconstructive effort of the imagination where subjective elements often intrude; whereas the visual arts are direct, immediate, and impose themselves with peremptory force.

The archaeological evidence on Etruscan life covers the whole development of its history, from its beginnings to the threshold of imperial Rome. In the case of figured monuments, the richest crop of documents was yielded by the golden age of the Etruscan civilization, that is by the sixth and fifth centuries B.C., to which period the greatest number of painted tombs belong. We shall therefore principally refer to this period, the period during which the Etruscan way of life was formed and defined; but we shall also take into account the variations that took place through the centuries, especially where customs are concerned. It should also be understood that the data supplied by monuments concern principally the higher or well-to-do strata of society: i.e. those classes whose financial means and requirements of prestige or of aristocratic pride allowed or imposed the building, decoration, and furnishing of grandiose and lasting funerary monuments.

Let us in the first place try to picture to ourselves the home, the centre of family life, its main features, and the activities of which it is the stage. There have been long discussions on the shape and layout of the Etruscan house: all too often it has been considered as an abstract architectural entity, as a type, reproducing substantially a single original plan, as in the case of the so-called 'Pompeian' house.[3] In actual fact the numerous documents that may be used in the reconstruction of Etruscan private dwellings offer considerable variations, variations that do not merely occur in an evolutionary direction, i.e. in the successive phases of the Etruscan civilization. Direct evidence is provided by the foundations of houses found in many parts of Etruria, but especially at Marzabotto near Bologna (where an entire residential centre may be seen), and at Vetulonia, Tarquinii, and Veii. From the very beginnings of the Etruscan civilization the house with rectilinear walls has everywhere replaced the ancient rectangular or ovoidal dwellings of Italian prehistory: a relic of the earliest phase of this movement is the 'cottage-shaped' cinerary urn of the Villanovan culture. It is likely that on the actual borders of Etruscan territory, as for example in Latium or at Bologna, this phase lasted right up to historical times. The belief that the dead man's life continued in the grave is chiefly responsible for the fact that tombs and urns were made to look like houses; and these were at times imitated down to the smallest detail of architecture and furniture. The rock-hewn tombs discovered in the Caere (Cerveteri) necropolis provide us with precious

documentary evidence of the various types of interior by
giving us the layout and general arrangement of the rooms,
the decoration of doors, windows, and ceilings, and even
the furniture (round tables, hampers, chests, beds). Details
as to the external architecture of the house may be obtained
from the rocky façades of tombs in the inner zones of Blera,
Norchia, Castel d'Asso. As for the house as a whole,
especially in its later phase, useful information may be
gathered from a number of cinerary urns found at Chiusi.

The house originally consisted of a rectangular building
comprising a single room, protected by a double-sloped
roof set at a low gradient. In its simplest form, this is the
type of house that spread from the East via the land route
and which forms the basis of the Mycenean *megaron* and of
the Greek temple. At a very early stage, however, it grows
richer and more complex in form by the addition of
external elements with porticoes, or by an increase in the
number of rooms. The sixth century tombs at Cerveteri
present in their most usual form a plan that may to some
extent be considered the ancestor of the Italic or 'Pompeian'
house: an unroofed entrance hall (corresponding to the
corridor in the tomb), a central room, possibly a small
courtyard (the future atrium?) on to which open two lateral
rooms, and, at the back, the main body of the house; this
consists of a transverse passage shaped like a transept with a
coffered ceiling or a double-sloped roof, which in its turn
gives access to one, two, or three rooms similarly protected
by a double-sloped roof. The three-roomed type became
the most usual and its resemblance to the Etruscan three-cell
temple is significant. The transverse passage would correspond on the one hand to the porticoed forecourt of the
temple, on the other to the *alae* of the Pompeian house;
whilst the back rooms are thought to be preserved in the
three rooms of the typical Pompeian house. It is worth noting that the transverse vestibule assumed in a few cases the

form of a portico supported by pilasters and columns; there is no lack of variants, which may take the form of circular or semicircular rooms, or of vestibules roofed with radially set beams.

Ancient sources appear to agree in attributing the invention of the atrium to the Etruscans: the very word *atrium* is said to be of Etruscan origin, and in fact the form *aθre* does occur in an Etruscan text. The atrium does not however appear in its typical form of a half-covered room with an *impluvium* at the centre in models of tombs belonging to the archaic period; it only becomes recognizable in later monuments such as in a rock-hewn tomb at Tarquinii whose ceiling is shaped like the roof of an atrium, or in a small urn from Chiusi kept in the Berlin Museum. From amongst the many examples that attest the variety and complexity of the various types of dwellings we may mention an urn in the Florence Archaeological Museum modelled in the shape of a small palace with arched doorway and two floors, and an urn from Chiusi featuring on its first floor a veranda supported by columns.

We have referred to the furniture, which must have been rather limited, as with all civilizations of the ancient world. [4] Funerary paintings depict beds with ornamental legs, cushions, and covers painted or embroidered in lively colours and geometrical patterns, rectangular or circular tables, chairs shaped like thrones, stools, foot-rests, etc. A typical piece is the wicker or wooden chair with a round seat and a wide splayed back found sculptured in a few Cerveteri tombs or, reproduced in bronze, amongst objects belonging to funerary *trousseaux* from Chiusi and Palestrina; it also survives in marble in that curious and late archaistic monument known as the 'Corsini chair': [5] its shape lives on to reappear in provincial figured monuments belonging to Roman Imperial times.

Bronze candelabra too may be included amongst the

furniture; many of these have come down to us as actual specimens or reproduced in paintings. Some are rather elongated in form, surmounted by a statuette and tips in the shape of a bird's beak on which candles or torches were fixed. We also possess many oil candelabra with a small dish at the top that were meant to hang from the ceiling, such as the famous carved candelabrum of Cortona (see plate 19A).

We ought to mention too the whole series of metal and clay containers, ranging from large archaic *lebetes* (cauldrons) supported on tripods or on circular pedestals, to vases imported from Greece or their Etruscan imitations such as *amphorae*, kraters (for wine), *hydriae* (with three handles, for water), jugs, pails, pans, plates, goblets, chalices, glasses, balsam containers in the shape of various animals, etc. Vases made of precious metals – gold, silver, or electrum (an alloy of silver and gold) – must naturally have been rare, though they occasionally appear reproduced in painting. Specimens in our possession are limited to silver and electrum and have mostly been found within graves belonging to the orientalizing period.

The oldest fictile vases (eighth to sixth century) were made with an unpurified and roughly mixed clay (the *impasto*) and have a slat-smoothed surface: they vary in colour (black, brown, red, or yellow) and in shape (occasionally imitating embossed types), and are ornamented with graffiti or paintings. Greek influence from the seventh century onwards helped to spread the use of potter's clay, decorated with figured and geometrical patterns: 'proto-Corinthian', Corinthian, Ionic, Rhodian, Laconian, Chalcidian and, lastly, Attic vases were imported and imitated locally. During the second half of the sixth century and throughout the whole of the fifth, Attic pottery alone was imported, black-figured vases preceding in time the ones with red figures. A type of native pottery, probably derived from the *impasto*, the *bucchero*, dominates in Etruria from the end of the seventh to the beginning of the fifth century with many varied forms; *bucchero* pottery is characterized by the use of surface-polished black or grey clay. The fourth century witnesses the spread of pottery decorated with red figures in imitation of the vases of Attica and of the Greek cities of southern Italy: the most important local school belongs to the Faliscan territory, but others are known at Vulci, Perugia, Volterra, etc. At a later period there is a predominance of clay vases gilded or varnished in black and red, with decorative elements stamped or in relief. From this late type of pottery was developed the great vase industry of Arezzo that was to flourish at the beginning of the imperial age to give rise to the characteristic pottery of the Roman world, the so-called *terra sigillata*. Besides these metal and clay vessels, we should also make a passing reference to vases made of ivory, alabaster, or wood, though it is only exceptionally that specimens made of the last-mentioned material have survived.

One monument which may be considered unique in the ancient world has provided us with an exceptional picture of all the objects that go to furnish a home: furniture, instruments, everyday objects, etc. This is the 'Tomb of the Stuccoes' or of 'the Reliefs' at Cerveteri (see plates 30 and 31). It consists of a large room shaped to resemble the inside of a house along the walls of which the dead were arranged in cells rather like niches with beds, whilst the actual surface of the walls and pillars is decorated with painted stucco reliefs representing objects that are supposed to be hanging there. Amongst these we can recognize weapons (helmets, shields, swords, thigh-pieces), vases, small flower wreaths, a fan, a double bag, a complete knapsack, kitchen knives, spits, tools (axe, tongs, knife), a round table, ropes, wooden trays, sticks, etc. These reproductions are remarkably impressive because of relief and colour and an extraordinary faithfulness to the chosen subject. We are filled with wonder at the resemblance, or rather the identity of some of these objects belonging to the third and second centuries B.C. with objects in use to-day: as for example the rectangular wooden kitchen trays or the knapsack. This picture of everyday life outlined by the tomb of the Reliefs is completed with materials found in funeral *trousseaux* of the various Etruscan cemeteries, both in the case of weapons and of instruments. Bronze fans, similar to the one found reproduced in stucco at the Tomb of the Reliefs or pictured on other Etruscan monuments (such as in the paintings of the Bruschi Tomb or of the Tomb of the Shields at Tarquinii) have been discovered in the 'Tumulus of the Fans' at Populonia. Objects belonging to the *mundus*, that is to the requirements of feminine toilet, must also be considered as household articles: *cistae*, bronze mirrors, small wooden boxes in the shape of animals for cosmetics, etc.

## Aspects of Etruscan Life

The reconstruction of the life led in the houses of the rich does not present excessive difficulties. We have already referred to the place of the woman in the home: how she participated in banquets and feasts on a footing of perfect equality with men. During the archaic period men and women banquet stretched out on the same couch: Aristotle is probably referring to this custom when he states in *Ath. Pol.*, 1, 23, d: 'The Etruscans take their food in the company of their women lying under the same mantle.' This statement has also been supposed to refer to a false interpretation of some sarcophagi on which husband and wife appear lying under a mantle, a symbol of marriage. The Etruscan marriage ceremony included in fact the rite – also found in present-day Jewish custom – of covering the bride and bridegroom with a veil: this is borne out by the relief, whose interpretation cannot be mistaken, on a little urn from Chiusi (see plate 14A). But it is also possible that the veil may have actually been used for the convivial couch. It is certain nevertheless that the Greeks tended to misunderstand the Etruscans, undoubtedly because of ancient political rivalries that made them find cause for scandal in the formal liberty of Etruscan women so unlike, at least up to the Hellenistic period, the segregation which was the lot of the Greek woman. It was easy and almost natural therefore to attribute to Etruscan women the character and behaviour of the *hetaerae*, the only women in Greece who took part in banquets with men. And thus, with that ease with which the classical world accepted and transmitted information, though unchecked, to be used as literary topics, were born and spread those libellous statements on Etruscan licentiousness insisted upon by Athenaeus (IV, 153, d; XII, 517 ff.) and re-echoed even by Plautus (*Cistellaria*, II, 3, 20 ff.). After the fourth century women no longer take part in banquets lying down on beds like the men, but seated, thus following the custom which was to remain firmly established throughout the Roman world. Paintings of banquets with several beds (generally three: hence the Roman *triclinium*) such as those found in the Tombs of the Leopards and of the *Triclinium*, both at Tarquinii, are full of natural and joyful simplicity. There are also a number of banquets in the Greek style, men only being present, culminating at times in abandoned orgies accompanied by dances and abundant libations (Tomb of the Inscriptions, Tarquinii). Banquets, like most other festivities and solemn occasions (e.g. games, funerals, etc.), were regularly accompanied by music and dancing.

A noteworthy series of paintings deals with games and entertainments (Tombs of the Augurs, the *Bigae*, and Francesca Giustiniani at Tarquinii, and the painted and relief tombs of Chiusi). It is evidently the Hellenic influence that dominates this aspect of Etruscan life; but the agonistic and professional character of Greek games and matches tends to give way in the Etruscan world to the spectacular. There is nothing more interesting or more suggestive in this respect than the Tomb of the *Bigae* at Tarquinii, where the artist has pictured a large sports field or circus bisected along its two axes, the long and the short, showing its arena and the wooden stands on which the spectators sit. In the arena we see charioteers on *bigae*, horsemen, wrestlers and boxers, vaulters with and without pole, an armed runner (hoplitodrome), umpires, and various other characters (see plate 22). On the stands, spectators belonging to both sexes take the liveliest interest in the result of the games, as the impassioned expressions on their faces clearly indicate. Quite possibly members of the most illustrious families took part in these sports. The Etruscan game of the Truia (*ludus Troiae*) is worth mentioning in this respect: it consisted of a horse race along an intricate course shaped like a maze: this is borne out by a graffito on an archaic Etruscan vase, and we know that it was still performed as an exercise for Roman youths at the beginning of the Empire.[6] Of a more popular character, the various activities of the showman (acrobatics, trick riding, clowning) are expressively portrayed in paintings at the Tomb of the Monkey in Chiusi (see plate 23). Lastly we must mention a bloodier kind of sport in which it is possible to recognize a forerunner of the Roman gladiatorial combats; these were in any case believed by ancient tradition to be of Etruscan origin (Athenaeus, IV, 153 f.): they certainly reached Rome by way of Campania which had come early under the influence of Etruria. They probably owe their origin to a funeral rite, an attenuation of the human sacrifices that accompany in many primitive civilizations the death of princes or of the illustrious. For in blood fights the stronger or the abler of the contestants has a chance of survival. A match of this kind is reproduced in the Tomb of the Augurs at Tarquinii: a masked figure, designated by the name of φersu (corresponding to the Latin *persona*, 'a masked figure'), with a hood and a ferocious dog on the leash, fights another figure armed with a cudgel and with head enveloped in a sack. Obviously if the latter manages to hit his opponent's dog with the cudgel victory will be his, and his adversary will be at his mercy; should the opposite come about, he will be torn to pieces by the dog.

## Economic and Technical Achievements

Outside the home, we have public life and the life of commerce, navigation, agriculture, and industry. We obviously cannot dwell on all the aspects of Etruscan production and economy especially as in the majority of cases we only possess documents that are of little worth, and as it is chiefly by comparison with the Graeco-Roman world that we derive the knowledge we have: we are thus unable to point out any specifically Etruscan characteristics. It is better therefore to stress those technical aspects which have, quite early, transformed certain districts of Etruscan territory into areas whose economy was mainly industrial, although the greater portion of the country remained faithful to a predominantly pastoral and agricultural life.

A sufficiently accurate picture of Etruscan production during the later phase of the nation's history is given by that well-known passage in Livy (XXVIII, 45) listing the contributions given by the principal annexed or federated Etruscan cities to Scipio Africanus' oversea expedition. Here is the list of the loans drawn up according to each district's resources:

Caere (Cerveteri):      corn and other foodstuffs;
Tarquinii (Tarquinia): sail-cloth;
Rusellae (Roselle):     corn and timber for ship building;
Populonia (id.):         iron;

Clusium (Chiusi):     corn and timber;
Perusia (Perugia):    corn and timber;
Arretium (Arezzo):   corn, weapons, and wrought tools;
Volaterrae (Volterra): corn and pitch.

We can see in this list, clearly defined within the Central and Southern zones, the agricultural districts (Caere, Rusellae, Clusium, Perusia, Arretium, Volaterrae) some of which were also given to exploiting the last remnants of the large forests that once covered the area; Populonia on the other hand appears as an iron-working centre, and Arretium as an important industrial city. The mining area in Etruria is mainly situated within the territories of Vetulonia (with its metalliferous hills) and of Populonia (which included the island of Elba). The extraction of metals, practised from the earliest times, is an activity whose importance has not perhaps been sufficiently stressed so far, for the bearing it has on the history and life of the Etruscans and, more generally, on the Mediterranean world: we need only consider that the Etruscan mines were the only ones of any importance to be exploited in the Central Mediterranean. The continuous pressure and menace of Greek colonists on the northern coasts of Etruria is a certain sign of the importance attached to the possession of the mining areas, to being able to influence them, or even merely to bring in their neighbourhood. We have no knowledge of the technical aspects concerning the extraction and the first working of the ores, unless we include a certain amount of archaeological evidence (shafts driven in certain parts of the metal-bearing hills, tools that have been found in them, slag produced during the smelting of iron around Populonia); a few ancient sources also tell us that Populonia was the first centre for the smelting of crude metal extracted from the Elba mines, and for its sorting and distribution, though no further treatment took place there.[7]

The whole of Etruscan production is determined by this abundance of mineral ores: the quantities of weapons, tools, and domestic objects in bronze and iron found in graves prove this. Archaeological data have allowed us to establish that, as regards the manufacture of bronze and iron articles, the most important cities were Perugia (for tripods and other objects in wrought iron) whence its products spread towards Umbria (the famous bronze chariot found at Monteleone di Spoleto, now at the New York Metropolitan Museum, was probably made at Perugia); Visentium (Bisenzio) with its manufactured articles, especially during the archaic period; Vulci with its tripods, candelabra, weapons, etc.; Arezzo too, as mentioned by Livy in the passage quoted above. Etruscan iron and bronze were also worked in Campania, and it is probably from here that both the crude metal and the finished products reached the Greek world (Diodorus Siculus, v, 13). Etruscan bronze trumpets and statuettes were also well known in Greece: a fragment of a tripod of the Vulci type was found on the Acropolis of Athens. [8] Nor must other aspects of Etruscan industrial production be overlooked, such as the textile industry, the leather industry, with especial reference to footwear renowned throughout the Mediterranean world (Pollux, VII, 22, 86).

The progress of Etruscan technical achievements is also manifested by the search, exploitation, and transport of water. The search for water was entrusted to the *aquilices*, or water-diviners. Pliny (*Nat. Hist.*, III, 20, 120) mentions the canals dug by the Etruscans in the lower Po valley; and only an advanced hydraulic technique, such as is attested by rock-cuttings at the *Ponte Sodo* in Veii (spanning one of the branches of the Cremera), can explain the conquest of the marshy lands of the lower Po valley wrested inch by inch from the river and its stagnant pools, and where cities such as Ravenna had still to be built on piles. Nor could such intensely active life on the marshy areas of the Maremma or of the lower Po be explained had malarial infection already been common during the golden age of Etruscan civilization; malaria must in fact have contributed, during the late Hellenistic period, towards hastening the decadence of many Etruscan coastal towns. [9]

## Weapons and Dress

A large bronze *situla* (a kind of pail) found in the vault of the *Certosa* of Bologna is an interesting witness of Etruscan provincial life during the first half of the fifth century B.C. (see plate 19B). It portrays military scenes, a procession, and episodes with domestic, hunting, and agricultural themes. Round the decorated top band of the situla a remarkable military parade unwinds itself: there are horsemen armed with battle-axes, three infantry platoons belonging to different services as shown by their armament, and a group of pioneers with axes. As to the Etruscan art of war, tradition tells us but little; we know however that the primitive military organization of the Romans owes much to the Etruscans. At first, battles were fought in chariots; after the sixth century, only cavalry was used. The three infantry services of the *Certosa* situla correspond perhaps to the three Roman orders of the *velites*, the *principes*, and the *triarii*.

As offensive weapons, the Etruscans had the heavy lance whose point and *saurocter* were made of iron or bronze; the light lance or javelin; the long sword, the use of which already seems to have ceased at an archaic period, and which was merely a relic of the armament of the late bronze age; the short sword or glaive; the curved sabre in use between the sixth and fourth centuries B.C.; the dagger; the battle-axe, which in oldest times possessed two blades, and, as already stated, probably belonged to the armament of chiefs. Their defensive weapons were the bronze helmet, the shield, the curiass, and greaves. Primitive helmets have a crest or a crown with cheek-pieces; but the use of Corinthian and Attic helmets spread quite early from Greece. The classic Etruscan bronze helmet has roughly the shape of a morion surmounted at times with a crest of plumes; many specimens of these have been found in tombs: one has appeared as a votive offering in the Hellenic sanctuary of Olympia, bearing an inscription to Zeus which tells how it was dedicated by the Syracusan tyrant Hiero, as war-booty after the naval battle waged by the Greeks against the Etruscans in the vicinity of Cumae in 474 B.C. Cuirasses were originally made of cloth with attached discs or squares of laminated metal: later they were made entirely in bronze with detachable parts, or all of a piece, moulding the muscles of the male torso. Round bronze shields appear both in archaic and in more recent periods; the *Certosa* situla however also shows elliptical and almost square shields probably made of wood or leather. A mention should be made of offensive and defensive cudgels in which may perhaps be recognized a relic of the ancient clubs used by primitive men; archaic monuments give one or two examples of such cudgels, whilst a type of stick with curved end, the *lituus*, tended to become more and more a mark of priestly office and as such was passed on to the Roman world.

Let us now examine the ordinary clothes worn by Etruscan men and women through the centuries. Though we have no direct evidence (unless we except jewellery and a few items made of time-resisting materials) we are very amply documented in this respect thanks to figured monuments. It is only natural that climate should influence the nature of clothes; but the force of tradition must also be taken into account, for it exerts in many cases a tyrannical influence on the development of fashion. Thus, masculine semi-nudity, a typically Mediterranean custom, was still very common in archaic Etruria. This custom, deriving as it did from the Eastern civilizations of Egypt and the Aegean, evolved in Greece into a complete athletic and 'heroic' nudity (though remaining foreign to everyday life). In Etruria and in Rome, however, it was limited to covering the lower part of the body by means of a short skirt or bordered loin-cloth. Even in the full civilization of the sixth and fifth centuries men went naked to the waist (especially in the intimacy of the home), though at the same time wearing expensive footwear and pointed caps on their heads. This traditional usage is reflected in the 'epic' dress worn by the banqueting dead, as shown by the carved lids of sarcophagi belonging to later periods. Only slaves and athletes went completely naked. A tight-fitting jacket that covered the whole trunk, derived from the bordered loin-cloth, was in vogue during the last years of the sixth century. It was then superseded by the tunic, an imitation of the Greek *khiton*.

The second most typical item of masculine attire was the mantle made of a thicker, coloured cloth, which protected the upper part of the body from the cold; its use was already quite widespread during the archaic period. As the items of masculine dress increased in number – and as the tradition of Mediterranean semi-nudity became progressively weaker – the mantle acquired an ever-growing importance until, enlarged and enriched with painted or embroidered decorations, it became the Etruscan national dress, the *tèbennos*, the direct ancestor of the Roman toga. Women and old people wore without any substantial variations, from archaic down to more recent times, a tunic shaped like a shirt that reached down to the feet, of light material pleated or decorated at the edges; over this was placed a painted mantle of heavier cloth. From about the end of the seventh to the beginning of the fifth century net-work patterned materials were used that are thought to have been embroidered: these may be seen made into tunics (on a Caere statuette at the Capitoline Museum in Rome, and on a canopic vase from Chiusi made in the shape of a standing female figure) or into mantles (on the *Certosa* situla).

Right from the earliest times one is struck by the very special care and interest which Etruscans devoted to their footwear. The archaic tombs at Visentium have yielded sandals in the shape of jointed wooden clogs with bronze reinforcements. Shoes could be of leather or of embroidered cloth. During the sixth century, the most typical form of shoe was raised behind the calf and curved upwards to a point at the front: these are the so-called *calcei repandi* of Ionic-Oriental origin, some characteristics of which still survive to-day in the *ciocie* of the mountainous regions of Central Italy; at a later period high ankle-boots were still in use, together with low sandals. All these various forms were passed, almost without change, to the Roman world.

For the head, a kind of dome-shaped cap in embroidered cloth was used during the sixth century; this was worn by both men and women and many variants of it were common. It is the *tutulus* of Oriental and Ionic origin, and it became the typical Etruscan head-dress. Other current forms are a pointed or hooded cap worn by certain personages such as priests and deities (as instanced by the above-mentioned *φersu* at the tomb of the Augurs); a woollen or leather cap with a wide base and cylindrical crown, as worn by haruspices and attested in various monuments;[10] finally, a wide-brimmed hat in the Greek style (*pètasos*) that seems to have been particularly popular amongst the lower classes (cf. the piper in the Tomb of the Monkey at Chiusi) and in the colder North (*Certosa* situla). Usually however both men and women went bare-headed, a custom that after the fifth century became quite general.

At first men wore beards and their hair long, well over the shoulders; but towards the latter years of the sixth century, young men already went clean-shaven and had their hair cut short, thus following the Greek fashion. The beard disappeared altogether after the third century B.C. and did not become fashionable again in Italy till four hundred years later under the emperor Hadrian. In earliest times (eighth to sixth century) women wore their hair long and knotted or plaited behind their backs; afterwards they allowed it to fall in ringlets over their shoulders, until finally (sixth to fifth century) it was knotted into a crown over the head or gathered in a net or cap. The bleaching of hair was a probable practice, for it seems attested by paintings in the tomb of the Leopards at Tarquinia. During the fourth century, the prevalent hair-style allowed the hair to fall in ringlets over the cheeks; later, when the Hellenistic period was in full swing, women preferred to wear their hair tied in a knot at the back of the head in the Greek style.

Jewellery played an important role in the attire of the Etruscans. Towards the end of the bronze age, the use of safety-pins or *fibulae* spread widely throughout the Mediterranean world: they are amongst the most characteristic objects found in tombs belonging to the iron age. Those worn by men differ from those worn by women in that the bow is broken and serpentine in shape. Fibulae were generally made of bronze though precious metals were also used; they were often richly adorned with paste jewellery or amber. Some specimens belonging to the orientalizing period, such as the disc-shaped fibula of the Regolini-Galassi tomb (see plate 28), are huge and lavishly decorated. The use of the fibula becomes less popular during the sixth century and practically ceases after the fifth: they are only preserved by traditional costumes such as those worn by haruspices. Other types of jewellery included diadems, ear-pendants, necklaces, bracelets, and rings. During the orientalizing period, the lavishness with which they were used was almost barbaric; and the same may be said of the Hellenistic age. The only time jewellery was worn in elegant measure by Etruscan men and, especially, women, was the golden age of the sixth and fifth centuries; and it is to this period that we attribute those magnificent necklaces hung with *bullae* and acorns, and ear-rings wrought by means of the exquisite technique of granulation (see plates 26 and 27).

## NOTES

1. A general treatment of the subject-matter of this chapter will be found in A. Solari, *La vita pubblica e privata degli Etruschi*, 1928.

2. We are dealing here with unpublished material kept in the Museum of Villa Giulia in Rome. Objects found at Vulci are mentioned in *Studi Etruschi*, III, 1929, pp. 109 ff. For the wooden objects, see *Studi Etruschi*, IX, 1935, pp. 267 ff.; X, 1936, pp. 361 ff.; XII, 1938, pp. 237 ff.; XIV, 1940, pp. 305 ff.; XV, 1941, pp. 267 ff.

3. G. Patroni, *L'origine della domus*, in *Rendic. Accad. Lincei*, V, XI, 1902, pp. 467 ff.; A. Gargana, *La casa etrusca*, in *Historia*, 1934, pp. 204 ff.; G. Patroni, *Architettura preistorica generale e italica. Architettura etrusca*, 1941, pp. 294 ff.

4. See G. M. A. Richter, *Ancient Furniture: Greek, Etruscan and Roman*, 1926.

5. P. Ducati, in *Monumenti antichi dei Lincei*, XXIV, 1916, col. 401 ff.

6. G. Q. Giglioli, *L'oinochoe di Tragliatella* (in *Studi Etruschi*, III, 1929, p. 111 ff.).

7. G. d'Acchiardi, in *Studi Etruschi*, I, 1927, pp. 411 ff.; III, 1929, p. 397; cf. also XI, 1937, pp. 305 ff.; XV, 1940, pp. 315 ff.

8. See note 3, p. 83.

9. Cf. P. Fraccaro, *La malaria e la storia degli antichi popoli classici*, in *Atene e Roma*, XXII, 1919, pp. 57 ff.; N. Toscanelli, *La malaria nell' antichità e la fine degli Etruschi*, 1927.

10. Cf. M. Pallottino, *Uno specchio di Tuscania e la leggenda etrusca di Tarchon*, in *Rendiconti Accademia dei Lincei*, 1930, pp. 47 ff., and *Studi Etruschi*, X, 1936, p. 463, plate L.

# PART THREE

*The Problem of the Language*

# CHAPTER TEN

# THE NATURE OF THE PROBLEM

## *The Interpretation of Etruscan*

IN 1936, in the Introduction to my *Elements of Etruscan* (*Elementi di lingua etrusca*), I wrote the following words: 'Unless we are biassed in our opinions, we feel the need, more than ever to-day, for a publication conceived along the lines of the present work; for the quick succession of ephemeral discoveries on the part of amateurs has brought in its wake the very natural disorientation of all those interested in the Etruscan language. At the other end of the scale, there is the obstinate scepticism of those who, sweeping aside the good with the bad, prefer to look upon the problem of Etruscan as the favourite playground of cranks or the "comic" section of linguistic science. We should be both greatly pleased and proud if the perusal of these pages were in some way to provide a better understanding of the difficulties involved and the direction to be followed. Our aim is to narrow the problem down to its real limits and to contain it within prudent, methodical, but also accurate and real statements, equally removed from the intransigent certainty of those who claim to have found the "key" as from the uninformed scepticism of Pyrrhonian critics.'

The situation has changed very little during the many years that have passed since the above passage was written. The slow and painful advance towards a solution of the language problem together with the doubts and prejudices of the majority on what may be considered as the 'Etruscan mystery' *par excellence* continue as before. It is thus most fitting that a work that has as its main task the examination of the most important problems concerning the Etruscans, should deal fairly fully with the language problem by giving an idea of its nature, an outline of its history, methods, and processes, and of the results that have so far been obtained; i.e. the complex achievements of linguists working in particularly unfavourable conditions, in a field bristling with dangers and difficulties, with only the prospect of gathering a meagre harvest or no harvest at all or, worst of all, of complacently following a mirage that will later reveal itself for what it is. And though we should deplore the activities of those – and they are not few – who, without adequate preparation, believed they had solved the problem as a whole, we should not fail to render praise to the patient painstaking labour of scholars to whom we owe the slow but real advances achieved by our discipline within the last two hundred years.[1]

The first and fundamental query: Have Etruscan inscriptions been interpreted, or do they still remain undeciphered (this is the form in which the question is usually put) only very roughly corresponds to a correct formulation of the problem. A categorical answer, whether in the affirmative or in the negative, would only be possible if the interpretation of Etruscan depended essentially upon external factors, i.e. the possession of a mechanical 'key' or 'translator': a known language, for example, so close to Etruscan that the meaning of Etruscan words would be intelligible to us, or a bi-lingual inscription written in Etruscan and in a second language known to us (e.g. Latin or Greek), or again a vocabulary or glossary of Etruscan words translated or explained in a known tongue. It is well known that the interpretation of ancient languages and alphabets whose meaning was lost to us (i.e. Egyptian, Assyro-Babylonian, Sumerian, Hittite (both hieroglyphic and cuneiform), Lydian, etc.) was at first almost wholly founded upon such a 'key'.

Despite the few and brief key-documents available for Etruscan and the frequent attempts made to establish connexions between Etruscan and other known languages and language families, we can definitely state that so far no key has been discovered. The history of the numerous attempts that have been made since the eighteenth century shows clearly that the knowledge gained and universally accepted as the most reliable has had to be wrested slowly, by degrees, never abruptly, from the very first elementary observations (such as the recognition of personal names) down to the present complex morphological and lexical notions. Everything points to the fact that, unless something unforeseen occurs, such as the finding of a lengthy bi-lingual text, discovery will proceed in slow gradual stages before reaching the final goal set by the limits of material possibility.

The problem, therefore, is more quantitative than qualitative in nature. What we ought to ask ourselves is not so much whether Etruscan has been deciphered, but how far has it been deciphered. The general meaning of a context is often acquired as the result of hard work in the slow circumscription of dark, obscure areas. Even in languages that are by now generally known, such as Egyptian, Hebrew, or even Greek, there still more or less obstinately persist, in spite of the advances of modern linguistic science, small dark corners of morphology and vocabulary, i.e. ἅπαξ λεγόμενα, isolated words scattered in the texts, reflections of individual or dialect 'languages' introduced in the literary language. Why should we be surprised then if Etruscan, linguistically isolated (at least so far as the possibility of useful comparisons is concerned), documented in brief and not very numerous texts unsupported by bilingual passages or glossaries of any importance, should offer so many deep uncertainties? In theory, Etruscan words that are still obscure can be considered as so many ἅπαξ λεγόμενα; with the difference that in known languages they do not affect the comprehensibility of the text, whereas in Etruscan their very considerable number is inevitably reflected in the general obscurity of the context.

In order to convey more concretely the nature and limitations of the problem a simile may be drawn from contemporary life: were an Englishman faced with a newspaper written in a language not directly related to his own (e.g. Hungarian or Polish), as long as he possessed average culture and intelligence, his general knowledge of the events and news presumably contained in it, the names of persons and places known to him, technical terms and words belonging to the 'universal' vocabulary, and, perhaps, the illustrations, would all help him to reconstruct and to understand the general meaning of the headlines, the shorter pieces of news, and sections of the longer articles. Such is the position of modern interpreters confronted by Etruscan inscriptions: and thus it is that difficulties grow in proportion to the length of the texts, and hence the vague and approximative character of the majority of the translations that have been put forward.

## The Development of the Chief Methods of Research

Until the last quarter of the nineteenth century, attempts to decipher Etruscan were mainly based upon etymological comparison with other languages and language families. The criteria employed in this process belong to the amateurish researches of seventeenth-century or even Renaissance enthusiasts (e.g. Annius of Viterbo or Pier Francesco Giambullari), the only difference being that attempts at deriving Etruscan words from the Hebrew (it was thought at the time that all languages derived from Hebrew) were slowly replaced, owing to the advance of general linguistic knowledge, by theories seeking to establish a relationship between Etruscan and the Italic dialects (Lanzi, Fabretti, Corssen, and Lattes) or hypotheses of a presumed affinity with Greek, Armenian (Bugge), Basque and Caucasian (V. Thomsen), Ugro-Finnish (Martha) or even Dravidian (S. Konow). Such attempts did not exclude the examination of various intrinsic features of the text, whether epigraphic, phonetic, morphological, or lexical (this is, in fact, the beginning of the 'combinatory' method), but the chief criterion in research consisted in deducing semantic and grammatical values from the outside, from languages of those linguistic groups to which it was thought Etruscan belonged. And in spite of much diversity of opinion, the system was founded upon a common axiom: the conviction that there existed one or more languages so close to Etruscan as to allow without great difficulty, by means of straightforward comparisons, the working out of its principal characteristics and the interpretation of the texts.

The almost wholly negative results of these various attempts – which by their very nature had to be accepted or rejected as a whole – and the progress of scientific criticism led inevitably to a reaction. This was prepared by the slow, conscientious, often unrecognized labours of collectors and epigraphists, notably Italian (e.g. Lanzi, Vermiglioli, Migliarini, G. C. Conestabile, and Fabretti), whose attention was mainly directed towards the isolation and direct examination of monuments. This work culminated in the publication of Fabretti's monumental *Corpus Inscriptionum Italicarum*, completed later by Gamurrini's *Appendix* (1880). It is to these first steps in critical research that we owe some of the fundamental discoveries in the interpretation of Etruscan: e.g. the conjunctive value of the enclitic particle -*c* (corresponding to Latin -*que*), the genitive or adjectival endings in -*s*, -*sa*, -*al*, the feminine endings in *i*-, -*ei*, the pronoun *mi*, the meaning of a number of words such as *ril* 'annos', *clan* 'son', *turce* 'has given', etc., especially in connexion with the very frequent onomastic formulas found on funerary inscriptions. Such victories were won without any recourse having to be made to other languages, by submitting the texts to an acute critical analysis and comparing one with another in order to wrest out, as in a puzzle, their original meaning.

But the insufficiency of the method of etymological comparisons with other languages only became generally established after the publication of a work by the famous latinist Corssen *Über die Sprache der Etrusker* (1874), stating that Etruscan belonged to the Indo-European family of languages and, in particular, to its Italic branch, and following this premise (with apparent methodological rigour) with a general attempt towards a morphological analysis and an interpretation of the texts. The thirty-nine pages of Deecke's *Corssen und die Sprache der Etrusker. Eine Kritik* (1875) were sufficient to bring down, like a house of cards, the imposing construction erected by Corssen.

This significant episode resulted in a change of direction in research. The uncertainty that still persisted as to the true linguistic relationship of Etruscan together with the inconsistencies proper to the etymological method led Deecke and other scholars such as Pauli, Herbig, and Torp to abandon external comparisons with other languages and take up the internal study of Etruscan texts and their reciprocal relations on the basis of facts previously ascertained by the straightforward epigraphic examination of monuments. The internal, or 'combinatory' method was thus born. New discoveries, such as the Capua tile and the manuscript wrappings of the mummy in the Zagreb museum, together with more up-to-date means of research such as the *Corpus Inscriptionum Etruscarum* begun in 1893 by Pauli and still in course of publication,[2] as well as the lexical indices drawn up by Lattes,[3] gave a vigorous momentum to research in this new direction. Much progress, mainly due to the work of Torp (*Etruskische Beiträge*, 1903–6), was made both in our knowledge of Etruscan grammar and in the interpretation of the texts, especially of the shorter ones. More recently, the activity of other etruscologists has done much to extend still further our knowledge of the subject. It is true that the etymological method, though superseded, has occasionally been used by scholars belonging to the 'combinatory' school (Deecke, Pauli, and even Torp) and obstinately followed for some time by Lattes and E. Goldmann; nevertheless it was by now mainly relegated to those amateurish improvisations that grew with tenacious persistence on the borders of Etruscan studies and which vainly sought to explain Etruscan by means of Greek, the Semitic languages, Egyptian, etc.

Meanwhile research on the linguistic relationships of Etruscan was progressing independently of the actual work of decipherment. Such research was much assisted by the more reliable and broader criteria furnished by modern general linguistics. The obvious, though not very close, similarities between Etruscan and certain Indo-European, Caucasian, and Asianic languages were explained in a number of ways: by postulating the existence of pre-Indo-European linguistic groups as understood by Trombetti, by recognizing in these similarities traces of a proto-Indo-European stratum, i.e. of an archaic Indo-European layer not yet differentiated in its various elements (Kretschmer), [4] or, finally, as suggested most recently by Devoto, as remnants of a peri-Indo-European structure, the result of the dissolution and transformation of the archaic Mediterranean substratum under the action of subsequent and repeated Indo-European infiltrations. [5] In each case it was a question of recognizing in the Etruscan of the historical period direct or indirect echoes of those pre-Indo-European Mediterranean languages that had already been largely extinguished in the course of the last stages of prehistory and which only sporadically remained unsubmerged. Toponymy, the science of place-names, was mainly responsible for providing a concrete basis for these theories: for even in present times there survive in many place-names fossil elements of very ancient languages that reveal a certain primitive Mediterranean linguistic unity and point to affinities uniting Etruscan with the Eastern group of pre-Hellenic languages and those of Asia Minor and even with the pre-Indo-European linguistic layer of the Italian peninsula and islands and with 'Ligurian'. Only the language spoken in the Aegean island of Lemnos before the Athenian conquest was recognized, not without a certain amount of discussion, to be linked more closely to Etruscan (see p. 59).

The possibility of classifying Etruscan with a fair degree of precision among the linguistic groups surrounding the Mediterranean was destined to re-open, but upon new bases, the problem of etymological comparisons. Alfredo Trombetti, who had already contributed so much to the genealogical classification of Etruscan and who, by the great breadth of his erudition, was singularly well placed to attempt the arduous task of comparing badly known languages or linguistic remains, cautiously re-introduced the use of the 'etymological' in conjunction with the 'combinatory' method in his *La Lingua etrusca* (1928). He succeeded in achieving some results before his untimely death, especially in the morphological analysis of the language and in integrating the interpretations of texts made by his predecessors, especially by Torp; these results, however, did not fulfil the hopes that had been nourished. After his death, the methodological principles which he had expounded were misinterpreted, for they were too intimately linked with his personal capacities and scientific preparation: this prompted a fresh outbreak of those amateurish attempts at finding an etymological and deductive explanation for Etruscan words, while at the same time official science adopted a policy of 'wait and see' for a few years.

Attempts at analysing phonetic, morphological, and epigraphical data and at reaching a satisfactory interpretation of the texts have been started again with renewed vigour, but only in recent years. In the meantime, prospects have changed in a truly decisive way: with very few exceptions, previous research had all been conceived and conducted at the purely technical level of linguistic analysis, not taking into account that a language, and especially its written documents, form a living part of the history of the people and times to which it belongs. To neglect such historical factors is equivalent to depriving oneself of an essential tool in the study of a language and the understanding of its texts. Only recently has this fact really been understood, but already a rich crop of results is being gathered as the result of the study of Etruscan with that of classical data, of cultural aspects as revealed by monuments, and of the contents and formulas of those literary and epigraphic texts belonging to the Greek, Latin, and Italic worlds with probable affinities with Etruscan documents (the 'bi-lingual' method). This is particularly true in the case of the interpretation of the longer texts such as those of the Zagreb mummy and of the Capua tile: here, the 'combinatory' method had, on the whole, produced only inconclusive results. Among those chiefly responsible for this new direction in research, mention ought to be made of Ribezzo, K. Olzscha, and the author of the present work.[6]

## NOTES

1. The following three chapters contain a fuller treatment of the matter contained in my article *Gli studi sulla lingua etrusca nelle loro condizioni attuali* (in *Archivio Glottologico Italiano*, XXXII, 1940).

2. The first volume (1893–1902) contains inscriptions found at

Fiesole, Volterra, Siena, Arezzo, Cortona, Chiusi, and Perugia. Of the second volume, four fascicules have been published: Section I, fasc. 1, 1907 (Orvieto and Bolsena); fasc. 2, 1923 (Coastal Etruria from Populonia to Vulci); fasc. 3, 1923 (Tarquinii); Section II, fasc. 1, 1912 (Faliscan territory). A supplement (1919–21) was also published containing the text of the Zagreb mummy. In preparation, a fascicule on the inscriptions of Campania and of Lower Etruria. The parts dealing with Northern Etruria, the *instrumentum*, additions and indexes are as yet in a state of project.

3. E. Lattes, *Saggio di un indice lessicale etrusco*, in *Memorie dell'Accademia d'Archeologia e Lettere di Napoli*, I, 1908; II, 1911; III, 1918; *Rendiconti del R. Istituto Lombardo*, XLV, 1912, pp. 303 ff., 351 ff., 412 ff.; *Memorie del R. Istituto Lombardo*, XXIII, 1914. This invaluable work is unfortunately incomplete and difficult to consult, buried as it is in various academic publications. The work is now being completely revised and brought up-to-date in a great scientific lexicon of the Etruscan language by the *Istituto di Studi Etruschi* in conjunction with the Universities of Florence and Rome.

4. For the most recent developments of P. Kretschmer's theory attributing Etruscan to a 'Tyrrheno-Pelasgic' linguistic stratum of Balkan–Danubian origin, see *Glotta*, XXVIII, 1940, pp. 260 ff.; see also *Glotta*, XXX, 1943, pp. 213 ff., where the author prefers to speak of a 'Raeto-Tyrrhenian' group. See also p. 31.

5. G. Devoto, *Pelasgo e peri-indoeuropeo*, in *Studi Etruschi*, XVII, 1943, pp. 359 ff.; *Etrusco e peri-indoeuropeo*, in *Studi Etruschi*, XVIII, 1944, pp. 187 ff.

6. On the subject of the history and methods of research on the Etruscan language the following studies will prove useful: E. Fiesel, *Etruskisch*, 1931, with reviews by S. P. Cortsen and E. Vetter, in *Glotta*, XXIII, pp. 144 ff.; XXVIII, pp. 117 ff.; M. Pallottino, in *Doxa*, III, 1950, pp. 29 ff.; F. Ribezzo, in *Studi Etruschi*, XXII, 1952–2, pp. 105 ff.

# CHAPTER ELEVEN

## THE SOURCES AND THE METHOD

*Present Means and Future Possibilities*

NEXT to the uncertainties due to the relative isolation of Etruscan and the lack of key-documents such as bi-lingual texts and glossaries, the major obstacles encountered in obtaining a full and accurate knowledge of the language are the scarcity, brevity, and limited contents of the texts. Present knowledge leads us to the conclusion that unlike the Greeks, the Etruscans were late and parsimonious in their use of writing, at least as far as monuments are concerned. With the exception of a very few texts of importance, our material is limited exclusively to brief, monotonous funerary or votive inscriptions amounting to little more than a few oft-repeated formulas containing a vocabulary pertaining to limited aspects of the religious life of the people. Etruscan literature is completely lost to us and, with it, that great variety of linguistic facets reflecting family, social, and economic life, abstract notions, and the structure of direct speech. Thus we can say that even if possessed the technical ability to translate precisely and completely all the texts in our possession, an important part of the vocabulary of Etruscan and many of its grammatical features would still remain unknown to us.

What possibilities have we of adding to our stock of Etruscan inscriptions? Every year, as a result of chance discoveries and regular excavations in the territory of ancient Etruria, a number of funerary and votive inscriptions are brought to light; they are usually short, however, and add little to our knowledge of the language. These are gathered and published in the epigraphic section of the review *Studi*

*Etruschi*. In spite of the apparent poverty of such material, it is occasionally of considerable value to us, especially in connexion with the analysis and discussion of known texts of greater importance: often, a single word, a single grammatical form may be sufficient to resolve doubts and problems of many years standing. Sometimes the epigraphic harvest is quite considerable, as in the case of the votive inscriptions on fragments of bucchero vases found on two separate occasions in the course of excavations on the site of the Apollo sanctuary at Veii.

But the hope that some day we may stumble upon an unforeseen discovery of real importance is still alive. We have already seen that the great majority of excavations in Etruria have been concentrated on the exploration of tombs: a type of search that is by far the easiest, most profitable, and economical. The excavation of sites of cities where the continuity of life down to present times has been interrupted has only been conducted in a sporadic and unsystematic manner or merely exists in a state of project: such is the case with Veii, Caere, Tarquinii, Vulci, and Rusellae, to mention just a few of the major centres. Now it is obvious that long inscriptions of a non-funerary character could only be found within ancient inhabited centres. Thus if we call for the excavation of Etruscan cities, it is also in order to increase our stock of epigraphic texts in the hope of furthering our knowledge of Etruscan.

What could we expect from the exploration of a city, should fortune be good enough to present us with a lucky find despite the passage of time and the inevitable upheavals suffered by an urban site? Above all, the much longed-for bi-lingual text: not merely meagre Etrusco-Latin epitaphs such as we already possess, but a full and complete text comparable to the Graeco-Egyptian inscription of the Rosetta Stone or the tri-lingual texts of Persepolis or the inscriptions in Phoenician and hieroglyphic Hittite recently come to light at Karatepe, in Cilicia: all documents that have led to the decipherment and interpretation of the writing and language of great Oriental peoples. Now since the Etruscans, from the fourth to the first century B.C., inhabited states federated to or included in Roman territory with other members of the Italic community, and since many Latin funerary inscriptions have been found in Etruscan cities, we are justified in believing that either public or juridical inscriptions may occasionally have been couched in both Etruscan and Latin. The discovery of one such inscription would revolutionize the whole development of research in Etruscan by providing external data fundamental to the interpretation of the texts and would, in all probability, solve once and for all most aspects of this centuries-old problem.

But even without the discovery of a bi-lingual text, a new long religious text comparable to the Umbrian tablets found at Gubbio, or a juridical text similar to the Latin laws of the Twelve Tables would greatly widen the scope of research. At the present stage of Etruscan studies, one single new source may be sufficient to lead scholars to a final and successful solution of the problem. But the gap presented by the absence of texts of a literary nature would almost certainly always remain open, a gap that removes all possibilities of our knowing Etruscan as well as the other languages of the classical world. In this respect our only hope, however fantastic and illusory, rests on the discovery of papyri in Egypt or at Herculaneum: such a miraculous find would re-echo the extraordinary discovery of an Etruscan text written on the linen wrappings of an Egyptian mummy.

### Direct and Indirect Sources

Let us now put aside future hopes and possibilities and examine the actual sources of our knowledge of Etruscan.[1]

These may be divided into direct and indirect sources. The first consist of those texts that have come down to us preserved on architectural monuments or through archaeological discoveries: in only one case can we speak of a manuscript; the rest of the material is epigraphic.

The manuscript is of exceptional interest not only to Etruscan studies but also as a unique document on the writing habits of the ancients: for it is the only preserved example of a *liber linteus*, or manuscript book on linen cloth. It was originally in the form of a roll or *volumen*, but was later cut into strips and used to wrap the mummy of an Egyptian woman in Ptolemaic or Roman times; the mummy was probably discovered in Middle Egypt, though we do not know the exact place. Important fragments of the original roll were lost in this process; we are also ignorant of the circumstances that determined the presence of an Etruscan religious book in Egypt. The mummy was brought to Europe by a Croatian traveller and later donated to the Zagreb National Museum; here, J. Krall identified the writing on the wrappings as Etruscan. When the separate strips were fitted together, it was possible to reconstruct the text within at least twelve vertical columns: it comprises 1185 words more or less clearly and completely legible, to which may be added about a hundred more words that can be accurately reconstructed with the help of the context. Since repetitions and parallel formulas are frequent, the number of distinct and original words becomes reduced to about 530. The Zagreb text is by far the most important, both for size and content, of the Etruscan texts in our possession.

Epigraphic texts – found almost exclusively in Etruria and Campania (small numbers have also been found in Latium, Umbria, Liguria, and in North Africa) – consist of carved or painted inscriptions on architectural monuments, cippi, urns, tablets, tiles, statues, bronzes, vases, etc. Including the most recent discoveries, their total reaches the figure of 10,000, but only a very few are worthy of special notice. First of all, an inscribed tile found in the neighbourhood of Capua and now preserved in the Berlin Museum: it comprises 10 chapters (separated by horizontal lines), 62 preserved lines and more than 300 legible words; the second part of the text is very damaged. The writing runs from right to left and from left to right on alternate lines. A stone cippus kept in the Perugia Museum (*C.I.E.* 4538) features on two of its faces an important inscription of 46 lines and 130 words. A round thin lead plaque found at Magliano and kept in the Florence Archaeological Museum (*C.I.E.* 5237) contains an inscription carved spirally on both sides and reading towards the centre, consisting of at least 70 words (it is difficult sometimes to decide whether a group of letters contains 1 or 2 words). On a sarcophagus kept in the Tarquinii Museum, the reclining figure sculptured on the lid holds an open scroll in his hand containing an inscription of 9 lines and 59 words (*C.I.E.* 5430).

Other inscriptions in our possession include a number (funerary for the most part) that contain a few lines of text with a certain variety in the words used; in the great majority of cases, however, they merely consist of a few words composed according to a few fixed formulas. The most numerous group is represented by funerary inscriptions (carved on the walls of tombs and on sarcophagi, urns, ossuaries, and tiles) consisting of the *praenomen*, the name of the *gens*, the patronymic and, occasionally, the matronymic of the dead person together with indications as to his age and, in a few exceptional cases, *curriculum vitae*. Votive inscriptions may be subdivided into an archaic group, with special formulas and the name of the dedicator, and a later group where it is the name of the divinity that is most prominent; they too, however, are generally very brief and stereotyped, with the exception of those found on a number of archaic vases. The few Etrusco-Latin inscriptions that we possess all belong to the funerary class and consist almost entirely of proper names. They provide nothing but the most meagre of morphological and lexicological clues: the title *netśvis trutnvt frontac* is, for example, translated *haruspex fulguriator* in the bi-lingual inscription of Pesaro (Fabretti, *C.I.I.* 69); the form *Cahatial*, the oblique case of the gentilitial name *Cahati*, is translated *Cafatia natus* in inscription *C.I.E.* 3763, etc.

Among the indirect sources in our study of Etruscan, we may distinguish the following:

(a) the glosses and other information provided by classical and post-classical writers;

(b) Etruscan elements that have passed into Latin and common Etrusco-Italic elements;

(c) Etruscan elements surviving in place-names;

(d) the supposed fragments of Latin versions of original Etruscan texts.

The *glosses* are Etruscan words with a Latin or Greek translation: they may be either found inserted haphazardly in texts by classical authors or gathered together to form actual glossaries. We possess about sixty such glosses, but their value in the interpretation of Etruscan texts is somewhat limited, just as in the case of Etrusco-Latin bilingual texts. Glosses of a varied nature appear in Varro (*de lingua latina*), in Verrius Flaccus (*de verborum significatione*, in the compendia of Festus and Paul the Deacon), in Isidore of Seville (*Etymologicum*) and especially in Hesychius' Lexicon. E.g.: *atrium* (Varro); *arse verse=arce ignem* (Verrius Flaccus); *cassis*=helmet (*galea*) (Isidore); ἄνδας, ἄντας=north wind, eagle (Hesychius). In exceptional cases Etruscan words are found quoted in the works of other authors such as Livy, Strabo, Plutarch, Dion Cassius, Macrobius, Servius, and John Lydus: e.g. ἄριμος=monkey (Strabo, XIII, 626), *capys*=

falcon (Servius, *ad Aen.*, x, 145). The original form may be preserved intact or may be modified by a Greek or Latin ending: e.g. αἰσάρ=god (in Dion Cassius), αἰσοί=gods (in Hesychius). The reliability of such glosses may be checked by means of the Etruscan texts themselves (*aiser*, 'gods'; *versum*, cf. *verse*, 'fire'?) or by a study of their form (e.g. *fala(n)do*=sky, according to Verrius Flaccus in Paul the Deacon: cf., for the root, such Etruscan words as *falaś*, *falzaθi*, and for the termination, *aranθ*). In a few cases the authenticity of the Etruscan gloss appears to be belied by the Latin character of the word: e.g. δέā, κάπρα (Hesychius). Specialized vocabularies are represented by glosses of medicinal plant names (Dioscorides, though here too some of the names are Latin), and of names of the months (Papias, in the *Liber Glossarum* of Leyden) which also seem to appear in Etruscan texts: e.g. *Aclus*=June, and, in the Zagreb text, *acale*. Phonetic and grammatical remarks of very little value may be found in Varro, in Agrecius' *Ars de orthographia*, and in Martianus Capella. [2]

A special study has been made by A. Ernout of those Etruscan elements that have passed into Latin. [3] They are thought to be characterized by their endings in -*na* (*atena*, *persona*: cf. Etr. φersu), in -*rna* (*santerna*), in -*mna* (*antemna*), in -*sa* (*favisa*: cf. Etr. *faviti*), in -*nt*, -*nd* (*fleḳuntes*, *mundus*: cf. Etr. *munθ*, *munθuχ*), in -*on* (*subulo*: Etr. *suplu*?; *fullo*: cf. Etr. *fulum*-), in -*it* (*veles*, *poples*), etc. The Etruscan derivation of certain words is explicitly stated by classical authors (*mantissa*, *histrio*, *lucumo*, *atrium*, etc.); in other cases it is hypothetical and may possibly be due to analogical formations, i.e. Latin words with endings imitating Etruscan derivatives; or again they may be remnants of the general pre-Indo-European substratum of Italy rather than actual borrowings from the Etruscan of the historical period. On the other hand, an Etruscan origin may be more correctly attributed to Latin words with obscure etymologies and an

Etruscan-looking ending related to the technical languages of religion, the army, the navy, or agriculture: such borrowings would be explained by the very strong cultural influence exerted by Etruria upon primitive Rome. There are also abundant examples where Etruscan acted as an intermediary between Greek and Latin: e.g. *groma* (an instrument used in direction finding and field measurement) from γνώμων, by way of a hypothetical Etruscan *\*cruma*. It is also quite possible that Etruscan may have had a limited influence on the phonetics and morphology of Latin. The whole question deserves more careful examination, if only for the help it may bring to the deciphering of Etruscan. Equally if not more obscure is the question of the possibility of Etruscan words surviving in the vocabulary of central Italian dialects; on the other hand, the hypothesis attributing an Etruscan origin to the aspiration of certain consonants in Tuscan dialects (the well-known *gorgia toscana*) appears to be acquiring more and more supporters. [4]

Despite the fundamental difference between Etruscan and the Indo-European languages of Italy, there are a number of words and roots common to both: e.g. Etr. *sac-*, *sacrn*: Lat. *sacer;* Etr. *eiser* 'gods, deities': Umbrian *esono-*, Volscian *esari-* 'sacred ceremonies, sacrifices'; Etr. *nefts* 'nephew': Lat. *nepos;* Etr. *prumts* 'great-nephew': Lat. *pronepos;* Etr. *vinum*: Lat. *vinum*, Umbrian *vinu;* Etr. *cletram*: Umbrian *kletra* 'trolley for sacred offerings'. These correspondences may be due to contacts established during the prehistoric period (as derivations from the 'Tyrrhenian' linguistic substratum, or as the result of very ancient Indo-European 'infiltrations' as understood by Devoto) or perhaps to reciprocal borrowings during the historical period. At any rate they throw light upon the Etruscan forms. The same phenomenon can be recognized in connexion with names of persons and gods. In the first group (masterfully treated by W. Schulze in *Zur Geschichte der lateinischen Eigennamen*, 1904) the resemblance first appears in the fact that the formula is composed of two or three members (the *praenomen*, the name of the *gens* and, eventually, the *cognomen*: Etr. *Larece Zuχu Mutu*, Lat. *Marcus Tullius Cicero*); this formula is common and limited to those peoples inhabiting the Italian peninsula (Etruscans, Latins, and Umbro-Sabellians), as we have already seen in considering the common social features of the most ancient Italian civilization (see p. 148). But in addition we note that a certain number of *praenomina* and a large number of gentilitial names are identical in Etruscan and Latin (e.g. Etr. *Aule:* Lat. *Aulus;* Etr. *Marce:* Lat. *Marcus*, amongst the *praenomina;* Etr. *Fapi:* Lat. *Fabius;* Etr. *Petruni:* Lat. *Petronius;* Etr. *Vete:* Lat. *Vettius*, amongst the gentilitial names). Forms of proper names belonging to the common Etrusco-Italic stock spring from Etruscan, Latin, and Umbro-Sabellian roots, with a certain preponderance of Etruscan roots.

In the case of names of gods and goddesses a number of common elements are also observed: Etr. *Menerva:* Lat. *Minerva;* Etr. *Selvans:* Lat. *Silvanus*. Such correspondences should be compared with such clearly marked divergences as Etr. *Tin, Tinia:* Lat. *Iuppiter;* Etr. *Fufluns:* Lat. *Liber*. Very ancient linguistic contacts are also revealed by correspondences of the type Lat. *Lar* (name of male genius) and Etr. *Lasa* (name of female genius): here the phenomenon of rhotacism should be taken into account, i.e. the passage of *s* to *r* in certain given positions. Many names of gods, both Etruscan and Latin, derive from the Greek; such names, together with a number of cultural terms (e.g. names of vases) also deriving from Greek, represent an important additional source to our knowledge of Etruscan, since the various changes which they have undergone provide us with a clue to the phonetic tendencies and morphological exigencies of the language. E.g.: Greek Ἀλέξανδρος: Etr.

*Alcsentre, Elaχśantre, Elaχśntre, Elχsntre, Aleχsantre, Elcste*,
etc.; Gk. Κλυταιμήστρα: Etr. *Cluθumusθa, Clutmsta;* Gk.
Ἑλένη: Etr. *Elina, Elinai, Elinei.*[5]

Despite the rich collections made by S. Pieri and the
studies, limited to single questions, of P. Aebischer, V.
Bertoldi, G. Bottiglioni, and C. Battisti,[6] the problems
relating to the Etruscan toponymy of central and northern
Italy are still a long way from being solved. The fundamental difficulty resides in distinguishing the various layers and
the various areas of diffusion of pre-Indo-European place-
names, such as, for example, place-names of the 'Ligurian'
type (found as far south as central Italy, as in the case of the
derivatives of the roots *carra-, pala-, gava-,* etc.), from place-
names belonging to the Etruscan of historical times.
Wherever the latter can be identified with absolute certainty, it is even possible to use them to assess the semantic
value of certain Etruscan words as attempted by Bertoldi
with place-names of the *falar-* type. Account should also
be taken of the close relationship existing between place-
names and personal names, as indicated by Schulze. Names
of Etruscan cities are particularly important in this respect,
for their ancient forms are known to us through the writings
of classical authors and from inscriptions: they are often
closely related to the name of a god or hero: e.g. \**Tarχuna*,
Tarquinii, with the hero *Tarχun-*, Tarchon; *Puplona*, Populonia, with the god *Fuflun*, Bacchus; *Manθua-*, Mantua,
with the god *Mantus;* etc.[7]

Finally, we should consider the hypothetical fragments of
Latin versions of original Etruscan texts. We already know
that the main body of Etruscan sacred books was translated
or abridged into Latin. In the congeries of indirect references, shortened or re-written versions of Etruscan texts
(some echoes of which have come down to us), there are
passages of especial interest to the study of Etruscan literature, but also, in certain aspects, to our knowledge of the

structure of the language: as in the passage taken from the Vegonic books and quoted by the *Gromatici* (Lachmann ed., I, pp. 350 ff.) enclosing the teachings of the Lasa Vegonia on the division of fields. [8]

## Methods of Research

Having examined the sources of our knowledge of Etruscan, let us now pass to the question of method. All attempts to make use of factual data without adequate linguistic preparation, a critical approach, and a good measure of prudence and common sense are bound to fail. Above all, it is important to keep in mind the basic axiom that a possible or even very likely solution need not necessarily be the correct one. The history of Etruscan hermeneutics is littered with failures due to the fact that scholars remained satisfied with more or less sensible and likely results, accepting them as final and correct. Often, in support of a given method or system, the fact that the translation made sense was adduced as an unanswerable argument. This, however, is by no means sufficient to prove the correctness of a given translation: it is quite easy to show that an Etruscan text can adapt itself to as many likely and reasonable translations as there are methods or presumed 'keys' with which to tackle it. Another requirement to which it is worth calling attention while still on this subject of method and common sense, is the humility and diffidence of the scholar before his own results. For though boldness and imagination are essential for fruitful research, it is impossible to dispense with rigorous self-criticism, methodical doubt, and cold detachment in evaluating the results obtained. The whole painful history of the failures with which the path of etruscology is strewn is little more than the story of men who became overfond of their own hypotheses and lacked the mental agility to abandon them as soon as unfavourable evidence began to accumulate. It is in the impartial estimation of one's own and one's colleagues' reconstructions – however brilliant and satisfying – that lies the prime condition for a steady, if slow, progress towards ultimate success.

To this general 'method', made up essentially of elementary preparation and common sense, should be added more specific methods, i.e. those tactical criteria to be adopted as we advance step by step over the difficult terrain presented by the uncertainty of linguistic phenomena and the obscurity of inscriptions. From the character of the documents in our possession and the retrospective examination of the attempts made during the past decades, we may exclude the possibility of a complete deciphering of Etruscan by means of an external agency, whether in the nature of one or more known languages with which it could be compared, or of a 'translator', be it a glossary or a bilingual text. The fundamental basis of research can only reside, therefore, in the direct examination of the texts in our possession, taking into account their purpose, the objects to which they refer, the figures that may accompany them and the onomastic formulas which they contain. Hence, it is naturally most important that an accurate archaeological estimate be made of the character, meaning, and chronology of the objects or monuments connected with the inscriptions. Lexical and grammatical values thus inductively obtained should then be checked by combining texts and passages with one another, i.e. by testing the reliability of the first hypothesis by means of new proofs. This is the classical procedure of the 'combinatory' method. Even when not rigidly adhered to, it remains irreplaceable as a means of control even in the case of information obtained from external sources.

Naturally the information obtained by the internal inductive method is, by its very nature, a good deal less precise than what might have been obtained from external sources.

In many cases, the function of a case ending is known only approximately or in part, as in the word *Menervas* found written upon a vase where final -*s*, added to the name of the goddess Menerva, may just as easily be a genitive of possession or a dative of advantage. The same may be said of lexical values as their differentiation is often generic, according to category, within the limits of the *genus proximum* rather than those of the *differentia specifica:* such is the case with terms referring to sacred ceremonies or political institutions and offices. We know quite well, for example, that the word *śacni* stands for a sacred place or institution, but are unable to tell exactly to what term it corresponded in Latin or any other language. Naturally, in the interpretation of words, the determination of meaning falls gradually from a maximum of accuracy and probability to vague and generic working hypotheses on which it would be rash to build further hypotheses. The uncertainty characterizing certain complex hermeneutic constructions built up entirely by means of combinatory processes is in fact due to this piling of hypothesis upon hypothesis till the whole structure appears to be devoid of all reality.

The weightier role played by the inductive or 'combinatory' method does not exclude the use of deductive processes based upon external data. Glosses and bi-lingual texts provide us, or, rather, have provided us, with certain lexical determinations, not, however, always absolutely reliable: e.g. *ais=god*, *arim*=monkey, *netśvis*=haruspex, etc. Other data could be obtained from an intelligent sifting of the Latin lexical material of supposed Etruscan derivation, so long as it is carefully checked by means of the combinatory method. Should we, for example, admit that Latin *mundus* is connected with Etruscan *munθ*, then the interpretation of the latter word as 'ornament', as proposed by Cortsen and accepted by Trombetti, would seem evident. But the meaning proposed is unintelligible in the context of the funerary inscription in which the word is found (*C.I.E.* 5470): it would lead to the odd translation 'he placed within the tomb twenty sarcophagi, ornament of the dead'! On the other hand, several other inscriptions include words derived from the same root *mun-*: it appears as if the meaning was rather that of 'repository for the dead, *locus* (in the funerary meaning of the Latin word)'. The connexion with *mundus* might then be established, if at all, in the way indicated by F. Leifer,[9] by way of the special funerary and religious meaning of the Latin word which, besides signifying 'world' and 'ornament', also stood for 'pit of communication with the underworld'. This example will suffice to show the importance of broadening our knowledge of Etruscan life and customs in order to gain a better understanding of the language.

From examples of etymological analysis of single Etruscan words, prudently carried out by M. Hammarström (for *natis, netśvis*)[10] and Devoto (for *ais, culsu*, etc.),[11] we are inclined to believe that the old etymological method, as long as it is not considered as an instrument capable of interpreting the whole of Etruscan by means of a known language or group of languages (which, as we have already stated, has shown itself to be critically impossible), but cautiously applied to single words or forms, is destined to furnish useful confirmations or even new contributions in the deciphering of Etruscan. In this connexion we should not forget the possibility of a tentative application of the methods of linguistic geography to the study of Etruscan, not only as a help in determining more accurately the position of Etruscan among the Mediterranean languages, but also in confirming, if only indirectly, some of its lexical and morphological values.

But next to the two traditional methods of Etruscan hermeneutics (etymological and combinatory), a new deductive principle has become established during the last twenty years as a major tool of research: the bilingual method. It operates in a completely different field from that of linguistic affinities and comparisons, tending instead to explain the meaning of words and phrases by using the same principle as the 'translators', i.e. bilingual texts or glossaries. Assuming that the Etruscan civilization was closely bound to the Greek and the Italic (as the comparative study of religion, art, customs, etc. clearly shows) and that such cultural affinities are reflected in analogies in modes of expression, in sacrificial, votive, and funerary formulas, we are justified in concluding that in many cases an Etruscan text may be compared with a Greek, Latin, or Italic text with presumably similar contents, and may be interpreted on the basis of such a comparison almost as if dealing with a bilingual inscription. Such a process was first applied by the writer in establishing the meaning of the Etruscan pronoun *mi* (=I, me), by comparing two formulas inscribed on two vases found on Faliscan territory: one in Etruscan: *mi qutun Lemausnas ...* ' the other in Faliscan (i.e., for practical purposes, in archaic Latin): *eco quto ... enotenosio ...* 'I (am) the pitcher of ... Enotenus (name of the possessor) ...* ' – identical expressions couched in two different languages. Practically at the same time, Olzscha recognized the great importance of Roman and Umbrian sacrificial formulas in the interpretation of Etruscan ritual texts, especially in the case of the longest and most important, that of the Zagreb mummy, to the interpretation of which he devoted studies of fundamental importance. Naturally, the bilingual method rests substantially upon the reciprocal translatability of words and expressions in Etruscan on the one hand and in Latin or Italic on the other, i.e. upon the existence of those 'translated loan-words' which inevitably follow the close cohabitation of peoples of different tongues within a common cultural orbit (as, for example, is the case with Romance and Germanic speakers in the modern world). Such a correspondence existed between the Etruscan title *zilaθ meχl rasnal* and the Latin *praetor Etruriae*, as we have already seen when dealing with the political organization in Chapter Six. This new method, used in the spirit of the new 'historical' directions taken by Etruscan hermeneutics and applied cautiously and intelligently with the assistance of the older, well-tried methods, opens up unhoped-for vistas of new conquests in this field.[12]

## Variations in Time and Space

It is chiefly owing to the work of Miss Fiesel that the attention of scholars has been drawn to the problem of the internal evolution of the language during the seven centuries of development for which we have material.[13] So evident a phenomenon is the rapid evolution of epigraphic Latin from archaic to imperial times that we may *a priori* suppose some similar development in Etruscan. Hence the need always to keep in mind the date, be it only approximate, of each inscription; this may be determined from the characteristics of the monument concerned and of its accompanying objects, the shape of the letters, etc. This attitude contrasts with the previous habit of studying and combining texts without taking their relative ages into account. Both from the palaeographic and phonetic points of view notable differences can be found between archaic inscriptions (seventh to fifth centuries B.C.) and later inscriptions. As an example, we may quote the fall of unstressed vowels and the reduction of diphthongs in the later texts: e.g. *lautn* (archaic Etr. *lautun*), *zusleve* (arch. Etr. *zuslevai*). In morphology too a number of differences are now beginning to be observed: the genitive ending *-al* corresponds, in archaic inscriptions, to *-a*. It would be advisable, therefore, to indicate the relative age of every lexical, morphological, or phonetic form quoted, by placing before it the abbreviations *a.Etr.* (archaic Etruscan) or *n.Etr.* (later or neo-Etruscan).

Much the same remarks could be made with respect to problems concerning topographical variations in Etruscan. The study of such phenomena is still less advanced than that of chronological variations. Only the completion of that great collection of Etruscan inscriptions, the *Corpus Inscriptionum Etruscarum*, which is to include the Etruscan regions of Campania and the Po valley, can provide sufficiently broad and reliable foundations for an attempt to disentangle regional – we may even say dialectal – peculiarities in vocabulary, phonetics, and grammar. Up to the present such research has proved extremely arduous owing to the rarity of preserved texts, especially in certain regions such as northern Italy. Nor is it always possible to establish up to what point the peculiarities of certain inscriptions are the result of local differentiations or reflect a given stage in the development of the language; such is the case with the archaisms found in the Capua tile or those (palaeographic and orthographic in particular) of the Po valley inscriptions. It is probable, moreover, that the outlying districts of Etruria, conquered and flourishing in archaic times, were slower to evolve linguistically compared with the central regions. Here, the language rapidly developed towards a neo-Etruscan which, without doubt, formed the basis of the literary κοινή of the Etrusco-Roman era. But neo-Etruscan too features a number of variants (e.g. in the treatment of sibilants) according to whether it was spoken in southern or in central and northern Etruria; it is such variants that allow us, for example, to establish that the text of the Zagreb mummy was written in the idiom of one of the central or northern cities. [14]

## NOTES

1. Cf. M. Pallottino, *Testimonia linguae etruscae*, 1954, a collection of the more notable texts and of the glosses.

2. Cf. G. Buonamici, *Fonti di storia etrusca tratte da gli autori classici*, 1939, pp. 354 ff.

3. *Les éléments étrusques du vocabulaire latin*, in *Bulletin de la Société linguistique*, xxx, 1930, pp. 82 ff.

4. See C. Merlo, in *Studi Etruschi*, i, 1927, pp. 303 ff.

5. Cf. G. Devoto, in *Studi Etruschi*, i, 1927, pp. 255 ff.; E. Fiesel, *Namen des griechischen Mythos im Etruskischen*, 1928.

6. *Studi Etruschi*, vols. I ff.

7. M. Pallottino, in *Scritti in onore di B. Nogara*, 1937, pp. 341 ff.

8. Cf. B. Nogara, *Gli Etruschi e la loro civiltà*, p. 420.

9. *Studien zum antiken Anterwesen*, quoted on p. 152, note 2.

10. *Glotta*, xi, 1921, pp. 213 ff.

11. *Studi Etruschi*, v, 1931; vii, 1933, etc.

12. On the bi-lingual method and its applications, see M. Pallottino, in *Studi Etruschi*, vii, 1933, p. 241; K. Olzscha, *Die Sprache der Etrusker. Probleme und neue Wege der Deutung*, in *Neue Jahrbücher für Wissenschaft und Jugendbildung*, xii, 1936, pp. 97 ff.; *Interpretation der Agramer Mumienbinde*, 1939, pp. 3 ff.; M. Pallottino, in *Studi Etruschi*, xiii, 1939, pp. 331 ff.; *Nuovi orientamenti nello studio dell'etrusco*, in *Archiv Orientalný*, xviii, 4, 1950 (*Symbolae Hrozný*, v), pp. 159 ff.

13. *Acts of the First International Congress of Etruscan Studies*, pp. 187 ff.

14. Cf. *Studi Etruschi*, xi, 1937, pp. 206 ff.

# CHAPTER TWELVE

# THE RESULTS

## *The Alphabet*

THE problem of Etruscan concerns the interpretation of the language and not that of its writing, for even though inscriptions cannot be clearly understood, they can be read with a fair degree of accuracy since we know the phonetic value of each Etruscan letter. These values were gradually established between the eighteenth and the beginning of the nineteenth century, by comparison with Greek and Latin alphabets to which Etruscan is closely related. Since 1833, when R. Lepsius determined the value of the Etruscan letter ‡ =z, the cycle of research has been considered closed as far as the alphabet is concerned: correct and complete reading of inscriptions was guaranteed in every case. Nevertheless, a very important and recent discovery has again brought the question of the alphabet to the fore by showing that even in the most recent studies, one of the symbols of the archaic Etruscan alphabet had been erroneously interpreted. This is the symbol ×, until lately confused with *t*, but demonstrated with all certainty by Miss E. Fiesel to be a sibilant which she transcribed ʃ.[1] As a consequence of this discovery, a whole series of suppositions concerning certain important archaic inscriptions had to be radically modified.

The origin of the Etruscan alphabet has provoked discussions that have not yet been completely settled.[2] On the basis of the equivalence ↓ =χ, it has been classified by some among the Western or 'red' alphabets and thought to have been transmitted to the Etruscans by the Chalcidian colony of Cumae. Others have spoken of an ancient proto-Greek alphabet or put forward even more unlikely hypotheses. The whole question of the origin of the Etruscan alphabet should be considered foreign to that of the origins of the Etruscan people.

What is certain is that during the seventh century, the Etruscans adopted an alphabet of twenty-six letters, whatever its origin, which may be found reproduced in its entirety on the margin of an ivory writing tablet (found at Marsigliana d'Albegna) and upon a number of vases: obviously didactic models. But the practical use of such an alphabet must have been the result of an elaborate process of adaptation. The letters $\beta$, $\delta$, Phoenician *samech* and *o* were discarded and do not appear in inscriptions for they do not correspond to any of the sounds present in the Etruscan phonetic system: the latter, in fact, lacked the series of voiced plosives while the vowel *o* was confused, at least originally, with *u*.[3] The letter $\gamma$ was not used to represent the voiced palatal plosive, but the unvoiced plosive (as with Latin *c*), together with the letters $\chi$ and *q*, the use of which becomes rarer in later inscriptions.[4] The complementary symbol $\times$, which in the eastern Greek alphabets carried the value of $\chi$, and in the western, and in Latin, of the consonant cluster *lks*, is only met in a number of archaic Etruscan inscriptions with the value of the simple sibilant *s*. In the case of the labio-dental fricative *f* (different from the aspirated bi-labial consonant $\phi$), the original alphabet lacked the appropriate symbol; at first, in the oldest texts, it was represented by the group *vh;* later, towards the end of the sixth century, a new sign 8, of uncertain origin, was introduced for it and placed last in the series of letters of the alphabet. The persistence of the two sibilants M and Z (corresponding respectively to the Phoenician letters *sade* and *śin*) is also worthy of note: it was justified by the existence in Etruscan of two allied sounds

| Typical Letterings | Archaic Letterings (vii–v cent.) | Late Letterings (iv–i cent.) | Modern Equi-valents | Typical Letterings | Archaic Letterings (vii–v cent.) | Late Letterings (iv–i cent.) | Modern Equi-valents |
|---|---|---|---|---|---|---|---|
| A | A | A | a | ⊞ | | | (s) |
| B | | | (b) | O | | | (o) |
| ℸ | ⟩ | ⊃ | c(k) | � | ⟨ | ⟨ | p |
| ⊲ | | | (d) | M | M | M | ś |
| ⊒ | ⧧ | ⧧ | e | Ọ | Ọ | | q |
| ⊣ | ⊣ | ⊣ | v | ⊲ | ⊲ | ⊲ | r |
| I | I | ⧧ | z | ⟩ | ⟨ | ⟨ | s |
| ⊟ | ⊟ | ⊟ | h | T | T | ✝ | t |
| ⊗ | ⊗ | ⊙ | θ(th) | Y | Y | V | u |
| I | I | I | i | X | X,✝ | | ṡ |
| ⋋ | ⋋ | | k | Φ | | Φ | φ (ph) |
| ⋁ | ⋁ | ⋁ | l | ↓ | | ↓ | X (ch) |
| ⋀ | ⋀ | 𝗆 | m | | 𝟪 | 8 | f |
| ⋎ | ⋎ | ⊓ | n | | | | |

Figure 6 – THE ETRUSCAN ALPHABET

which were originally quite distinct; they are generally transcribed *ś* and *s*. Apart from the adoption and the rejection of certain signs, the evolution of the Etruscan alphabet features a number of variations in the shape of letters which allow the dating, if only approximative, of inscriptions.

In modern transcriptions of Etruscan, the corresponding Latin letters are used, modified at times by diacritical signs, with the exception of the aspirates (*ph*, *th*, and *ch*), for which the Greek letters $\phi$, $\theta$, and $\chi$ are used.

Writing proceeds from right to left in the great majority of inscriptions, contrary to the usual direction of Greek and Latin writing. In a few exceptional cases, writing runs from left to right or alternates the direction with each new line. In archaic inscriptions, words are run together, whereas in later texts one or two dots are often interposed. A recent and important discovery in the study of Etruscan is due to Vetter's researches on Venetic punctuation: working back from the latter to archaic Etruscan inscriptions, Vetter established the characteristics of a system where simple open syllables (e.g. *ma*, *lu*, *ke*, etc.) are considered normal and left, therefore, unpunctuated; whereas isolated letters, whether vowels or consonants, appear distinguished by one or more dots. This system is very widespread in archaic inscriptions, especially from southern Etruria, and it is present even in the Capua tile. Is it perhaps a relic of a syllabic system of writing?[5] It is worth noting, in this respect, that an archaic vase found at Caere possesses, besides the alphabet, a complete syllabary.

### Phonetics

After the fundamental preparatory work by Lattes in the field of Etruscan phonetics, research on phonetic problems came to a comparative standstill, from which it only recovered as a result of the work by Trombetti, Devoto, and Miss Fiesel. The latter two have concentrated their attention upon Etruscan phonetic tendencies as revealed by the transformations undergone by Greek mythological names in Etruscan inscriptions. Mention should also be made of F. Slotty's contributions on syllabism.

The elementary sounds of Etruscan seem to have been the following:

(a) four vowels: *a, e, i,* and *u* (*o* is confused with *u*);

(b) one semi-vowel: *v*, which, at times, replaces the vowel *u;*

(c) one aspirate: *h*, found almost exclusively at the beginning of words;

(d) six plosive consonants: *c, t, p* (unvoiced), and *χ, θ, φ* (aspirated);

(e) one labio-dental fricative: *f;*

(f) three dental fricatives: *s, ś,* and *z;*

(g) two liquids: *l* and *r;*

(h) two nasals: *m* and *n.*

It should be noted that fricatives, liquids, and nasals may all possess at times syllabic value and become sonants, i.e. behave as if they were vowels, as in words like *cnl, clθi.*

The Etruscan vowel system is a good deal more developed in the earlier than in the later phases of the history of the language. There is much instability in the quality of vowels, as in *Ràmaθa, Ràmeθa, Ràmuθa, Ràmθa,* all variants of the same woman's name. There are also many examples of vowel harmony, i.e. of the assimilation of vowels in neighbouring syllables, as in the form *Cluθumusθa* derived from the Greek *Κλυτάιμήστρα*, and in the frequent occurrence of words with a predominant vowel, e.g. *siricima, Fuflunsul, acnanasa.* Five diphthongs are known: *ai, au, ei, eu,* and *ui,* but *ai* generally tends to change to *ei* or *e,* whereas *au* and *eu* tend to become, in later Etruscan, *av* and *ev.*

The most characteristic phenomenon affecting Etruscan

consonants is the so-called *Lautverschiebung:* the tendency of
unvoiced plosives to become aspirates and of aspirates to
become fricatives. Thus, *c* tends to change to $\chi$, *t* to $\theta$, and
*p* to $\phi$ or *f*: e.g. a.Etr. *zac* becomes in later Etruscan *za$\chi$*.
In the most recent texts, there is oscillation in the spelling
of unvoiced and aspirate consonants; both are used indiffer-
ently: e.g. *suti* and *su$\theta$i*, *zic* and *zi$\chi$*, *uple* and *u$\phi$le*. In the
initial position, aspirates and fricatives weaken sometimes
to the simple aspirate *h:* e.g. *Fasti* and *Hasti*. The absence of
voiced plosives (*b, d,* and *g*) in Etruscan may perhaps have
been originally due to the same phenomenon, i.e. they may
have changed to the corresponding unvoiced consonants
in prehistoric times.

In the matter of stress, the most noticeable and striking
characteristic of Etruscan is the strong initial stress of the
word and the consequent fall of unstressed vowels (syn-
cope). It is most marked in neo-Etruscan and results in the
formation of complex consonant clusters and the development of sonants: e.g. a.Etr. *lautun:* n.Etr. *lautn;* Greek
'Aλέξανδρος: Etr. *Ale$\chi$santre, El$\chi$sntre*.

## Grammar

Considerable progress has also been made during the last
few years in the domain of Etruscan morphology. We are
indebted to Trombetti for stressing the importance of
morphological phenomena in the interpretation of Etruscan, on the ground that the understanding of a text cannot
be arrived at merely by knowing the lexical values (i.e. the
meaning of word-roots) concerned, but requires in addition
an accurate appreciation of syntactical relations and grammatical functions. Trombetti was the first to attempt, upon
a sound critical basis, the splitting of the Etruscan word into
its formative elements, and it is to him, as also to Rosenberg
(within the framework of the combinatory method), that

we owe the concept of a grammatical structure for Etruscan independent of that of Indo-European languages. This is especially evident in the singular indifference with which different suffixes are used in word-formation, the vague fluidity of certain grammatical categories, the probable nominal character of the verb, the poverty of development of plural and feminine formations, and especially in the superposition of suffixes. We have defined as 'morphological redetermination' (a term suggested to us by Trombetti) the group of facts pointing to the typical tendency of Etruscan grammar to reinforce or redetermine the syntactical function of a form by the superposition of suffixes. For example, *Larθ*, a masculine personal name, becomes *Larθ-al* in the genitive, which, in its turn, may acquire another genitive ending *-ś* to form *Larθ-al-ś*, used indifferently instead of *Larθ-al*. We may truly speak of an actual inflexion of forms that have already been grammatically inflected, as in the case of *Uni-al-θi* 'in the (sanctuary) of Juno' from *Uni-al*, the genitive of *Uni* 'Juno'. The concept of morphological redetermination, however repugnant it may appear to the structure of classical languages, has to-day been universally accepted by scholars as fundamental to the interpretation of Etruscan grammatical phenomena.

The Etruscan noun does not possess a characteristic ending for the nominative, with the exception of a few masculine proper names that end in *-s*. Adjectives are formed by means of special suffixes: e.g. *śuθi* 'tomb': *śuθi-na* 'funerary'. Feminines only show differentiation in personal names (both proper and common) by means of special thematic suffixes and endings in *-i*, *-ia*, *-a*, and *-θa*: e.g. *pui, puia* 'wife'; *śeθra*, the feminine form of *śeθre*, a *praenomen; Mutunai*, the feminine form of the gentilitial name *Mutuna; lautniθa* 'freewoman', from *lautni* 'freeman'. Also in the case of plural formations, it is difficult to establish a rule: we know of several plural and collective nouns characterized by the suffixes -r, -l, and -a: e.g. *clan* 'son': *clen-ar* 'sons'; *murś* 'sarcophagus': *murs-l* 'sarcophagi'.

As regards the declension of the noun, we can distinguish groups of genitive and dative suffixes (-a, -l, and -al; -s, -ś, -si, and -sa), a locative suffix (-t(i) or -θ(i) ), and other endings belonging to oblique cases with advantage, instrumental and locative values, etc. (i, -e, -eri). It is not easy to draw up actual paradigms of inflexions, though it is possible to consider cases such as the following:

| nominative | *meθlum* |
| genitive | *meθlum-eś* |
| dative of advantage? | *meθlum-eri* |
| locative | *meθlum-θ.* |

Broadly speaking, we are able at present to distinguish two separate groups or 'declensions', characterized principally by their genitive endings: one in -s, the other in -l (a.Etr. -a). To the first group belong all nouns ending in a vowel, with the exception of feminines in -i, and the majority of nouns ending in a consonant; to the second, feminines in -i and certain nouns, mostly personal, in -s, -θ, or -n. E.g. for the first group, *hamφe:* gen. *hamφe-ś; ramθa:* gen. *ramθa-ś; fler:* gen. *fler-ś;* for the second group, *ati* 'mother': gen. *ati-al.* Morphological redetermination, particularly in the declension of proper nouns, was much developed: we have already mentioned genitive forms obtained by adding the suffix -s to a genitive in -l; when, on the other hand, it is the suffix -la that is added to a genitive in -s, the result obtained is a 'genitive of the genitive', i.e. a genitive in the genitive case. E.g. *Vel Avleś* 'Vel, (son) of Aule': gen. *Vel-uś Avles-la* 'of Vel, (son) of Aule'. Complex forms are thus obtained in which no less than three genitive endings may be found superimposed: e.g. *Arnθ-al-iśa-la.*

The identification of the particles *mi, mini* with the personal pronoun of the first person (they were at first believed to be demonstratives), was first made by Sittig and confirmed by the author by the application of the method of comparison of parallel texts, and is now generally accepted. [6] The following demonstrative adjectives and pronouns are also known: *ca, eca, ta* and, perhaps, *ei*, together with some of their declensional forms (e.g.: *ca, cś, cla, cn, cei, clθi*, etc., where forms in -*n* appear to be accusatives). It is probable that the demonstratives, used as noun determinants, came to be reduced to mere articles and ended by being employed enclitically as particles incorporated in the noun itself: e.g. *esvi-tn, huslneś-tś, śacni-cla, śacni-cleri*, etc.; the phenomenon was first noticed by Torp and has to-day been accepted by the majority of scholars. Other particles of a pronominal type, such as *θi, χi, in, an, ipa*, etc., may have been demonstratives, relatives, or indefinites, but their employment and interpretation are still far from clear. The composition of pronominal roots in forms such as *ancn, cnticnθ, ipeipa*, etc., is, on the other hand, fairly obvious.

The classic problem of the Etruscan numerals resides in the correct identification of the six words written on the facets of the well-known Tuscania dice (now kept in the Louvre in Paris) with the first six digits. It is as yet unsolved. If the thesis upholding that the majority of the numerical formulas in the text of the Zagreb mummy are dates becomes, as we believe, generally accepted, the series proposed by Torp ($\theta u = 1$, $zal = 2$, $ci = 3$, $śa = 4$, $ma\chi = 5$, and $hu\theta = 6$) will doubtless become recognized as the most probable. At most there may be some discussion as to whether $hu\theta$ may not represent 4 (owing to the classic comparison of the pre-Hellenic place-name Ὑττηνία = Τετράπολις) and *śa*, 6.[7] Other numerals are represented by *cezp-, semφ*, and *nurφ-*. The word *zaθrum* was probably equivalent to 20. Multiples of 10 are formed by the addition of the suffix -*alc* or *alχ*: e.g. *cialχ, śealχ, huθalχ-, muvalχ-*,

etc. Counting appears to have proceeded additively as far
as 6 (e.g. *huθiś zaθrumiś* 'on the twenty-sixth (day)?') and
subtractively from 7 to 9 (e.g. *esl-em-zaθrumiś* 'on the
eighteenth (day)?'; cf., also, Greek δυῶν δέοντα εἴκοσι,
Latin *duo-de-viginti*). Mention should also be made of the
numeral adverbs, formed by the addition of the suffix *-z* or
*-zi*: e.g. *ci-z* 'thrice'.

Many and important problems arise out of the study of
the Etruscan verb. Pauli's opinion, that it had a nominal
origin, appears to be back in favour: many forms derived
from verbal roots and with verbal meaning do, in fact,
possess both structure and inflexions identical with those of
nouns. The only really certain verbal forms, from the point
of view of morphological structure, are the third person
singular 'perfects' in *-ce*, such as *mulveneke* 'has dedicated',
*turce* 'has given', *svalce* 'has lived', etc. Other suffixes frequently encountered with verbal roots are: *-a, -e* (e.g. *ama,
ame*), *-u* (e.g. *lupu* 'has died'), *-ri* (with a value probably
identical with that of the Latin gerundive: e.g. θezeri *'faciun-
dum est, fieri oportet'*), *-aś, -θas* (with participial or relative
meaning: e.g. *svalθas* 'having lived, who has lived'). There
are also hypotheses, built on fairly sound foundations and
tested by the combinatory method, concerning the possible
passive nature of the Etruscan verb as in the case of the
Basque verb. [8]

Very little is known for certain on the subject of adverbial
expressions and copulative particles. It is generally difficult
to distinguish between pronouns and pre- or post-positions.
The old fundamental discovery of the enclitic conjunction
*-c*, corresponding to Latin *-que*, has been joined by that of
enclitic *-um*, generally used to co-ordinate sentences and
possessing a slight antithetical value. Some still doubt,
though wrongly, the conjunctive value of the particle
*etnam*, also found, as it seems, in an enclitic form *-tnam*: it
probably corresponded to Umbrian *inumek* and to Latin

*item, etiam.* A few more adverbial or conjunctive particles are known, such as θui 'here'; *matam* 'above'?; *iχ, iχnac* 'as'; etc. Very little attention has been given as yet to questions affecting the syntax, word-order, and style of Etruscan texts. [9]

## Interpretation of the Texts

In the present condition of our knowledge of Etruscan, it may be affirmed that the very great majority of inscriptions can be understood and translated perfectly. This statement may surprise the general public and all those who continue to retain Etruscan as a sphinx enveloped in impenetrable mystery. It is necessary, however, to add that by far the greater part of epigraphic material in our possession consists of very brief explicative texts (accompanying the painted or carved figures of mythical personages), of a number of legends on coins and sundry objects (giving, in the latter case, the name of the owner), but especially of funerary inscriptions with the name, and, occasionally, the age, of the dead person; all documents, in fact, that contain little but proper names. On the basis of certain inflexions found in funerary inscriptions (such as the genitive of the patronymic or matronymic) and by the comparison of the epitaphs of related persons buried in the same tomb, it has been possible to establish from the very beginning of etruscological research the meaning of certain very common words, such as *clan* = son, *seχ* = daughter, etc. At the same time, the meanings of the words for 'to live', 'to die', 'years', and 'age' were also fixed. Here is an example of the complete formula of a funerary inscription, with a literal translation:

| *Partunus* | *Vel* | *Velθurus* | *Satlnal-c* | *Ramθas* |
|---|---|---|---|---|
| Partunu | Vel | of Velthur | and of Satlnei | Ramtha |

| *clan* | *avils* | *lupu* | *XXIIX* | |
|---|---|---|---|---|
| son | of years | dead | 28 | *(C.I.E.* 5424) |

i.e. 'Vel Partunu, son of Velthur and of Ramtha Satlnei, who died when 28 years of age.'

Difficulties begin to arise when we pass to funerary inscriptions containing information on the life and career of the dead person, or inscriptions recording the dedication of monuments and furnishings. Words of obscure and uncertain meaning begin to make their appearance, and their meanings become all the more arduous to determine as the etymological problems which they present are further complicated by archaeological and historical difficulties. The combinatory method, even when assisted by the new bilingual processes, has not yet allowed us to pin down the value of, say, political, administrative or priestly titles that accompany the names of the dead, or the exact significance of sacral and funerary terms such as *śacni* (whence the verb *śacnisa*), *acazr*, *atrś*, etc. The value carried by the words for 'tomb', 'sarcophagus', 'to do', 'to give', etc., is, on the other hand, much clearer. Biographical funerary inscriptions are quite frequent, and may assume the character of the Latin *elogia*, such as the well-known inscriptions in the tombs of the Scipios. Here is a brief and simple example of such an inscription:

| *Aleθnas* | *Arnθ* | *Larisal* | *zilaθ* | *Tarχnalθi* | *amce* |
|-----------|--------|-----------|---------|-------------|--------|
| Alethna | Arnth | of Laris | *zilath* | in Tarquinii | was |

(*C.I.I.*, Suppl., III, 322),

i.e. 'Arnth Alethna (son) of Laris: he was *zilath* (probably= *praetor*) in Tarquinii'. Here is a longer and more complex inscription:

| *Arnθ* | *Xurcles* | *Larθal* | *clan* | *Pevθial* |
|--------|-----------|----------|--------|-----------|
| Arnth | Churcle | of Larth | son (and) | of Pevthi |

| *zilc* | *parχis* | *amce* | *marunu* |
|--------|----------|--------|----------|
| *zilc* | *parchis* | did belong to the | *maru* (college of the |

| *spurana* | *cepen* | *tenu* |
|---|---|---|
| civic | priest (who) | held office? |

*marones?*)

| *avils* | *maχs semφalχls* | *lupu* |
|---|---|---|
| of years | seventy-five? | dead |

(Fabretti, *C.I.I.* 2070),

i.e. 'Arnth Churcle, son of Larth and of Pevthi: he was *zilc parchis*, with the functions of priest of the town "marones"?, died when seventy-five? years of age'. In this inscription, we meet titles of office the precise meaning of which it is naturally impossible to determine (see, however, pp. 146 ff.). The longest biographical funerary inscription in our possession is, as we have already mentioned, the one carved on the sarcophagus of Laris Pulena (*C.I.E.* 5430). Beginning with a very full genealogical account of the dead man (going back to his great-grandfather), it lists the offices and religious honours of this important personage; but the text is unfortunately still very obscure, except for the introductory formula and a number of isolated words. It appears that Pulena was the author of books on divination (*ziχ neθśrac acasce*), had filled an important civic office in his native city of Tarquinii (*creals Tarχnalθ spureni lucairce*) and was connected with the worship of the gods Hermes, Catha, Pacha (Bacchus), and Culsu. Among the inscriptions that do not refer to individuals but to a tomb in general (a record of its foundation and ornamentation), the most notable is that belonging to the hypogeum of San Manno, near Perugia (*C.I.E.* 4116), commemorating the opening of the sepulchral chamber and its decoration with urns and other furnishings by members of the Precu family.

The inscription of the great cippus of Perugia (*C.I.E.* 4538) is particularly noteworthy. From the time it was first discovered, it has provoked the greatest interest among etruscologists, with especially keen attempts to interpret it correctly on the part of Torp, Trombetti, Ribezzo, Goldmann, and Devoto. Two distinct families are recorded in the inscription, the Velthina and the Afuna, and explicit reference is made to the tomb of the Velthina; the text also deals with borders (*tularu*), measurements (*naper*), property and cessions (*turune, ścune* = he gave, or similar phrase) and the writing of documents (*ziχuχe* = he wrote). It is now almost impossible to doubt the juridical character of the text: it probably records a purchase-and-sale transaction or a donation of funerary properties, analogous perhaps to the *iura sepulcrorum* of certain Latin inscriptions. It is possible to explain not only single words, but even whole phrases, and the general meaning of the document is understood. Many obscurities, uncertainties, and unsolved problems are still scattered widely in the text, however, and there are still insufficient data to fix an accurate and precise translation of many words (c.g. *vaχr, tezan, fuśle, falaś, spelθi*, etc.).

Votive inscriptions are the most common texts pertaining to the religious sphere. They are numerous on archaic vases and follow the classic formula:

*mini    mulvanice      Mamarce    Velχanas*
me      has dedicated  Mamarce    Velchana
(Caere: *Notizie degli Scavi*, 1937, 388),

i.e. 'Mamarce Velchana dedicated me'.

In these formulas, many are the known forms and variants of the 'perfect' of the verb *mul-* = Greek ἀνατίθημι, and, with it, other verbs with analogous meaning (e.g. *tur-, al-* 'to give, to offer'). The longer archaic votive inscriptions are usually extremely obscure, partly owing to the difficulty of separating the words from each other. Neo-Etruscan dedications found on statuettes and other objects are generally easier to decipher, though not always fully intelligible; next to the name of the dedicator, they often bear the name of the divinity to whom the offering is made. A sacral document of considerable importance is contained in a leaden lens-shaped plaque found at Magliano and spirally inscribed on either side (*C.I.E.* 5237): it contains the names of a number of gods (*Cauθa, aiseras, Marisl, Calus, Tins*) and records of funerary offerings. Despite the valiant attempts made by Torp and Trombetti to decipher it, it is still impossible to offer even a partial translation of the text. Other inscribed lead tablets in our possession consist most certainly of '*tabellae defixionum*', i.e. the consecration to infernal deities of persons whose death was ardently desired. The most notable, found at Monte Pitti, near Populonia (*C.I.E.* 5211), contains the curse of a freewoman upon a number of partly related persons, a type of document well-known to the Greek and Roman worlds. Unique, on the other hand, is the bronze model of a liver found at Piacenza, to which we have already had occasion to refer in our chapter on religion, with the names of gods, mostly abbreviated, inscribed in the appropriate spaces, presumably for the use of divinatory priests.

Finally, there remain to be considered the two longest Etruscan texts in our possession: the text of the Capua tile and that of the wrappings of the Zagreb mummy. They are the only two that appear to contain transcripts of complex ritual documents, if we except occasional brief prescriptions found inscribed upon objects. They have in common the prescriptive formulas proper to a liturgical manual for the guidance of sacrificing priests, a characteristic shared by the Umbrian texts of the Iguvine tablets and by Roman rituals as handed down in literary sources (e.g. those contained in Cato's *de agricultura*). The difference rests in the nature of the ceremonies described. The Capua tile is closely connected with funerary rites performed in the honour of infernal deities (*Šuri, Leθam, Aφe-, Calu, Larun, Fulinuśna, Natinusna(i), Tinun-, Seθum-*, etc.; but there is also mention of Tinia, Uni and, perhaps, Bacchus). Within the text, it is possible to distinguish brief sentences, rather uniform in structure, with the verb in the imperative, the indication of the offering preceded at times by a numeral and the name of the divinity in the genitive case. Of a more difficult nature, on the other hand, is the determination of the exact technical meaning (i.e. the correct translation) both of verbs expressing sacred acts (*acas-*, *picas-*, *sac-*, *tul*, *ilucu*, *apir-*, *utu*, *scuv-*, *fani-*, *nunθ*, etc.), as of the nouns describing the offerings or the things offered (*vacil*, *tartiria*, *cleva*, *riθna*, *zusleva*, *turza*, etc.). Here, for example, is how the meaning of one of the prescriptive phrases may dimly be seen:

| *Leθamsul* | | *ci* | | *tartiria* | *ci-m* |
|---|---|---|---|---|---|
| To (the god) Letham | | three | | *tartiria* | and also three |

| *cleva* | *acasri* |
|---|---|
| *cleva* | ought to be offered (or similar phrase). |

Mention is probably made in the text of officiating priests (*cipen*), and perhaps also of the family (*lavtun*) of the dead man. We have already noted the possibility that the Capua ritual may be connected to the 'salvation' sacrifices contained in the *Libri Acherontici* and remembered by some late classical authors.[10]

It is only natural that the greatest effort in the deciphering of Etruscan became concentrated on the longest text available, the *liber linteus* of Zagreb, which owing to good editing, the evenness of the script and regular word-division, the recentness of the language and the frequent recurrence of words and formulas, offers the most favourable conditions for decipherment. The text was first studied with only partial success by Lattes, Torp, Rosenberg, and Trombetti; more recently, it has become the object of repeated and more thorough probings on the part of Runes, Cortsen, Olzscha, Vetter, and the author of the present book.[11]

The hypothesis that the text contains a funerary ritual in some way connected with Egypt and the mummy on which the wrappings were found has now been definitely discarded in favour of the view that it comprises a series of prescriptions connected with partly public ceremonies regulated by a religious calendar. The most remarkable section of the text consists of a liturgical sequence, repeated, with small variants, at least four times, in honour of the 'gods' (*eiser śi-c śeu-c*), of a god *in crapśti*, and of Neptune. As in the case of the Iguvine tablets, the sacrifices were made on behalf of institutions of a religious nature (a sanctuary) or a political nature (a city or nation?), indicated by the words *śacnicleri cilθl śpureri meθlumeri-c enaś*. Less important paragraphs prescribe, more or less summarily, ceremonies in honour of other divinities (Veltha, Tin, Culsu, and Uni). Each paragraph appears to be preceded by a date (day and month): e.g. *eslem zaθrumiś acale* 'on the eighteenth of the month of Acale (June)'. Of the words found repeated in the text, some are understood with sufficient clarity and precision (e.g. *vinum* =wine; *ais, eis* = god; *fler* =sacrifice, offering; *tur* =gives; etc.). Others are understood only in a general sense and no precise translation can be given with any certainty (e.g. *zeri, vacl, faśe, eśvi, zusleva* =sacred ceremonies, offerings; *fardan, nunθen, θezin, tul*, all verbs connected with religious worship, etc.). Finally, there are a number of words on whose meaning there is much doubt and disagreement among scholars.

In this case too, the step most likely to lead to a complete decipherment of the text consists in the isolation of the syntactical units corresponding to complete phrases and the identification, as far as it is possible, of the essential elements of such phrases: subject, verb or nominal predicate and complements. To achieve this, much help is obtained from the isolation of conjunctive elements (like the enclitic particles *-c* and *-um*, and, perhaps, also the word *etnam*) and, especially, from the distinction of nominal and verbal forms and the definition of the syntactical functions of certain morphemes. In many cases, no satisfactory result can be

attained or seems attainable, but in the most favourable
instances, the structure of the Etruscan text is revealed as a
complex net of syntactical relations where only the semantic
content of the lexical elements is missing. Thus, in the phrase
*cis-um pute tul θansur haθrθi repinθi-c*, it is possible to recognize in *tul* a verb in the imperative, *θansur* as the object and
*haθrθi repinθi-c* as the complement in the locative. Occasionally, however, even the semantic values of the component
words may be arrived at with a greater or lesser degree of
accuracy, so that the general meaning of the phrase can be
made out, as if through a gradually lifting fog. Here are
some examples:

(1) Column vi, lines 9 ff.:

*zaθrumsne*                  *lusaś*      *fler*
on the twentieth (day?)   of *lus-*    the offering
*hamφisca*                  *φezeri*
that concerns the *hamphe-*?   should be made,
*laivisca*                   *lustreś*      *fler*
that concerns the *lae-*?   of the *lus-*?    offering
*vacl-tnam*                  *θezeri*
and moreover the *vacl* (libation?)    should be made.

(2) Column viii, lines 3 ff.:

*Celi*                               *huθiś zaθrumiś*
(on the month) of Celi (September),    the twenty-sixth
      *flerχva*              *Neθunsl*
(day)?    the offerings to the god   Neptune
*sucri*
should be consecrated (or established or similar verb)
*θezeri-c* . . .
and should be made . . .

(3) Column ix, lines 6 ff.:

*raθχ*       *tur*    *heχśθ*    *vinum*     *trin flere*
to the left?   give   place    the wine,   invoke (or propitiate)

*Neθunśl un*       *mlaχ*       *nunθen*
the god Neptune,?    the vow,    beseech (him)
*zuśleve . . .*
(with the offer) of one *zuśleva . . .*

(4) Column XI, lines 14 ff.:

*cntnam*       *θesan*       *fler*       *Veiveś*
and on the same   morning   an offering   to Vejove
*θezeri*       *etnam*       *ais(na) . . .*
should be made   and moreover   the divine service . . .
*huθiś zaθrumiś.*
as on the twenty-sixth (day)?

The strenuous efforts made to interpret the Zagreb text
with the help of the combinatory and the bilingual methods
are now well on the way to success. The journey is long and
difficult and the goal can only be reached in slow successive
stages. But we may confidently state that, once the major
hermeneutic problems of the Zagreb text have been solved,
the obstacles that still bar our way to the comprehension of
the other texts will become much easier, even if new
Etruscan texts of some length were to be added to our
stock, as we most ardently hope.

## Lexical Values

So as to provide a more complete picture of the state of our
knowledge of Etruscan, we now give a list of those words
whose meaning is known with certainty or near-certainty,
classified according to their semantic content:[12]

I – DEITIES AND RELIGIOUS WORSHIP:

*ais, eis* 'god'; *aiser, aisar, eiser* 'gods'; *aisuna, aisna* 'divine,
     divine service';
*fler* 'offering, sacrifice'; *flerχva* 'offerings'; *flere* 'god, deity';
*śacni, śacni-cn, śacni-tn, sacniu* sacred place or action; *śacnisa*
     'consecrate';

*zeri* sacred act;

*vacl* sacred act, perhaps 'libation';

θez, θezi, θezin, θezine, θezince, θezeri 'to make (an offering)';

*mula, muli, mulu, mulune, muluni, mulunice, mulvanice, mulvenice, mulvunce, muluvanice,* etc. 'to dedicate'; *mulaχ, mlaχ* 'vow, anathema';

    *tur, tura, ture, turi, turu, turune, turce, turuce, turunce* 'to give'; *turza* 'gift'?

    *al, ale, alce, alice, aliqu* 'to give'; *alpan, alpnu* 'gift'?

*acas, acasa, acasce, acasri* 'to do, to give';

*nunθ, nunθen, nunθene, nundenθ* 'to beseech (with an offering)';

*cver* 'gift';

*trutnut, trutnvt* 'divinatory priest, soothsayer'?

*netśvis* 'haruspex'; *ziχ neθśrac* '*liber haruspicinus*'?

*frontac* '*fulguriator*';

*cletram* 'trolley for offerings' (cf. Umbrian *kletra*).

## 2 – THE FUNERARY WORLD:

θaur, θaura 'tomb'; θaurχ 'funerary';

*suθi, śuθi* 'tomb' (prop. =Lat. *sedes*): *śuθi neśl, śuθi zivas, śuθi hinθiu* 'abode of the dead =tomb'; *śuθina* 'funerary';

*cela* 'cell';

*munisule-, munsle, munθ,* 'repository, *loculus*';

*murś* 'sarcophagus, urn';

*mutna, mutana* 'sarcophagus';

*cesu, ceseθce* 'to lie';

*lupu, lupuce* 'to die';

*leine* 'to die'?;

*hinθial* 'soul'; *hinθiu* 'of the souls';

*φersu* 'mask'.

## 3 – MAN, FAMILY RELATIONSHIPS:

*clan* 'son';

*śec, seχ,* 'daughter';

*pui, puia* 'wife';

*ati, atiu* 'mother';

*tuśurθir* 'married couple';

*ati nacna* 'grandmother'?;

*papa* 'grandfather'?;

*papacs, papals* 'grandson'?;

*nefiś, nefts* 'nephew';

*prumaθs, prumts* 'great-nephew'.

### 4 – MAN, LIFE AND ACTIONS:

*ama, ame, amce* 'to be';

*svalce, svalas, svalθas* 'to live';

*ar, arθ, ara, araś, arce* 'to do';

*caru, carsi, caresri, cerine, ceriχu, cerχunce* 'to make, to build'; *cerur* 'pottery'?;

*śaθe, śaθena, śaθene, śaθas, setirune* 'to establish';

*suθ, sutanaś, suθce* 'to place, to stand'?;

*heci, heχśθ, heczri, hecce, hecśce* 'to put, to do';

*teśamsa* 'to heal'; *tesinθ* 'healer';

*ziχuχ, ziχne, ziχuχe, ziχunce* 'to write'; *ziχ* 'written, book'.

### 5 – POLITICAL AND SOCIAL ORGANIZATION

*lautn, lavtn* 'family, gens'; *lautni* 'gentilitial';

*lautni* 'freeman'; *lautniθa* 'freewoman';

*etera* 'servant' or member of the lower classes; *eterau* 'relating to the *etera*';

*śuplu* (Lat. *subulo*) 'piper';

*θanasa* 'actor';

★*θruna* (Hesychius δροῦνα) 'power, sovereignty';

★*lauχume* (Lat. *lucumo*) 'king, prince'; *lucairce* 'to fill the office of *lucumo*'?;

*zilc, zilχ, zilaθ* magistrature, probably = 'praetor'; *zilaθ meχl rasnal* 'praetor Etruriae'?; *zil(a)χnu, zilaχnθaś, zilaχn(u)ce* 'to be a *zilath*';

*maru, marunu, marniu, marunuχ* magistrature = Umbrian

maro; marunuχva 'belonging to the *maru*'; marunu,
marvaś 'to be a *maru*';

camθi magistrature; canθe, canθce 'to be a *camθi*';

cepen, eisnevc, ceχase, celu priestly titles;

macstrevc 'magister';

tenve, tenine, tenu, tenθas, tence 'to have the functions of . . .';

spur, śpur 'city, *populus*'; spureni, spurana 'civic';

tudθi, tuθiu 'state'?;

meχl, meθlum 'nation, league'?; meχl rasnal 'Etruria'?;

raśna (Dionysius *Ρασέννα*) 'Etruscan, Etruria';

rumaχ 'Roman'.

## 6 – NATURE, HOUSEHOLD OBJECTS AND BUILDINGS:

\*anθa- (Hesychius ἄνδας, ἄντας) 'north-wind, eagle';

\*arac (Hesychius ἄρακος) 'sparrow-hawk';

\*arim- (Strabo ἄριμος) 'monkey';

\*capu 'falcon';

hiuls 'screech-owl'?;

\*θamna (Hesychius δάμνος) 'horse';

θevru 'bull';

leu 'lion';

vinum 'wine';

verse 'fire'?; versie 'concerning fire'?;

zamaθi 'golden'?; zana 'precious'?;

cape, capi names of vases;

culiχna (Greek χυλίχνη) 'cup';

cupe, χupe 'cup';

θapna 'cup';

leχtumuza (Greek λέχυθος) 'small pitcher';

pruχum, pruχś, prucuna (Greek πρόχους) 'pitcher';

putere, putiza (Greek ποτήρ) name of vase;

qutun, qutum (Greek κώθω) name of vase;

aθre part of building, 'atrium', '*aedes*'?;

θamce 'has built';

tular, tularu 'border, limit';

*naper* measure: 'feet'?;
*sren* 'figure'; *śrenχve* 'figured'?.

## 7 – TIME AND ITS DIVISIONS:

*tin* 'day';
*θesan* 'morning, day';
*tivr* 'months';
*avil* 'year, years';
*ril* 'at the age of . . .';
*\*velχitna*? (*Velcitanus*) 'March';
*ampiles* 'May';
*acale* (*Aclus*) 'June';
*θucte* name of a month?;
*\*t(u)rane*? (*Traneus*) 'July';
*\*hermie*? (*Ermius*) 'August';
*celi* (*Coelius*) 'September'.

## NOTES

1. In *American Journal of Philology*, 1936, pp. 261 ff.

2. On the whole question of the origin of the Etruscan alphabet, see G. Buonamici, *Epigrafia etrusca*, pp. 133 ff., with bibliography; see also M. Guarducci, in *Studi Etruschi*, XIV, 1940, pp. 281 ff., and R. Carpenter, in *American Journal of Archaeology*, XLIX, 1945, pp. 452 ff.

3. The exceptional presence of *o* in *frontac* (= *fulguriator*) in the bi-lingual inscription of Pesaro (C.I.I. 69) may be explained by the fact that this very late inscription belongs to the border region of Etruria.

4. The Latin use of the letter *c*, derived from Greek γ, is certainly due to Etruscan influence. In archaic times there probably also existed small differences in the pronunciation of the letters, *c*, *q*, and *k*, as attested by their use with the different vowels: *c* was normally followed by the front vowels *i* and *e*, *k* by the middle vowel *a*, and *q* by the back vowel *u*.

5. E. Vetter, in *Glotta*, XXIV, pp. 114 ff.; XXVII, pp. 157 ff.; G. Buonamici, *L'interpunzione sillabica*, etc., in *Studi Etruschi*, XVI, 1942, pp. 263 ff.; F. Slotty, *Beiträge zur Etruskologie*, I, *Silbenpunktierung und Silbenbildung im Altetruskischen*, 1952. The latter author tends to

regard the phenomenon as due to purely phonetic causes, as a mark of syllabic division; objections to this view will be found in K. Olzscha, in *Gnomon*, 1953, pp. 271 ff.; M. Pallottino, in *Studi Etruschi*, XXII, 1952–3, pp. 478 ff.

6. S. P. Cortsen, in *Glotta*, XXVI, 1937, pp. 10 ff.

7. See K. Olzscha, in *Neue Jahrbücher für Wissenschaft und Jugend-bildung*, 1936, p. 105.

8. K. Olzscha, *Interpretation der Agramer Mumienbinde*, 1939, pp. 103 ff.; see also V. Pisani, who, in *Archivio Glottologico*, XXXIV, 1942, pp. 116 ff., prefers to speak of an 'intransitive' nature of the Etruscan verb.

9. On the subjects of Etruscan phonetics and m orphology, see also M. Pallottino, *Elementi di lingua etrusca*, 1936, with the modifications required by recent progress in the science. H. L. Stoltenberg's recent synthesis on Etruscan grammatical structure, *Etruskische Sprachlehre mit vollständigem Wörterbuch*, should be consulted with care.

10. See F. Ribezzo, in *La Parola del Passato*, I, 1946, pp. 286 ff.; M. Pallottino, *Sulla lettura e sul contenuto della grande iscrizione di Capua*, in *Studi Etruschi*, XX, 1948–9, pp. 159 ff.

11. Cf. *Studi Etruschi*, vols. VI ff.; E. Vetter, *Etruskische Wort-deutungen*, I, 1937; K. Olzscha, *Interpretation der Agramer Mumienbinde*, 1939, and *Glotta*, XXXI, 1948, pp. 105 ff.; XXXII, 1953, pp. 283 ff.

12. See Müller-Deecke, *Die Etrusker*, 1871, II, pp. 508 ff.; S. P. Cortsen, *Vocabulorum etruscorum interpretatio*, in *Nord. Tidsskrift f. filol. fjerderæke*, VI, 1917, pp. 165 ff.; A. Trombetti, *La lingua etrusca*, 1928, pp. 211 ff.; M. Pallottino, *Elementi di lingua etrusca*, 1936, pp. 87 ff.; E. Vetter, *Etruskische Wortdeutungen*, I, 1937; H. L. Stoltenberg, *Etruskische Sprachlehre mit vollständigem Wörterbuch*, 1950 (with reservations as to many of the proposed translations).

Works on particular aspects of Etruscan studies will be found
listed in the notes to the relevant chapters of this book.

*Acts of the 1st International Congress of Etruscan Studies*, Rinascimento
del Libro, Florence 1928.

BUONAMICI, G., *Epigrafia etrusca*, Rinascimento del Libro, Florence
1931.

DENNIS, G., *Cities and Cemeteries of Etruria*, London 1883 (3rd ed.);
also in Everyman's Library.

DUCATI, P., *Etruria antica*, 2 vols., Paravia 1927.

DUCATI, P., *Storia dell'arte etrusca*, 2 vols., Rinascimento del Libro,
Florence 1927.

DUCATI, P., *Le problème étrusque*, Leroux, Paris 1928.

GIGLIOLI, G. Q., *L'arte etrusca*, Treves, Milan 1935.

HÜLSEN, C., *Etruria;* THULIN, C., *Etrusca;* KÖRTE, G., *Etrusker;*
SKUTSCH, F., *Etruskische Sprache*, in *Paulys Real-Encyclopädie* by
WISSOWA, G., VII, 1907, cols. 720 ff.

LOPES PEGNA, M., *Saggio di bibliografia etrusca*, Olschki, Florence
1953 (to be consulted with care).

MÜLLER, K. O. and DEECKE, W., *Die Etrusker*, 2 vols., Heitz, Stütt-
gart 1877.

NEPPI MODONA, A., *A Guide to Etruscan Antiquities*, Florence 1954.

NOGARA, B., *Gli Etruschi e la loro civiltà*, Hoepli, Milan 1934.

PALLOTTINO, M., *Elementi di lingua etrusca*, Rinascimento del Libro,
Florence 1936.

PALLOTTINO, M., *Gli Etruschi*, Colombo, Rome 1940 (2nd ed.).

PALLOTTINO, M., *L'origine degli Etruschi*, Tumminelli, Rome 1947.

PARETI, L., *Le origine etrusche*, Bemporad, Florence 1926.

PARETI, L., *Etruschi: Storia;* DEVOTO, G., *Lingua;* NEPPI MODONA,
A., *Religione;* DUCATI, P., *Archeologia e arte;* CESANO, S.L.,
*Numismatica*, in *Enciclopedia Italiana*, XIV, 1932, pp. 510 ff.

PONTRANDOLFI, G., *Gli Etruschi e la loro lingua*, Barbèra, Florence
1909.

RENARD, M., *Initiation à l'étruscologie*, Lebègue, Brussels 1941.

RENARD, M., *La question étrusque*, in *L'antiquité classique*, Brussels 1940.

SOLARI, A., *Topografia storica dell'Etruria*, I–IV, Spoerri, Pisa 1915–20.

SOLARI, A., *La vita pubblica e privata degli Etruschi*, Rinascimento del Libro, Florence 1928.

TROMBETTI, A., *La lingua etrusca*, Rinascimento del Libro, Florence 1928.

# INDEXES

## 1. HISTORICAL AND GEOGRAPHICAL INDEX

*(The names Etruria, Etruscans, and Tuscany will not be found listed in this index. Numbers in italic refer to plates)*

## 2. INDEX OF ANCIENT AUTHORS

# 3. INDEX OF MODERN AUTHORS

## Malden'

The doorway that had been jammed shut by the demon's bulk collapsed in front of him, its stones shattered by the creature's thrashing. Suddenly the way back to the moonlit corridor was open—and Malden was given a chance at survival.

He had nearly squandered it. Because even as the tower was collapsing over his head, when the stone was shrieking and roaring and smashing all around him, he had heard a voice calling him. A voice of authority that demanded respect. A voice that could have commanded nations.

*Thief*, the voice had said. And that was all. It had not been his ears that heard the voice, of that he was certain. Though it had sounded exactly like someone shouting just behind him, he knew the voice was inside his head.

He had turned away from escape and safety to see who had spoken. It was not the demon—the thing had no voice, and even if it could speak, it would not have sounded like that. It was a human voice. Which meant, absurd as it might sound, that it was the crown that spoke.

The simple golden coronet of the Burgrave.

Books by David Chandler

*The Ancient Blades Trilogy*
DEN OF THIEVES: BOOK ONE
A THIEF IN THE NIGHT: BOOK TWO
HONOR AMONG THIEVES: BOOK THREE

# DEN
## OF THIEVES

### THE ANCIENT BLADES TRILOGY:
### BOOK ONE

# DAVID CHANDLER

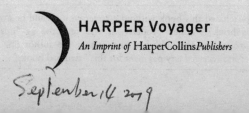

**HARPER Voyager**

*An Imprint of HarperCollinsPublishers*

September 14 2019

**HARPER Voyager**
*An Imprint of HarperCollinsPublishers*
10 East 53rd Street
New York, New York 10022-5299

Copyright © 2011 by David Wellington
Excerpts from *A Thief in the Night* and *Honor Among Thieves* copyright © 2011 by David Wellington
Cover art by Richard Jones
ISBN 978-0-06-202124-3
**www.harpervoyagerbooks.com**

First Harper Voyager mass market printing: August 2011

Harper Voyager and ⟩ is a trademark of HCP LLC.

Printed in the U.S.A.

10 9 8 7 6 5 4 3

*For F.L., M.M., and R.E.H., the Grand Masters*

# Acknowledgments

I didn't think you would ever see this book. I wrote it for myself, for therapy, for fun. I wrote it intending to put it in a desk drawer (well, the back of my hard drive) and forget about it. Nobody else was ever supposed to see it, but Alex Lencicki stood outside my cave shouting insults and dire threats until I threw some pages at him to make him go away. After that it was out of my hands. Russell Galen saw it next, and he beat me over the head with a club until I let go of the manuscript. Diana Gill and Will Hinton took it from there and made it into something better, something I'm proud to show the world. Without these people it could never have happened, and I'm very grateful.

DAVID CHANDLER
New York City, 2011

THE
ASHES

SWAMPWALL

PARKWALL

SKAIT RIVER

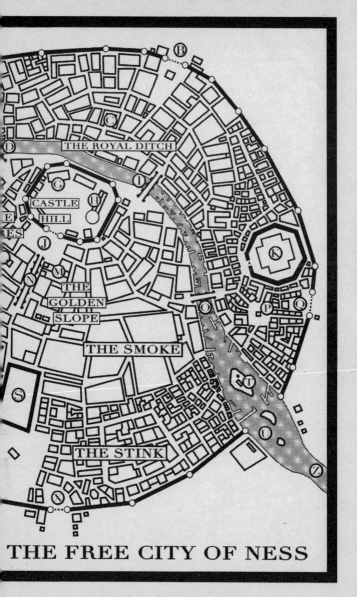

THE FREE CITY OF NESS

# DEN
## OF THIEVES

# PROLOGUE

Nearly one hundred thousand people lived in the Free City of Ness, stuffed like rats in a sack too small to contain them all. The city was less than a mile across and filled every cranny of the hill encircled by its high defensive wall. At midnight, seen from a hill two miles to the north, it was the only light in the nighttime landscape, a bright ember smoldering in the midst of dark fields that rolled to the horizon. It looked, frankly, like all it needed was one good gust of wind to stir it up into a great whoosh of flame.

Bikker grinned to see it, though he knew it was only a trick of perspective. He was a giant of a man with a wild, coarse beard and a magic sword on his belt. He did not know how the other two members of the cabal felt, but for himself, he'd love to watch the Free City of Ness burn.

The lights he saw came from a thousand windows and the forges of a hundred workshops and manufactories. The city supplied the kingdom of Skrae with all the iron and steel it needed, most of the leather goods, and an endless river of spoons and buckles, as well as lanterns and combs made of horn. The guilds worked through the night, every night, filling the endless demand. Streamers of smoke rose from every chimney, rising like boiling columns of darkness that obliterated the stars, while half the windows in the city were illuminated by burning candles as an army of scribes, clerks, and accounters scratched at their ledger books.

On the near side of the river, gambling houses blazed with light, while whores marched up and down long avenues carrying lanterns to attract passersbys. Half the city, it seemed, was still awake. "D'you suppose any of 'em know what's coming?" Bikker asked.

"For the sake of our scheme, I pray they do not," his

employer said. Bikker had never seen the man. Even now
the mastermind of the cabal was ensconced in a darkened
carriage pulled by two white horses that pawed at the turf.
The horses bore no brands or marks, and the driver wore
no livery. The coach might have belonged to any number of
fine houses—all its insignia had been removed.

A slender white hand emerged from a window of the
coach, holding a purse of gold by its strings. Bikker took the
payment—the latest of many such—and shoved it inside his
chain mail shirt. "For your sake, I advise sealed lips."

"Don't worry, I can be discreet when I choose," Bikker
said with a laugh. "Though what a juicy tale I could tell!
In a month the city will be torn in half, and the streets will
be lined with the dead. How many lights do you think will
show then? And no one will ever know what part I played
in it all."

"No, they will not," the third member of the cabal said.
Bikker turned to face Hazoth, whose visage was covered
in a thick veil of black crepe. As much as Bikker disliked
this business of unseen associates, he supposed he was glad
for that veil. It was not good to look on the naked face of a
sorcerer. "If you cannot maintain silence, I can enforce it on
you. Don't forget your place. Your part in this is minimal."

Bikker shrugged. He knew that perfectly well. He'd been
hired to perform a variety of small services, but mostly
because he was probably the only person in the city who
could stop these two, if he so chose. When he'd agreed to
meet with them—and then agreed to their tentative, secre-
tive offer—they'd been comically grateful. His reputation
preceded him, and they didn't dare offend his vanity. But
they never truly let him forget that he was their lackey. "I do
what I'm told . . . when I'm paid. Gold has a way of stifling
the tongue. I know better than to ask of him," Bikker said,
jutting one thumb toward the occupant of the coach, "but
what are you getting out of this, wizard? What could he pay
you that you can't just magic up on your own?"

"I've agreed to turn a blind eye to Hazoth's . . . experiments," the coach's occupant said, "once I rule the city.
Does that trouble you?"

There had been a time when that would have given Bikker pause, indeed. Sorcerers could be dangerous. Hazoth stank of brimstone and the pit, and he was capable of things mortal men should never try. Sometimes sorcerers made mistakes and the whole world paid. The sword at Bikker's side was a testament to how high the price had once been— it was sworn to the defense of the realm against the demons a sorcerer could summon up but couldn't always control.

There'd been a time when Bikker was sworn to that same defense. But the world had changed. Times had changed. He too had changed. Any belief he'd had in nobility or service was ground down by a mill wheel that moved very slowly, but never stopped. Once, he'd been a champion of human-kind.

Now he only shrugged. He peered down at the city. From here, it might have been a nest of termites clambering over themselves and their dung heap. "Slaughter 'em all. Feed 'em to your pets, Hazoth, if you like! By then I'll be far enough away not to care."

"Indeed. The gold in that purse will take you far. And there is more to come, once you have fulfilled your part of our design. You know the next step?"

"Oh, aye," Bikker said. He spat in the direction of the city as if he would put out all those fires with one gob. "Next thing to do is find our unwitting fourth." A fool was required, someone who would have no idea what he was doing. Without such a pawn, the plan could go nowhere. "I need to scare us up a thief."

# PART I

# A Thief's Ransom

# CHAPTER ONE

There were evil little things skulking in the shadows, their eyes very bright in the gloom. In every burned-out shell of an old house, Malden could hear their tiny footsteps and the occasional whisper. No lights at all showed in this part of town, and the fog hid both moon and stars. The lantern Malden carried could paint a crumbling wall with yellow light, or show him where the cobblestones had been pried up and deep pools of mud awaited an unwary step. It could not, however, pierce the darkness that coiled inside the ruined houses and stables, nor show who was watching him so intently.

He didn't like this.

He didn't like the time of the meeting, an hour past midnight. He did not like the location: down by the wall, near the river gate, in the wasteland called the Ashes. In the same year he was born this whole district had been consumed by the Seven Day Fire. Because the doss-houses and knackeries down here belonged to the poorest of the poor, no effort was made since then to rebuild or even to tear down the gutted remains. No one lived here if they had any choice, and the Ashes had been abandoned to decay. Now limp weeds were sprouting from between the forgotten cobbles, while vines strangled the fallen roof timbers or slowly chewed on the ancient smoke-damaged bricks. Eventually nature would reclaim this zone entirely, and Malden, who had never set foot outside the city since he was born, found this distinctly uncomfortable—the concept that part of the city itself, which was his whole notion of permanence, could rot and die and be effaced.

Behind him something dashed across a forgotten street. He whirled to catch it with his light. Despite well-honed reflexes he was still not quick enough to see what it was, only that it disappeared through the gaping hole where a window had once looked out on the street. His hand went to the bodkin he kept at his hip but he dared not draw it. You never showed your weapon until you were ready to strike.

Malden stopped where he was and tried to prepare. If an attack was coming, it would come quickly, and being braced for it would make all the difference. His eyes showed him little—the scorched beams and the soot-stained street were all of a color by his little light. So he turned to his other senses in his search for signs. He heard nothing but the creaking of old, strained wood, the sifting of ash. He could smell the smoke of the fire, so many years gone.

Behind him he heard soft footsteps. The sound of bare feet slapping against charred timber. Only for a moment, before the sound stopped and he was left in silence again. Silence so profound—and so rare in the clamoring city. It sounded like a roaring in his ears.

He turned slowly on his heel, scanning the empty door frames on every side, the twisting little roads that curled between the buildings. He longed to get his back against something solid. There was a brick building up ahead, or at least the husk of one. Its roof was gone and one wall had come down. The other three still stood, however, and if he could get inside them, at least he would not have to worry about being attacked from behind. He hurried forward, his lantern held high—and then a noise from quite close by stopped him in his tracks.

One of the watchers had stepped out into the street behind him. He heard its feet splashing in a puddle. This time, however, it did not rush off as he turned to see it. This time it held its ground.

Even before he completed his turn his hand was on the hilt of his knife. He hesitated to draw, however, when he saw the creature he faced. It was a child, a girl no more than seven years old. She wore a stained shift of homespun and had rags wrapped around her feet in place of shoes. She also had a hammer clutched before her in both hands. Her eyes stayed on his face and they did not blink.

Malden spread his own hands wide, showing her they were empty. He took a step toward her, and when she did not flee, he took another. He reached down toward her—

—and suddenly the street was full of ragged children. They seemed to emerge from the mist as if generated spontaneously from the cold and the damp, like fungus from a rotting log. They were of both sexes, and varied in apparent age, but were dressed all alike in torn shirts and tunics too big for their skinny frames. And they all held makeshift weapons. One had a carpenter's saw. Another held a cobbler's awl. Bits of wood with protruding nails. A length of iron chain. One of them, a boy older than the rest, had a woodsman's hatchet that he held down against his thigh as if he knew how to use it.

A gang of orphans, Malden thought. A band of urchins joined together in their poverty to waylay any traveler foolish enough to come here by night. A ragged little army. There were dozens of them, and though he was certain he could best even the older boy in a fair fight, he could see in their eyes they held no concept of fairness or justice, such things as impossible and mythical in their experience as the continents the sages claimed lay beyond the sea. They would be on him in a heap, slashing and hitting and pounding and mauling him until he was dead. They would offer no quarter or mercy.

They were waiting for him to make the first move. To try to run, or fight. Not because they were afraid to attack, but because they wanted him to make some mistake, to calculate the odds incorrectly. They would take advantage of whatever weakness he showed and make short work of him.

Malden licked his lips and turned slowly this way and that, looking for an opening. There was no way out, it seemed. Unless . . . unless there was another reason for their silent waiting, for their constant unblinking stares.

"You want some password or sign," he said, "but all I have is this." He reached inside his cloak. They moved toward him, closing the circle they formed around him. They were ready to attack at the first sign of aggression. But he was not reaching for his bodkin. Instead his nimble fingers reached into his purse and drew out the scrap of parchment that had beckoned him to this dreadful place at this beastly time. He unfolded it carefully—the old paper cracked down the middle but he held the pieces together—and showed them the message he had received:

> This house is ONE OF OURS,
> and its owner under my protection.
> At next *Witching Hour* come ALONE
> to the Ashes hard by Westwall—or
> you're DEAD before next *Dawn*.

"I found it tacked to the windowsill of a house I was in the process of burgling. This is what you want to see, yes?"

Could they read it? he wondered? But no, of course they couldn't. It was foolish to think these children had ever been tutored or given even religious education. And yet they seemed entranced by the brief missive. Ah, he thought. They recognize the signature, a crude drawing of a heart transfixed by a key.

He did not know what that sign meant, not for certain, but its power on these children was intriguing. One by one they came close and touched the paper, as superstitious merchants will sometimes touch a statue of the Lady before sitting down to some tricky negotiation. When they had seen the sign for themselves and perhaps decided it was no forgery, they filed away, back into the darkness. All except the girl with the hammer, the first one he'd seen. She still held his eyes with her own. When they two were alone again, she finally broke his gaze and started walking toward the brick ruin he'd thought to shelter in. She led him right up to a doorway and then gestured inside with one hand. Then she made a perfect curtsy and ran off to join the others.

Clearly this was the place. Holding the scrap of parchment before him like a talisman, Malden stepped through the door.

# CHAPTER TWO

Inside the ruined building three old men dressed in rags sat on a long wooden box. Two of them had long white beards, while the other was bald and clean-shaven. Age had withered their muscles but their eyes glinted with cunning—no dotards, these. Malden had the sense there was a great deal more to them than what he saw.

He nodded to the men but did not speak yet. First he studied the interior of the building—its fallen and shattered roof beams, the piles of scorched plaster in the corners. The floor was covered in a thick layer of debris. There did not seem to be anywhere an assassin could hide, though between the lack of light and the tendrils of mist that coiled around his lantern, it was hard to be sure.

"What if I had brought the city watch with me?" Malden asked, because he felt there was no need for polite small talk. He had, after all, been threatened with death.

The bald man smiled wickedly. "We would not be here. You would have never found this place. And before morning your throat would be slit."

Malden nodded in understanding. "This isn't a bad setup. The children out there keep an eye on the place for you, right? Make sure nobody gets in uninvited. I'm guessing that even now if I tried something, you'd be ready for it."

One of the whitebeards raised a long, crooked finger and pointed into the air. With his eyes, Malden followed the direction of the finger until he could just see a spire looming out of the mist two blocks away. Most likely it had been the steeple of the local church, made of stone, so it survived the fire. While he was staring through the gloom, something whistled past his cheek and slammed into a charred wooden plank behind him. He glanced sideways and saw the shaft of an arrow there, still quivering. The arrow was as long as his arm and it had struck the wood so hard the iron point was completely embedded.

For a while after that Malden did not breathe. His lungs clamped shut and every muscle in his body went rigid. He waited patiently for the next arrow, the one that would find his guts or his throat. But it did not come.

He understood rationally what had happened, and why. The arrow was a message—a reminder that here not all was what it seemed, and that he was still in mortal danger. It was not a reminder he'd truly needed.

"I'll pay you the courtesy of noticing you didn't flinch," the whitebeard said. "That's good, lad. Very good."

Malden gave him a brief bow, once he could move and breathe again. "I think I understand where I am. I'm not sure who you three are, but I assume you aren't the ones I'm supposed to meet. Yet you can show me the way to my meeting. You're the guardians of the doorway, yes? And more than that, certainly."

The bald one touched his chest. "I am called 'Levenfingers. These," he said, gesturing at the whitebeards, "are Loophole and Lockjaw."

"Well met," Malden said. "Wait. Wait . . . I've heard of him, of Loophole. It was a little before my time, but they still tell the story up in the Stink. If you're the same man, then you got that name when you robbed the garrison house up by the palace. Is it true that you climbed in through an arrow slit, fifty feet up the curtain wall?"

Loophole wheezed as he laughed. "Another time, I'll tell ye all, if you wish. Assuming you survive tonight."

Malden nodded. "I'd be honored. And you—'Levenfingers—how'd you come by that name, if I might ask?"

"I was the king of the pickpockets in my day," the bald man said with obvious pride. "They used to say no man with ten fingers could be so dab at it, so I must have eleven." He held up his hands, which were gnarled and spotted with age but otherwise perfectly normal. "Just a nickname."

Malden smiled at the third man, expecting an explanation of his name. It was Loophole who gave it, however.

"Lockjaw? He holds his secrets well, that's why. Never gives anything away for free."

"Does he ever speak?"

"Not to the likes of you," Lockjaw grumbled, in a hollow voice like a floorboard creaking in an empty house. "Not yet."

"I see," Malden said. He was impressed despite himself. Thievery was a dangerous occupation. If you didn't die in some trap or under the spear of some overzealous guard, the law was always waiting. In the Free City of Ness, lifting even a copper penny from some fat merchant's purse was punishable by hanging. These three men, daring rogues in their day, notorious for grand exploits, had survived long enough to grow old without being caught. That must mean they were very, very good in their prime. Malden wondered what they could teach him. Of course, there was more pressing business at hand. "I was called here to meet with someone."

"Are you ready for your audience with our boss, then?"

"I suppose I'd better be," Malden said.

Lockjaw grunted out a noise that might have been a laugh. The three of them stood up in unison, then moved aside to let Malden have a better look at the box they'd been sitting on. It was a coffin made of plain wood, tapering in width at both ends. 'Levenfingers lifted its lid and Loophole gestured for Malden to get inside.

Malden had never thought himself squeamish or, worse, superstitious. Yet a cold dread gripped his vitals at the thought of lying down in the coffin. "Only a fool or a dead man would get in there happily," he said.

"If you don't get in," Loophole told him, "you're both, anyway."

Malden snuffed out the flame of his lantern, then placed it carefully on the ground. There would be no room for it. Then he clambered inside what, he assured himself, was truly no more fearful than a packing crate. The lid was closed and then nailed shut. He tried not to breathe too hard. He'd come this far, he told himself. He must see what would happen next.

# CHAPTER THREE

The darkness inside the box was a solid thing, as if the air had turned to obsidian all around him. All sounds that came through the wood were muffled and thick. Malden hoped very much he would be let out soon. The same moment the lid was hammered shut, he found that he had trouble breathing inside—perhaps it was just his mind playing tricks on him, but it seemed there was not enough air in the coffin to support his life. He began to panic, to lose control of his faculties. It took a true effort of will to calm down and resign himself to what was happening.

One fact alone sustained him, one thing he was relatively sure of. The master of this place had already had many chances to kill him. Which meant that, for whatever reason and however temporarily, he was expected to survive this.

That kept most of the panic at bay. The fear tarried longer.

The box was lifted—the three oldsters must be stronger than they looked, or they had help—and carried a short distance before it was lowered again, foot end first, into some variety of chute. For a moment Malden had the sense of rapid downward movement, and then the box struck a solid surface very hard, hard enough to push all the air out of his lungs. Not knowing what to expect, he forced himself not to inhale again.

His body protested and he started to gasp for air but he managed to hold his breath a moment longer. The only way to determine where he'd ended up was by listening to his surroundings. Though the sounds that came to him were distorted by the wooden box, he was able to make out a few things. He could hear voices, people laughing among themselves. A woman's giggle. So he was not alone.

Then there was a knock on the lid of the coffin, and he

sucked in air at last. "Anyone home?" someone asked, the voice thick with mockery.

"Let yourself in and have a look around the place," Malden replied.

The owner of the voice laughed wickedly but said no more.

It did not take Malden long to realize no one would come to release him from the coffin—that he would have to find his own way out. He was able to draw his bodkin easily enough, but then found it difficult to maneuver it within the coffin without stabbing himself. It was not much of a weapon, a triangular piece of iron that tapered to a sharp point. By law it was the largest knife he was allowed to own, the blade no longer than his hand from the ball of his thumb to the tip of his middle finger. It had no edge, just the point, and was only good for stabbing in a fight. But then, he wasn't a violent man by nature, and the bodkin was more than it appeared to be. He'd found many uses for it in the past, and killing had so far not been one of them. It served him well as he jabbed the point into the thin seam between box and lid. Without leverage it took some time to pry the lid upward, but when he did he was rewarded by a thin stream of light and—much more blessedly—a new breath of air.

The nails in the lid shrieked as he worked to free himself. Eventually he had the lid open enough to push it outward with his hands. Returning the knife to its sheath, he sat up and looked around.

The room was broad but low, its ceiling propped up on stout beams so it looked not unlike a mine shaft. The walls were bare, close-packed earth that glistened with condensation. The place was well lit by more than a dozen candles, some backed by reflectors of copper that added a rosy tint to the light. On a divan on one side of the room sat a man in a leather jerkin and particolored hose. He had the thick shoulders of a warrior, not a thief. Upon his lap was a red-headed girl with her bodice unlaced. She laughed prettily as he tickled her. Neither of them spared him a glance. In another corner of the room a group of men in colorless cloaks were throwing dice against a wall and cheering or groaning the result.

The final occupant of the room was a dwarf who might have been the epitome of his people. Dwarves were rare in Ness—rare anywhere in Skrae—but enough of them had come down from their northern kingdom, looking for work, that Malden was jaded to their presence. They were master craftsmen, brilliant artificers who could make better tools and finer wares than any human artisan. Dwarves alone knew the secret of making proper steel and thus were highly prized and given special rights wherever they turned up in human lands. Like all his folk, this one was skinny, perhaps four feet tall, and his flesh was as white as the belly of a fish. He had a wild mop of filthy black hair and a tangled beard. He was dressed only in leather breeches and was sewing pieces of metal into a silk glove. He glanced up briefly at Malden, then shook his head and went back to work.

Malden looked away and turned in a slow circle to make sure he'd seen all of the room. He did not want to miss some hidden threat, not now. Directly behind him, he saw the chute through which he had descended, a construction of thin hammered tin. It had been smeared with brown grease that glimmered dully in the candlelight. He could probably get back up that way, given enough time—and assuming no one tried to stop him.

The man on the couch had a sword at his hip, and Malden did not doubt that the others were armed as well. Someone, he figured, would try to stop him. After all, he'd been summoned here for a reason. If he tried to run away now he would be thwarting that purpose. Based on what the oldsters had said aboveground, he would not be allowed to escape in one piece.

A little stiffly, Malden climbed out of the coffin and regained his feet. He dusted himself off and strode over to the divan, intent on learning what he was expected to do next. The bravo on the divan looked up expectantly. "You must have made an impression on the three masters above," he said. Malden instantly recognized his voice as the one that had spoken to him when he was inside the coffin.

"Oh?" he asked.

"They let you keep your clothes and that knife at your belt. Sometimes the ones they send down here come naked."

"I'm quite personable when you get to know me," Malden said. "Now, if you'd be so kind as to direct me to your master? I'm told he wishes to speak with me."

The bravo's eyebrows drew together. "And what makes you think the master of this place is not here, right before you?"

Malden bowed in apology. "Organization like this, in such a secret place, leads me to believe only one man in the Free City might be master here. A man I know only by reputation, but that reputation leads me to believe certain things about him. I doubt he's one of these gamblers, who kneel and dice for pennies. I am relatively certain he is no dwarf, and she—well . . ." Malden searched his memory. "Her name is Rhona. She's one of Madam Herwig's girls, from the House of Sighs up on the Royal Ditch." The girl looked up at him with wide eyes, but he merely smiled at her in return. There were very few harlots in the city who Malden could not recognize on sight. "As for yourself, well, I do not think you are the chief here. While you cut a striking figure, sir, I will not believe you if you say your name is Cutbill."

At the sound of the name everyone in the room glanced over their shoulder. Even the bravo and his playmate frowned. Yet in a moment all concerns were forgotten again and the bravo laughed boisterously, which got the girl giggling as well. "You're smarter than we credited," he said.

"Yet not so arrogant in that wisdom, as to have avoided this summons in the first place," Malden said.

The bravo picked the girl up in his strong arms and put her back down on the divan as he rose and came bounding over to take Malden's hand. "I'm Bellard. I serve the one you named on those occasions when subtlety has failed."

"Well met. I'm called Malden."

Bellard laughed again. "Oh, I know your name all right. And you're correct, the master is waiting on your pleasure. He's just through there." Bellard made a sweeping gesture toward the far wall, where a stained curtain hung.

"So I just go through there, do I?" Malden asked.

The bravo smiled. "If you can, you're well on your way."

Malden bowed and headed to the curtain. Twitching it back, he found a wide door set into the wall, made of stout oak with massive iron hinges. A thick iron ring would open it. There was just one problem. A thick bar of iron passed through the ring and was anchored in either wall. It was held shut by the largest padlock he had ever seen.

# CHAPTER FOUR

Well. He knew what to do with locks.

Malden drew his bodkin and held it by the blade. The grip was formed of a very long piece of stout cord wrapped countless times around the hilt, ostensibly to create a more comfortable handle for the weapon. In fact the cord served far less obvious purposes. He picked at it until one end came free, then spooled it out with a practiced motion. Woven into the cord were his tools: picks, rakes, hooks, and a pair of tension wrenches. Two different skeleton keys for different size locks. These tiny pieces of steel were the most valuable things Malden owned, worth far more than their weight in gold. Worth his life if he were ever caught with them, for they had no legal use—their only function was to allow locks to be opened by someone who lacked the proper key.

He placed the tools carefully in order on the floor beside him, then knelt before the door to examine the lock more closely.

"Right there's a famous example of the locksmith's art," Bellard said from behind his shoulder. "Originally it secured the door of the seraglio of the northern·chieftain Krölt. Imagine the exotic and untamed beauties it locked away, eh?"

Malden wondered if they had been half as comely as the lock itself. It was a thing of exquisite craftsmanship, no doubt—probably built by a dwarf, considering its complexity. The recurved case was wider than his two hands put together. It was made of bronze worked with copper, which sadly had grown furry with verdigris over the ages. The front was lined with rivets of brass sculpted to resemble handsome female faces. So profoundly intricate was the workmanship that each face had recognizably different features, and each was more lovely than the next.

The lock's shackle, also of brass, was cast in the shape of a maiden's braided hair. The massive keyhole was covered in a sliding plate to keep out dust and moisture that might foul the mechanism inside. When Malden drew the plate back he saw that the keyhole was big enough that he could reach inside with two fingers—if he dared. The key that opened this lock must have been the size of a shortsword.

The room's fitful light did not permit him to see much inside the lock mechanism, but picking a lock was a skill of the fingers, not of the eyes. He selected a saw rake from his tools and the larger of his tension wrenches. He hoped it would be large enough. He willed his hands not to tremble as he inserted the rake most carefully inside the keyhole and began feeling around for wards or tumblers.

When his rake made contact, the entire lock seemed to thrum as if a spring had been released inside. He just had time to see the rivets move before he jumped backward and caught himself with his hands on the floor. His picks went flying and clanged musically on the stones, but for the moment he forgot all about them.

"You're quicker than we credited, as well," Bellard said. He did not laugh this time.

The rivets shaped like the faces of women were not rivets at all, Malden saw. They were more similar to the dust plate covering the keyhole in that they could slide away from concealed holes in the face of the lock. From each of these holes now emerged a needle as big as a carpentry nail. Had he not jumped back in time, those nails would have scratched his hands in a dozen places. He looked closer and saw that the tip of each nail was coated in a straw-colored fluid.

"Poison, of course," he said.

"Old Krölt was a jealous cove, and he hated thieves. Of course, his poison dried up and flaked away centuries ago. The stuff we replaced it with isn't lethal, since the lock is meant for training new recruits. Which is not to say it's pleasant," Bellard said with a shrug. "It would leave you in a fever for three days, during which time you would suffer such agonies you would most devoutly wish we'd used hemlock instead."

Malden rubbed at the sweat rolling down into his eyes. Though he made his living at an occupation beset with certain risks, tonight he was being threatened with death and pain far too often for his liking.

And of course it wasn't over yet. If he failed to get through this door and keep his appointment with Cutbill, his life remained forfeit. He needed to pick the lock—but in such a way that he touched none of the needles. He would have to take great care.

He recovered his picks and then gripped them tightly by their free ends, to give them as much reach as possible. He had hoped it might be enough to let him pick the lock without touching any of the needles. Yet no matter how he tried, no matter how he strained or bent his hands into uncomfortable angles, the tools still didn't make it all the way inside the lock.

He sank back in frustration and anger and dropped his tools on the stone floor. What to do? What to do? He was not ready to give up. Sadu alone knew why he was being forced to this ordeal, to this series of gruesome tests, but there had to be some reason—he did not believe the master of this place would be such a sadist as to put him through so much just for grim amusement.

So there had to be some solution to the problem. Some simple, elegant answer that would lend itself to a man who knew how to think. Malden had always counted himself quite clever. He wasn't very strong—a bad diet had seen to that—nor was he accounted particularly handsome. He had the kind of face that no one remarked on, or remembered for very long. What he was, was smart. Quick, like Bellard had said. His best weapon now was his brain, his ability to think this through.

There would be a solution. It must be in this room, since he was not permitted to leave. And it had to be something he could discover if he would just open his eyes. He looked around, trying to see what he had missed before.

He glanced over at the dwarf. He hadn't paid the little creature much attention before. He had barely been aware of what the dwarf was doing. Now he gave the dwarf's piece-work his full attention.

The dwarf was sewing pieces of metal onto a pair of silk gloves.

Malden went over to him with his friendliest expression on his face. "My, those are rather fetching."

The dwarf sneered. "They might fetch a fair price," he said.

Malden could feel all eyes in the room turned on his back. He ignored them. "May I?" he asked. He picked up one of the gloves and studied it. The dwarf had sewn several dozen small tin plates onto the back and palm of the glove. They wouldn't work very well as armor in a fight, but they would be perfect for his current purpose. So perfect, in fact, that he could see no reason for their construction other than to help pick the poisoned lock. Malden opened his purse and took out a handful of farthings—copper coins cut into four pieces each. "I'm not sure how much you—"

"It'll do," the dwarf said, snatching them from his grasp. He counted them quickly, rolling the coins in his hand. "Miserly thieves. Half what they're fucking worth." He held out the gloves and Malden took them. "Now, that's just for hire," the dwarf informed him. "I take them back when I feel you've had 'em long enough."

"But of course," Malden said. He pulled on the gloves and hurried back to the lock. He had no doubt now they'd been made expressly for this purpose. The silk was quite delicate and would tear after even a little use, but it was also thin enough that it did not deaden the sensitivity in his fingers that was necessary for lock picking. The tin plates wouldn't protect the hands from any but the feeblest blows—but when he attempted to pick the lock again, he found they easily blocked the needles from scratching his skin.

Even with the gloves, though, opening the padlock wasn't easy. The lock was enormous and had dozens of pin tumblers inside. He had to tease each one into the proper position with his hooks, then hold it there with a rake while he applied just the right amount of torque with his wrench. It required perfectly still hands, but if he did not lapse in concentration even for a moment . . . yes . . . *there*. When the lock clicked again, he nearly jumped away a second time— but there was something different about this click. It was weightier, more solid, more final.

The needles retracted into their holes with a series of soft *thunks*. The shackle came loose and the lock hung swinging from the iron bar.

It was open.

Malden wound his picks back up into the hilt of his bodkin, then sheathed the weapon with a sigh. He removed the lock from the bar, though it was so heavy he could barely lift it, and set it down carefully on the floor. He stripped off the gloves, turning them inside out in case any of the poison had transferred to the tin plates. He tossed the gloves to the dwarf, who caught them easily. Then, going back to the door, he slid the bar out of the ring and pushed gently. The door opened with a creak.

He looked back at Bellard.

"He doesn't like to be kept waiting," the bravo said.

Malden nodded and stepped inside.

# CHAPTER FIVE

Beyond the locked door was a snug little office, heated by a charcoal brazier and kept insulated by heavy tapestries hanging on the walls. A massive desk faced the door, carved out of some expensive wood that had turned black over time, a very large and detailed map of the city posted behind the desk, a basin for washing one's face and hands, and a sideboard with a flagon of wine and several goblets. No one sat behind the desk, however. Instead, the room's sole occupant perched on a stool in the corner, scratching entries in a broad ledger held on a lectern before him.

He was a very thin man with long, mournful features and eyebrows that arched high onto his bare forehead. His black hair had receded well back onto his scalp and was shot through with two streaks of gray. His eyes were at once very dark and very bright—narrow, merciless eyes that did not look up at Malden as he came in.

Malden closed the door behind him and waited patiently for the man to finish his task. There were chairs, but he did not sit down, unsure what to expect inside this cozy room.

The man's quill pen scratched out a few more figures and then stopped.

"Your mother was a whore," he said, quite without inflection.

Malden's chest clenched but he understood what was happening. The man—who was certainly Cutbill, whether he looked like a mastermind of thievery or not—was testing him. Attempting to see if he would come at him in a fury or perhaps merely whine in offense.

There was no denying the truth of the statement, however. "She was. A good woman in a bad situation, who did her best to raise me with care and patience. She died of the sailor's pox when I was not yet a man."

Cutbill nodded, as if merely accepting this new bit of

information as something to enter into his account book. "Your father?"

"Half the men in this city might claim the title, yet none ever have."

"Sit down. You may be here awhile," Cutbill told him. Malden chose a chair near the door. "You lived in a bawdy house for most of your youth, performing small tasks and running errands for the madam. In that time you probably saw your fair share of illicit activity. I daresay you might have engaged in some yourself—rolling drunks, cheating paying clients—or at least tricking them into overpaying—procuring small quantities of various illegal drugs for the harlots. It wasn't until after your mother died that you began extending your activities to the larger sphere of the city, though."

"There wasn't much choice in the matter," Malden confirmed. "There's not much room in a brothel for a young man—not when there are so many unwanted boys around to clean the place and run errands. I was given a few coins but told to go forth and find my own fortune. I decided I'd see how honest folk lived. It turned out the city had little use for a whoreson with no estate. This place isn't kind to those who were born on the wrong side of the sheet."

If he'd been hoping to evince sympathy from Cutbill, he was disappointed. The clerkish man didn't even look up.

"I looked for work in various trades. I was too old already—no guild would take me on for prenticing at the advanced age of fifteen. I tried to find occupation as a bricklayer, as a carpenter, even as a stevedore down at the wharves. Each place turned me away—or demanded bribes. The gang bosses who organized such labor all wanted a cut of the pennies I would earn."

"And you were unwilling to pay such fees."

"How could I, and survive? It takes money to live in this world, money to eat, money for rent, money for taxes and tithes. The pay that work offered would have put me in debt the first week, and it would only have gotten worse. I'd seen this scheme before, and the ruin it caused."

"Oh?"

"It is exactly how the pimps keep their stables of women in line."

"Indeed," Cutbill said.

Malden fidgeted with the sleeve of his shirt. "There were no opportunities for one like me. None at all. Yet I needed money to survive. I could go out on the streets and become a beggar. Or I could turn to a life of crime. You know which I chose."

"And found you had a flair for it."

"You wish to know my life story entire?"

"I already know it. I'm simply confirming it. For the last five years you've been making a paltry living pilfering coppers from the unwary. Occasionally you've run a trick of confidence, but your real skills seem to lie in your fingers, not your voice. It was only recently you turned to burglary. For only a few months now you've been breaking into houses. Care to tell my why you changed your game?"

"People in this city know better than to carry much money when they go out. They know no purse is ever safe. The real money they leave behind, at home. It only seemed logical to follow the money, not the people."

The master of thieves made a small notation in his ledger. "You know who I am," Cutbill said. "You spoke my name outside."

Malden waved one hand in the air. "All of the Free City knows the exploits of great Cutbill, master of thieves, procurer extraordinaire, purveyor of unlawful euphoria, betrayer of confidences, extortionist to the high and mighty—"

"Spare me."

Malden sat back in his chair, a little dumbfounded. He had not expected the man to speak so plainly—or so abruptly. It was all he could do to keep up.

"You know that I run this city, or, at least, the clandestine commerce within it. That I have organized and consolidated the criminal class. That I have taken in hand the scattered gangs and crews that exist in any city of this size and made of them something more cohesive, something efficient." Cutbill put down his pen and sat up on his stool, lifting his chin in the air. "You know my reputation. I recounted your history to show I know yours as well."

Malden held his peace.

"I do not appreciate arse-licking, nor false modesty, nor unplain speaking. So I will say this simply: I have kept a close and admiring eye on you, ever since I became aware of your activities. I keep accounts of all who commit crimes in the Free City of Ness, whether they work for me or not. But you, Malden—you I've watched quite closely. You have the skills of a born thief: the lightness of step, the deftness of hands, the ability to keep a secret. And you learned these things all on your own. No mentor guided you, no school drilled you up in the ways of our profession. I find this quite impressive. Or I did so, until tonight.

"Tonight, you went in secret into the house of Guthrun Whiteclay, a master of the worthy guild of potters, and took from him a quantity of silver plate, some fancy cutlery, and a sack of silver coin he had hidden under his bed. Yet you failed to prepare for this jaunt properly."

Malden frowned. No one, he thought, could have been more prepared than he. "I cased the house for three days. Watched Whiteclay and his wife leave for a fete up at the moothall, saw him lock his front door but forget to latch a window at the side. I wrapped my shoes in cloth to deaden my footsteps. I studied the patrol patterns of the city watch and knew exactly how long I had to get in and out unseen. I even waited for a night when the fog would conceal the moon, and so darken the alley I used for my entrance and escape."

"Yes," Cutbill said, "but you forgot to ask anyone if Guthrun Whiteclay had *protection*. Do you even understand this concept? I have an arrangement with him. Nothing formal, nothing written down, of course. Yet I receive from him each month a certain sum of money. In exchange for this small payment, he is guaranteed against burglary, robbery, blackmail, and murder at the hands of his business rivals. You may think it easier to simply take all that is his and be done with it—but I assure you, over the years I have made many times as much money from this arrangement than you might ever see from reselling his household goods. Now you have cost me money, because I must send out my agents to recover the things you stole and have them returned to Whiteclay's house before he notices they are missing. Do you understand the magnitude of that task? Do you understand what it will cost me if I fail in it?"

"I see," Malden said, shifting in his chair. "So this is a shakedown. You wish me to return these things and to give you the silver I worked so hard to acquire. Well, I don't like it—but what choice have I? You can have your pet swordsman out there skewer me like a pig on a spit if I refuse."

Malden had the impression that Cutbill had never smiled in his life. One corner of his mouth did pucker, though, as if he were savoring some tasty morsel of knowledge that he had not chosen to share.

"Yes, yes, all of that. But more as well. I want you to join my operation."

Malden frowned. "I'm sorry?"

"I wish to offer you a job."

# CHAPTER SIX

Neither of them spoke for a while, as the meaning of Cutbill's words sank in. Malden had expected something quite different when he answered Cutbill's summons. Mostly, he'd expected to have to pay back the money he'd taken, and then receive a savage beating (if not worse) by way of a receipt.

"I've always worked alone," he said finally.

"And I cannot allow you to continue doing so. You are too good at this to be independent," Cutbill informed him.

"I don't like competition. I'd much rather have you in my stable. There are compensations you'll gain from accepting, of course. You know I have a considerable fraction of the city watch on my payroll, and more than one noble in the palace as well. Right now if you are caught stealing so much as one penny from a church collection box, you'll be hanged for your trouble. Under my wing, you will have some measure of safety from that fate. Furthermore you'll be allowed the services of my dwarf, Slag, who can provide tools of a fineness and quality you'll never gain from any human blacksmith. You can continue to pick your own jobs, though of course you must abstain from burgling any of my clients. And I have something else to offer you."

"Oh?"

"Your heart's desire. The thing you truly covet. I can offer you freedom."

"Every man in Ness is free. There are no slaves here," Malden pointed out. It was what made Ness a Free City. Outside of its walls most men and women were villeins, peasants, cotters—little more than slaves. They owned neither land nor livestock nor the clothes on their backs. They could not be married without the approval of their lord, nor could they move away from their farms unless they were sold to some other liege—and even then they could take nothing with them but their children.

But in Ness a man was his own. He could work to make a life for himself and his family, or he could laze about and eventually starve in the street. But it was his own choice. The city's charter guaranteed the right of a man to do either.

"I didn't say you were a slave. Rather, you're a prisoner. You have no family, no birthright. You dress like a common laborer and you have the accent of a peasant. If you tried to leave this city—if you stepped outside its walls—you would be scooped up by the first reeve who saw you. He would sell you to some petty baron and you'd spend the rest of your days tilling some field. Ness is a very large prison, Malden, and the door of your cell is wide open. But only because the powers that be know you'll never leave."

"If I had enough money—"

"But you don't, and living the life you do, you never will. If you keep operating independently you'll end up swinging from a rope or, if you're lucky, dying in poverty in some hovel. Come work for me and we'll change that. It will take time. You will work harder for me than you ever would for some shopkeeper. But your money will be your own. And with enough money, even the son of a whore can be a man of importance. He can go where he likes and live as he chooses. Freedom, Malden, is what I offer. True freedom."

Malden found his heart was racing. Cutbill did know him, heart and soul. How many times had he thought the same thing? How many times had he cursed fate for making him his mother's son?

"I will admit," he said, choosing his words carefully, "that is a strong incentive. May I ask what you get out of this arrangement?"

"I'll take a cut of everything you earn for my trouble. Let us say, nine parts of every ten."

Malden gaped in surprise. That deal was shameless robbery—worse than any demand a pander would make. But of course he must consider its author. There was in Cutbill's face a certain hardness of line that told Malden the numbers were non-negotiable. "And if I refuse your offer?"

"Then you are free to go, to walk out the door you came in by. Of course, in my disappointment I might forget to give Bellard the all-clear sign, and he may think you are trying to flee against my wishes."

"Of course," Malden said. "Well, in that case, I suppose my answer must be—"

Cutbill interrupted him. "You're probably thinking, right now, that you can rob me in some way. That you can short the money you turn over to me. Find some way to make my terms more agreeable. You've proved you're clever. Perhaps you think yourself more clever than me."

"Perish the thought," Malden said.

"I have no reason to believe you will play fair with me. So for a while, at least, you'll be under probation. You may eventually earn full position in my organization. I fancy our business here to be like unto one of the trade guilds.

Each new member must serve a period of apprenticeship, at the end of which he demonstrates his ability to perform the duties and the functions of the craft. For instance, one of Guthrun Whiteclay's apprentices might make an especially elegant and large drinking vessel—which would be called his masterpiece, because he made it to impress his master."

"I'm too old for prenticing," Malden insisted.

"Agreed. And I think we can consider your burglary to-night your masterpiece, because it certainly did impress me. So we'll start you off as if you were a journeyman, the next rank and title in our hypothetical guild. But there is another bar to entry at that level. One must pay one's guild dues, to be considered a member in good standing. So I'll expect a payment from you immediately, before you may enjoy any privilege of your new employment."

Malden clamped his mouth shut. What he wanted to say was this:

*Why, you loathsome double-dealing toothfish of a blasted cheat, is there no limit to the depths of your ignobility, your mendacity? You've held me here at threat of death, and bled me dry, and now you wish a gratuity for the service?*

What he actually said was this:

"How much?"

Cutbill flipped through the pages of his ledger. He consulted an entry near the beginning of the book, then looked up and for the first time directly into Malden's eyes. "I think one hundred and one golden royals should be enough. Or do you think that too little, after all the trouble you caused me tonight?"

"I . . ." Malden was briefly unable to speak. "I imagine . . . I think that I will laud your generosity to all I meet."

"Good. You can go now." Cutbill picked up his pen again and returned to writing in his book.

Malden rose from his chair. His legs shook. His hands had been steady when he picked the poisoned lock. He had not flinched when an arrow passed through his shadow. Yet now his body was rebellious to his commands. He turned toward the door. "You know, you never actually gave me the chance to say yes or no."

"I never do. In any business negotiation, if the outcome is not certain before you even begin, then you are fated to get the lesser hand. Remember that, Malden. Oh, and don't go through there."

Malden looked at the door. It was the only exit from the room that he could see. "But of course. You haven't given the all-clear signal."

"There is no such signal. If you walk through that door, Bellard will run you through, no matter what I do or say. I think that might sadden him—he seems to have a liking for you. So go through there instead." Cutbill flicked his pen toward one of the tapestries behind him. When Malden lifted it he found a very long corridor ending in a flight of stairs leading upward. Not looking back, he climbed until he found a trapdoor that opened on an alley in the Stink— the district of poor people's homes that lay just inside the city wall. The neighborhood of his own home, though he still had a long walk ahead of him.

He had only one thought as he headed there.

*One hundred and one royals.*

It was a fortune. It was a bondage—until he paid it, he would be Cutbill's slave, working for nothing but the payment of that blood price. It might take him a year to earn as much, even if he redoubled his efforts, even if he picked only the richest plums—plums, he was certain, that were already on Cutbill's list of protection.

One hundred and one! Royals! Coins so valuable the average journeyman in an honest guild might earn but one for a year's work. All of the plate and cutlery he'd taken from Guthrun Whiteclay, if sold to a very forgiving and generous fence, would earn him but two royals, perhaps three.

One hundred and one!

He reached his lodgings barely cognizant of the path he'd taken. He had a room above a waxchandler's shop, not much at all, but it was clean. He had a mattress full of straw which he went to as soon as he arrived. The plates and silver he had stashed underneath, below a loose floorboard. He was not surprised to find them gone. One of Cutbill's thieves must have broken in here to get them back. In their place was a bottle of cheap wine. A strip of paper was wound around its neck. When he unfolded the note he read:

*Welcome to the guild.*

It was signed, of course, with a crude drawing of a heart transfixed by a key.


# CHAPTER SEVEN


He drank the whole bottle and got rather drunk and lay in his bed with the world whirling around him, alternately cursing and blessing Cutbill's name. The guildmaster of thieves had held him to ransom—a ransom so large as to be absurd. Only a fool would take the offer, only an idiot would think he could make a hundred and one gold royals before he was stooped and old.

And yet . . . and yet . . . he kept coming back to what Cutbill had said. Freedom. Not a slave, but a prisoner. But he could break those shackles. Free himself, if he had the cash. Money meant everything in Ness, just as it meant everything the world around. A man with money was his own—he could buy fine clothes, buy a house of his own, buy, in short, respect. The good honest folk spat at him in the street now. With enough money they would tip their hats when he walked past. No, when he rode past, in a fine carriage, with a liveried servant driving the horses . . .

It was unimaginable. Impossible. And yes, alone, he could never do it. He could never be more than a petty thief, a second story man, fated to an ignominious death. But with Cutbill, with the power of the guild of thieves behind him . . .

His whole life could change. It could *mean* something, just like his mother had always wanted. Just like she'd dreamed of. Despaired of, on her deathbed.

All that was standing between him and that future was a stack of gold coins.

What could he do, then, but go back to work? But what kind of work, ah, there was the problem. His brain was seized by a fever of schemes and plans, but none of them paid off. At first he thought to burgle his way out of the debt, but that turned out to be . . . problematic. All the wealthiest citizens of the Free City were already on Cutbill's protection list. His options were therefore limited, and a couple days later he was back at the old routine, in the city's central Market Square. Right in the shadow of Castle Hill and its twenty foot wall.

No better place for the game he had planned.

"Forgive me, good sir, and the blessings of the Lady upon you!"

It was the oldest trick in the book, but that was how they got so old: they still worked. Malden had his right arm in a sling tied around his neck. Three mangled fingers and a fourth badly infected stump protruded beyond the edge of the cloth—a grotesque wound that would make most people look away rather than risk a closer inspection. With Market Square as crowded as it was that day, it was inevitable that the splinted arm would bump the occasional passerby. So far he had accidentally jostled a lady of quality with her hair in cauls at the sides of her head, the liveried servant of a noble house in black and green, and a fat merchant in a plumed hat wider than his shoulders.

"Pardon me, miss, it's this blasted arm," he would say, or "May the Lady save your grace, sir, I am sorry." They would turn to sneer and perhaps kick him away, but once they saw the arm they tended to murmur some words of empty forgiveness and then hurry off before he could start begging.

By then, of course, he already had their purses open. The broken arm was a fakery. Slag the dwarf had carved it from wood and then painted it to perfectly match Malden's skin tone. It was hollow inside and open at the bottom, so his real arm fit easily into the gap. In his actual right hand he had a tiny pair of sharpened shears and a square of damp felt. It was the work of a moment as his mark was turning away from him to cut open their fat purses and let the coins inside fall soundlessly into the cloth. Mostly he was securing pennies, groats, and farthings, nothing too worthy. At this rate, he calculated, he would pay off his debt to Cutbill in about twenty years.

Still, on a day like this, volume of business could make up for poor pickings. The Market Square was thronged from side to side, even though this was not a market day. The anonymity a big crowd offered made it easy, too.

Malden stopped for a while to take in the sights. It was impatient greed that carried more thieves up the gallows than any watchman or thief-taker. It was not wise to take too many purses even from so thick a crowd, lest someone raise the hue and cry and every man check their purse at once. Then it would be up to his feet and not his fingers to keep him alive. Anyway, even a working man like himself could enjoy the spectacle laid out for this day's entertainment.

Where the shadow of Castle Hill best cut the sunlight and the heat of the day, a wooden viewing platform had been set up, and there the mightiest men of the city sat with goblets of mulled wine, waiting on their entertainment. Men whom even Malden recognized. Ommen Tarness, the Burgrave himself, had come. The ultimate ruler of the city sat on a carved wooden throne, his simple coronet of gold polished and gleaming at his temples. He was dressed in cloth-of-gold and brocade, with an ornamental brass key hung around his neck. Despite the gaudy clothes, his face was that of a man used to command, the stern-eyed countenance of a ruler. There was little of mercy in that face, and much of resolution.

On his right hand, under a canopy, sat Murdlin, envoy of the Dwarf Kingdom. It was quite rare to see a dwarf by daylight—they were subterranean creatures by wont, and hated the sun. Murdlin had a wide-brimmed hat pulled low over his eyes but still he seemed agitated. His legs kicked at the air where they dangled from the seat of a human-sized chair. The dwarf's hair had been slicked down with bear fat for the occasion, and his beard had been braided in a hundred plaits, each set with a carnelian bead.

On the left of the Burgrave was the sorcerer Hazoth, his face veiled in black crape as befit one of his dread profession. There were stories about that man to chill the blood. It was said Hazoth had lived in Ness since ages past—no one knew exactly how old he was, but he had lived far past his allotted span. In the olden times supposedly he had summoned demons to save Skrae from the elves and then the dwarves in the endless wars that marked the kingdom's early years; that he had made the earth quake and the sky rain fire. Of course he didn't do things like that anymore. Summoning even a minor imp was enough to get a man burnt at the stake. Still, people drew back and turned their eyes aside wherever Hazoth went, and whispered stories that no one dared to disbelieve.

Behind these three stood the bailiff Anselm Vry and his reeves, the Burgrave's retainers, minor nobles, knights, ladies, and countless servants, enough so the wooden platform groaned with all their weight.

Below them, standing on the cobbles of the square, were the grand people of the Golden Slope, the district of the city inhabited by merchants, burgesses, guildmasters, and those of independent means. A colorful lot in their fitted hoods and gathered tunics, their checked and particolored hose, their snoods and wimples and wide baldrics. None so gaudy, of course, as their liveried servants, who wore hues bright enough that anyone could tell them apart at a distance. There were a scattering of drab cloaks and doublets as well, of course, for any such gathering could not help but attract beggars and the hawkers of sweetmeats and wine. Then there were the bravos and the hired guards, who favored black silk or leather dress, to show how serious was their profession. Yet even these made some concession to the gaiety of the crowd by draping garlands of flowers around the brims of their kettle helmets or tying the favors of their ladies to the hafts and hilts of their weapons. Today, by decree, everyone was to show some sign of pomp and excitement.

After all, it wasn't every day you got to see a public hanging.

# CHAPTER EIGHT

The accused was brought into the square on a hurdle, hoodwinked and bound. He wore nothing but a pair of breeches and a white nightshirt. His hair was blond and cut very short, and his chin had been shaved for his execution. Even with a filthy cloth tied around his eyes, Malden could see he had the face of a poet but the body of a warrior. Under the loose shirt the man's body rippled with muscle. More than one woman in the crowd turned to whisper excitedly to her neighbor as the cart trundled past on its voyage to the gibbet.

Malden hated the man instantly, just on principle.

Leaping down easily from the gallows, the masked hangman grabbed up the prisoner's bound hands behind his back and heaved. The bound man's back arched in pain and he grimaced (showing off perfect white teeth), but he refused to make a noise of agony. Struggling to stand up properly, he kicked out with his legs and found the first step of the gallows. Without hesitation he climbed to the top.

The crowd pressed close, murmuring with excitement. With barely checked glee. Up on the platform the criminal was on proud display, and the little chill of terror a hanging always evoked ran in waves ran through the people gathered to watch.

A list of charges was read out, but Malden didn't listen. He was far too busy at that moment lifting purses. The real trick to it wasn't deft fingers, really. It was choosing the perfect moment. You had to wait until your mark's attention was fully on something else, until he was totally unaware of the people all around him.

Then it was child's play. *Snip-snip* went the shears, and coins fell into Malden's hands. The fat merchant in front of him didn't even turn around to see who'd touched him.

Up on the gallows the show was just getting started, it seemed. Mouths fell open and eyes went wide as the condemned man lifted his chin and interrupted the reading of the charges. "May I not see my accuser, before I am put to death?" the prisoner asked in a voice as clear as a bell.

Over on the viewing stand the Burgrave rose from his throne. A sardonic smile twisted his lips. "I suppose you have that right, as a peer. Let him see me."

The executioner pulled off the prisoner's hoodwink, and for a moment the blond man simply blinked and squinted in the bright sunlight. Then he looked up and saw Ommen Tarness gazing silently in his direction.

"Ah," the prisoner said. "Greetings, milord."

"Exactly, Sir Croy," the Burgrave replied. "I am still your lord."

The crowd erupted in surprise. Apparently they had no idea that the man waiting to be hanged was, in fact, a knight of the realm. A man of property and good family—which made his execution that much juicier. Most interestingly, the dwarf envoy, Murdlin, jumped up on his seat at the news. The dwarf looked conflicted by varying emotions—in which state he mirrored the people who surrounded Malden on every side. A great chaos of voices and opinions raised itself, and it seemed no two citizens could agree on what this meant.

Tarness held up both hands for silence. "Croy, I warned you, when last we met, that I would not suffer you to return here. Yet you broke the letter of your banishment. I hope you have a very good reason."

"I do," the knight said, bowing his head. "I came for love."

The crowd erupted in noise. Some jeered, some expressed the utter disbelief that Malden felt on hearing this.

Others, many of them, cried out in sympathy. Tarness shook his head and sat down on his throne. "Enough of this nonsense. Proceed."

"Wait! Let me speak in my defense, I beseech you!" the knight shouted. "When you hear my tale, I am sure—"

Tarness made a gesture with one hand and the hangman struck Croy across the face. The Burgrave looked away in disgust and said, "Gag him so I don't have to listen to this. And then proceed."

Even Malden had to admit he found that a trifle unfair. The man was about to die—he ought to be allowed to prattle on if he liked. He gave in to his instinct to join the chorus of boos and hissing that welled up from the crowd.

Still, he had not come to see the knight's final distress, but only to do a little hard labor and reap a harvest of coin. He looked away from the scene on the gibbet and moved through the boisterous crowd, now looking for a final victim before he retired for the day. It would be easy to take a purse at the moment the hanged man dropped. At that moment every eye in the square would be turned to the same place. Few easy marks presented themselves, however, and suddenly Malden was in danger of being trampled. Some among the crowd had begun to shout for the prisoner's release, raising their fists in the air. They drew closer to the gallows, as if they might storm it and save the man themselves. The bailiff waved for the watch. The town's policing force, dressed alike in cloaks patterned with embroidered eyes, rushed into the throng and pushed back with their quarterstaffs until the crowd gave some way.

Knowing it would be folly to try to take another purse right under the noses of the city watch, Malden shrank back, away from the gallows, and stumbled backward directly into what felt like a wall of jangling iron.

He whirled about, a curse on his lips, but this he forestalled as he saw whom he'd tripped over. A man much broader and taller than himself who loitered at the back of the crowd, aloof from it as if immune to its bloodlust. He wore a hauberk of chain mail covered by a jerkin of black leather. His head was covered in a wild tangle of brown hair that didn't end until it wrapped around his chin in a full and glorious beard. The man peered down at him as if from a considerable height. A jagged scar crossed the bridge of his nose, nearly bisecting his face.

"Steady on there, boy," the big man said. "Are you hurt? Ah, but now I see you are. I'm a blasted pillock for not seeing you there."

Malden licked his lips. He'd been ready to call the man far worse than that until he saw the massive sword strapped to his back. So instead he kept his mouth shut, because he had a brain in his head. He never argued with a man wearing a sword. He held his peace for another reason as well. Under his sling, his long thin fingers had touched a fat purse on the swordsman's belt. By the way it hung low and heavy, it must contain something more precious than copper.

Up on the viewing platform the dwarf Murdlin was trying desperately to get the Burgrave's attention. Malden was barely aware that anyone else in the square existed. He was too busy running his fingertip across the milled edge of a coin inside the swordsman's purse. It must be silver, he thought, just based on how it felt.

It was folly to steal from a man so heavily armed, recklessness of a sort Malden never permitted himself. Yet the oaf had bruised him. Malden feigned unsteadiness and let the swordsman grasp his left arm. With his right hand he made a quick pass with his shears and felt the weight of the coins that dripped from the cut purse. They were heavy enough to be gold, even though he wouldn't know until later when he could examine them in private.

"The fault was mine, and I will beg your pardon, rather than insult you further," Malden said. He reached up and touched the cowl of his cloak in salute, then twisted away and pushed into the crowd before the swordsman could say another word.

Up on the gallows, the hangman draped the noose around the knight's neck, then pulled it fast. Better you than me, Malden thought. Best to get away now in the noise when the poor fool dropped. He took no more than a few steps into the comforting anonymity of the throng, however, before the swordsman behind him spoke the two words Malden dreaded most.

"Hold! Thief!" the man shouted.

From no more than five strides away, a watchman in an eye-covered cloak looked up and right into Malden's eyes. The watchman took a step toward him—but then something miraculous happened.

"Wait!" the dwarf envoy bellowed, up on the viewing platform. "I cannot let this go on. This man is beloved by the king of my people. Lord Burgrave, I demand you spare his life!"

It was enough to turn the square into a bedlam. The watchman had all he could do to hold the crowd back from tearing the gallows down with their own hands. Long before he and his fellows had the mob under control, Malden was off and away, his scrawny legs flashing under his cloak. It was the best chance he would get to make good his escape, and he planned on milking the opportunity for every drop of grace. Yet his luck was not unalloyed at that moment. As he fled he glanced behind him only once—and then only to confirm what he dreaded. The watch had lost sight of him, but the swordsman had not. The big man was right behind him.

# CHAPTER NINE

Malden pushed through the crowd, which tried to push back. He was a slippery fish, though, and ducked easily under raised arms or around fat bellies and even between skinny legs. His small size was an asset in a life spent always running away from something. He ducked around a party of student scholars too drunk to react as he whipped past them, then clambered on top of a cart full of fruit before the vendor could grab him. He plucked up a skinned melon, overripe and bursting with juice after being out in the hot sun all day, and waited for his moment.

"You there," the vendor began to shout, "come down and—"

Malden flipped the vendor a thruppence and the hawker turned away as if he'd never seen him. It was a dozen times what the melon was worth.

The bearded swordsman shoved his way through the students, knocking half of them down like ninepins. "Thief, hold, I only want to—"

Malden hurled the melon with pinpoint accuracy. It exploded across the swordsman's face and chest, the pulp forming great yellow clots in his beard and across his eyes. By the time he recovered from his shock and started scraping the mess off his face, Malden was off and running again.

Market Square was a central location from which one could reach anywhere in the Free City of Ness. Malden chose none of the half-dozen streets that led away from the square. He knew a better road, a kind of highway, where he could make much better speed: across the rooftops, where few could follow.

First, though, he had to get up above the crowd.

Along the south edge of the square there was a massive multitiered fountain, a gift from the third Burgrave to the people. It was in the shape of a series of bowls held by the handmaidens of the Lady, the Burgrave's favorite deity. Malden dashed for it and then leapt up one tier after another, his feet barely getting wet as he stepped on the stone rims of the bowls. Balanced precariously at the top, one foot on a handmaiden's cocked elbow, he looked back to see if his ascent was drawing the ire of the watch. He needn't have bothered. The people had mobbed the gallows en masse and were busy cutting down the imprisoned knight, while the Burgrave and the dwarf envoy bellowed conflicting orders at their various servants and retainers. Malden easily made the leap from the top of the fountain to a pitched roof beyond, dropping to all fours to get a better grip on the slick lead shingles. He had landed on the top of the civic armory, which normally bristled with guards, but they were busy rushing out to join the general melee in the square. He clambered over the roofline of the armory and up one of its many spires to leap over to another roof, this the top of the tax and customs house.

It wasn't the first time he'd climbed these heights. The district around Market Square was full of old temples, public buildings, and the palatial homes of guildmasters and minor nobility. It was called the Spires for its most common architectural detail—all of which were so heavily ornamented, carved, and perforated they were easier to climb than a spreading oak. Combined with how close the buildings pressed to one another, Malden could move through the Spires almost as easily as he could walk on flat cobbles.

Arms spread for balance, he hurried down the roofline of the customs house, one foot in front of the other like he was walking a tightrope. The sun glared on the pale shingles of the roof, made from slabs of stone cut thin as paper. At the end of the roof he slid down the steeply pitched shingles and sprang up onto a rain gutter, then launched himself across the narrow gap of the Needle's Eye, an alley that curled around the back of the university cloisters. The cloisters had a nearly flat rooftop running a hundred yards away from him, an easy place to gain some time in case he was still being pursued. Of course, that was impossible. There was no way a man wearing thirty pounds of chain mail on his back could—

"Oh, that's unfair," Malden breathed.

A puffing, roaring noise like the bellow of an exhausted bull chased him across the roof, and then the clanking noise of chain mail slapping on shingles. The swordsman clambered up on top of the customs house, dragging himself upward despite all the weight he carried. The bastard must be as strong as a warhorse, Malden thought.

"Just—want—to—talk," the swordsman grunted, hauling himself up onto the steeply peaked roof, staring at Malden across the alley between them. "Listen, thief," he said, "you needn't run—any further. I just—just want to talk."

"Is your tongue as sharp as your sword?" Malden asked. "Come no closer." Witty banter wasn't coming as easily as he'd hoped. Maybe he was too terrified to crack jokes. Well. Never mind. He drew his weapon. "This," he said, "is a bodkin."

"So it is," the swordsman replied, the way a tutor might speak to a student who had just mastered the first declension of a regular verb.

Malden sneered. "It may not look like much. But it's designed for one thing, and one alone. It has a wickedly sharp tip so it can punch right through chain mail and into an armored man's vitals." Of course, of the hundred odd uses Malden had come up with for his knife, that was the one he'd never actually tried. He imagined it would take a lot of strength to push it through the fine mesh of metal links. He would have to get his back into it. Assuming the swordsman hadn't cut his own spine in half before he had a chance to try. "If you attempt to follow me further—"

"I don't want to follow you over there. Bloodgod's armpits! That's the last thing I want to have to do today. I just want to talk to you. Truly."

Malden pointed the weapon directly toward the swordsman's midsection.

The swordsman responded by getting a running start and then leaping over the gap between the customs house and the roof of the university cloister. As the enormous man came flying toward him, Malden let out a yelp and broke into a run. Behind him the swordsman came down hard on the lead tiles of the cloister's roof and landed altogether wrong on his leading foot. He slipped and twisted around and fell with a great clanging noise that must have alarmed every student and scholar inside the cloister—unless they were all up in the square. The students of the university famously loved a good riot. The swordsman's legs and then his lower half slid over the edge and dangled in space, while his hands scrabbled at the roof tiles, looking for any kind of purchase. It was all the swordsman could do to keep from rolling over the edge and dropping into the Needle's Eye. From that height the impact would almost certainly break bones.

"Blast," the swordsman said. Then he shouted, "Cythera! Stop him!"

Malden was already running down the long lane of the cloister's rooftop. At its far end, he knew, was the Corn-market Bridge, which was lined in allegorical statues. If he launched himself off the edge of the roof and angled it just right, he could easily snag the top of the Bounties of Harvest Time. That particular statue had wide hips and a cornucopia full of fruits and grains, which would give him plenty of handholds to climb down to safety on—

Malden had to stop short when a woman in a velvet cloak materialized out of thin air, directly in his path.

He gawped like a fish on a pier, from the shock of her appearance, of course, but also—also—from the nature of her appearance. His mind felt like it had slammed into a brick wall, and his eyes felt pinned to the spot. He could not look away from her.

The woman was astonishingly beautiful, though it was hard to tell. Dark, complicated, *disturbing* tattoos covered her cheeks and forehead and the bare arms she revealed as she swept the cloak back over her shoulders. Her eyes were very large, very blue, and altogether too heartbreakingly sorrowful to look at for more than a moment.

She smelled of some perfume Malden had never smelled before. Her hair looked softer than sable, and despite the circumstances, he took a moment to imagine what it would be like to bury his face in her curls.

It would be . . . very pleasant, he thought.

"Are you Cythera?" Malden asked, because he could think of nothing else to say to this bewitching woman. He knew he should be running, knew that the swordsman would be right behind him. Yet if he ran away now, that would mean tearing his eyes away from her exotic beauty.

She smiled. It was the single least mirthful smile Malden had ever seen. "I am." She took a step closer. That was when he realized what was so disturbing about her tattoos. They were moving. The complex patterns of interweaving tendrils, leaves, briars, thorns, flowers, and the like were slowly rearranging themselves on her face, seeking out new arrangements and complications, forming arabesques and elegant knots that resolved themselves while he watched into wholly new patterns, which . . . it was quite mesmerizing, really, just watching them. Just—

Malden tore his gaze away. He'd felt entranced, and well he should have. Something about the tattoos had dazzled him, clouding his mind. He never enjoyed being tricked— he was the one who was supposed to trick *other people*. He roared as he brought his bodkin around, the point angled toward her throat.

"That," she told him, "would be a singularly bad idea." It was not a threat. Somehow the tone of her voice conveyed the sense that she wanted nothing less than to see him hurt, that she really didn't wish him ill, but that he was playing with fire all the same. Or was that just another illusion? Perhaps she was some kind of witch and was quite happy about leading him to his doom.

Best, he thought, to break the spell and flee.

Slowly he lowered the bodkin. "I don't know what manner of creature you are," he told her, "but I really must be going."

"Oh no you don't," the swordsman said, coming upon Malden from behind. He grabbed Malden's head under one massive arm and squeezed. Apparently the swordsman had recovered from his stumbling fall. There was no way for Malden to break the hold: the oaf had the strength of a bear. He rather smelled like one, too. "You and I," the swordsman said, giving Malden's head another squeeze, "are going to have our talk now. All right? Promise me you won't," yet another squeeze, "run off?"

"I promise, of course, how could I have been so rash as to—as to—I promise! Just stop that! Your mail is digging into my neck."

"Very good," the swordsman said. He let Malden loose to stagger around on the roof, grasping at his throat. "My name, by the way, is Bikker. We weren't properly introduced before."

"I'm Malden." The thief bent over double for a moment. "Well met."

"Indeed. So. Malden?"

"Yes?" Malden said, lifting his head.

"This is for the melon," Bikker said, just before punching him right in the face with one massive mailed fist.

# CHAPTER TEN

Approximately three hundred yards to the northwest, Market Square had erupted into a melee as angered citizens brawled with the watch in their eye-patterned cloaks. It didn't take much to start a riot in a city of this size. The students of the university were deep in the thick of it, laying into the watch with bare fists, fueled by strong drink and the excitement of a day away from their dry and dusty studies. Most of the wealthier folk were attempting to flee the square, with varying degrees of luck.

To Sir Croy, up on the gibbet, it was like looking into the pit. He could not believe that all of these people were battling because of him. He had spent his whole life defending these people, keeping them safe, and now they were warring amongst themselves. That they were arguing over his fate was too much to bear.

"Friends! Please, I beg you, peace!" Sir Croy shouted. He wanted to wave his hands in the air to gain the attention of the throng, but of course could not, as his hands were bound. The noose around his neck didn't help either. The executioner beside him looked confused, uncertain as to whether he should release the trapdoor that would drop Croy to his fate.

Somehow Anselm Vry managed to climb up onto the gallows. The bailiff was the city's chief administrator and keeper of the peace, answerable only to the Burgrave. Sallow-skinned and lean of features, Vry looked like the kind of man who should spend his whole life with his nose in a book, but Croy had known him once and could see beyond the man's looks. Vry was an able administrator, a skilled organizer of men and matériel. He was above all a rational man. Croy couldn't resist beaming at someone whom he had once called his friend. The bailiff whispered in the executioner's ear, and at once the hooded man jumped down from the gallows and waded into the riot, aiding the watch.

"Anselm!" Croy called. "I knew you wouldn't let this— Oh."

Vry had taken up the executioner's post, his hand on the lever that would release the trapdoor.

"I see," Croy said. "You've come to see me off personally."

"Indeed," Vry said, shaking his head in disgust. "I hope you understand this was not my choosing. I pleaded with Tarness not to slay you, in fact."

"I'm much obliged."

Vry snorted. "I told him we could simply give you a commission and ship you off to fight barbarians in the eastern mountains. They would have killed you for us. But that wouldn't have worked, would it? You would have deserted your post and returned here in haste."

"Defy a commission of duty? Never!"

"Oh? Truly, you would have gone away and never returned?"

Sir Croy was not a man for deep thoughts or meditations on the future. He pondered this for a moment, then smiled. "I would have whipped the barbarians in six months. Then I could have come back here with a clear conscience."

Vry rubbed at his eyes with one hand. "Croy, please, for once in your life try to be realistic. Whatever quest is driving you this time won't let you stay away. Yet Tarness cannot allow you inside the city walls. You know things he wishes kept secret. I know you would never betray him, but there's always the chance someone would get the information out of you—if not by torture, then by wizardry. Banishing you the first time was an act of great mercy on his part, and it will not be repeated."

"I understand. Well, I forgive you old friend. We serve the same masters, you and I, and perhaps you are simply more loyal than me. That's hardly a quality to be condemned. Now, if you must—obey your orders." Croy lifted his chin and straightened his back. If he was going to die he would do so with proper posture.

"Noble as you ever were," Vry said, "and just as stupid." He started to pull the lever.

His hand was stayed, however, at the last possible moment. There was a flash of light that was instantly swallowed up by a thick cloud of yellow smoke. Croy's lungs filled and he was overwhelmed by a powerful reek of rotten eggs that made him gag and cough. He tried to stay upright and maintain his composure but the stench was just too great. He worried he might vomit—not exactly what the people would expect of a knight of the realm, not in public—

"Hold still, you freakishly large livestock copulator," someone hissed in the midst of the yellow cloud. The noose was lifted away from his throat, then a knife cut through the rope holding Croy's hands together. Small hands pushed him from behind. He went staggering forward and over the edge of the gallows platform. It was all he could do to land on his feet. Down at ground level the yellow smoke was rarefied and he could breathe again, but still he could see nothing.

Fortunately a figure with a cloth across its face was there to guide him. He was dimly aware that the figure was only about four feet tall. A child? Some magical sprite, with the appearance of a child?

"Stop standing there manipulating yourself in an erotic fashion. We don't have much time before the feces-smelling watch is upon us!"

Ah. No child. There was only one sort of creature in the world with such a vulgar tongue, yet such an academic grasp of human language. "Murdlin?" Croy asked. "Is that you?"

"It won't be either of us in a moment, if we're both dead as horse urine!"

They wasted no more time. Using the melee as cover, the man and the dwarf hurried out of the square. Once they were clear of the yellow smoke, Croy was able to understand why Murdlin had covered his face with cloth. It must have filtered out the worst of the stinking smoke and allowed the dwarf to breathe easy even in its midst. Was there no end to the cleverness of the diminutive folk?

"Murdlin, I am deep in your debt now," Croy said as he was led around a corner into Greenhall Street.

"Considering what you did for the dwarf king's daughter, the debt is crossed out," Murdlin told him.

"I only did my duty, as bid by my king," Croy pointed out. A year earlier the dwarf princess had been traveling to Helstrow, to be received at the royal court of Skrae. Along the way she'd been abducted by bandits who intended to hold her for ransom. Croy had spent six weeks tracking the bandits down and eventually rescued the princess. The dwarf king offered him anything he desired—steel, gold, even the princess in marriage—but Croy had never considered there might be a reward. A crime was committed, and someone had to put it right, that was all.

Clearly Murdlin felt some recompense was still owed.

"This way, most hurriedly, like a rabbit making love," Murdlin called.

Even as they dashed across the cobblestones, a wagon full of hay pulled up beside them. The driver was a dwarf with a hood pulled low across his face to keep out the sun. The wagon rolled to a stop as soon as it reached them.

"By the Lady, you work fast," Croy said.

"The moment I realized it was you on the gallows, I knew what course things must take. I sent one of my servants at once to fetch this conveyance. Now please, get into this body-odor stinking hay. It will hide you from view.

The wagon will take you outside the walls. By the time you arrive I'll have a horse waiting for you, so you may run off like a goblin that has fouled its own pants."

"You make escape sound less sweet that I would have thought it an hour ago," Croy admitted.

"It's only a figure of speech. A common expression in my first language," Murdlin told him. "I am taking a great risk doing this, Croy. Now, please! Into the hay that itches like pubic lice."

Croy rubbed at his chafed wrists. Then he started walking backward, away from the dwarf, almost breaking into a run. "You have my eternal thanks, envoy. But I've work to do yet, here in the Free City. My lady is still enslaved. What is freedom to me when she is in chains? Fare thee well!"

The dwarf cursed him and shook his small fists in the air, but Croy was already on his way, turning a corner into Brasenose Street and back into danger.

Just the way he liked it.

# CHAPTER ELEVEN

For a while Malden's world was only a terrible ringing, as if a bell were struck right next to his ear, and darkness, a kind of darkness that hurt. He could feel his body being moved about, but only from a distance, as if he were watching some other poor bastard being carted around. The pain he felt made no sense, really, and he kept probing at it with mental fingers, trying to remember what had happened.

Eventually he heard sounds over the ringing in his head. Gasps and shouts, and then the shriek of chairs being pulled back. His poor body was dumped without ceremony on a flat surface, and suddenly he rushed back into it, though that just made things hurt more. Gradually he managed to tease out voices from the noise all around him.

"—might have killed him with a punch like that. And we'd be back where we started. You really ought to learn some discipline."

"What? That little tap? I've hit flies harder than that. Look, he's already waking up. I couldn't possibly have done more than jiggled his brains a bit."

The voices were vaguely familiar. Malden couldn't quite place them, though. He was having a lot of trouble stringing thoughts together, even though the horrible ringing noise had faded away from his ears. He attempted to make a catalog of the things he knew for sure. He was certain, for instance, that he was lying on a very hard surface. Also, that his face hurt.

Suddenly his face hurt a very great deal.

"Oh," he moaned. "Oh, by the Bloodgod. Oh . . ."

"Open your eyes now, boy," Bikker said. "There's a good lad."

Malden looked around without sitting up. He was in a tavern, lit by smoking oil lamps. The few patrons present at that time of day were all staring at him. The alewife, a heavyset woman of middle age, was coming toward them with a tankard full of beer.

"Which one of you is paying for this?" she asked. "This isn't a sickhouse."

Slowly, Malden got his elbows under him and sat up. He had been laid out flat on a long table, a slab of oak that felt as hard as stone. It was patterned with old dark rings where tankards had overflowed, and was held together with strips of iron that dug into his back and legs.

Cythera—the tattooed woman—handed the alewife a farthing and passed the tankard to Malden. It was of the kind that had a lid on a hinge, to keep out flies, an earthenware vessel sealed at the bottom with pewter. An expensive bit of crockery. That told Malden roughly where he had to be—on the Golden Slope, the region of rich houses and expensive shops just downhill from the Spires. Had to be, as there were no taverns in the Spires, while if his two strange captors had carried him any farther downhill, the tankard would have been made of leather sealed with pitch. Knowing that was important. When he made his escape from this place, he would need to know where to run to first.

Wherever he was, though, he had to admit he was very thirsty. He lifted the lid and sipped carefully at the contents, thinking it must be some medicinal draught—but in fact it was only small beer. A drink fit for children.

"You like that, boy?" Bikker asked.

"I'm not an infant," Malden said, taking a long drink. "I'm almost twenty. Please stop calling me 'boy.'"

Bikker smiled broadly, showing off the gaps where some of his teeth used to be. "You going to try to run off again, boy, as soon as you can stand? Or are you going to talk to me now?"

Cythera glanced around the room. Whenever her blue eyes passed over one of the staring patrons, they flinched and looked away. "Bikker," she said, "we need more privacy than this. Where should we go?"

"I'm tired out after chasing this cur," Bikker told her. "I like this place just fine. You lot, out now. Barkeep, you can go, too."

"By Sadu's eight elbows, I will not," the barkeep told him. "Just run off like a scolded brat, and leave you here with my till and all my stock?" She snorted in derision.

Bikker shrugged hugely. Then he reached behind him and drew his sword.

It made a strange slick sound as it came out of its scabbard, and when revealed, was not the shiny length of steel Malden had expected. Instead it looked like a bar of iron, three feet long, with no real edge. The iron was pitted and rough, like something that had been left in a tomb for centuries before it was picked up again. It looked a little slick, too—and as Malden watched, bubbles formed on its surface, then congregated in thick clots until it looked like the sword was drooling. A drop of the clear fluid ran down the sword's edge and dripped on the dirt floor, where it hissed and smoked on the packed earth.

"You may wish to move aside," Bikker said to Malden, who jumped off the table quickly, ignoring the throbbing pain in his face and head. Bikker swung the sword around in a wide arc that brought it crashing down on the oak table. With an explosive hiss like a dozen angry snakes striking at once, the blade sank through the thick wood and through the other side. The table fell in two halves, split clean down the middle, against the grain of the wood. The wetness of the blade—it must be vitriol, Malden realized, of some very potent type—gave off foul vapors that stung his nose. For a moment he could do naught but look at the sundered table. It was still bubbling and dissolving wherever the acid sword had touched it. Then he looked up and saw that everyone—patrons and barkeep alike—had fled the room.

"There," Bikker said. "Privacy."

Cythera sighed deeply, though there was an affectation to the sound that made Malden think she was accustomed to being annoyed with Bikker's antics. "They'll be back soon enough. And they'll probably bring the watch."

Bikker shrugged. He sheathed his sword. Malden saw that the interior of the scabbard was lined with glass, no doubt to keep the acid from burning its way through. The big man said, then, "So let us speak quickly to the boy, and then we can all be on our way. Boy," Bikker called.

"Malden. At least use my name."

"Boy," Bikker said, walking over behind the bar and pouring himself a pitcher full of strong ale, "you are a thief, is that correct? This wasn't the first time you ever cut a purse. Judging by the way you scampered up those rooftops, I imagine you've done this sort of thing before."

"Listen," Malden said, "the silver I took from you, it's all—it's here somewhere." He reached down across his chest and realized that his sling and his fake arm had been removed. Looking up, he saw that Cythera held them—and his bodkin, too. "I'll give it back, right? And everything else I took today, you can have that as well. Just let me go."

"Bugger the silver! There's plenty more where it came from!" Bikker shouted. He lifted his pitcher and drank lustily from it until foam drenched his beard.

"We don't wish to punish you," Cythera said. "We wish to hire a skilled thief for . . . well, our purposes must remain unspoken, of course. We wish to hire a master thief for a certain job."

More where it came from, Malden thought. More silver. Enough the brute didn't even bother keeping hold of the pittance he'd had with him. More. "Are you?" he said. "Well, luck is with you, for I—"

"Can you recommend anyone like that?" Cythera asked.

"I—I can indeed," Malden said, and raised himself up to his full height. "I know a thief with no equal in the Free City. One more than up to whatever task you set him." He gave her his most dashing look.

"Yes?" she said patiently.

"Milady, I am at your service."

She frowned. "No, I mean, what is his name, this paragon of thieves?"

"It's—well, me."

Bikker laughed so hard he spilled his ale. Cythera's face didn't change, but her icy blue eyes looked Malden up and down and then flicked away.

"We don't want a pickpocket, boy! We want a *thief*. A . . . a burglar, a . . . second story man, a—"

"And I tell you, you've found him." Malden brushed past Cythera—she gave a short gasp as he nearly touched her— and over to stand before Bikker. He had to look up to meet the swordsman's gaze but he held it. "Why, just the other day, Cutbill, the master of thieves, expressed his deep admiration for my skills. He listened to the story of how I stole plate and silver from Guthrun Whiteclay's house and said he'd never heard of a finer scheme enacted so skillfully. And he should know."

"Cutbill." Bikker glanced across at Cythera. "You're one of his crew?"

"Indeed," Malden said.

"Only—we need this to stay between us. It can't get back to him, or the world will know our business. At least, it will if it has the coppers to buy the information."

"Discretion is my watchword. Though it does cost extra."

Bikker shook his head and quaffed more ale.

"You've seen how quick I am," Malden insisted.

"We did, at that," Cythera agreed. "He would have gotten away from *you*, Bikker, if I hadn't been there to distract him. And the man we need will have to know how to climb. He showed us that as well."

The swordsman hunched his shoulders. He was half convinced, Malden knew, and he already had Cythera on his side. Time to close the deal, before Bikker could reconsider.

"For this job I will require the sum of one hundred and one gold royals," Malden announced.

Bikker smiled. "You haven't yet heard what it entails. We might be getting a bargain for that price."

A bargain at one hundred and one royals? *More silver where that came from*, Bikker had said. How much more? "Of course, that does not include incidentals, the fees of the dwarf who makes my gear, bribe money, hazard bonuses, surcharges for quick resolution, gratuities—"

Bikker leaned back against the bar. "Don't get ahead of yourself, Malden."

# CHAPTER TWELVE

The sorcerer Aelbron Hazoth lived in an imposing four story edifice where the Lady's sacred parklands abutted the city wall, most of the way downhill from the palace, in the district called Parkwall.

It was not the safest district in town, though it had its recommending features. Like the Ashes, it had originally been a residential district for the poor until it burned down in the Seven Day Fire. Unlike that wasteland, Parkwall had been laboriously cleared, the remains of the old houses scraped away and the land allowed to go to seed. Now Parkwall was a zone of lush grass, a green common kept cropped by the sheep and goats of the people of the Stink, a spacious greensward in a city that had very little green space. The tall crowded houses of the Stink drew away on either side to let in the air. It was rumored to be the healthiest place in town—the plagues that swept through Ness every few winters often skipped Parkwall entirely—but its openness and lack of well-lighted streets had drawn footpads and thieves, and it was counted terribly dangerous by night. A few fine houses had been built in Parkwall to take advantage of the pleasantly rustic environs, but these were all surrounded by their own walls and wrought-iron fences to keep out the uninvited.

Such as Sir Croy, for instance.

The knight had found lodging at a nearby villa. After escaping from the gibbet, he thought he would be a hunted man, that no place would be safe for him, but in fact it did not take long before he had a place of refuge. He did not lack for friends in the Free City, some of whom were stalwart enough to hide him from the watch. A rich merchant had found him wandering in the Golden Slope and begged to bring him home. Croy accepted, though he had no money to pay the man. The merchant insisted none was required, and Croy had praised his good heart in all the words he knew. The merchant assured him that Croy would bring him great fame and social status, but Croy knew the man was just being kind. He gave Croy a suite of rooms all to himself and ordered his servants to see to his every wish.

This night he was laying spread out on a bench in a roof garden, pretending to take his ease. It was a likely enough occupation. This close to Ladymas and the hottest time of year, anyone with sense was up on a rooftop or in a garden, trying to catch a breeze. Anyone who saw him might think him yet another pampered noble attempting to stay cool. In truth, he had come up to the roof garden to watch Hazoth's house. Croy was a man of action, but this evening he had spent almost motionless on the bench, taking only a little wine and some nuts for sustenance. One thing only would bid him tarry so. For hours he had kept an eye on the place, watching who came and who went, hoping to spy a glimpse of Cythera.

After midnight he got his chance. She and Bikker came traipsing over the grassy common. The place had a reputation for being full of footpads after dark, but the two seemed to pay no special heed to their surroundings. Instead they were deep in conversation. Croy even got the sense they might be arguing.

He placed a salted almond between his lips and bit down hard. He longed—oh, how he desired it!—to call out, to wave, to get her attention somehow. He longed to jump down from his perch and run to her side, to catch her up in his strong arms (even knowing what a mistake that would be) and carry her off to his castle. Failing that, he would have been glad even for a moment's soft conversation, for a renewed exchange of promises and honeyed words.

But it would not happen tonight. Tonight he could only watch.

The guards at Hazoth's door challenged the pair, but Bikker reached for his sword's hilt and the armored sentries fell back. The two of them stopped just inside the sorcerer's gate, however, and waited for something Croy could not see. When it came, he felt it instead. There was a sudden change in air pressure, or perhaps merely the crickets in the grass all fell silent at once. It was like the night itself held its breath.

It lasted a bare moment. Then it was over, and Cythera and Bikker entered the villa's grounds and went their separate ways. He, toward a low shed at the side of the house that Croy knew served as barracks for the sorcerer's guards. She, into the house through the stables—like a common servant.

How he felt the need to rush down there and follow her, to reach—quite gently, of course—for her hand in the shadows, to breathe her name and see recognition in her eyes. But not tonight.

Not while the house was shielded so patently by some spell—a spell even she must wait to pass.

Not tonight. Not until he could get his weapons back.

It was time to find out what friends, if any, he had left in the palace.

# CHAPTER THIRTEEN

The next day Malden spent in preparation.

It was mad even to consider going through with this. The job he'd been hired for was, if not impossible, distinctly ill-advised. It was going to make of him a pigeon in the midst of a pack of dogs. If the plan failed in the slightest particular, it would mean a quick but nasty death, a spear through his lights, or an axe through his skull. Cutbill's influence could not protect him from that.

Yet if it worked—it couldn't, of course, it was the worst kind of folly, but—*if it worked*, he would be clear of his debt to the guildmaster of thieves before the sun rose tomorrow morning. He would be a full member of the guild, with all the rights and privileges thereunto pertaining. He would be a free man again. Better, by far, because he would be on his way to wealth. On his way to being a man of means.

In the Free City of Ness, that was the only thing that counted.

He made his way to the Ashes early, just as the sun was rising over the city's wall. The gang of children that guarded Cutbill's headquarters did not show themselves—they already knew he belonged there. Loophole, Lockjaw, and 'Levenfingers were inside the ruin already, though. As far as he knew, they were there all day, every day, sitting on the empty coffin. The old men greeted him warmly and asked him what schemes he had planned for the day. They asked every time he visited. "A little of the same," he told them. "Though to be honest, my heart's not in it."

"Be of good cheer, lad," Loophole told him. "Money comes to them that keep their eyes open."

"I'm sure you're right." Malden would gladly have spoken with the old men, for he'd learned they were a sure font of wisdom. If any of them knew how this job could be done, this fantastically impossible job, surely it was one of them. Yet he knew that anything he said to them—even to Lockjaw—would be reported to Cutbill at once. In addition, Bikker and Cythera were quite clear that his fee included a hefty sum to make sure Cutbill never learned of the plan. So he kept his peace and headed inside.

He had learned on his second visit, some days ago, that it was not necessary to travel by coffin every time you visited Cutbill's burrow. That was just for new arrivals, a kind of object lesson to remind them their lives were forfeit if they crossed Cutbill in any way. Actual employees had their own entrance through a trapdoor hidden in the debris of the fallen house. It led to a door below, hidden behind a curtain. There were many doors in Cutbill's domain, and all of them were hidden. Malden was certain he'd seen only a fraction of the guildhall in his visits.

In the main room, Bellard was throwing darts at a target on one wall. The permanent dice game was going on in the corner, but only two players had risen so early. There were others there, thieves like himself, pimps come to pay their tithe to the master, procurers dividing up their stash, and one fellow dressed in dusty traveling clothes that Malden did not recognize. There was something odd about the man, but in the dim light he couldn't get a good look.

The traveler was sleeping on the divan when Malden came in, but before he could take two steps into the room, the man bolted upright and reached inside his tunic, probably for a knife. His beady eyes twinkled in the candlelight as he shot them back and forth, and his lips pulled back in a sneer as if he expected Malden to attack him.

"Be at ease," Bellard said. The dust-covered man nodded, lay back down and immediately returned to sleep.

Malden glanced over at Bellard, who nodded and said, "That's Kemper. An unsavory character if there ever was one."

"He's a thief, like me?" Malden asked.

Bellard cocked his head to one side. "Hardly. Little more than a sharper—a card cheat. A vagabond by nature, never stays in any one place for long."

"What's he doing here? Is he one of Cutbill's?"

Bellard snorted in derision. "He's no member of this guild but he pays his respects when he passes through. We wouldn't abide his sort at all if we had a choice, as he's wanted by the reeves of every village within a hundred miles of here. He's called on an old tradition of sanctuary, though, so we must let him lie here until he thinks it's safe to head out again. Of course, the tradition doesn't preclude Cutbill from charging him rent."

Malden shrugged. Good to know such a tradition existed, he supposed—who knew when he might need it himself? Yet his business was with Slag, the dwarf, so he made his way quickly to the workbench and brazier at the far side of the room.

"Need somewhat?" the dwarf demanded, looking up as Malden approached. He was no less ugly in daytime, though of course the sun never shone down in Cutbill's hiding hole. "Or you just wanted a kiss?"

Malden smiled. "There's a job I'm casing right now," he said, "and it's going to be tricky. I need a few things to see it out."

"If I can't build it, you're not good enough to need it," Slag replied.

Malden listed his requirements and the dwarf nodded. He said he had everything in stock—the items Malden requested were not too exceptional—and would provide them for hire, for a price. The price was steep, but Malden could cover it with the coins in his purse, just barely. Good thing, too, as the dwarf expected payment in advance.

"That way, when your arse is killed on the job, I don't have to go down into the fucking Bloodgod's underworld to get what you owe me."

"Your confidence in me is inspiring," Malden said. He waited for the dwarf to go to his storeroom and fetch the things. It took quite a while, so he played at darts with Bellard to pass the time. He managed to lose another tuppence before the dwarf returned. Malden had deft hands, but Bellard had the keener eye.

The tools came wrapped in sailcloth that had been treated with tar to make it waterproof. It would keep the rust off. "Return 'em in the shape you found 'em, or there's an extra fee," Slag told him.

"And so I shall. Farewell, Bellard. Farewell, all." Bellard grunted a response but no one else even looked up as Malden headed back to the light of day. The three old masters were a bit more cordial, but he didn't spend long speaking to them.

He had some time to squander, so he walked all the way uphill to the old Chapterhouse of the Learned Brothers, which was said to be haunted, before heading south around the curve of the city wall, down through the warren of close-spaced houses that marked the eastern extent of the Stink, then farther south to the homes of the fishermen and sailors who took the goods of Ness to ports around the world. It was a very long and pointless route, but it kept him always in the broad streets where most honest people traveled, and away from dark alleys and sheltered closes.

It also led him past the King's Gate, so called because it opened on the road to the royal fortress of Helstrow, a hundred miles away. Malden paused a moment to muse that Helstrow might as well be on the far side of the moon. He had never traveled more than a mile in any given direction in his life. He could not, bound as he was by the city's walls.

The gate stood twenty feet high—tall enough for knights to ride through with their lances raised. It was made of the same bluish stone as the city wall, and on this side was fronted by a massive triumphal arch celebrating some military victory or other. Malden doubted anyone living in the Stink could have told him what battle it commemorated. He let his gaze wander briefly over the carved figures of soldiers fighting wicked elves, but what really drew his eye was the land beyond the gate.

It was green, for one thing. Green grass grew out there, catching the sun. It was so wide and open, and not a soul in sight. Malden took a few steps into the narrow tunnel of the gate and found the guards there didn't even look at him. No, of course not—they had no brief to keep people from leaving. The people of Ness were free to go outside if they pleased. They just weren't free to come back in.

The sun on the grass out there looked so warm and inviting. A summer breeze played with the blades of it, stirring them gently, then letting them fall back. Behind Malden, in the Stink, all was noise and grime and desperation. Out there it would be quiet, he thought. Quiet and peaceful and—

"Make way, you little fuck!" someone shouted, and suddenly a brown and black dog was snarling at him, its wet teeth snapping shut on his cloak. Malden looked up in startlement and just had time to jump back as a mounted man came thundering through the gate, heedless of where his horse's hooves fell. The owner of the dog, a footman wearing the same coat of arms as the rider, shoved Malden back against the wall of the gate with a cudgel. "There's people of importance trying to use this gate, and you're just standing here gawking?"

Malden tried to stammer out a reply. "I assure you, I was simply—"

The footman knocked him down with the cudgel, and probably would have beaten him senseless if he hadn't needed to run off then, to keep up with his master. Down in the dust Malden felt at his ear where the footman had struck him. He was glad his fingers didn't come away bloody.

"Oh, just get out of there," a guard said, grabbing his arm and pulling him away from the gate. "You're lucky I don't dump you outside and let the reeve take you."

Lucky indeed. The green grass out there might look inviting, but the second he trod on it he would have legally become a villein. A slave, in all but name.

But if he had a little money to his name—if he could purchase even a small plot of land in some cheap place . . .

the story would be different. And that was what Cutbill had
promised him, wasn't it?

Cutbill had said he was a prisoner in Ness. Malden had
never felt that way before—now he could think of himself
in no other terms. A prisoner. And Cutbill had the means to
set him free.

It could happen tonight, for the price of a little risk.

The rest of the morning he spent cutting purses down at
the fish market by Eastpool. He needed to earn back all he'd
spent or be penniless by nightfall. He supped on cockles at
a little shack by the river gate and then rented a room in
a doss-house frequented by sailors. He would gladly have
gone back to his own rooms above the waxchandler's but he
had to make sure none of Cutbill's people saw him when he
met Cythera later.

Much of his movement during the day had been for this
purpose. He knew that Cutbill would have spies watching
him, especially if he seemed bent on some specific task.
Then there would be the unaligned thieves, the pickpockets and grifters of too small account to join the guild. They
tended to follow Cutbill's people around the way gulls will
follow a galleon, hoping to pick up scraps left behind by
the more established thieves. Malden knew he had to make
sure none of either sort were aware of what he was doing, so
he spent the day acting as if he had nothing planned at all.
There had been no reason to rise early, and in fact he spent
the afternoon asleep in his rented bed. It was just past midsummer, with the festival of Ladymas less than a fortnight
away, and the sun would not set until well into the evening.

When he rose, he brushed the bed's freight of insects
from his hair and clothes, then climbed out the window and
up onto the roof of the doss-house. He was relatively certain
no one was following him, but to be sure he crossed three
streets by the rooftops, leaping silently from one building to
another. When he dropped down to street level again he was
at the very edge of the river Skrait. He traveled northward
again, upriver, by moving from pier to dock to wharf—hundreds of them stuck out from the riverbank, as each house
along the Skrait had its own. He ended up deep in the Smoke,

the region of manufactories and workshops where tanners, papermakers and bookbinders, hatters, blacksmiths, brewers, and bakers all plied their trades. The shops stained the air with their fumes and turned the river black with their dumping, and the smell was intense—the region downwind of the Smoke was called the Stink for good reason. It was here that Malden was to meet Cythera.

He had time to consider what he was doing. He had time to wonder if he was mad, or if he truly expected to live through this. He had time to think of that green grass beyond the gate, and how good it would feel under his feet. Eventually the sun went down and he had no more time to think.

When she came for him, gliding out of the vapors in a tiny boat she rowed herself, she asked him if he was ready. He spoke no word, but simply dropped into the boat and grabbed a pair of oars.

# CHAPTER FOURTEEN

As they hauled away from the Smoke and up the river toward the Golden Slope and the Spires, the docks and piers that stuck out into the water grew fewer in number. The river narrowed and grew faster, so they had to row all the harder. The water turned clean again, with only the occasional floating bit of sewage or debris to mar its churning surface. The river Skrait had driven its channel right through the northern half of Castle Hill, creating a winding canyon through half the Free City. Conforming to the slope of the hill, the ground along the riverbanks grew higher until it had to be held back by retaining walls, so that eventually they traveled between two high and sloping walls of ancient brick, with moss slowly eating away its mortar. Here and there a tree had taken root directly into the bricks, and its branches swayed over them, its leaves making the moonlight flicker through the mist that hung over the water.

The river bent away from them, concealed by the rising wall. Malden saw a glimmer of light. "Hold, someone's coming," he whispered, and reached back to grab Cythera's arm. He was strangely hurt when she yanked her arm away before he could touch it.

What he saw took all his concentration and kept him from thinking why. A long boat came nosing around the corner—little more than a dugout, really, its sides well-patched. An old woman stood in the stern, poling the boat downriver, while half a dozen children leaned over the thwarts. They skimmed the water with long hooks, snatching at every piece of jetsam they passed. One held an oil lamp just above the surface, illuminating a milky patch of water.

"Move aside and let them go past," Malden said. Cythera steered her boat over toward the last of the docks on the southern side of the Skrait. One of the children raised his dripping hook in thanks.

"What are they looking for?" Cythera asked, her voice a tight whisper, no louder than the rustling of leaves.

"Anything they can sell. A cloak dropped into the water from the bank of the Royal Ditch. Waste leather from one of the tanneries in the Smoke." Malden shrugged. "A dead body that might still have a purse on its belt."

He heard Cythera gasp. "Truly? They might find such a gruesome haul? Those poor children!"

Malden frowned. He knew she had money to spare, but could she really be so sheltered by it that she didn't understand basic necessities? "They would cherish it. It would mean they could eat for a week."

The old woman waved cheerily at them as she pushed past. Malden waited until the boat of mudlarks was gone from view, then signaled to Cythera that they could move again.

"It's not well that they saw us," she suggested, but as if she hoped he would reassure her.

"Even if the city watch found them and asked what they saw this night," he said, "they'd never describe us. They know if we're abroad this late we're of their kind—of the great confraternity of desperate folk. They'd never betray us."

Behind him, he heard her sigh in relief. He wished he could assure himself so easily. But there was nothing for it—they couldn't turn back now. Pushing on, they made their way up the river until the walls surrounded them on either side.

There was no sound but the dripping and knocking of their oars. They saw no more boats, not at that late hour. Malden kept an eye on the tops of the retaining walls, making sure no one was looking down to follow their progress. He did not see anyone.

It was hard work, rowing upriver, and for a while they did it in silence. It was boring work, too, however, and eventually Malden started talking just to have something to do. He kept his voice very low, knowing that sound travels far over water, but she did not try to silence him.

"I'd pay good coin to know how you pulled that trick yesterday. When you just appeared like that on the roof of the university. It was magic, was it not?"

"If you could define what magic is, and what it is not, you would be wiser than the world's great sages," she told him. "It was simply what you called it. A trick."

"Hmm. And do you know many such?"

"Not many."

Malden saw that up ahead a zigzagging set of stairs had been carved through the wall, which at this point was nearly thirty feet high. The stairs ended at a solitary dock, but there were no boats at it. All the same, he held his tongue until they were well past.

"And the way you held my gaze? I could not look away, even with that great mountain of a man coming up behind me. Surely that was wizardry."

"What are you talking about?" she asked. There was no guile in her eyes.

"You charmed me," he said, looking over his shoulder, intending to take her to task for enchanting him. Yet she looked as puzzled as he. "You used some spell."

"You give me too much credit. I know no such incantation."

Yet of course it had to be a spell she'd cast on him. Didn't it? What else could have explained his sudden interest in her eyes, her hair? What explanation would satisfy the facts, other than that she had ensorcelled him?

Malden had grown up in the company of harlots, and knew well the ways of physical love. He'd often heard them talk of the other kind, of romance and true love. They'd even talked of the fabled love-at-first-sight, though most had considered it a myth. He himself had never considered he might feel that way about another human being, much less an enchantress covered in tattoos.

So it must have been magic. There was no other possibility. Was there?

He decided to talk of anything but, rather than continue in that line of thought.

"You intrigue me, Cythera. You seem a lady of quality, yet you associate with the likes of Bikker."

"He's not so bad. Honest, in his way."

"He's a ruffian. Cheerful, perhaps, but uncouth. I don't think you chose his company. You work with him because you were ordered to do so. I think you both work for someone else. Someone who wants my services, who—"

"Who shall remain nameless."

"Very well. Though the number of citizens who could afford your services must be small."

"Not every wage is paid in coin."

It was a funny kind of thing to say, and it birthed all manner of questions in Malden's mind. But it was clear it pained her to speak of it, so he let it go. He had another thing to ask her about anyway.

"Those tattoos on your face and your arms—"

"They are not tattoos." Her voice grew sharp when she said it.

"The designs, then. Did I really see them move?"

"Yes. They are never still."

"What artist paints them? What kind of pigment does he use?"

Cythera sighed. "No artist. No paints. They are a curse. Or rather, they were imposed on me as a gift by my mother. Or perhaps she meant to curse another."

"Your mother was a sorceress? I can believe that, for you certainly enchanted me." There it was again. That thought he couldn't explain.

She seemed unwilling to discuss it herself. "You'll hold that scoundrel tongue of yours, if you know what's good for you. My mother was never a sorceress. And she still lives. She *is* a witch."

"Naturally," Malden said.

Cythera sighed. "Must you always be so glib?"

"It's part of my charm."

"Oh, you have charm? I hadn't noticed." But she was smiling.

"You wound me to the heart," he said. "But it's all right. We'll find some way you can make it up to me. When this is over, what say you we both—"

"Stop," she said, interrupting his half-serious attempt at courting. "Ship your oars."

He did as she said. "Is this the place? Have we really come so far?"

"Conversation makes any night fly. Yes—look. There is the pipe I was told to seek out. This is exactly the right spot."

The pipe in question stuck directly out of the wall. Filthy water drained from its end in a constant trickle. It was big enough around for a man to climb through, if it hadn't been closed by an iron grating. Such a man would have been a fool, of course, for the pipe led nowhere but into the dungeons of the Burgrave.

Malden looked up—and up. The gentle cambered wall above him rose no less than one hundred and fifty feet into the air. Straight to the top of Castle Hill. Up there, far, far in the air, was the Burgrave's palace.

Malden knew one thing for certain. On Cutbill's secret

protection list, the Burgrave's name did not appear. The Burgrave, of course, had his own garrison of troops for protection and did not need the aid of the master of thieves.

Malden had never been given a reason why he could not break into the house of the ultimate ruler of the Free City of Ness and pilfer his most prized possession. Most likely this was because no one had ever thought him so stupid as to try it.

At least not until Bikker and Cythera had come along.

"When you reach the top, do not scamper over the parapets directly," Cythera whispered. "Remember—Bikker will create a diversion in the courtyard. The guards up there will rush to investigate. That is your only chance to get in unseen. Move quickly, though not so quickly you fall prey to a trap. Recover the . . . the item we asked for, then come back here as fast as you can. Do not take anything else. It is critical that you do not leave any evidence you were there, or create any suspicion that the thing is gone."

He was very aware she would not say aloud what it was she wanted, not now when they were so close to it. He filed that away under the myriad things about her he found curious and interesting.

"Start your climb now. I'll make sure Bikker knows when to do his part."

"How about a kiss for luck, before I go?" Malden asked.

Cythera laughed.

"From me, such a kiss would token anything but good luck. Quickly, now!"

Malden carefully stood up in the back of the boat. He waited for Cythera to brace herself, both her oars in the water to steady the tiny craft. Then he took a quick step and jumped at the wall, his hands out and fingers spread to find whatever purchase was there.

It was not difficult. The bricks were sturdy, but the mortar between them had crumbled away over time. His fingers fit easily between each row of bricks, so that it was like grabbing at the rungs of a ladder.

Once she saw him dangling from the wall like a lizard,

Cythera bent to her oars and got her boat moving away from the wall. Malden didn't waste time watching where she went. Instead he started to climb, hand over hand.

Straight up.

# CHAPTER FIFTEEN

Malden had learned to climb almost from the time he could walk.

He was not so unusual in that—every child in Ness learned to climb, since so much of the city was on a hillside. The streets were so winding and switch-backed that often the fastest way from one house to another was to go over the house in between rather than around. It was easy enough to move around up on the rooftops, in a city where the streets were so narrow and the second floors of houses almost came together over the alleys. There were places in Ness where if a woman left a pie cooling on a second-story windowsill, the man across the street could reach through his own window and help himself to it. Even small children could jump from one house to another with little danger of falling. A relatively nimble child could run from one end of the Stink to the other across the rooftops without having to do more than occasionally hop. There were few enough opportunities to play in the crowded streets, so children often headed upward to find space for their games.

Malden had shown a real talent for climbing at an early age. He'd had no fear of heights and a love of clean, fresh air, so the tops of the city proved his natural element. His few friends always dared him to climb to the top of a steeple or dance atop a high chimney. Later, when he turned to crime for his livelihood, he found that a man who could run across the rooftops was a man rarely caught by the watch. So he trained himself to climb faster and jump farther than anyone else.

This climb was like many he'd made before, he told himself. It didn't matter what was up top—hanging on and not looking down were all it would really take.

The wall of Castle Hill leaned away from him, so instead of a sheer surface it was like a very steep slope. Only a few of the bricks had crumbled with time, though many were cracked. It was not so hard a climb, or rather, it would not have been, if it weren't so long. Taking his time, choosing every handhold carefully, pausing now and again to rest, all kept Malden from falling, but nothing could keep the cramp out of his fingers forever. He looked always for features of the wall to aid him, and found a few. Here and there a dripping pipe emerged from the bricks. On occasion he passed a narrow window, wider than an arrow slit but never so big he could have fit through. These allowed him good spots to stand and massage his hands, to ready them for further climbing. Such spots were far apart and few in number, but they helped. They even gave him a chance to free his hands long enough to take a drink of wine from the flask he kept on his belt.

By the time he was sixty feet up in the air, however, his hands were pained claws. Another ten feet and he could no longer feel his fingertips. The whole front of his tunic was stained with brick dust, and sweat had begun to pour down the back of his neck.

At seventy-five feet up he had a new peril to worry about. Across the river's channel, the opposite wall gave out—the hill was lower over there, and topped with a strip of parkland thick with chestnut and oak trees called the Royal Ditch. Lanterns hung from some of the lower branches, tended by the proprietors of the gambling houses and expensive taverns that lined the Goshawk Road there. He could hear music playing and occasional bursts of raucous laughter carried across by the wind. Should anyone there chance to look over, toward Castle Hill, he would be quite visible—

and he had no doubt they would sound some alarm. The
Free City of Ness was eight hundred years old and had never
been properly sacked by invaders, but there was always a
first time.

He had his cloak turned inside out, to show its paler side.
It was like a hawthorn leaf in color, a deep forest green on
one side, a lighter sage green on the other. The lighter hue
would make him harder to spot against the wall, but still,
when he moved he would certainly give himself away.

There was nothing for it, however. He would have to trust
to luck that no one would chance to look across the water.

His luck was with him in that, at least.

Starting at eighty feet up the wall had been carved by ancient hands. A row of human figures was sculpted into the
brick, each of them twelve feet tall so they could be seen
easily from the Royal Ditch. Malden had seen them often
from that not-so-distant vantage, but they looked smaller at
the time. They represented the direct male descendants of
Juring Tarness, the first Burgrave of the Free City of Ness.
Each of them had been Burgrave in his turn. They were crude
images at best, and the artists who carved them had made
one foolish choice in their designs. The Burgraves were depicted each in full armor, their heads hooded with chain mail
and square helmets mounted with the crown of the Burgravate. As a result it was almost impossible to tell them apart.
One had a mustache, another a full beard—perhaps such
facial hair had been fashionable in their day. Malden had
never cared to learn their names or the dates of their respective reigns. He did not care to learn them now, though he was
grateful to them for one simple reason: the carvings were
even easier to climb than had been the bare bricks. He made
a silent apology to the ancient Burgrave whose shoulder he
trod upon, and made for the top without pausing.

One hundred feet up and his hands were frozen in the
shape of hooks. He jammed them again and again into
the cracks between bricks and continued hauling himself
upward. One hundred twenty feet and he felt like all his toes
were broken from repeatedly pushing them into gaps too
small to admit them.

One hundred thirty feet—and he heard a voice from above. Instantly he froze in place, pressing himself as close as possible to the bricks. Not twenty feet over his upstretched arms a guard was walking patrol along the wall of the palace grounds. If they should look over the crenellations, if they looked down—

"Tell me if anyone's coming," the voice said. Clearly the owner of the voice must be speaking to someone.

"No, no, it's clear," a second voice said, proving Malden's suspicion.

Then came a grunt, and a noise like chain mail rattling. And then something caught the moonlight as it fell past Malden at incredible speed.

He came very close to falling off the wall then and there. He was so desperately afraid of being hit by the jetsam from above that he pulled one hand free of the wall and swung away from his perch. A moment later he realized what was happening and cursed himself silently for his lack of forbearance.

A stream of foul-smelling liquid was coming down from on high, a stream that spread out and turned to mist a few dozen feet below his position. The guard was pissing over the side.

Malden's lip curled in disgust. Was the man too lazy to find a privy? But there was nothing he could do but hold tight, and wait, and hope the wind didn't change. He spared a quick glance down to make sure Cythera was well clear. He couldn't see her little boat down there, though he was mightily impressed by how far down it was. He had no fear of heights, but it would take a man of far greater courage than himself to look down into that abyss and feel no vertigo.

When the guard had finished and moved on, Malden looked back up, toward the top of the wall. It was close now. One quick sprint and he would be on top. But his hands were so painfully cramped he knew he would arrive unable to use them for anything but climbing. He needed to rest a moment, to rub the blood back into his whitened fingers. He also needed to make sure he would not be seen when he reached the top. Looking around, he saw a window off to his left, no more than a dozen feet away. Moving carefully, as silently as a cat on a carpet, he shifted himself over in that direction. The window was broader than the others he'd seen, though it was also lined with iron bars. Still, it would make a great place to stand for a while. Just a few minutes, he promised himself. Just until he could feel something in the balls of his thumbs.

Yet as he approached the window he heard someone moving around inside. He had to freeze in place again and wait for the people there to go away. And that could have been when his luck ran out.

For exactly at that moment Bikker provided the promised distraction.

# CHAPTER SIXTEEN

Croy hated subterfuge, but sometimes the direct approach was just not appropriate. For instance, when one needs to recover one's property from a locked room inside the palace, and one is under an order of execution, it behooves one to act in a clandestine fashion.

So instead of marching up to the Burgrave's door and asking politely, he had come to this. Masquerading as the lover of a lady-in-waiting, and then sneaking into the most secure room in the city.

"I have the key here, somewhere on my person," Lady Hilde said, and placed a hand on the bodice of her gown. She seemed to be breathing very hard and her eyes were wide as she stared into Croy's face. "It wasn't easy to get, you know. I had to wait until the castellan fell asleep at his desk. Luckily for you he's so old and decrepit, he didn't wake up even when I took it from his belt. But now—where did I put it?"

He supposed she might be frightened. It was an understandable emotion. They were inside the Burgrave's counting house, a place no one of any rank was permitted to enter after it was locked up for the night. Even by day only the castellan and the bailiff had keys to the place. It was so secure that the castellan hadn't bothered posting guards out front—after all, anyone approaching it from the courtyard would have had to pass dozens of guards already.

Of course, if you had access to one of the Burgravine's ladies-in-waiting, and she was willing to do you a favor, there weren't a lot of places in Ness that were off-limits. Croy felt distinctly uneasy about what he was doing. This was very much counter to his moral code, and he was a man for whom ethics meant everything. Still, he was able to assuage his conscience a bit. He wasn't hear to steal—he was no thief. He had only come here to recover that which belonged to him. That which he was pledged to honor and uphold, in fact: the sword he counted as his soul.

The counting house was built into the wall that surrounded the palace grounds, and had to be the most secure structure in the Free City, because it was where the Burgrave kept his gold when he wasn't spending it. It was a vast trove, stuffed full of bags of coin, coffers overflowing with silver plate, great heaps of gems, and the jewelry of Ommen Tarness's wife, the Burgravine.

None of which was what Croy had come for. His swords had been taken from him when he was arrested, and brought here, placed with the most important relics and treasures of the Free City of Ness. Just behind the locked door he faced. Hilde had claimed she could get the key for him only if he brought her inside with him so she could see the treasures for herself. Lacking a better plan, he had agreed.

"I seem to be having trouble finding the key," she told him. "Perhaps you can help me look?"

He knelt with his lamp and looked around the floor at her feet.

"No, you foolish man," she said. "It's somewhere in my dress."

He opened his mouth to speak, and then found he could not close it again. Hilde was unlacing her corset. "Well? You were so handsome yesterday in Market Square, Croy. So dashing. It made my knees tremble. And other parts of me as well. Of course, it might just be that I haven't had a man all year. My mistress keeps me so busy. Maybe if the Burgrave could perform better his own husbandly duties, I could slip away more often. Oh, no, that's exactly where I want you," she said, as he began to rise to his feet. She giggled and put a finger on his shoulder, pressing him back down to a kneeling posture.

"Milady," he said, jumping up, "I fear I misheard you."

Hilde rolled her eyes. "Don't tell me you're one of those men who doesn't know what to do with a naked woman." She twitched her shoulders and her kirtle fell to the floor. Underneath it she was wearing nothing but a chemise and knee-length hose.

Croy blushed and averted his eyes. "Milady, I would never spurn, ah, true affection from your quarter, but . . . my heart belongs to another."

"You're . . . serious."

He bowed his head and tried to keep his thoughts pure. It was not easy with Hilde's underthings rustling so close to his face.

"Here," she said, and pressed a long iron key into his hand. "Do what you have to, while I put all this back on. I have no idea how I'm going to lace up this corset without a big, strong man to help, but—oh, never mind."

"Thank you," Croy said, and quickly opened the locked door. Beyond was a tiny room with a barred window. For a split second he thought he saw a shoe outside the bars, but that was quite impossible—outside that window would be a sheer drop to the river Skrait, more than a hundred feet down. He turned to look around the room, expecting to have to search high and low for his swords.

In fact, they were the only things present. Where were the religious relics the Burgrave was required to parade through the streets every Ladymas? Where the city's charter, for that matter? Perhaps they'd gone to the same place as the city's gold reserves. The swords lay perfectly alone on a shelf below the window, two long blades in shagreen scabbards. They were all he'd brought with him when he returned to the Free City. He hung them in their proper places on his baldric and stepped back out of the room.

Hilde waited for him near the door, tapping her foot with impatience. "Come along," she said. "I'll take you through the kitchens so no one sees you. Though it would probably do my reputation some good to be seen in connection with you."

"I'm a wanted criminal," he protested.

"You don't understand this city at all, do you?" she asked. "Surely you—"

A high-pitched scream of terror and pain split the darkness outside the door. Croy leaned over Hilde's shoulder to look out into the courtyard just in time to see a man of the city watch come staggering through the main palace gate. A dark stain spread across his cloak-of-eyes as he clutched at an arrow sticking in his side. Before he'd taken a dozen steps he collapsed face first onto the flagstones.

A second scream followed close, and a guard toppled from the battlements of the palace wall. An arrow had pierced him through the neck.

"Murder!" someone shouted. "Murder!" And then an alarm bell started to ring, high-pitched and wild.

# CHAPTER SEVENTEEN

M alden listened to the clamor beyond the wall for only a moment, then scurried up over the last twenty feet of bricks faster than a spider. He slipped over the crenellations at the top of the wall and found himself on a broad walkway. No guards were in sight. He crept to the far side of the wall and peered through an embrasure, down into the courtyard.

Castle Hill was the residence of the Burgrave and the seat of his administrative functions. It was also a fortress, a keep designed to forestall any invading horde. Within its walls stood the garrison where the Burgrave's personal retinue of soldiers lived, and the central Watch Hall from which the bailiff's civic guardians were dispatched. Both these structures were alive with light now as men in various states of uniform dress came pouring out of their gates to fill the broad courtyard and parade ground. There was a great deal of shouting and confusion, and knots of watchmen in their cloaks-of-eyes were gathered around two bodies that lay lifeless in the grass. A klaxon bell rang with a deafening strident tone. Meanwhile, a detachment of soldiers were storming up and around the walls and towers on the far side of the hill, over where it looked down on Market Square. They were thrusting torches into every shadow, stabbing their iron swords into troughs and haylofts, looking for whoever had shot the two men with arrows.

What, in the Bloodgod's name, had Bikker done? He'd killed two men in cold blood—just to create a moment of chaos.

Of course, Malden had to admit it made a most excellent diversion. Not a single soldier or watch man remained in the northern half of the courtyard. The counting house, the Burgrave's private chapel, and the kitchens were all deserted. So was the palace.

This last was a tall, el-shaped structure made of quarried stone elegantly carved and pierced on its lower level with many arches and broad windows of fine glass. It was airy and light and held up with slender flying buttresses, topped with gargoyles and peaked gables. Even the Ladychapel, the great church that stood across Market Square, was not so delicate in appearance nor more refined in ornament. The palace was a masterpiece of architectural skill. One determined barbarian with a sledgehammer could probably bring it crashing down. It was built around a much older and more sturdy structure that looked like a wart on the face of a princess.

Malden surmised that the tower at the end of the el shape probably supported most of the palace's weight. It stood five stories high and he guessed that its walls were five feet thick, pierced only by a few narrow arrow-slits. This was the original holdfast of Castle Hill's first inhabitants, where the first few settlers had fled whenever the elves came a-raiding. It had stood up against those bloodthirsty devils and the dwarves who came after them (back when the dwarves still had some fight in them), and even the human barbarians who scourged Skrae three hundred years ago, back before King Garwulf the Merciful had swept their tribes across the mountains far to the east. It stood as strong as it had ever been, and was still the highest structure in the Free City.

The tower was where he happened to be headed that night. He was going to break into it, when elves, dwarves, and barbarians had never been able to. Of course, back then the palace hadn't been there. It looked like an anemic toddler could break into that airy confection.

The palace stood about thirty feet clear of the wall, separated from Malden's perch by a wide patch of manicured garden. It was that gap he needed to cross.

He ran along the top of the wall to where he could stand directly opposite the palace roof. He took a moment to reverse his cloak so its darker side was outward, then took one of Slag's tools from his belt. It was a grappling hook made in two parts joined by a central hinge. Folded, it could lie flat on his hip, but when he opened its arms fully the two parts locked into place. The prongs were wrapped in padded leather so that when it connected with stone, the hook would not clang or rattle, but make no more sound than a dull thud.

Of course, with the alarm claxon sounding and the shouts of the men in the courtyard, Malden thought it unlikely that he would be heard if he were beating a drum. But it never hurt to be quiet.

He paid out a long double length of rope through the ring in the grapple's haft, then started to swing it back and forth. When he had the momentum right, he made his toss and watched it arc through the moonlight to kiss the palace roof. It slid for a while, then came to a stop.

Slowly, he drew it back to him by tugging on the doubled rope, twitching it now and again to try to get the hook to catch on a chimney pot or the leg of a gargoyle. The best purchase it found was in the join between two lead roof tiles. It wasn't as secure as he might have liked, but he thought it would hold his weight. Though he tugged and yanked at the rope to make sure, there was only one way to test the grapple's hold. He took the two ends of the rope and tied them tight around the nearest crenellation of the wall. Then he climbed out onto the rope—and hung from it like a monkey, crossing his legs around it and holding on with both hands so his back dangled toward the Burgrave's rose garden, twenty feet below.

The rope sagged a bit but held. Malden exhaled all the air in his lungs. He made his way across hand over hand, sliding his feet forward as he went. In short order he was able to clamber up onto the roof of the palace, where he waited a moment for his heart to stop racing. Then he recovered his grapple and his rope. By doubling the line and tying it off, he'd made a very long loop and was able to pull on one side of the rope until the knot came to his hands. It was a simple matter to untie the knot, then draw the whole rope toward him until he could coil it around his waist. He would have much preferred to leave it in place, and thus have a ready escape route, but couldn't dare leave it where it might be discovered. Looking down into the courtyard, he could see that the soldiers were already extending their search to the

northern part of the fortress—it would not be long before
they came to search the wall where he had just been.

The diversion had served its purpose well enough. Yet
now it was having the opposite effect. Before Bikker started
peppering the place with arrows, probably the bulk of the
guards had been asleep or otherwise distracted. Now every
man in the palace grounds was wide-awake and looking for
a furtive trespasser. Malden knew that if they caught him,
they would assume he was the phantom bowman—and
would kill him before he could even speak in his defense.
He cursed Bikker under his breath. Getting in had been easy
enough: all told, simply a matter of the strength in his fingers and a little talent at throwing a hook. Getting out would
be a great deal harder.

He might as well make it worth his while. Just below
him, on the top floor of the palace, a balcony projected from
the wall. He could see no lights down there, so he dropped
easily to the railing, then pushed open the doors and darted
inside.

# CHAPTER EIGHTEEN

Malden found himself in a small bedroom that looked
like it belonged to a lady-in-waiting, with a canopied
bed and a large clothing chest. Rushes were strewn on the
floor and perfume had been sprinkled around liberally to
hide any odors. There was no one inside, so he hurried to
the door and pressed his ear against the keyhole. When
he was sure no one was patrolling the corridor outside, he
slipped out the door and down a hallway lit with oil lamps.

Cythera had told him that what he sought was in the

tower, on the same level as this top floor of the palace. "It is in a room that once served as the first Burgrave's bedchamber. It is placed there every night while the current Burgrave sleeps. Beware: it will be guarded well." One layer of its defense, at least, had been removed. Malden imagined that normally this hallway would have been full of soldiers, but Bikker's diversion had drawn them to the courtyard.

"They'll be away from their posts, but don't think that's the only way to guard a treasure. Men at arms are too easily overcome. Walls can be climbed, and locks picked. The Burgrave knows as much. So he'll have other defenses waiting for you."

He had paid close attention to her words. Now, he kept his eyelids stretched as he hurried down the corridor and around the el of the building, into the wing that led to the tower room. As he approached the door at its end he was already unraveling the grip of his bodkin and removing his picks and wrenches. A lock with a dead bolt had been built into the massive iron-bound door, but it gave him little trouble.

"Will there be spells on it, enchantments of protection?" he had asked.

"Unlikely. Magic is too unreliable under the best of circumstances. Not to mention expensive to maintain. No, it is not the handiwork of enchanters you need fear. It is the work of dwarves."

Beyond the door lay a corridor perhaps twenty-five feet long. Tall windows stood every ten feet or so down its length, and moonlight spilled in to form pools of silver on the wooden floor. Between each patch of light lay impenetrable shadows. It was as if the hall were one column of a game board with alternating spaces of light and dark.

"I cannot tell you what traps you may find," Cythera had said. "I can only tell you to beware any room that seems unused. The palace is a busy and a crowded place, so dust on a floor, or rooms that seem completely empty, are avoided for a reason."

There were no doors leading off the moonlit corridor, nor any furniture within it. At its far end he could just see the glint of something metallic. Malden stayed outside, beyond the door, and pondered what lay before him. No dust lay on the floor here, at least none he could see in the pale light. Yet there was a sense about the corridor, a feeling of distinct absence he couldn't quite explain. It didn't have the feel of a place that was used often. Ness was an old city, overcrowded even in its infancy. Every stone had been touched by a million hands over the years, every wall brushed by clothing until it was smooth and worn. This hallway, in contrast, looked as if it had been just constructed—by skilled and masterful hands.

Which of course was the hallmark of a dwarf's handiwork. Yes. This was the place.

Cythera had been quite clear. "There are more than three score dwarves living in this city. Their services are sought by all the wealthiest citizens, for they alone can build the cunning devices which are proof against thieves and murderers in the night. A human engineer might devise these fiendish pitfalls, but only a dwarf could build them. The Burgrave will have employed the services of the best among them, and the traps he has laid will be of unusual cunning and danger."

Well, he had a dwarf on his side, as well. Slag had raised an eyebrow when told what he required, but then, for the first time, Cutbill's dwarf had looked at him with something other than disdain. It wasn't exactly respect he had seen glowing in the dwarf's eyes, but it was at least an acceptance that he wasn't a complete fool.

Malden reached into a pouch at his belt and took out a lead ball wrapped in leather. It was as heavy as a cobblestone in his hand. With an underhand motion he rolled the ball down the hallway, then quickly took a step back from the doorway.

For a moment he felt quite foolish, like a boy playing games in an alley. The ball rolled merrily along through the first pool of moonlight, then disappeared into the darkness beyond.

Malden's heart pounded, however, when a moment later a portcullis gate crashed down from the ceiling, right where his leaden ball was rolling. Six long bars of iron crashed down and smashed into the floor.

He did not so much as breathe as he watched them slowly retract back into the ceiling. There was the ratcheting sound of a spring reloading itself, and then a click as the portcullis snapped back into place.

He peered through the half-dark hallway. The leaden ball he'd rolled was pierced right through its middle, nearly cleaved in two by one of the falling iron spears. Its end must have been razor sharp.

He took another ball from his pouch and threw it with a little more force this time, lofting it so it landed in the midst of the second pool of moonlight. It bounced once, without triggering anything, then rolled into another patch of shadow. A second portcullis identical to the first crashed down, jarring his senses.

"There will be a way through," Cythera had told him. "Every night the castellan must bring the treasure to the tower room, and every morning he must recover it. For his convenience, the route must not be impossible, nor even onerous. If you know the trick of it, it should be quite easy to make your way through the traps."

And now Malden thought he had the lay of the thing. The floor was rigged, designed to register any amount of weight that fell on it, but only in the dark sections. Those touched by moonlight would be safe. He got a good run-up, then jumped into the hallway, bounding from one pool of light to the next, careful to never let his feet touch any patch of shadow. One leap, two—he was feeling very pleased with himself for figuring it out—a third leap, directly to the final pool of moonlight at the corridor's end. And that was when he remembered something else Cythera had said.

"These traps are not made to be circumvented, they are made to kill thieves. The dwarf who designs them will know what you are thinking, and will find ways to confound your logic, to surprise you when you least expect it."

Despite heeding her advice in all other things, he was still not ready when his feet came down on the final pool of moonlight—and the floor gave way. A trapdoor there had been set to hinge open when any weight fell on it, and though Malden was slender and short of stature, he was more than heavy enough to trigger it.


# CHAPTER NINETEEN


Malden's feet kicked wildly at nothing as his body dropped like a stone into the pit. His blood sang in his ears and his heart galloped in his chest as he felt himself falling, plummeting. It was all he could do to keep a shriek from bursting out of him. His arms flailed out to his sides for balance and his fingers just barely grasped the edge of the pit. His body slammed forward into the wall of the pit, and that hurt so much it made him gasp and lose the grip of one hand.

But the other one held.

Gasping to refill his lungs, his face pressed up tight against the pit wall, he glanced down. There was a flickering light from below, not enough to see much but it showed him that it was a very, very long way down if he let go.

Carefully he reached up and grasped the lip of the pit with both hands. His fingers protested at taking all his weight. They were still sore and swollen from the long climb up the palace wall from the Skrait. He ignored their pain.

From below a distant sound came up, echoing in the shaft of the pit so it sounded distorted and hollow. Yet he could not mistake it: a scream of agony. It was followed by the noise of a great wheel turning, and then more sounds of pain. The pit must lead straight down to the dungeon, far below the palace. Should he fall now, he would be saving the Burgrave the trouble of having guards drag him thence.

He doubted very much there was a pile of soft straw at the bottom either.

Very, very slowly he pulled himself up and out of the pit. Once he had a shoulder above its edge it was much easier, and once he had a leg up and out of the shaft, he was able to just roll out and lie on the floor a moment. He was about to spread out his aching arms when he realized that would put his hand down in one of the shadowy zones of the hallway floor.

He was very fond of that hand. He did not wish to see it pierced by a razor-sharp iron spear. So he kept it by his side and just shook for a while, letting the fear drain out of him. He had expected danger on this job—any burglary was a risky proposition. He had never met such devious hazards before, though. Well, he supposed that should be expected, considering the value of the thing he'd come to steal.

Eventually he recovered his feet and stood up, at the end of the hall.

He must be very close to the tower room he sought. It must indeed lie beyond the very wall ahead of him. Yet he saw no door. Instead he found a niche that held a bronze statue of Sadu, the Bloodgod.

He searched the wall around the niche, looking for some hidden panel that would open to admit him to the tower. He could find none. He tapped the wall with the pommel of his bodkin, thinking to find any kind of hollow or thin place in the wall through which he might break through, but the wall seemed to be made of solid stone, of the same thickness throughout.

It was only after this exhaustive and pointless search that he chose to look at the floor, and noticed an obvious seam in the wood. The crack formed a semicircle five feet in diameter. He was standing within its bound, in fact. He tapped the floor in several places but found it as solid as the wall. Perhaps—yes, perhaps this was a door after all. If somehow the floor could be made to rotate, and the whole wall with it . . . but there must be some trigger, some way of activating the change.

The statue of the Bloodgod, of course.

The Burgrave was known to be a devout of the Lady of Abundance. Sadu was a much older god, one whose worship was not officially forbidden in the Free City but certainly frowned upon. The Bloodgod was the patron deity of the poor and the oppressed, a symbol of ultimate justice and even vindictive revenge. Sadu punished all men alike in the afterlife, and each according to his sins. He was hardly the sort of god a man like the Burgrave would ever want to meet.

The Bloodgod did have eight arms, though, and that leant itself to the obvious purpose of this particular idol.

The bronze statue depicted Sadu in the typical fashion, as he was worshipped in tiny shrines all over the city. The idol had seven arms on the left side of its body, each holding a different weapon: a sword, a falchion, a spear, a trident, a net, a flail, and an arrow. Different images of the Bloodgod always had different weapons in his hands, since Sadu was the master of them all. On the right side he had only one arm, holding an ornate crown, as it always did. Sadu's face was depicted as that of a snarling demon with massive tusklike teeth and wide, staring eyes. Malden had seen more terrifying versions, though this was a common depiction. Yet as he examined the statue quite carefully he noticed two things that were unique to this image in all his experience.

For one, the eyes were not just open—they had been hollowed out. Two sharp points of metal glinted from within their depths. Malden thought of the needles that sprang from Cutbill's lock. Perhaps these were the same—or worse, tiny darts that would fly through the air to poison him if they pierced his flesh. And of course this time the poison would be fatal.

The second thing he noticed was that all eight arms of the Bloodgod were attached to the body by stout hinges. One could move them, if one desired, independently from the rest of the statue.

Clearly he would have to push the correct arm to open the way to the tower room, while pushing any other would result in instant death.

He rejected the crown arm immediately. It was far too obvious.

Of the weapon arms, the net appealed to him first. It was the least deadly of the weapons, while the others could all kill you easily. The arrow was a bit confusing—it really should have been a bow Sadu held, should it not? But the arrow was also very similar to the darts hidden in the eyes.

Yet wouldn't that appeal to some dwarf artificer's twisted sense of irony? Perhaps you pushed the arrow arm to say you did not wish the darts to fire.

It was a gamble, but it seemed most likely. Malden stood well back of the statue, but still within the circular seam on the floor, and reached over to tap at the arm that held the arrow. Nothing happened. He applied more pressure, bending the arm backward.

There was a rumbling of massive gears, a shrieking of poorly oiled metal—and then the whole wall swung on its axis, propelling him directly into the tower room. The place where the Burgrave kept his crown when he wasn't wearing it.

# CHAPTER TWENTY

"You're—You're mad," Malden had said two days before, when Cythera finally revealed what she was after. "The crown of the Burgrave? What possible reason could you have to steal *that*? Why would anyone? If I'm caught with it, I'd be drawn and quartered!"

"You needn't be caught, if you stick to our plan," Cythera said. Though he could see in her eyes that she knew no plan was ever perfect, that events could always conspire to catch a thief. She was asking him to take an enormous risk.

"But—why? It's made of gold, to be sure, but it's only so big. Melted down, it isn't worth a tenth of what you're paying. And you would have to melt it down. No fence would ever touch it. If you so much as showed it to a fence, they would have no choice but to call in the watch."

"We have our reasons for wanting it. Intact," Cythera said.

"As soon as it goes missing, every watchman in the city will come looking for it." Malden shook his head. "They'll tear down the Stink looking for it, and for *me*. I don't—"

"No, they won't," Bikker said. He'd been standing by the fire, staring down into the flames. They danced in his eyes like light from the Bloodgod's pit. He came clanking over to where Malden sat and loomed over him, his face split by a grin. "That's the best part. As you say, there's not much to the crown on its own. A good goldsmith can make a replacement in a day. If the Burgrave appears in public without the crown even once, he'll look a fool. Everyone will ask where it is, and what will he say? That he just forgot to put it on that morning?"

Malden had to admit he had never seen the Burgrave without it.

"That's the heart of the plan," Bikker said, thumping the back of Malden's chair so he nearly fell out of it. "Do you see? He and his advisors will be too embarrassed by its absence to say a word. They won't call out the watch—they'll keep this a secret, from everyone they can. They will never let it be known, anywhere, that the crown was ever stolen. They won't even dare to come looking for it, because then they'd have to tell the watch what to look for. Do you really believe every watchman in the city would keep such a thing secret? No, the bailiff and the Burgrave will just pretend it was never stolen. They'll trot out a replacement, and that will be the end of it."

Bikker squatted down in front of Malden and cuffed him lightly on the shoulder. Just hard enough to leave marks. "So what do you say?" he asked, his eyes bright. "Are you the man for this job?"

# CHAPTER TWENTY-ONE

The crown—technically a coronet—was not a work of great art in itself. It was a plain circlet of gold, crenellated in the same pattern as the Free City's walls. No jewels adorned it, nor was it lined in fur, nor was anything engraved upon it. It was the crown of a leader of free men, not a king who ruled serfs, and so it was not meant to glorify unduly its wearer or set him apart from the common weal.

Honestly, to Malden it looked a little cheap. Even the head of the fuller's guild wore more ceremonial gold than was in the city's coronet.

But of course the crown had far more symbolic value. It could only be worn by a Burgrave. It was the symbol of his lordship, the image of his right to rule the city as he pleased. It was what separated him from the citizens, what imbued him with all of his power. The Burgrave wore it every time he went out in public—when he led civic processions, when he sat to watch a tourney, when he handed down judgments in the law courts. He'd worn it the day Malden saw him in Market Square, the day he'd condemned that blond fool to death. The crown *was* the Burgrave's power.

Malden was dimly aware in his untutored way that he lived in a kingdom called Skrae, that beyond the Free City's walls there was a grand feudal system of nobility with, at its head, a single monarch who had granted the city its charter and appointed the Burgrave's great-great-etcetera-grandfather to be the city's ultimate ruler. He had never paid taxes to that particular king, and had certainly never seen him. Even the portrait stamped on the larger denominations of money in the Free City was not that of the king, but of one of said king's distant ancestors. Inside the city's walls, the Burgrave was the only power that mattered, and Malden didn't care a jot for anything outside them.

The Burgrave ruled by the authority invested in the crown. A thief who could take the crown away would be sending a message: that the Burgrave's authority was not sacrosanct. That in Ness, in the so-called Free City, every man was vulnerable and no man was truly better—superior—to another.

Malden kind of liked that idea. He'd grown up the son of a whore, a man with no status whatsoever. A man who wasn't even respectable enough to clean the Burgrave's privy. That he could strike such a blow was a great triumph for the equality of men. It would be justice, of a sort. Of course, no one could ever know that he had achieved the theft, more's the pity.

As for the Burgrave, how much would he pay to keep its theft a secret? Surely that was the point of this ridiculous scheme. To extort the Burgrave for as much as his position was worth. It was certainly a dangerous plan, no matter what Bikker said, but still it seemed like it could be quite lucrative.

Malden was now close enough to the crown to reach out and grab it. The tower room was almost empty. Its walls were lined with old campaign banners and tattered flags. Its floor was strewn with sand that ground noisily under his feet. Of furniture, the room possessed a single piece, set exactly in its center: a simple stone pedestal, atop which sat a crystal bowl three feet in diameter.

The bowl was full to its brim with clear water. Inside the bowl, magnified strangely by its curvature, was the crown—and something else.

Cythera had given him one last piece of advice when they planned this theft together. "Such a treasure will always be guarded, of course. It cannot be left alone and unsupervised

at any time. Yet I doubt you will find human guardians
inside the chamber. Most likely it will be some variety of
cursed beast or even a demon, bound to the defense of the
crown. Such a creature will perhaps be the hardest obstacle
you must overcome."

"Is this what you meant?" Malden asked now, whispering to himself as he watched the thing in the bowl squirm
around in its tiny prison. It was a pulpy thing, with leprous
skin and long boneless arms. It looked somewhat like an
octopus, though it had no head that he could see, nor suck-
ers on its tentacles. A particularly flexible starfish, perhaps.

Malden could easily have held it in his hand. As he
watched, it writhed its way through the crown, wrapping
one oozing arm around the golden band. He supposed, if he
were feeling especially fearful (and he was, after his near
brush with the pit in the corridor outside), that the beast
might possess deadly venom. Or teeth—somewhere—sharp
enough to take his finger at the joint, should he be so foolish
as to reach into the bowl with a bare hand.

He had a better idea. He took the grappling hook from
where it hung on his belt and paid out a few feet of rope.
Then he dipped the hook into the bowl and fished for the
crown. The spineless creature attacked the hook immediately, grasping at it with all of its legs at once, thrashing
so hard at this intruder that it caused the bowl to rock back
and forth on its pedestal. Malden tried to pull the hook free
but the little monster's grip was strong as steel. Struggling
against it merely aggravated the bowl's swaying motion.

"Release, you tiny bastard," he grunted, and yanked the
hook free of its assailant. It came clear—but not without
knocking the bowl completely off its perch. It fell from the
far side of the pedestal and crashed upon the sandy floor
with a noise so enormous that Malden was certain it must
have alerted half the guards on Castle Hill.

He held his breath. He closed his eyes to try to hear
better. No shout came to his ears, however, nor any sound of
men rushing toward the tower. When he was certain it was
safe, he opened his eyes and stepped around the pedestal to
retrieve the crown.

The tentacle creature still had it, however, gripped in one unsolid arm. It flopped impotently on the floor in the wreckage of its bowl and a puddle of water that was already soaking into the sand. It was strange—but had the thing not looked smaller when it was in the bowl? Now it was larger than the crown it held, whereas before it had appeared smaller.

No matter. Malden drew his bodkin from its sheath. He did not wish to have it sting or bite him, so he supposed he would have to just kill it and take its prize by force. Not the way he normally chose to operate, but—

It was definitely bigger. Even as he watched, it seemed to swell. It was hard to say for certain with such an amorphous blob of a creature, but he was certain it was as big now as a dog. One of its flailing arms brushed across his shoe and he jumped back. It was like a sponge, which grows when full of water, Malden thought. With every squirming undulation of its being, it seemed to expand in size. Its arms were long enough to grasp the top of the pedestal, now. To grab Malden's belt if he wasn't careful.

He stepped quickly around it, looking for something to stab. It had no head, nor any eyes, nor even a body in the proper sense. It was more like a clutch of snakes all tied together in knots than a singular being. He took a swipe at one of its arms and connected but did it no injury—its flesh was rubbery and shied away from the point of his bodkin without so much as a scratch appearing on its mottled skin.

Not like a sponge placed in water, he realized, but the opposite. Water kept the foul thing in a manageable size, hence the crystal bowl. When it was exposed to air instead, it swelled—and the larger it got, the faster it seemed to grow.

It was as big as a horse suddenly. Much bigger than himself. Its arms smashed across his shoulder, his knee, his face. Battered and confused, Malden staggered backward, back against one wall.

The thing grabbed him around the waist and *squeezed*.

# CHAPTER TWENTY-TWO

Bile rushed up Malden's throat and his head swam. The breath exploded out of him and he nearly let go of his bodkin. The demon's arm throbbed around his midsection and constricted his guts until he thought for sure he would be pinched in half.

Then it picked him up off the floor and slammed him against the ceiling of the tower room. His vision went black for a moment and when he came to his ears were ringing like bells.

It had grown still larger, until it nearly filled the room. Its myriad arms waved limply in the air and slapped against the stone walls. One of its arms still held the crown, gripped carefully in a thin twist of flesh. It held the thing well clear of Malden's reach, even if he'd had the presence of mind to make a grab for it.

Malden stabbed wildly around him with the bodkin, but even when his knife struck true it merely sank into the pulpy flesh, then came out again without leaving so much as a mark on the creature's arms. The thing was sickeningly fluid, barely solid enough to keep a form, it seemed. Yet where it held him, its muscles were like ropes of steel. The thing was . . . unnatural. Unworldly.

Now Malden understood why the room was guarded by a statue of the Bloodgod. This was no natural beast. It must be a very demon, loosed from out of Sadu's pit of souls. It did not belong in the world of light and air. Whatever sorcerer had summoned it from its natural environment must have understood that. He or she must have known that it would grow, and continue to grow, when exposed to air. They had placed it in the crystal bowl of water to keep its size small. If he could submerge it again in water, perhaps it would shrink once more and—

It thrust him against the walls again and again, trying to

batter him to death. For a while he could not think or even see clearly as he was lashed against the flags and banners that lined the walls of the tower room. Pennons and standards crashed to the floor as his body knocked them free of their pegs. His left shoulder struck the stone wall hard and went instantly numb, and he could barely feel his legs.

*Water—there must be some water—son ewhere—*

He could hardly think straight. He could hardly think at all. There had been water in the bowl, but it soaked into the sand that covered the floor. That must be what the sand was there for. The river was nearby, if he could somehow trick the beast into climbing over the wall and falling into the canyon beyond—but how he would manage that when he could not free himself from its grip was past his imagining.

*Water! He must have it! He—*

He had no water. But he had wine. The flask at his belt was still half full. Would it have the same effect on the creature? He could not be sure.

The beast had grown still larger. It filled the tower room entire now, and was crushing him against the walls with its bulk. As it waved its arms around, it smashed the stones to powder—its arms were as thick around as tree trunks now. Would it keep growing, would it grow so large it burst the walls of the tower? Would that be enough to kill it, when the upper stories of the tower collapsed upon it?

Malden doubted it. But he was certain of one thing—he, himself, would never survive such a collapse.

There was no more time for thinking. He reached around the tentacle at his waist and grabbed the flask of wine. It was leather sewn together with gut, the seams worked with wax to make them waterproof. It sloshed as he lifted it up to see it. When he bought the thing, he'd chosen shrewdly, picking a vessel that wouldn't leak, that would stand up to rough treatment. Now he cursed himself that he hadn't just bought some cheap skin he could burst with one hand. The damned flask was too sturdy. He brought his bodkin around and stabbed it. Wine squirted out of the hole he'd made and red drops ran down the back of his hand.

One drop fell onto the beast's skin. The arm that held

him pulsed wildly and he was thrown hither and yon, but the grip around his waist eased a trifle. Yes! The wine had some effect on the thing. He held the flask toward the tentacle and squeezed it as hard as he could, spraying wine all over its pulpy flesh.

Suddenly, blood rushed down into his legs and they burned with new sensation. His guts relaxed inside his abdomen and he belched as his stomach nearly loosed its contents. He squeezed the flask again and he was free, flying through the air as if the demon had thrown him like a ball.

The wall of the tower came toward him very fast, and he nearly crashed into it head first. He threw his arms up in front of him and managed to catch the wall with his sore fingers and then cling there like a spider before he fell back into the demon's arms.

Below him the beast thrashed like a mad thing, bashing against the walls convulsively. Stone crumbled and shattered and pulverized. A wide crack opened in the wall and then a whole section of the tower's stonework fell away, letting in a rush of cold night air.

The tentacles snapped at Malden's ankles and back, trying to get a grip, but they were slow and he was able to avoid being grabbed up once again. The main problem he faced was that the beast had grown so large there was precious little room in the tower it didn't fill, little enough that Malden had to press himself against the wall to keep from being crushed by its sheer bulk.

More of the wall fell away. The tower above began to groan as its timbers shifted, no longer able to support the weight. The tower that stood for so many centuries, that seemed eternal, now lurched and swayed like a ship in a gale. In a moment the room would collapse and he would be crushed. He had escaped one gruesome fate only to befall another, it seemed. And yet—perhaps—

Malden looked down and saw that he was very close to the statue of Sadu that was the secret lock to this room. The creature had enough respect for its creator, it seemed, not to smash the idol or even brush it with its tentacles. Malden waited until the tentacles were as far from him as possible, then dropped to his feet next to the image. He wasted no time pushing down on the arm-lever that controlled the door.

The pivoting section of floor and wall began to turn, and Malden readied himself to dash through it as it revealed the moonlit hallway beyond. Yet when the wall had swiveled only a few degrees through its arc, with only a sliver of moonlight coming through from the other side, the motion stopped.

The cause was immediately apparent. The tentacled beast's mass was pressing against the wall, keeping it from swinging open. Malden pushed at the wall, trying to force it to open, trying to squeeze his shoulders through the small gap, but to no avail. "No!" he screamed at it. "Get back, you infernal bastard! Let me go!"

The beast made no response but to redouble its thrashing motion. Malden laid into it with his bodkin, stabbing and thrusting wildly at its ever-moving arms. It was no use, though, because the thing was *still* growing, still expanding to fill more and ever more of the available space—

—and then the tower began to rumble, as if it were being shaken to pieces. Rock dust sifted down from the ceiling and the stone walls began to give way.

# CHAPTER TWENTY-THREE

A great crashing noise stopped Croy in his tracks. "That came from the palace," he whispered. "From the tower—did it not? And so soon after those two men were killed. Something's wrong here."

Hilde grasped his hand and dragged him farther into the

shadows beside the kitchens. "It's nothing to do with me or you. Come quickly. We can't let the guards see you here."

Croy held his ground, though, as another thunderous sound issued from the tower. The edifice began to shake and a block of stone fell from its top to crack the flagstones below. Then a fissure appeared in the side of the tower, about halfway up. The men of the watch who were out in force in the courtyard all turned to look as one, and there was a cry of surprise and alarm that could be heard even over the ear-shattering klaxon.

"It's going to collapse," he said, just before the tower's wall exploded outward, showering the courtyard with broken chunks of stone. The upper floors of the tower tottered over with a most horrible slowness, then all at once collapsed in a massive cloud of dust and debris. The watch were everywhere at once, shouting and calling for each other, for the guards, for anyone who was close enough to help.

"There might have been people in there," Croy said, turning toward the lady-in-waiting. "Hilde, you go seek shelter in the—" He didn't bother to finish, as she was already gone. She hadn't stopped to let him save her, but instead ran for dear life. Well, that was probably wise. He hoped she would find safety, and quickly. She might be a little confused, but she was a good woman at heart and he wished her luck.

The moral qualities of ladies-in-waiting was suddenly less important to Croy, though, than the groaning rumble that shook the very mass of Castle Hill and threatened to knock him off his feet, as the tower collapsed further and massive stones went bouncing and rolling across the courtyard.

Was it an earthquake? He'd never heard of such a thing in the Free City. Perhaps some sorcerer had attacked the palace? But Hazoth was the only sorcerer in a hundred miles who had the power for such a thing, and this hardly seemed like his handiwork. Croy drew the smaller of his two swords and made to run for the tower, either to rescue anyone inside the ruin or to slay whoever had knocked the tower down, he wasn't exactly sure which. He got no more than two steps, however, before a hand wrapped in chain mail grabbed his baldric. It threw him off balance and his sword went flying.

He rolled across the flagstones and got his elbows under him, bending his knees so he could leap back to his feet. Then an all-too-familiar face loomed out of the shadows and put a boot on his chest. The big swordsman pressed down hard enough that Croy could barely breathe.

Bikker.

Croy could hardly believe his eyes. He'd known, certainly, that the two of them would meet again. It was destiny. But here? At this time? It seemed fantastic.

"What in the name of Sadu's flaming arse are you doing here?" Bikker asked.

Croy could only stare up at the massive warrior. "I might ask you the same."

"I live here. This is my city," Bikker snarled.

"I meant—"

"I find myself in no position to answer your questions, Croy. But I will have answers to mine. I say again, what are you doing here? You were banished from Ness, never to return. I remember it well, since I was the one tasked with riding you out of the city gates on a rail."

Croy remembered that moment himself. The rail had been tied to the back of Bikker's horse at the time. He had been left bruised and abraded ten miles north of the city with nothing but his swords—even his clothes were ruined by the rough treatment.

"I returned for Cythera, of course," Croy said. "Once I have guaranteed her safety and her freedom, and once I take care of a few other standing engagements, I'll leave in peace. You have my word."

"Doubtful," Bikker said. "Oh, don't look so shocked. I know you're telling the truth. I also know that by 'standing engagements' you mean me. You mean my death. And since that's not likely to happen, well . . . Never mind. Tell me what you're doing here, tonight. Your presence is most inconvenient to my plans."

In the courtyard something crashed to the ground with a thud that shook Croy's teeth in his skull. He tried to rise and see what had happened but Bikker just pressed him down again.

He decided the best way to recover his feet was to answer Bikker. "I came to get my swords back. The Burgrave took them from me when he sentenced me to death. I imagine you were there at my hanging—surely you wouldn't have missed that."

"I had to leave early," Bikker said. He wasn't looking at Croy, but at the ruins of the tower. "I hear it didn't end well."

"Oh?" Croy asked.

"You got away. Croy, please do me a favor and keep reaching for the hilt of Ghostcutter. Please, please, try to draw your sword. It will give me the excuse I need to hack you to pieces right now."

Croy opened his hands wide and stretched them out at his sides. He had known Bikker for a long time. He was quite certain the man was willing to stab him where he lay on the ground, to take his life without the slightest shred of honor or dignity. And yet . . . he hadn't so far. He had every opportunity but still let him live. Was it just because Bikker wanted information? Or was it possible there was something still alive in Bikker, some shred of the honor he'd cast off like a stained tunic?

"Surely Hazoth didn't send you here to kill me," Croy said. "He could not have known I was here—unless he has been following my movements with a spell."

Bikker snorted in derision. "The wizard? I doubt he even remembers your name. He has no interest in you one way or another. He *has* ordered me to be discreet when I'm out in the city. Which is enough to save your life, at least for tonight. Blind me, what is that thing?"

Croy turned his head to look as best he was able at the fresh ruins. He gasped at what he saw. It was as if a nest of gigantic blind asps or equally large worms had been crammed inside one room of the tower and now they were writhing and striking at the air. Yet by the way they moved in concert, he could tell it was a single beast with many arms. Some of its numerous appendages grabbed at the fallen rocks in the courtyard and threw them at the guards

that rushed toward it. Other sinuous limbs pushed against
what remained of the tower as it tried to drag its enormous
bulk out into the night. It made no sound other than a wet
slithering.

"Fiend from the pit, do you think?" Bikker asked, with
professional interest.

"Or a sorcerous abomination, at the very least," Croy
confirmed. A thought occurred to him. Maybe he had a way
of getting back on his feet. "Between Ghostcutter and Acidtongue, we'd stand a chance against it."

"Just like old times, hmm?" Bikker asked. "Is that what
you're thinking?" He pulled at his beard, the way he always
did when he was unable to make a decision. Croy understood, despite himself. The old times had never seemed
older. Yet the two of them took an oath once, an oath on
their souls. Such things died hard.

"That, and that we could save a number of innocent
lives," Croy said.

"Bah," Bikker said, but Croy could tell his heart wasn't
fully in the disdain.

The guards and the men of the watch were already peppering the demon with arrows. The missiles seemed without
effect, so a detachment of guards were approaching it with
halberds at the ready. As they watched, a tentacle lashed
out and threw one poor guardsman half across the courtyard. The man landed in a crump of dented mail and broken
bones from which he did not rise.

"Both you and I have good reason to flee this place before
our faces are seen," Bikker said.

"And better reason to stay," Croy insisted. "When was
the last time Acidtongue did what it was made for? A bloodied sword—"

"Is a sword that doesn't rust," Bikker finished. He looked
disgusted for a moment. Disgusted, perhaps, with himself.
Then he took his boot off Croy's chest and offered him a
hand up.

# CHAPTER TWENTY-FOUR

It was all Malden could do to hold on. His strength was no match for the demon's, even with half its arms crushed under the fallen tower.

But he would not let go of the crown.

In the last moment before the tower collapsed, Malden's luck had returned in trumps. The doorway that had been jammed shut by the demon's bulk collapsed in front of him, its stones shattered by the creature's thrashing. Suddenly the way back to the moonlit corridor was open—and he was given a chance at survival.

He had nearly squandered it. Because even as the tower was collapsing over his head, when the stone was shrieking and roaring and smashing all around him, he heard a voice calling him. A voice of authority that demanded respect. A voice that could have commanded nations.

*Thief,* the voice had said. And that was all. It had not been his ears that heard the voice, of that he was certain. Though it sounded exactly like someone shouting just behind him, he knew the voice was inside his head.

He turned away from escape and safety to see who had spoken. It was not the demon—the thing had no voice, and even if it could speak, it would not have sounded like that. It was a human voice. Which meant, absurd as it might sound, that it was the crown that spoke. The simple golden coronet of the Burgrave.

Malden's childhood had been full of tales of statues that could speak, and of talking animals that were secretly men under the curses of dire sorcery. Those were simple tales, made to entertain. Yet magic was real enough. He was almost willing to accept that a crown could talk, even if he hadn't heard it himself.

When it spoke again, all doubts flew away.

*Thief, do not let me be entombed here.*

Malden reached out then, heedless of the demon's thrashing arms, and grabbed the crown out of the air. The fact that a slender tentacle was still wrapped around its other side did not matter. When that voice spoke, something inside Malden had no choice but to listen. He had grasped the crown, and then thrown himself clear of the collapsing tower, into the trapped palace corridor beyond. When the earth stopped shaking and the demon was crushed under a dozen tons of broken stone, Malden found himself lying on the floor dazed and bruised but with the fingers of one hand still clutching the crown.

He looked up to see the corridor transfixed. When the tower came down it must have shaken the entire palace like an earthquake. The vibrations had been enough to trigger every one of the traps in the corridor. The portcullises were all down, their spear points embedded in the floor. No matter how long he watched them, they did not retract—the delicate springs that controlled them must have snapped. He was trapped inside the corridor, between a massive pile of rock debris and a portcullis that looked uncomfortably like a set of prison bars.

He tried to rise carefully to his feet, intent on figuring out what to do next. "You wouldn't have any clever ideas, would you, crown?" he asked the thing in his hand. It did not answer—perhaps it only gave commands, and did not accept them. He started to dust himself off and consider his plight.

Which was when he was yanked off his feet again, to fall painfully to the floor. He looked in horror at the crown and saw that he was not the only one still holding onto it. The demon's slender tentacle was still wrapped around it in an unbreakable grip.

Slowly, with jerks and starts, the tentacle began to withdraw back into the pile of broken stone. The damned thing was still alive—and intent on keeping its treasure.

But so was Malden. He grabbed the crown with both hands and braced his feet against the pile of debris. He pulled with all his might, heedless if he bent the crown in the process. The muscles in his skinny arms bunched and tightened like lengths of rope, and he gritted his teeth as sweat broke out on his brow. It was certainly a losing battle. The demon was many times stronger than he was, he knew. As it tugged at the crown he felt the power in its gelatinous muscles straining against him. But Malden had heard that voice. The voice that could send men to their deaths, and make them believe they went only to glory.

He refused to let go.

# CHAPTER TWENTY-FIVE

Croy's blood thrummed with excitement, as if his veins were harp strings plucked by righteousness. As he and Bikker approached the fiend they were laughing. Each drew his sword, and the very air seemed to throb with potential.

The blades were made for one purpose alone. It had been a long time since they'd had a chance to perform that function.

Acidtongue seethed in Bikker's hand, its pitted metal slick with power. Ghostcutter leapt from Croy's sheath and shone in the moonlight like a torch of might. Croy's sword had no magic in it—instead, it had been made to cut *through* magic. Its blade was as long as Croy's arm, made of cold-forged iron as black as the pit. No man now alive—nor any dwarf—remembered the method of its manufacture: alone in the world, it possessed its special characteristics. One edge had been honed to razor sharpness, and had to be specially ground out when it dulled—no heat could be applied to the blade or the iron would lose its special properties. Silver had been fused along the other edge, carefully poured along the cutting surface to make a uniform coating. Trails and runnels of the silver streaked the central ridge and fuller like the drippings of candle wax. The iron edge did more damage to demons than the best steel ever could, while the silver could disrupt magic spells and curses, and, aye, even cut the ectoplasmic flesh of a ghost. It was a potent weapon, and it had served Croy well on more occasions than he could count. He knew its every peculiarity, had learned its balance and its heft so thoroughly that when he held it, Ghostcutter became an extension of his arm—an extension of his desire for justice and the right.

In many ways he thought of himself as an extension of Ghostcutter, instead of vice versa. The sword had a destiny, and a longer span of life than Croy ever would.

Now he waded straight into the arms of the demon, flourishing the sword above his head, totally without fear. He brought the iron edge down with a strong overhead swing that should have sliced one of the demon's tentacles in half.

Except that it didn't.

The rubbery tissue scorched where the iron blade touched it—the stench was overpowering—but it was like trying to cut water. The sword went through without resistance but the flesh simply flowed around it. Croy shouted his defiance and swung again, this time a low, sideways cut that could have cleaved a man in half at the waist. The tentacle before him split open—so it could be cut!—but oozed away from the stroke even before Croy had followed through.

He had failed to harm the demon much, but succeeded in one thing: he had gotten its attention. A tentacle lashed toward him even as he was recovering from his attack and wrapped itself around his neck like a living whipcord. There was no time to parry, much less dodge out of its way. In the Lady's sacred name the thing was fast.

The fleshy rope was dry and its skin was cracked, as if it had been exposed to the hot sun of the desert for days. It smelled of corruption and vileness, and had the consistency of a custard. At least, until it constricted. Then it felt like an iron chain lashed around Croy's throat.

A second tentacle wrapped around his thigh and staggered him. It yanked backward, and it was all Croy could do to keep his feet. The fiend would pull him down if he did not find some way to break its grasp. Croy struck at this second arm with his blade, but it held resolute, even as the cold-forged iron seared its skin.

The tentacle around his throat constricted until he felt his throat start to crush. Every breath became a hard-fought effort. He lost all interest in keeping his footing, as just staying alive became his main focus. His vision filled up with throbbing blood and his eyes bulged out of their sockets as the demon dragged him off his feet and toward its center. Was there a mouth in there, full of teeth to grind his bones? He could see none—perhaps it merely wanted to bring more of its arms to bear on crushing him into paste.

"Bik-k-k-k," he choked, ashamed to call on the scoundrel's aid but knowing he could not free himself.

"What's that, lad? You need to speak up," Bikker said. A tentacle tried to reach around Bikker's chest but the bearded swordsman punched it away with his free hand. Another lashed him across the side of the head, a glancing blow but strong enough to knock Bikker sideways. "Blast your eyes," Bikker said. "This is not what I expected of our reacquaintance." Bikker's sword whirled through the air, droplets of acid falling like rain on the beast so it recoiled in pain. The pitted blade sliced through the tentacle around Croy's throat as easy as it could cut paper. The stump of the cut arm waved desperately in the air, its wound cauterized by the hissing acid. Another swing and Croy's leg was free.

"My thanks," Croy called as he dodged away from another tentacle bent on snaring his sword arm.

"Save them. The damned thing is still growing. If we're going to kill it, it's best done soon. I'll clear you a path—go for its heart, if it has one!" Acidtongue swung around and around like a scythe mowing wheat. Bikker did not even bother with proper flourishes and cutting strokes, instead engaging the demon with a series of sweeping moulinet cuts. Though he barely touched the demon's arms, they were severed right and left, the tapered ends of the tentacles dropping all around them to writhe and die separately on the ground.

Acidtongue looked like a piece of rusted old iron, like a sword cast aside in a field, left out in the sun and rain for centuries. Yet when its wielder slogged into battle its true virtue made itself known. It secreted a concentrated vitriol more powerful than any alchemist's *aqua regia*, an acid that could cut through any substance known to man. The sword had to be kept in a special glass-lined scabbard just so it didn't eat its way through and burn the man who wore it at his belt. It was one of the most powerful weapons in the world, and Bikker was a master at its use.

Croy had to admit, not without a twinge of professional jealousy, that it made short work of the demon that had nearly overwhelmed him.

"Now," Bikker shouted, and Croy ducked under a flailing arm and into the gap Bikker made. A seeming wall of severed stumps lay before him. The demon had continued to grow even after the tower fell on it, and now it seemed as big as the palace. Severed arms beat at his head and shoulders, and smaller tentacles reached to grab his arms and legs, but Croy laughed as he brought Ghostcutter around with both hands wrapped about its hilt. He brought it up to his shoulder, then drove it down with all its might into the join between two tentacles. The blade met some resistance at first but then pierced the tough skin and sank deep into the demon's body, all the way up to its quillions.

That, it turned out, was enough to make the demon scream.

Its voice was high and chirping like a bird's, but loud enough to shatter glass windows in the palace. Its scream was wordless and atonal, a simple heart cry so pure and piteous that it could mean only the creature's death. It screamed with its mind, not with any audible voice, like many demons of Croy's experience. His brain was battered by a trillion small voices speaking gibberish, but pleading, begging, beseeching him to withdraw his sword. When Croy refused, the demon tried to pull back physically, to roll away from the sword, to thrash itself free. It redoubled its attacks, its arms wrapping around Croy's body so thick they covered him head to toe. But its strength was already ebbing and he only held fast, grunting in pain. By the time Bikker reached him and cut him free, the demon was already dead and its tentacles slithered off of him as if he'd been buried in a pile of so much rope.

Croy stumbled over its severed arms where they littered the courtyard and out into the moonlight, gasping for air. When he had a little breath back, he started to laugh. Bikker slapped him hard on the back and he nearly went down on one knee.

By the mercy of the Lady, that had felt good. To do the thing he was sworn to do, once more. Demons were so rare upon the land these days that he'd had to find other uses for Ghostcutter's puissance, and not always things he was proud of. He'd nearly forgotten the purity and the clear conscience that came from fighting demons.

Beside him, Bikker looked possessed of the same emotion. He was smiling from ear to ear, all malice gone from his eyes. Perhaps, just perhaps, there was something of the hero in the man yet. Perhaps the man who Croy had once know was not yet dead. He'd thought Bikker lost to the tide of cynicism and shifting morality that sullied this world, but perhaps . . .

The castellan came running from the palace, pulling a dressing robe around his withered frame. "Water!" the old man cried. "The Guardian must be doused in water, or it'll keep growing until it chokes the world! Fetch water from the well, bring more from the river! Water! Water!"

Eventually the castellan saw the corpse of the demon—his eyes had never been very good, and age had worsened them—and stopped his shouting. "Water," he said with a dejected air. "Water would have made it shrink."

"Cold iron and acid seem to work, too," Bikker said, taunting the old man. He laughed heartily. "Don't tell me, castellan, that you've been harboring a demon inside these walls. Don't tell me you made a pet of a pit fiend."

The three of them stared at the body as it began to smoke and dissolve. It was not a creature of this world, and lacking now its vital force, it had nothing to protect it from the abhorrence of nature. In moments its corpse would resolve to nothing but a stink of brimstone and a blackish residue on the stones.

"It's the Guardian of the—the—" The castellan's face turned dark with congested blood. It was a high crime for any man to summon a demon or to keep one hidden. For decades Croy and knights like him had been hunting down sorcerers capable of performing the necessary rituals. Now only a handful of them remained, and all of them closely watched. If it could be proved that, say, Hazoth had summoned this demon, he would be burnt at the stake. Even for one as powerful as the Burgrave, harboring a demon could be a hanging offense. Should Bikker or Croy bring news of this to the capital—

But then the castellan's face creased with shrewdness. He pointed one long and trembling finger at the two swordsmen.

"You are an escaped prisoner. And you have no right to be here," he said.

Croy looked at Bikker. "I'd hoped when we saved the palace from the demon, all might be forgiven."

Bikker grinned wickedly. "Did you expect justice in this life, lad? Have you learned so little of my teachings?"

"Guards!" the castellan shouted. "Take these two under arrest!"

Suddenly the walls of Castle Hill were crowded with archers, while men of the watch in their cloaks-of-eyes came streaming in through the Market Square gate.

"I had hoped to talk to you more. But we'll meet again," Croy said.

"You may be assured of it," Bikker agreed.

And then they split up, running in opposite directions as fast as their legs could carry them.

# CHAPTER TWENTY-SIX

"Curse you, leave off," Malden whimpered. His strength was nearly gone. The joints in his arms and shoulders burned, and his legs had cramped where he used them to brace himself against the pull of the demon. He would not let go of the crown, but inch by inch, inexorably, the tentacle was pulling it closer to the debris of the tower room. Sweat poured down into Malden's eyes but he didn't dare wipe it away. He heaved backward with every muscle in his body but still gained no ground.

And then—he did. He was able to straighten out a fraction, to pull the crown closer to his body. The tentacle throbbed and started to whip back and forth. Its grip loosened and then the crown slithered free of its embrace.

Malden fell back, panting like a dog. He stared at the tentacle, expecting it to renew its grasp, but it did not. In fact, it flopped across the floor and did not move at all. As if the demon had perished, unseen by him, and could fight no more. Even as he watched, the thing began to melt.

He could hardly believe it. He stared at the crown in his hands. It had not stretched or bent at all in the struggle, though it was made of gold, one of the softest of metals. Its crenellations had dug deep gouges in his palms and fingers, and his blood slicked its surface. He longed to put it down, to tend to his cuts, but he dared not let it out of his hands, even for a moment. He couldn't bear the thought.

Of course, he didn't have to put it down, if he just set it on his head . . .

*You have done well, thief*, the crown said.

"Say no more, I beg of you," Malden moaned. He thought how much he had risked for this prize. He could easily have been killed in that final moment before the tower fell—yet the voice had commanded him, and he obeyed. Now he knew it wanted more. It wanted him to put it on his own head.

Surely that was sacrilege. Wasn't it? He was no Burgrave. He couldn't legally wear it. If anyone saw him with it on, he would be arrested at once for impersonating a noble.

And yet . . . what sweet justice it would be, wouldn't it? It was almost maddening, it was so appealing. For a common thief, the son of a whore, to wear even for a moment the coronet of temporal power.

Malden began to raise it toward his head.

The thing was magic. Who knew what powers it might have? Maybe it would grant him wishes. Maybe it would turn him instantly into a man of estate, of power. Such things were told of in stories, sometimes, such things were . . .

. . . were . . .

. . . too good to be true.

Malden lowered the crown again. He didn't let it go. No, that would be too much to bear. But he forced down the urge to put it on.

He had a horrible presentiment—a certain hunch—that if he put the crown on his head, he would never willingly take it off again. And that would have presented more problems than it was likely to solve.

He felt the thing pulse in his hands, a little jolt of anger. He had thwarted its design and it wasn't happy. Malden had to fight with himself to contain his natural impulse, which was to do anything, anything at all, to make the crown happy again.

*If you will not wear me, then carry me to the castellan. He will see to my safety.*

"Be still!" Malden said, though he felt like a field mouse issuing orders to a lion. The strength in that voice, the resolute, firm quality of it, was hard to resist. "I'll do no such thing. I'm leaving now, and you shall accompany me."

*Find the castellan.*

"He would have me slain on the spot." Malden shook his head. He could feel the disdain radiating from the crown. It cared not a jot for his life or well-being. It only wanted its orders carried out. As far as the crown was concerned, he deserved whatever he got. Was he not, after all, a thief? And were not thieves hanged in this city?

An upright citizen, a more honest man, would never have disobeyed. Any such would have marched to their doom, just for the honor of serving the crown—or been seduced into putting it on, whatever horrors that might entail. Whatever intellect might inhabit it, it remained a symbol of ordained power, a representative of an iron-bound class system where every man knew his place. Even in the Free City of Ness men were born into a system of rank and from childhood had one lesson drummed into them: know your betters, and respect their wishes to the letter. Those who disobeyed faced beatings and upbraidings. Those who went along were left alone. Though the free citizens were proud people, they were not unlike the bondsmen outside the city walls in this regard—they knew better than to challenge power.

Yet Malden had never been a true citizen. He'd never been raised to be an honest man. His people were among the lowest of the low, and no one had ever cared to remind him of his rank because they assumed he would never rise above his station.

That expectation, or lack thereof, had given him ambition. And ambition bred will. Taking care, he removed one hand from the crown and flexed the fingers to get the blood flowing through them again. Then he placed the crown on the floor. Oh, that was hard, but once done, he felt so much better. He knew at once he'd made the right decision. He eased his other hand and wiped blood from his palm.

Then he began to consider, once again, how he was going to escape.

The hallway was blocked by the portcullis spears, and even if he could have fled through the palace, he would only arrive in the courtyard where doubtless every armed man on Castle Hill was waiting for him. The tower was collapsed and impassible. It seemed he had but one choice for egress, though he liked it not.

He could climb down the oubliette, the pit that nearly swallowed him before he reached the tower. He peered down into its inky depths now, and remembered what he had thought before—it could lead nowhere but into the Burgrave's dungeons, some hundred feet straight down.

It was the only way out.

Jumping into that pit would be folly, of course—he would never survive the fall. He could attempt to climb down, but from what he could see of the shaft, its walls looked slick and free of easy hand- and footholds to facilitate such a descent. Fortunately he still had the rope he'd used to gain entrance to the palace, and Slag's folding grapnel. The rope would be just long enough, if he could drop the last ten feet.

He wasted little time. No doubt guards were headed to the palace already, to check on the Burgrave and his retinue and make sure they had not been injured when the tower collapsed. At least some of those guards would be coming to check on the crown as well. The crown. Best to secure it now, so he wouldn't lose it. He picked it up again.

*Thief.*

"Be still!" Malden hissed. He would not let it control him again. He would let no man be his master, ever again.

Well. Save for Cutbill. And Cythera and Bikker, of course. He scowled at himself, but wasted no more time on that line of thought.

He threaded his belt through the crown—touching it gingerly, as if it were like to burn him—then fastened it again about his waist so he would not drop it in the shaft. Then he wrapped his grapnel around one leg of the statue of Sadu—it had been badly dented in the cataclysm, but was still sound enough to hold his weight—and lowered himself foot by foot down into the pit, with only the vaguest notion what he would find at its bottom.

# CHAPTER TWENTY-SEVEN

Warm gusts of air chased up the shaft and made Malden's hands sweat until he could barely hang onto the rope. The shaft was narrow enough that he could walk his way down, keeping his feet pressed against one wall while he climbed down hand over hand, but the walls were slick with condensation and gave little purchase to his soft shoes. For the first fifty feet or so of the descent he was in near total darkness, but as he passed the halfway point, the light from below grew strong enough that he could see the water forming thick, greasy droplets that held for a moment, then streaked down the walls around him.

From below he could hear the roaring of warm air as it rushed up the shaft. And something else—something he had dreaded as he came down the narrow chimney, something he had formed a fledgling hope he would not hear at all. A quiet moaning, the fatigued sighs of a prisoner. He had hoped that the clamor in the courtyard would have brought the gaolers of the dungeon running. That when he reached the dungeon, he would find it empty of guards. Judging by the continued sounds of torment issuing from below, that hope was forlorn. Getting down into the dungeon was going to be the easy part. Dealing with its occupants might be decidedly more difficult.

*One problem at a time,* he told himself, and kept descending.

The light was not enough to reveal the bottom of the shaft until he was almost upon it. When he reached the last few feet of his rope and peered down with great curiosity to see where he would land if he just let go, his heart flipped over his chest.

The floor at the bottom of the shaft was studded with spikes. Iron spikes mounted securely, three feet long and worked to nasty sharpness.

Reaching the end of the rope, he hung onto it by one hand with his feet stretched down as far as they could go. Seven feet of empty air still remained between him and those wicked points. If he just let go, the fall would not break his legs but he was like to be skewered.

He had no more rope to tie to the end, nor anything to extend his descent. Twenty feet of good stout cord were wrapped around the hilt of his bodkin, but it was not strong enough to hold his weight.

Malden ran one hand down the wall of the shaft next to him. It had been cut through solid rock with metal tools that left marks in its surface, no more than shallow dents—hardly enough to get his fingers or toes into. Yet perhaps if his strength had not completely left him . . .

He braced his feet against one wall as best he could, then pushed against the opposite wall with one hand. If he kept his legs bent and his arm straight, he could just about hold his weight up against the force of gravity. And if he used both hands, and if he was headed downward—it would not be a graceful descent. It would be more like a barely controlled fall. But that was better than an uncontrolled plummet.

It took a great deal of courage to let go of the rope. Malden might have been indolent, and not a valiant fighter, but when his life was in jeopardy, he rarely lacked for bold-ness. He let go of the rope and thrust both hands out against the wall at the same time, bracing himself in the shaft. The impact of his hands on the wall made a wet slapping sound that echoed up and down the walls, but he did not have time at that point to stop and listen to hear if anyone remarked on the sound. He was too busy rushing down toward the spikes, his feet and hands clutching at the tool marks on the walls for whatever small purchase they offered.

The rough wall tore and picked at his hands, already sore from the long climb up the wall of Castle Hill. The air rush-ing past him whispered of doom and folly and why there were so few old thieves. His teeth pulled back in a terrible rictus as he smashed his feet and hands again and again into the walls, trying anything, anything at all, to slow his de-scent.

The spikes hurtled toward him like javelins. If he didn't time this perfectly—

Just as his hands reached the bottom of the shaft and ran out of wall to grip, Malden ducked his head and kicked hard with his legs against the stone. He shot forward through the air, narrowly clearing the spikes, and curled himself into a ball as he made contact with the floor beyond them, to perform a perfect somersault and wind up sitting on the floor, his breath whooping in and out of his lungs.

"Wuzzat?" someone said. Someone nearby. Someone whose voice suggested to Malden that he would be quite a bit larger than himself. A slow shuffling step started toward him, drowning out the tired wails of the unseen prisoner.

Malden looked around him in a panic, searching for a place to hide. There was none whatsoever. He had dropped into a narrow room with a vaulted ceiling—a ceiling from which hung sundry articles of iron, many of them with sharp points, others made of heavy chain. The tools of a torturer. The shaft's opening was just a square of darkness on the ceiling, the spikes inconspicuous among so much hardware. Arches led away in four directions, with light coming from cressets set between each arch. Beyond one arch lay a flight of stairs heading up—surely the normal method for accessing this underground hell. The echoing footsteps came from another arch. He could have gone left or right and hoped the torturer was slow enough in chasing him—but he saw a better idea and took it. Jumping to his feet, he ran backward up the stairs until he reached the first landing, then walked back down them at a more leisurely rate.

As the torturer ducked through the arch, the man would only see him coming down the stairs as if he had just arrived.

"Who the blazes're you?" the torturer asked when they came face-to-face. He was an enormous man, though not overly tall, his body bloated and lumpy, his hair falling out in clumps. He looked half like an ogre and half like something that should not have been able to crawl out of its sickbed.

"The new kitchen boy," Malden said. "I was sent down to

fetch you. Fire's broken out above, and they need every man to help put it out. Hurry, you must get up there at once! Are there any others down here who can also help?"

"Just me." The torturer's mouth fell open and his eyes turned to slits. Malden had the impression he was squinting at him. The big man already had a massive wen over his left eye, so it was hard to tell. Other purplish growths adorned his chin and one side of his neck, like a grotesque beard half shaved. "Fire, you say? No great concern of mine, that. Naught to burn down here."

"Nor any other way out but these stairs," Malden insisted, hoping very much this was not true. "If the palace falls down on top of us—"

"Oh," the torturer said, his right eye opening wide. "Oh! Fire! I'd best get up there, see what I can do to help!"

He rushed past Malden on his way up the stairs, nearly knocking him down. Malden cheered him on as he thundered up the risers. Then he darted through the arch the torturer had just vacated, intent on finding another way out before the brutish man thought to wonder why a man of his age was working as a kitchen boy.

He had not gotten more than a dozen strides into the dungeon, however, before someone called out to him.

"You! Yes, you—ye're Cutbill's man, ain't you? Thank the Lady, ye've come to rescue me!"

Malden considered keeping on, ignoring the cry for aid. Had he truly been one of Cutbill's thieves, those honorless blackguards (whom he had been doing his level best lately to emulate), he would not have faltered in a single step. But he was, in some ways, still his mother's son. He turned aside from his path and went to look for the man who'd called him.

# CHAPTER TWENTY-EIGHT

Croy dashed into the shadows, keeping his head down as arrows buzzed past him left and right. If he could just get to where the archers couldn't see him— Yes. The wall of the kitchens proved exactly the cover he needed. Its shadow cut through the moonlight like a scythe. Of course, there was one problem. The kitchens abutted the defensive wall, so he had just trapped himself in a corner.

He turned around quickly and saw four men of the watch come hurtling toward him. Their cloaks billowed around them as they came, the eyes woven into the fabric seeming to blink as the cloth snapped back and forth. The four of them spread out as they approached, forming a half circle before him. That was smart. He could easily have taken them on one by one, but if he tried to attack any of them now, he would be leaving his left flank dangerously exposed.

The blades of their halberds flashed out and toward him, the weapons swinging in unison, just as their drill instructor had surely taught them. Croy had taught enough guards in his own time to recognize the technique. He couldn't see their faces under their hoods but he understood. These were men handpicked for duty on Castle Hill, trained well and ready for anything.

Croy reached over his shoulder. Ghostcutter he left in its scabbard—it was only for fighting demons and sorcery. Instead he drew his shorter, nameless blade. Nothing but honest steel to meet their iron.

"I don't want to hurt you," he said. "I know you're just doing your duty. However, I cannot allow you to arrest me tonight."

One of the watchmen snickered at that, an ugly sound. Another took a step forward and made a feint of cutting at his blade. Croy did not respond, drawing the sword back rather than let the halberd make contact.

"The Burgrave wants your head," the snickerer told him. "They say he'll pay good new-minted silver for it. There won't be any arresting."

Croy frowned. That did complicate things.

He knew exactly how much these guards earned. Once upon a time, when he'd lived on Castle Hill, he drew the same salary in the Burgrave's service. He knew they would be grateful for a chance to supplement their income.

Yet they must be good men at heart. They served a properly anointed lord and protected the Free City of Ness. So he couldn't just kill them. He knew Bikker would have—in fact, Bikker was probably doing that just now on his own way out of Castle Hill. Yet Croy prided himself on being made of different stuff. He would have to find another way out of this predicament.

"Last chance, gentlemen. I ask you, as honorable men, will you let me go in peace?"

A halberd spike came jabbing toward his face—and this time it was not a feint. He had received his answer. He smashed the point aside with the forte of his sword and then dropped low into a ducking sideways hop, moving like a crab as the four of them advanced as one. Two halberds clashed where his head, a moment before, had been, their wooden hafts thudding like drums. Another came low and nearly swept him off his feet. Croy jumped forward and smacked that watchman in the temple with the flat of his blade. It was a stunning blow, not a killing attack. The watchman staggered backward, nearly dropping his heavy weapon as he reached up to grab his ringing head.

Halberds were powerful weapons, half spear and half axe so they gave the user a wide range of effective fighting styles. They were slower than swords, however. By the time the next blow came toward him—this one a cutting swing aimed at the top of his skull—Croy had danced back and was able to lean away from the chop. As the weapon flashed past his face, he reached out with his free hand—his off hand—and grabbed the halberd right in its middle. Putting his back into it, he twisted the halberd sideways and out of the watchman's grip and then rushed forward, knocking down two of his opponents in a heap. He threw the halberd away from him and then sheathed his sword. He could kill all four of these men easily, but he had no stomach for it. They were honest defenders of the public weal—what good could possibly come from their deaths?

The last standing watchman ran at him, but Croy side-stepped the charge. Then he dashed to the side of the kitchen building and clambered up its wall. It was a half-timbered structure with protruding beams and nearly as easy to climb as a ladder. A halberd blade whistled past his feet as he made the roof, but it missed cleanly.

From the top of the kitchens it was simple to reach the parapet along the top of the defensive wall. Where he went from there was another question. He stood atop a length of curtain wall that lay between two watch towers. From both of them, men were pouring out of doors or jumping down from the tower tops to get at him. He seemed to be out of options.

Then he looked down and saw the river Krait, flowing briskly by a hundred and fifty feet below him. He tilted his head back and laughed heartily. The men of the watch would be on him in seconds, with orders to slaughter him where he stood. There must be a full company of them coming at him—far more than enough to take him down, fancy swords or no.

Jumping into the river from this height was utter folly. If he didn't hit the bottom hard enough to shatter his bones, there was a good chance he would drown. Of course, there was the slimmest of chances that he would survive.

He jumped, of course.

The air whistled past him as he fell, as fast as the pro-verbial stone. He could see nothing—it all flashed past him so quickly—and he could barely tell which direction was up. Somehow he managed to get his legs pointed downward with the toes extended so he hit the water like a knife blade.

Still, he hit it hard enough to jar every bone in his body. The shock of immersion in the cold river nearly stopped his heart. The breath exploded out of him in a torrent of silver bubbles. His brains reeled with the impact and his legs stung as if the skin had been flayed from them. Then he opened his mouth to inhale—he had no choice, his body was not accepting the commands of his will—and his lungs flooded with water. He flailed blindly, trying to swim up, unable to tell what direction he was facing, barely cognizant of the difference between right and left.

His head collided with something hard and wooden, adding injury to injury. His vision spun with blackness and he knew he was about to die. He nearly gave up then and there—if this was the time the Lady had appointed for his death, who was he to gainsay Her wish? Yet there was something in Croy that failed to stop even when lesser men could do naught but yield. He grasped at the wooden obstruction above him and pulled himself up and over it. His face hit the night air with a gasp and he sucked in breath—then turned his head sideways and coughed up a great gout of cold water. He shook his head to clear his eyes and finally looked at where he was and what he was holding onto. It was the rail of a tiny boat.

Sitting at its oars was Cythera.

The woman he'd risked all to find. The woman whose love he would defy even death to beseech.

Surely only one explanation could satisfy this great co-incidence. The Lady had smiled on him. Far from choosing this night to bring him to Her bosom, She had let him live, so that he could see Cythera once more. He nearly let go of the boat, wanting to raise his hands to the heavens in thankful prayer.

"You'd better get in, as we're going to be spotted any minute," Cythera said. "Stop playing around and— Hold. You're not Malden."

She made no attempt to help him. She did not reach for him. But then, it would be his death if she embraced him. Her curse made it so. She peered over the gunwale, searching his face with wide eyes.

"Croy?" she asked, looking horrified.

He pulled himself over the rail and into the boat. For a while he could do nothing but lie there gasping, looking up at the sky. At the top of the wall tiny faces were peering down at him, tiny arms pointing with urgency at the little boat.

"Row, Cyth. Row away from here," he panted. He couldn't help but smile.

"I'm supposed to meet someone—"

A rock hit the river, not three feet from the boat, and sent up a great column of water that splashed them both.

"I don't think they have boiling oil," Croy told Cythera. "But I know they have plenty of archers."

"Let us away, then," she said, and bent to her oars.

# CHAPTER TWENTY-NINE

As a child growing up in a brothel, Malden had possessed few friends his own age or sex. Yet whenever he chanced to find himself in the company of other boys, one of the favorite topics of conversation had concerned this very room—the torture chamber of the Burgrave. The boys would name and describe all the instruments of torture they could, and speculate wildly on their possible applications. One frequent debate was held over which device one would least like to be subjected to. It had all been in good fun, of course, a gruesome contest of oneupmanship. He had never considered the idea he would actually be in this room, or see its true inventory.

"O'er here, lad, and sharpish! I can't take much more. Oh, oh, I'll kiss the Bloodgod on the lips for this, when I meet him," the prisoner announced.

As Malden headed through the arch to the torture chamber proper, he was more afraid than he had been facing down the demon above, or when he first climbed into

Cutbill's coffin. On every side were the nightmares of his youth. The boot, and also its cruel if prosaically named cousin, the instep borer—which drove a screw through the fleshy part of a man's foot. The tramp chair, which didn't look so bad until you realized you would be locked inside it, unable to stand. The heretic's fork lay on an anvil where the torturer had been sharpening its prongs. Iron-rimmed breaking wheels lined the walls, while a selection of bone-breaking hammers hung by straps from the ceiling. Close by the arch, leaning up against one wall, was the scavenger's daughter (sometimes called the reversed rack). In pride of place stood the dread crocodile shears, which were only ever used on the slayers of nobility, for that which they took away could not be seen. At least not while the victim wore breeches. There were at least three sets of branks, or witch's bridles—specially designed headgear with an iron spur arranged in such a way that it projected into the mouth and placed a spike against the tongue. Any sorcerer who tried to speak a curse or cast a spell while wearing such a bridle would shred their tongue instead. A handy appliance to have, Malden thought, in a place like the Free City, where wizards vied with Burgraves and sent thieves to do their mischief.

"I heard yer voice, I know ye're still there. Come on, boy!"

But of all the things that could be done to a human body, all the bits of iron that could be plunged into soft parts, all the different ways to stretch sinews and ligaments until they burst, one device was always rated the worst. None could really say why—it did not seem half so horrible as the choke pear. Yet generations of boys had passed down the sure and certain knowledge that the paragon of suffering-inducing machines had to be the strap.

The prisoner's hands had been bound behind his back, then a hook inserted between his wrists. He had then been hauled up on a pulley until he dangled from the ceiling. His arms were twisted around behind him, and as a result his chest thrust forward at an awkward angle. To make this worse, a chain was wrapped around his feet, and from this chain depended a large, round stone. The weight pulled down on joints already strained by the strap that held the man aloft.

"Ah, and there ye are, ye clever son. There, over there— that knot!"

Malden stared with gaping mouth at the prisoner, and not only because of his state of distress. The man was naked, gaunt, and haggard of expression. He was also someone he recognized. It was the vagabond he'd seen in Cutbill's lair, the one who'd claimed right of sanctuary.

"You're the thief Kemper, are you not?" Malden asked.

"For the nonce. Sooner'n I'd like, I'll go by a different name," Kemper agreed.

"I'm . . . sorry?"

"They'll be calling me 'the late' thief Kemper, if'n you don't get me down."

Malden recovered his wits with a start. "Of course, at once," he said. He hurried to the wall where the other end of the strap was tied around an iron hook. He undid the knot with shaking fingers and lowered Kemper carefully to the floor.

For a while the vagabond merely rolled about on the flagstones, his face split by a piteous grin.

"Oh, I've never found such happiness at the bottom of a flagon, nor between a girl's legs," Kemper moaned. "Ye'll never know such ecstasy, lad, and ye should be thankful for that."

Malden had many questions for the man. "How did you come to be here? It was just this morning I saw you, at Cutbill's. You were safe enough there—how were you taken so soon after?"

Kemper grimaced. "A man can only abide so much stale bread and water. Cutbill gave me sanctuary, to be sure, but his hospitality was a mite lacking, if you catch me. Of all things, water to drink, ye'd think I was a horse! If I wanted real victuals, I decided I must go abroad. I snuck forth just afore dawn, made right for the Smoke, where I knew I could catch a game."

Kemper rolled over onto his side and moaned in pleasure.

"Found it easy enough. Didn't reckon one o' the players was a cloak-of-eyes on his off-shift. The bastard recognized me just fine and tried to haul me out o' there. Figured I was safe enough, as I've always been. Been caught more times'n you've kissed a girl, I figure, and always got free again before. Never thought they'd ken out me one weakness. Now, if ye please, me hands and ankles."

Malden went to free the vagabond's extremities and found they were bound by matching chains of bright metal, seemingly far too thin to hold up Kemper's weight. They tinkled merrily when he pulled them free.

"Keep'm as souvenirs, if ye like," Kemper told Malden, when he saw how the thief stared at the chains. "I've no desire to see'm again. Should be worth a mite, seein' they're solid silver."

"Silver?" He could make no sense of it. He knew nobles could demand that they be hanged with a silken rope, rather than the hempen cord commoners received. But why in the world would a petty thief be strapped with silver? It made no sense.

"Good 'gainst curses," Kemper said, as if that explained everything. "Mind, I'll need a cut on what ye sell'm for."

"But of course," Malden said. He pulled the chains free and stared at them in his hands. Why bind a man with silver? What had Kemper meant about curses? He lifted his eyes to ask the man directly, but in vain. Without a sound, without so much as a fare-thee-well, Kemper had disappeared.

# CHAPTER THIRTY

Malden rushed back through the arches, thinking Kemper must have slipped up the stairs while he wasn't looking. He sought only to warn his fellow thief that no good would come of heading that way. Yet as he reached the bottom of the stairs he thought better of chasing Kemper up the steps. No doubt the vagabond would be caught as soon as he made the surface. He would only be sacrificing his own freedom if he followed too close on the man's heels.

He had freed the prisoner from his chains. Surely, that was enough of a good turn, and he could be forgiven for thinking of himself next. He had to escape, with the crown, if he didn't want the night's fiasco to be in vain. And he thought he knew a way.

Malden cast about him, looking for something on the floor. He found it back in the torture chamber—a round iron grate that came up easily when he lifted it. It had to be the drain that led out to the river, via the outlet pipe he'd seen when coming in.

The problem with having a dungeon cut into the bosom of a hill was that it would flood every time it rained. The drain was there to alleviate such a shortcoming. It would also make a fine way of disposing of any victims who didn't survive their interrogations—or any parts of them they didn't need anymore.

Putting aside such grisly thoughts as best he was able, Malden dropped down into the drain, then pulled the grating back over his head, cutting off some of the light. The drain proved to be a pipe lined with bricks furred white with niter, about three feet wide, leading down at a steep grade. There was no light in the tunnel, of course, but part of the way down its length he saw a glimmering and started crawling toward it. Compared to some of the things he'd been through since he started working for Cythera and Bikker, the drain was an easy traverse. The worst thing about it was the smell.

It was foul at first. It quickly rose to a level of unbearability. The fetor of the drain made his eyes water, and even when he covered his mouth and nose with the hood of his cloak he could barely breathe. His body fought for clean air but there was none to be had. The source of the stench was no great mystery, Malden thought. The garderobes of the palace must empty directly into this same pipe—a clever enough alternative to having the Burgrave's ordure carted out every week. His guess as to the drain's purpose was confirmed when he reached a patch of light in the tunnel. It was coming down from above, through a shaft much like the one that led to the dungeon—though this time there were no spikes at the bottom. Looking up, he could just make out a circular opening, high, high above him, lit by flickering candlelight. The smell here was much stronger than elsewhere, and the condition of the shaft walls is certainly best left undescribed.

The smell made him want to retch, and the yielding texture of the floor he crawled over made him wince with each foot he covered. Nothing but the promise of freedom and safety kept him moving forward. Still, he supposed it could be worse. There was a fortune in gold waiting for him once he was out of this—no matter how briefly it would remain in his possession. Malden pitied the servant who must come down here and clean this drain every time it filled up, and was probably paid only in room and board.

There were more shafts intersecting the drain as it headed down toward the river. One of them was even in use. He waited patiently until the user was finished, then continued on his way.

At last he came to a point where they could see the outflow pipe. Moonlight streamed in through its grate, though its lower half was clogged with filth and detritus. Malden rushed forward and grabbed the iron bars with his much-abused fingers. He rattled them but they held.

He looked out through the bars, hoping to signal Cythera. Perhaps she had a way of bending iron bars he lacked.

But where in Sadu's name was she? The boat should be waiting for him—it was his agreed upon method of egress. If she wasn't there . . .

Then he would just have to swim for it, wouldn't he?

With a sigh, Malden drew his bodkin and began to work at the bars, trying to loosen them enough that he could make good his escape.

*Thief,* the crown at his belt said when he was quiet awhile. *Thief, go back.*

Malden growled at the thing, never slowing in his work.

# PART II

# An Unquiet Crown

# INTERLUDE

Bikker made his own exit from Castle Hill, though in a less dramatic fashion than Croy or Malden. In the confusion following the death of the demon, he merely stepped into some shadows by the wall, then through a doorway into a well-lit room near the main gate. Inside, a servant was waiting for him. The withered old man offered to take his cloak—Bikker declined—then offered him a cup of hot mulled wine. This he took, draining the goblet in a single gulp. "Is he here?" Bikker asked.

The servant nodded without looking up. He was busy mending a torn tunic, pulling his bone needle through the old fabric then plunging it down again. The old man was the castle's tailor, and he had a pile of clothes beside him, each item waiting his attention. "When things have calmed a bit, I'm to take you to the chapel. He'll meet you there."

Bikker eyed the tailor carefully. Was it possible this man was, in fact, his employer? He'd never seen the man who brought him into the cabal. It could be anyone in Ness, anyone with a compelling interest in bringing down the Burgrave. It wasn't an ideal situation for one of Bikker's talents, not knowing who he worked for. He was more accustomed to working for lords and merchants who insisted that he wear their personal livery. After all, what was the point in having a famous knight in your retinue if no one knew he was yours?

Still, Bikker supposed he could understand the need for secrecy. If anyone knew what the cabal was really meant to do, the jig would be up. The Burgrave would make short work of them all, probably hanging them in chains from the castle gates so everyone in Ness could see the wages of treason. Secrecy was paramount. Even Hazoth hadn't been filled in on all the details, and Bikker was certain there were elements of the scheme he didn't know about himself.

He shrugged and demanded another cup of wine. It didn't matter to him what happened to the city. What mattered was that he be far away when it happened. Far enough away not to smell the blood or hear the screams.

When enough time had passed, the tailor handed him a cloak-of-eyes, the traditional garb of the city watch. For the first time, Bikker realized why the castle's tailor would be a useful pawn of the cabal—uniforms and regalia of every kind came through the old man's hands. Any number of disguises would be at his disposal. Bikker threw the too-small cloak over his shoulders and let the tailor lead him through the dim corridors of the chancery, the unassuming building where the city's administrative work was carried out. They came through a dark refectory and then down a short passage that led to a chapel. A gilded cornucopia, symbol of the Lady, hung there above a modest altar. There were no pews, just a scattering of straw-filled cushions on the floor where supplicants could kneel. This was not a chapel for the use of the Burgrave and his family, but for the clerks and scribes of Anselm Vry's ministries—commoners, if well-paid commoners.

With a thin smile, the tailor bid Bikker to kneel. Perhaps he thought it would be amusing to see the knight in an attitude of prayer.

For Bikker it was anything but diverting. There had been a time when he stood vigil in far ruder churches. He'd been a sworn vassal of the king once. A champion of virtue. He took his place on his knees, the muscles of his back locking obediently into place. There was a certain method one learned to kneeling all night, a way of staying upright even when your body demanded sleep. He resisted the urge to place Acidtongue before him, his hands folded neatly on the pommel. He would not mock what he had once been, no matter what Croy might think of him now.

*Croy. Croy was here.* Bikker's skin itched at the thought. The foolish knight could cause all kinds of problems if he chose to poke his nose in where it wasn't wanted. Croy still considered himself one of the noble order of the Ancient Blades—which meant that whenever he discovered wrongdoing or malfeasance, he was honor-bound to root it out, uncover the criminals, and bring them to punishment. If Croy even guessed at the work of the cabal . . . but Bikker knew he could handle Sir Croy, if it came to that. He had trained Croy—had taught the younger knight everything he knew about holding a sword. But he hadn't taught Croy everything he knew himself. Bikker still had a few tricks up his sleeve that Croy had never seen.

"It's done," a voice behind Bikker said, startling him. "The crown has left Castle Hill. Good." Bikker did not turn to see who was speaking. His employer had been quite clear from the start that he did not wish his face to be seen. "Not as neatly as I'd hoped. But plenty of people saw the guardian demon before it was slain—that was to my liking. It will further humiliate Tarness."

"If you like, I can ride tonight for Helstrow. There I can inform the king that the Burgrave of Ness has been harboring demons," Bikker mused. He didn't relish the prospect—he was not well-loved in the royal fortress just now. But it would further their aims, and it would get him far from Ness before things went to perdition.

"Not just now. We'll hold that charge back as insurance. No, Ladymas is almost upon us. When Tarness appears in public without the crown, he'll be unable to explain himself. If we're lucky, the people will riot on their own, without further provocation. By manipulating their anger, we can inspire them to true revolt. The city will collapse under civil strife, and the king will have no choice but to intervene."

Bikker frowned. He stared up at the cornucopia as he asked, "That's the part I haven't fully grasped. The Burgrave will look a fool if he appears without his crown, true enough. But he's a man of formidable intellectual resources. Surely he'll find some excuse and the people will believe it. They love him, after all."

"They love *him*. They will not love what they see on Ladymas." The voice seemed to find this highly amusing.

"Trust me, Bikker. I've had years to plot this out. I know exactly what I'm doing."

"I'm sure," Bikker said. He wondered if he should tell his employer about Croy. But no. If the cabal thought Croy was a threat, they would take steps to slay the knight errant as a concerted front. Bikker didn't want that. He wanted Croy all to himself. So he held his tongue.

"Now. You know what you must do next? What your role is now?"

"Aye, I'll secure the crown. Get it to Hazoth's villa where it can be hidden."

"Exactly. Get the crown from the thief—pay him whatever he asks, it doesn't matter."

Bikker smiled. "Sure, since as soon as the crown is in my hands I can just kill the little fool and take the money back."

"What? No, you mustn't kill the thief. You're already a wanted criminal after tonight's endeavors. It's still against the law in this city to kill a man, and I don't want Anselm Vry's watchmen to pick you up for such a minor infraction. Not while I still need you. No, just pay the thief and let him be."

Bikker grunted in frustration. "This doesn't sit well with me. The thief knows too much, and he's hardly to be trusted. Leaving him alive is foolhardy."

"Yes, I'm aware of it. Which is why Hazoth is going to kill him. No need to get your hands dirty when we have one of the world's greatest sorcerers on our side."

"As you wish," Bikker said. Though it still rankled him. Not because he thought Hazoth wouldn't do it. Because he had intended to give Malden—whom he had actually come to respect, after a fashion—a clean death. He could only imagine the particulars, but he was sure that what Hazoth did to the thief would be downright gruesome in comparison.

# CHAPTER THIRTY-ONE

Croy and Cythera spent much of the night in furtive silence, as they wended their way from Castle Hill all the way down to Parkwall. The city watch was out in force and looking for them, and they had to take great pains to avoid capture.

Twice they came close to discovery. They had docked their little boat in the Smoke, in a place where two tanneries discharged the contents of their vats directly into the Skrait. Cythera thought the smell would keep the watch away and they could debark unseen. They nearly walked right into an armed guard who stood watching a pile of untanned hides that had just been delivered. The guard challenged them as they came up the riverside stairs, and they had to run as he chased them with a club. Croy could have made short work of the man, of course, but that would have just drawn more attention.

The second brush with the watch was more serious. They had arrived nearly at the edge of Ladypark Common, within sight of Hazoth's villa and the house where Croy was staying—only to find the grassy sward crawling with watchmen. The two of them retreated to a tavern a few streets away, where they were able to find out why the common was so heavily guarded. It transpired that a footpad had murdered the footman of a money-changer there earlier in the evening. It had been a particularly bloody killing, and the watch was called down in droves to find evidence and look for the assassin.

"They won't find him," Cythera said, when she and Croy could speak privately again. "That was Bikker's work."

"Are you sure?" Croy asked, looking as if he would grab his swords and run out into the night to find the big swordsman.

"No," she said. "I can't prove anything. But he was supposed to set a number of diversions, all the better to keep the watch away from Castle Hill. I didn't think he'd be so . . . expedient about it."

Croy settled down then. In his personal book of accounts, Bikker already had enough crimes under his name. One more didn't change how he felt.

They took a room at the tavern under assumed names and spent the night waiting for a knock on their door or the sound of hobnailed boots rushing down the hall. No one came to arrest them, though, or even to ask them difficult questions. When morning finally came it seemed they were safe. The patrols of the watch had diminished in size and frequency, and both of them began to breathe easier.

"I have to go back soon," Cythera said as she led Croy through the Ladypark Market, a winding street of shops and stalls just uphill from Hazoth's villa. Fishmongers wheeled their carts from door to door—this early, the day's catch had not yet begun to stink—as linkboys hurried home to bed, to wait out the day until their services were again required. Minutes before, the two of them had had the place virtually to themselves, but now the city's throngs closed around them. Bakers and brewers were already at their stations, of course, long before the dawn. With the sun, the market truly came to life, however, filling with women getting their daily shopping done.

Croy found himself strangely unwilling to give up the heightened emotion of their night outrunning the watch. As fraught as it had been with apprehension, he'd savored the time with his lady fair. He supposed, though, that every night, no matter its freight of sweetness or of terror, must end. The morning had broken crisp and clear while they were renewing their old acquaintance—he had longed for the sun to tarry beneath the horizon, but alas, every day must follow in its course.

"If I'm late," Cythera said, "Hazoth will want to know why. And he has a method of discerning falsehoods."

"One that works, even on you?" Croy asked. "I thought you were immune to sorcery. Is his too strong for your curse to bear?"

She smiled without mirth. "There is no sorcerer in this world who could break through my curse. But Hazoth, well . . . not every trick he pulls is by magic," she told him. "He's the cleverest man I've ever met."

"Cleverer than me?" Croy asked with a hurt look.

"By far," she said, and this time laughter creased the skin around her eyes. He was glad only that he could still bring her some small joy. There had been a time—a lifetime ago, it seemed—when he would cut capers and dance for her until she clapped her hand over her mouth to keep from guffawing like a fool. Now her aspect had changed for the morose.

"I didn't want to leave, back then," he said with sudden seriousness. "The Burgrave was my liege lord. When he ordered me away, I had no choice."

She did not reply. Instead she ducked inside a bakery and emerged again a moment later with a round loaf. When she cracked it open, steam burst from the spongy brown bread inside.

"When was the last time you ate?" she asked. "You were always so busy dashing hither and yon, you would forget to feed yourself. Don't pretend to me, now. I've learned some of my master's art and will see it in your eye."

"I suppose it's been no more than a day," he said, thinking of the almonds he'd eaten while he watched her go inside Hazoth's house the day before. He had to admit the bread was making his mouth water. "Not here, though. Let's break our fast properly."

They found an inn that had just opened its doors, and for a piece of silver they were given a private room. The hostler looked askance at the shifting tattoos on Cythera's face but said nothing, nor was he slow in bringing wine and a half wheel of cheese when they called for them.

"Sit. There," she said, and pointed at a bench by the room's sole table. Croy did as he was told. "Will you take a cup?" she asked, lifting the flagon.

"You don't need to serve me," Croy said, and took it from her hands. His fingers touched hers—only the lightest, gentlest of meetings, but enough to make her wince and nearly drop the wine. Croy made as if he hadn't seen her fearful gesture. "You're not my slave. Nor my wife. Yet."

"Oh, Croy, dreams are fine things, aren't they?" she said.

"Call it no dream. Say vision. Or prophecy." He cut the bread and the cheese with his belt knife and handed her a slice of the former. She took it very carefully. He studied her face while she ate. The painted vines that curled around her cheekbones sprouted new leaves—and new thorns—while he watched. Around her throat they were as thick as a tangle of briars, with shadows deep and black between them. Once, he saw a pair of bestial eyes glowing in that darkness, but they winked out before he could meet their gaze.

He knew perfectly well what those images meant. Cythera's mother—a woman of fierce demeanor and considerable power—had placed this enchantment on her, that Cythera would never be harmed by curse or spell. Such magic could never penetrate further than the top layer of her skin. Yet that arcane energy must go somewhere, and thus manifested itself as these fell images. The curses lingered on her skin until such time that any man tried to attack her physically—and then they would be released, like a shock jumping from an iron door latch to one's finger in the winter, only with far more lethal results.

It was rare that a woman of Cythera's character was the object of a truly vile curse, though. When Croy had met her—back when he was still employed as the Burgrave's bodyguard—there was only a single tendril of curling vine then, and that disappeared up her sleeve. She might have gone a lifetime without acquiring much more in the way of images, had she not needed money. Penniless, with no skills to earn her keep, nor the willingness to prostitute herself, she had found employment where she could.

Hazoth had taken her into his service when she was still a girl. He made an amulet out of a lock of her hair, which extended the protection of her enchantment to himself. And a sorcerer like Hazoth attracted his fair share of curses—cast by his enemies, of which he had many. He compelled service from the demons of the pit. Such creatures liked not making such bargains, and once they were free of his influence, sent magic to destroy him, or to pull him down into the pit with them where they could torment him forever. Now Cythera bore the brunt of those curses. Since entering Hazoth's service, her collection of tattoos had grown denser with each day.

Cythera's skin crawled with magic, far too much for her to safely contain. Magic never stood still—it was pure action, pure energy, and it hated being bound or constrained. Her skin could hold an enormous magical potential but it had its limit, and once that maximum had been reached, the magic constantly sought to be discharged. The slightest jar, the most well-meaning touch, could release that magic instantly. If Croy grasped her hand in a fit of passion, if he crushed her lips with his own—it would be his end.

He had to admit it was going to make the wedding night complicated. But perhaps they could find a way to release her from her magical burden.

"Come away with me," he said. "Tonight. Get away from the villa and meet me. We'll be on a ship, sailing for some pleasant southern beach before he even knows you've left him."

"You think it's that simple?"

"I think it can be, if we choose it."

She lowered her crust of bread to the table and looked at it very carefully, as if she could read the future there. Perhaps she could. "He would not allow it. I must be near him for our connection to work. He would grow wroth."

"Let him pout! What harm can he do us? He wouldn't dare hurt you."

"It's not myself I'm worried about," she told him. She looked up into his eyes. Her own were untouched by magic images. They were clear and very honest, and brooked no falsehoods. "He has my mother under his thumb. Should he desire it, he could extinguish her life with a wave of one hand." She reached toward his cheek but did not touch him, only mimed the gesture, her palm hovering a fraction of an inch above his skin. She'd had a long time to learn how not to touch other people. A very long time to live with no one touching her. "Oh, Croy. You should never have come back."

He stood up quickly from the table, scattering the crumbs of cheese he'd been toying with. "You said you needed to report in. That it would mean trouble if you were late."

"So I did," she told him. She rose from the table and wrapped her cloak tightly around herself, furling it over her arms so her hands were safely inside the garment. "You can't escort me any further, of course, or he'll see us together." She headed for the door, but turned before she slipped through it to take one last look at him. "Try to forget me. I'm lost, Croy."

"You're enslaved. Which is exactly what your mother was trying to protect against when she enchanted you. Hazoth is precisely the kind of enemy she wanted to forestall. Yet now he uses her against you. You've been captured by him as easily as if he *had* used sorcery to compel you." The words were harsher than he'd meant them to be. He had no right to speak to her like that, he thought, and shame burned in his cheeks.

"It's like I said," she told him. "Not every trick he pulls is by magic." And then she was gone.

# CHAPTER THIRTY-TWO

It took Malden the better part of the day to scrub the shit out of his clothes. He couldn't afford to hire a washer-woman, and he certainly didn't want to answer any questions she might have had, so he did it himself down by the river Skrait, rubbing his cloak against smooth rocks until its color was almost back to normal and it didn't stink. When the time came, he told himself—when he was in Cutbill's firm employ, and able to earn for himself—he would never have to wash his own clothes again.

Perhaps it would happen tonight.

He had been very worried after leaving Castle Hill that he might be arrested at any moment. The torturer got a good look at his face, after all, and could have reported his description to the watch. So he had spent the predawn hours slinking from one darkened part of the city to the next, spying on every cloak-of-eyes he could find, watching them to see if they were alerted and searching for a thief. And they had been—a woman, in a velvet cloak, in a little boat. Cythera. They were looking for Cythera.

Which perhaps explained why she had not been waiting for him when he left the pipe and unceremoniously fell into the filthy river. He supposed he could not blame her for fleeing once the guards spotted her. In the midst of the confusion in the palace above, they would be unlikely to listen to whatever story she spun for them. She could have ended up in the strap herself.

He would just have to make contact with her or with Bikker somehow, and make proper arrangements for handing over the crown. Which might be difficult if they were being sought by the watch—most likely they would have gone to ground. Still, he possessed ways to find them the authorities lacked. It would just take a little digging.

On his way back from the river he decided, though, that he could afford to rest and lie low for a day. He was exhausted from his nocturnal jaunt, and his hands ached and desperately needed to be idle for a while. He was also starving, as he hadn't eaten since the day before.

So he took his time heading home. Down in his part of the Stink, the river ran flat and wide through a district of fishermen's homes, all built on stilts to weather the annual springtime flood. He climbed up a bank thick with salt grass, where coracles and punts lay overturned, the tar between their timbers softening in the sun. The fishermen sat in their boats, to keep them from being stolen, waiting for the tide to turn. In the meantime they laughed and joked amongst themselves as they repaired their nets with thick, scarred fingers. They eyed him warily but without comment. Surely it wasn't the first time they'd seen a furtive figure, his clothes drenched with river water, come up the bank and slinking away in the early morning light. He hoped it happened often enough they wouldn't remember him when he was gone.

A short flight of stairs brought Malden up to the high street, where he bought a day-old loaf and three gulps of wine ladled out of a barrel. It was better fare than he often ate, but he was hungry enough to spend the extra coin. He picked apart the bread as he wended his way up the street, careful not to step in anything that might ruin his newly clean shoes. The houses here leaned over the roadway, their upper stories built out so far they were nearly touching. Even in the midday the shadows were thick under the eaves. He sat for a while on a horse trough to finish the meal, and watched the comings and goings of his neighbors.

The people of the Stink dressed plainly, and few among them had clean faces—in fact, most bore the pockmarks of long-healed disease, or other signs of bad diet and unsanitary living. None of them could read or write, and by the age of twenty-five even the most comely of girls looked old and stooped.

"'Ware below," someone shouted from above his head, and a cobbler's apprentice in the street had to dodge a cascade of garbage and filth poured out a second floor window. His leap sent him sprawling into a sawyer and they both went down in a heap, the woodchopper's load of firewood spilling out onto the cobbles. The man pulled the boy's ears for that, and demanded that he help pick up the wood, but the boy merely made a rude gesture and hurried on. Across the street a goodwife stepped out into her dooryard, her face flushed from the heat in her kitchen. She fanned herself with her apron for a moment, then hobbled back inside and back to her endless tasks. She had to work constantly to feed her family, and to have enough left over to sell so she and her husband could make the rent.

These people were miserable, and their lives meant nothing. Malden had never felt like one of them, even if he lived among them. And yet he wondered, as he often did, what his life could have been had he tried to be an honest man.

Not, of course, that he'd had much choice in the matter. The son of a whore—the bastard son of a whore—could never rise far. He had learned both letters and figures as a child, and kept the books for his mother's house, but such skills were useless to one of his station. No merchant would ever have trusted him to add up accounts. By the time he'd left the brothel, he was too old to apprentice in any lucrative trade. He could have given himself over to unskilled labor, and broken his back unloading ships or carrying goods to market for farmers too poor to own a cart. He thought he would not have lasted long at that business, though. He would have turned to drink, to soothe his sore muscles, and wasted that tiny pittance of money he earned.

He finished the last of his bread and got up again. He headed up a side street, a narrow, winding passage between two closes, piles of houses built around tiny, stinking courtyards full of livestock. He heard voices from all around him, snatches of conversation dripping from every window thrown open to catch a breath of air. Hundreds of people lived in the closes, pressed into a space the size of a rich man's parlor. Some of the houses were six stories high. Imagine, he thought, to every day go down to the river to fetch water and bring it back up all those stairs. He saw in his mind's eye an endless course of pails, sloshing and losing a bit of their contents with every step they climbed, a river of water moving up and down inside those tall houses every day. And every pail needed a poor blighter to carry it.

He shook his head and hurried up the street. His own room was in the next block over, above a waxchandler's shop. The shop turned out candles, whole barrels full of them every day made of beef tallow that stank when it burned or more expensive and reliable beeswax. His room stank always of paraffin, and the stairs leading to it were used to store extra spools of wicking and blocks of rancid tallow. Still, the room at the top of those stairs was warm all winter from the heat of the wax kettles underneath, and he didn't have to share with anyone else. He headed up the exterior stairs to his door and lifted the latch, thinking only of his bed. It was a simple mattress stuffed with straw and sagging in a frame of ropes. He wondered if he would care enough to tighten them before he climbed inside. He wondered how long he would stay awake once his head touched the scratchy sheets.

He hurried inside and closed the shutters. It wouldn't be the first time he'd slept through an afternoon, wishing to be rested for the night to come. Yes, just a few hours with his head down and then—

*Thief. Hearken to me, thief.*

The damned crown!

When he first touched it, it had spoken to him. During his escape from the dungeons it had mostly been quiet, but only because there was enough noise to drown out its voice. Now, when his room was still, when he was alone with his thoughts and his exhaustion, he could hear it whisper to him.

It never stopped.

*Thief, I can help you. I can save you from all dangers. Simply listen to what I have to say. Thief! Listen to me!*

Malden stormed over to the middle of the room, where he'd hidden the crown beneath the loose floorboards. He stamped on the spot, hard enough he thought he might stave in the boards and ruin his hiding place. Like a man pounding on the floor to tell his downstairs neighbors they are too loud.

*I've seen what you desire, thief. And I can help you get it. I ask only one thing. Place me upon your head.*

His stomping was of no use. The damned thing would be quiet just long enough to let him crawl into his bed. Then, before he could even close his eyes, it would speak again, inside his head where he could not block it out.

*Thief, put me on. Place me on your head and I shall tell you secrets. Thief, I can tell you where treasure is buried. I can tell you how to make wealth out of thin air, how to acquire all the riches you desire. Thief! I can make you free!*

The thing had hardly stopped talking since he stole it.

And much worse—he was starting to believe the things it said.

All he had to do was put it on his head. All he had to do was wear it for just a moment and it would tell him anything he wanted to know. It would tell him why Bikker and Cythera wanted it so badly. It would teach him all the secrets of the Burgrave.

*And so much more, thief. I know the way to a woman's heart. The witch's daughter can be yours, thief. I can make her obey your every command. I can make her long for you until her body aches for your touch. Just put me on.*

The crown wouldn't let him get a wink of sleep. Long before dark he surrendered. Not to its suggestions, of course, but to the fact that he would go out again, as tired as he was, and find Bikker or Cythera immediately.

It couldn't wait another hour.

# CHAPTER THIRTY-THREE

Finding Bikker was easily enough done, for a man with the right connections.

Malden headed across the city again, this time taking the bridge that ran high over the Skrait to the Royal Ditch. He kept clear of the Goshawk Road there—that place was only for the sons of rich men, idle and carrying too much coin for their own good. They would have been an attraction for a man with his deft fingers if not so well-guarded. At every corner of the Goshawk Road armed men lounged, looking out for people like Malden. The guards, employed by the gambling houses and upscale brothels of the Road, would take him down an alley and beat him senseless without bothering to ask any questions first.

Besides, Malden's destination was in a far more humble part of the Royal Ditch. A part of the city he knew very well. He should, since after all it was where he'd grown up. As he headed down Pokekirtle Lane, a few haggard whores leaned out of doorways to shout propositions at him, but he ignored them. Too drunk to recognize him, they let him pass without impugning his manhood too severely.

Malden had to knock on the door of the Lemon Garden for ten minutes before he was answered—and then only from a window on the second story. Elody, the madam of the house, leaned out into the dusk, her shoulders barely covered by a frayed silk shawl. She clucked her tongue down at him. "Sorry, love, we're not open yet. Come back after dark."

"Afraid a customer will see the pox sores on your rump if they aren't hidden by darkness?" Malden asked.

Elody's painted face turned dark with anger—until he stepped back away from the door so she could see him. Then a wide grin split her face, showing her missing teeth. "Malden! It's been ages!"

It was true. It had been years since he'd returned to his childhood home.

Elody slammed the door shut, and he heard her racing down the stairs to get the door. She must have alerted the others inside to his presence, because half a dozen girls were squeezed in the portal when it opened, all of them giggling and simpering for him. He favored them with a warm smile, and a dozen soft hands pulled him inside and shut the door after him. The older "girls," some of whom had worked alongside his mother, tousled his hair and poked him in the ribs to see if he'd gained any weight. The younger doxies reached for other parts of him, only to have their hands slapped away by Elody.

"He isn't here for that," she scolded, "you spavined sluts. Malden's not a *customer*. He's *family*. He could have girls younger and more talented than you for the price of asking but he never does."

"Maybe he just hasn't tried someone his own size yet," a slender girl said.

"Or maybe he doesn't like seafood," one of the oldsters told her. "You might try washing it out after you use it all night."

"Maybe he doesn't like girls."

"You do like girls, don't you, Malden?"

"Don't you like me?"

"Learn some manners!" Elody shrieked. "Mirain, fetch him some wine. Gerta—you get some pillows together, make him a pile to lie on. The rest of you go finish putting your faces on, it's only an hour till we open. You don't get paid for fawning over our boy! Malden, Malden, it's good to clap eyes on you. How you've grown. Come in, come in!"

Elody was a madam who knew more of hospitality than any ostler. After all, she'd been entertaining men all her life. She let him take her plump arm and directed him into the courtyard garden that gave the house its name. A single withered lemon tree swayed there over piles of freshly strewn rushes. It was here the tupenny whores entertained their clients—the penny trulls (called penny uprights, sometimes) never bothered to lie down. In the rooms above, which had curtains instead of doors, wealthier clients might be entertained by girls who advertised themselves as virgins (unlikely) or by their varied specialties, which ranged a wide gamut.

Malden was led beneath the tree and provided with a bed of cushions and a cup of mulled wine. It wasn't very good, but he pretended to sip at it to appease his hostess. She smiled and saw to his every need and asked a million little questions about his life since leaving this place that had once been his mother's house. These questions he answered only vaguely, or with outright lies—Elody knew perfectly well how he earned his living, and wasn't asking for real information anyway.

He imagined he could have found this same reception in any brothel between the Golden Slope and the city walls. One of his jobs when his mother had still been alive was to run errands back and forth between the various houses of prostitution, and he learned early on that whores had three special talents other women lacked: one was the obvious, but another, less widely advertised, was that they took care of their own. They had to—even by the liberal standards of the Free City of Ness, a working woman was on the absolute bottom rung of the societal ladder. If they had problems, they turned to one another to solve them, because no decent citizen would ever stoop to aid a whore. The children of whores were treated like royalty among their number—because outside the walls of the brothel, they would be treated worse than livestock.

"It's been so long," Elody said, playing with a curl of her hair. The henna she used for dye left it thin and fragile, but she could never stop playing with it. "Why didn't you come back sooner?"

Malden smiled at her but made no answer. When he left, when he'd grown too old to be a baby of the house, when the previous madam of the place shoved him out in the streets, she'd not been unkind but was firm. There was no place for him there any longer. The house that had been his only home when he was a boy had suddenly seen him as a seed between its metaphorical teeth, and spat him out into the streets of Ness with as little ceremony. He could still remember the look on the faces of Elody and the other "girls" that day. They'd fought with themselves not to show him any pity. And they'd won.

For a while afterward, while Malden tried to find honest work—and then when he began his life of crime—he'd sworn to himself he would never return.

Now, seeing how Elody received him, he realized what a fool he'd been.

The madam patted his hand and let his silence go. She filled it with her own words instead. "So much has happened that I must tell you about. Wenna had her baby, she's a pretty little thing, and Gildie actually made good on all her promises, and bought out her contract, and is living with a wood-carver now, she's an honest woman at last. She who was the most scurrilous of commodities once, as you'll no doubt remember."

"Really? I thought she was all bluster, that one."

Elody laughed. "Nothing stands still for long these days. Even old baggages like me can change our ways when the wind blows—oh, and have you heard the latest? It's all the talk today. The Burgrave's tower fell down! It seems a wonder, even now when I've had time to grow accustomed to the notion. Eight hundred years it stood. They say it was lightning that done for it."

"I hadn't heard," Malden said.

"You must be the last." She squinted at him suddenly. Malden tensed, thinking she might guess he'd had some hand in the tower's collapse. She was a shrewd woman, Elody—one had to be to get to run a bawdy house in Ness. Could she see it written all over his face? "There's something different about you," she said finally.

"I'm the same as ever," he protested.

"No. What is it? What do I sense here?" Her face opened wide with a bright smile. "You've met a woman! You must tell me all, at once!"

Malden's shock could not be overestimated. "I—I—ah—yes," he finally said, simply glad to change the subject, not thinking overmuch on what he said. "But—how did you know?"

"You've combed your hair!" Elody said, exploding in laughter.

Malden reached up and touched his short hair. It was true he'd groomed himself before heading out that morning. He'd wanted to look presentable when he turned over the crown. It did not occur to him that he had done so thinking that he would see Cythera again, but—

"It's nothing," he protested. "She's a beauty, and far beyond what I might hope to attain. I've done nothing but make a fool of myself when I'm around her. Surely she's not interested."

"Some women like that," Elody told him. "But I can see your discomfort talking on this, so I'll let it be. For now. Tell me, Malden, why you've really come here," she said, a sparkle in her eye. He knew he hadn't heard the last of this. "I know you aren't here just for advice on love."

He set his cup on the ground and looked up at a shriveled lemon hanging from a branch above him. "I'm looking for someone. Either of two people, actually—a man and a woman."

"We've plenty of the latter, to meet all requirements," Elody japed.

He smiled and looked her in the eye. "How much of this place does Cutbill own?" he asked. He still wished to keep the master of thieves as far out of the job as he could manage, just as Cythera and Bikker had asked.

"That scrawny weevil? None," she insisted.

"In truth?"

Elody sighed. "You know we're not the finest house, nor the most lucrative. Truth be told, we've fallen on hard times, Malden. Cutbill could buy this place ten times over, doors, windows, coneys and all, and not feel the pinch. He never made so much as an offer. He steers clear of us because he doesn't want to absorb our debts."

Malden nodded understandingly. "I'm not sure if the people I'm looking for were ever clients of yours . . . or of any woman plying the trade. But perhaps you've heard tell of them." That was the third great talent of the harlots: they heard things. Men were famous for talking in moments of extreme relaxation. The working girls tended to share the juicier bits of gossip they acquired with each other. Had the Burgrave himself a dark secret to hide, if he whispered it into the ear of his favored concubine at midnight, for certain it would be the small talk of streetwalkers in the Stink by midday.

"Let's see what we can learn." Elody offered him a hand to help him rise from his cushions and led him up the stairs to the private rooms, where the girls were getting ready.

Once there, he described the shifting tattoos on Cythera's cheek to a girl who billed herself a Barbarian Princess (in truth, she was only tanned by the sun). While a trull twice his age coated her face with white lead to hide her wrinkles, he spoke of Bikker's acid-spitting sword. A girl of fifteen put powder of belladonna in her eyes while he elocuted on Cythera's ability to appear from thin air. When she was done, she looked as surprised as he'd been on the roof of the university, but she had no news to share with him.

It wasn't until he reached Big Bess's closet that he found what he was looking for. Bess was taller than Malden by a full head and broader through the shoulders. She wore a tight bodice that made her substantial bosom look as big as Castle Hill. Perversely enough, her specialty was for dwarves—the diminutive craftsmen liked their women sturdy, and far from home they would settle for Big Bess's powerful frame. It seemed they weren't the only ones.

"A bit wild, but a smooth talker, you say. Big sword over his shoulder, oh, aye." Bess grunted. "He leaves his chain mail on when he ruts." She rubbed red powder onto her cheeks to make them look permanently flushed, then smeared some between her breasts as well. "You say he's called Bikker? Milles is the name he uses, but of course it's not what they call him at home. He doesn't come often, but when he does I make him pay for the full night because I know I'll be bruised and no good for anyone else in the morning."

"I imagine we're speaking of the same man," Malden told her. "Bess, do you know where he lives? Or at least where I might find him?"

"Are you going to kill him?" the trollop asked while gluing on a set of horsehair eyelashes. "Because I won't have that on my conscience."

"No, no," Malden said. "Perish the thought. He owes me money."

"Ah!" Bess exclaimed. "In that case—"

# CHAPTER THIRTY-FOUR

When the Seven Day Fire finally burned itself out, leaving nearly half the Free City in smoldering ruin, a great wave of religious mania ran through the people. Both Sadu and the Lady were exalted for stopping the fire, and their adherents carried their icons through the streets in endless processions. Zealots of the two faiths came to blows in the streets, and thus began a civil war that might have finished what the fire began. The Burgrave stepped in then, crushing the leadership of the Bloodgod's mob with brutality and a lack of discrimination. When the bodies were cleared away, he declared the Lady the official tutelary of the city. In honor of this patron deity, he seized an entire neighborhood of houses where Sadu was the only god and had them pulled down. Every timber, every stick of furniture, was demolished and carted away. The people who had lived in those houses went to live with family members if they could, or to the streets if they must. The very ground where the houses had stood was cleared to bare soil, so no sign of the neighborhood would ever be found again.

Protests had been minimal. There were already plenty of martyrs with their heads on pikes up by Castle Hill, and even the most devout were loath to join their coreligionists there. Besides, the houses the Burgrave tore down had mostly been destroyed by the fire already. Yet the Burgrave's intention was clear—he had demonstrated that the faith of the Bloodgod was no longer an accepted religion in the city. If he allowed it to be practiced at all it was strictly at his pleasure, and he could clamp down on it whenever he saw fit. He needed a monument to that intention, and the cleared ground would be the place for it.

A stone wall ten feet high had been constructed around the six acres thus reduced. There were no gates in that wall, nor any way to enter the ground inside once it was completed. All sign of human habitation was removed from what came to be known as the Ladypark. Plants and wild animals were allowed to flourish there unchecked. Rumors persisted—and were reinforced by the roars and howls that plagued the district by night—that the Burgrave had introduced some large predatory creatures to the preserve before sealing it up. It was well known that anyone who climbed over that wall, perhaps looking to steal fruit from the many trees inside the park or to poach some of the holy game, would never climb back out in one piece.

It was a dangerous place, and a sacred one. Which meant that the watch never bothered to guard it. Perfect for Malden's needs.

The top of the wall surrounding the park made a narrow avenue winding through half of the Stink and all the way down to the common of Parkwall. Malden ran along its top, where an endless row of wrought-iron spearheads stuck up from the capstones. One slip and he'd be impaled, but Malden never slipped.

When he reached the end of the wall he squatted down and peered through the darkness. A sliver of moon lit the scene, while vapors of mist curled on the grass of the common where a few stray sheep slept on their feet. Beyond the Ladypark's south wall a hundred yards of open ground surrounded a grand villa. Parkwall was known for its enclosed houses, which belonged to those citizens rich enough to afford mansions yet willing to live so far away from the crowded merchant neighborhood of the Golden Slope. This house was the largest of them all: a massive three story pile of white stone, busy with gables and flying buttresses. Its walls were pierced in a hundred places by broad windows of clear, smooth glass—expensive—and in the front by a twenty-foot-wide rose window of stained glass, worked with cabalistic symbols—ruinously expensive. It would look very much like a cathedral, Malden thought, had it possessed any spires.

Smaller outbuildings clustered the forecourt, while in back of the house was a broad and meticulously tended garden of topiary and fountains. The whole was surrounded not by a wall, but by a simple fence of iron bars, pointed at the top to discourage anyone from climbing over. The fence looked imposing, but Malden might have laughed at the security it provided (had he not been trying to stay quiet as a mouse). A boy, or even just a very thin man, could slip between those bars by turning sideways.

He was not a fool, of course. He knew whose house this was, and that the fence would be the least of its defenses. It belonged to Hazoth, the only sorcerer of real power in the Free City of Ness. Malden knew of the man by reputation. Growing up in the city, unruly children were often threatened with a visit from the sorcerer, and even some adults used his name as an oath. Though Hazoth was accepted as a leading citizen (the only prerequisite of that status being gold), he was a reclusive figure who only came out of his home for grand public occasions. Such a character naturally attracted his share of attention and superstition—a reputation that was worth a dozen walls and moats and palisades. Whether Hazoth was truly as powerful as the legends made him out to be, no thief with natural survival instincts would risk drawing the man's attention.

Trespassing on the grounds of a sorcerer was reckoned a kind of self-slaughter. There was no telling what dread curse Hazoth might levy on a trespasser. He might turn your guts to water or make your eyes burst in their sockets with a simple wave of his hand. No doctor could heal that kind of injury, nor would any touch you for fear of suffering a like fate.

No, only a fool would bother Hazoth in his own home.

Even without the threat of magic, Malden had eyes in his head to see that there were armed guards patrolling the garden behind the house. They went with shining lanterns around the corners of the stables and the kitchens, looking for anyone who dared to slip through that fence.

Malden would never have approached the place in a hundred years—had he not had legitimate business there. His investigations told him this was where Bikker was to be found, and likely Cythera as well.

So he assumed that Hazoth had to be his ultimate employer. It must have been Hazoth's orders that sent Cythera and Bikker after the crown. What in the Bloodgod's name could a sorcerer want with it, though? Clearly it was enchanted—normal crowns didn't talk to people. Perhaps, Malden thought, the wizard merely wanted to study the magics imbued in the simple coronet of gold. Most likely he would never know the true answer. The motivations of Hazoth's kind would always be mysterious to the uninitiated.

The main result of Malden's discovery was to make him all the more eager to be quit of the thing. Hand it over, collect his pay, never think of it again. It seemed the only proper course.

Of course, it would have to be done with care. Hazoth had sought to escape scrutiny, hiding his complicity in the crown's theft behind a double layer of employees. He would not take kindly to even his own hired thief walking up to his gate with the crown in hand, not now.

Malden made his way along the wall until he was directly over the darkest part of the common. As he had expected, it was not completely deserted. A boy in a dark-colored cloak was crouched in some bushes just below the wall. He had a cudgel on the ground next to his right hand and a sloshing jug clutched close to his chest. He also had a scarf wrapped around the lower half of his face, which was a bit of a giveaway.

Malden drew his bodkin, then stepped carefully over a spearpoint until he was directly above the boy's head. The young footpad didn't even look up. He was too busy watching the common, looking for any poor shepherd who might have come late to collect his sheep. The take would be piss-poor, but for a certain class of desperate criminal no score was beneath plucking. Even shepherds had clothing, and there were places in the city where you could sell clothes in the middle of the night where no questions would be asked.

Without a sound Malden dropped down onto the footpad's back. The robber struggled and started to cry out, but he placed the point of his bodkin in the join between the boy's jaw and neck.

"If I wanted to slit your throat, I'd have done it already," Malden said. "Now, will you be quiet? I want a word."

The boy started to nod—and stopped when he realized that doing so would impale him on Malden's weapon. "Certainly, milord," he sputtered out. The alcohol on his breath was enough to make Malden's head spin. He supposed that lying-in-wait was thirsty work.

"You've a chance to earn some coppers tonight, lad," Malden said, and moved his knife a fraction of an inch away from the boy's jugular vein. "But first you must answer me a question true. Who do you work for?"

"My own self! That's all! I swear, your honor, I'm a good fellow, I say my prayers as often as I remember, and I've never done anything like this before, I—"

"You don't report back to Cutbill? He doesn't take a share?"

The boy squirmed violently. Perhaps the lad thought he'd been sent by Cutbill to kill him for unauthorized thieving.

"That answer's good enough," Malden said, easing up a little more. "Now let us converse like gentlemen of fortune."

# CHAPTER THIRTY-FIVE

The boy's face was freckled and his chin weak, when the scarf was removed. Malden held onto his cudgel and his jug while he conveyed the message. Walking like a man on the way to the headsman's block, the boy crossed the common and went right up to Hazoth's gate. He gave one last look over his shoulder—even though he couldn't possibly see Malden so far away in the dark—and then stepped inside the open gate.

The effect was immediate, and startling.

A crackling sound rustled through the grass, and then the boy lifted into the air, as if he'd been snatched up by some invisible hand. Inside the sorcerer's laughable fence all was suddenly action. Guards rushed out to see who the intruder was, and Malden heard dogs barking in their kennels and horses stamping in their stalls.

Slowly the boy sank back down to earth. There was a sudden flash, not of light but of darkness—like the pulsing of shadows after lightning strikes. Malden's eyes narrowed. He was glad he'd sent the boy in his place. Apparently the iron fence was only a symbol for a quite different kind of protection.

The guards circled the boy and drove him to his knees. The boy lifted his hands above his head as a spear was jabbed into the small of his back. Malden could hear him wailing out his message, the one Malden had made him rehearse several times to get every word right.

*You never told me it could talk*, the message ran. *Let us three meet at midnight, at the Godstone.*

It was a risk, sending this message. Someone might be listening—someone who belonged to the city watch or some other enemy. If they were, he had given them the time and place where they could seize him with ease. Hopefully the words were obscure enough to confuse anyone who didn't know all the particulars of what had happened.

The boy was released unharmed. The guards held him a bit roughly, perhaps, but they didn't break his bones for his impudence. Once he was beyond the gate again, the boy ran off toward the Stink, not even bothering to return to Malden for payment. Perhaps in his fear he had forgotten the thruppence promised him. Malden dug in the soft soil underneath the bush where he'd found the boy concealing himself. There, he buried the cudgel, the jug, and three pennies, wrapped up in the filthy scarf. If the boy was brave enough or bright enough to return for his things, he well deserved the money.

Then Malden fled back into the night, running the way he'd come, along the top of the Ladypark's enclosing wall. There was much to prepare.

The fact that his secret employer was a master of the arcane sciences worried him greatly, but not near so much as Bikker did. The big swordsman had killed two men just to create a diversion, and Malden had no doubt that Bikker would be willing to kill him as well. Either the swordsman would want to keep the gold for himself—or more likely, would want to keep him quiet, in the most expedient way possible. When he'd taken this job, Malden believed it was little more than a prank. The crown would be replaced with a duplicate, and no one would ever be the wiser—the Burgrave wouldn't even publicly acknowledge the theft, out of fear of embarrassment.

Now things had changed. The crown was enchanted, and thus far more important than just some well-wrought lump of gold. The Burgrave would want it back, and stop at little to secure its return. Bikker and his master would want to maintain total secrecy, and the only way they could assure that was to slit his throat and dump his body in the river.

Malden sighed as he ran atop the wall. No one had ever said his new life as a daring burglar was going to be easy. He came to a corner of the wall and slipped down to the street below, a shadowed lane running toward a row of houses in the Stink. The houses there closed in quickly, filling the available space around the common like a miser jealously throwing his arm around a pile of pennies. It felt good to be back on cobblestones, back in a district he knew well. He'd spent his life on these streets, and though he knew all too well their dangers, he knew how to manage them as well. He felt almost safe as he headed uphill, toward the eastern section of the Stink.

Not completely safe, of course. But he felt like he was the master of his destiny again. He felt like he could pull this off. If he was careful. There were still ways he could get his gold and keep his life, but it would take much planning and—

"Hold, if you please."

Malden's heart stopped beating, but only for a moment. He'd seen no one following him, had thought it impossible. Who could this be?

Whoever it was, he did not wish to meet him now.

He leapt back toward the wall of a half-timbered house. Its eaves cast a deep rich shadow on the street below that would hide him. He made no answer to the call. He did not so much as breathe. He considered closing his eyes so they would not glint in any stray beam of starlight. But no, he needed to see what was coming for him.

"It is not my design to hurt you," the voice said.

Light burst all around him. The other must have had a dark lantern and suddenly drawn back its shade. For a moment Malden could see nothing, and his eyes, adapted as they were to the darkness, burned with pain. Throwing his cloak across his face, he dashed to his left, intent on getting away from the spearing light—

—and near impaled himself on the point of a sword. He dropped his cloak just in time and drew up short as the tapering point bobbed in the air just inches from his throat. It was no blunt iron weapon either, but good, bright steel of the kind only a dwarf could forge. It would have run him through like a skewer through a sausage.

Squinting, Malden glanced over at the lantern. He could see now that it was sitting unattended on the cobblestones. If he had run toward it and kicked it over, he would be away into the shadows by now and free of this danger.

For the first time he looked down the blade of the sword at the man who held it. He was no watchman, at least. He was a blond man perhaps half again Malden's age, wearing a jerkin studded with iron and a fine samite cape. A man of some wealth, then, though his boots were muddy. He was smiling, but with warmth—not with the predatory grin of a cat pinning a starling with its claws.

It took a moment for Malden to recognize his accoster. When he did, he was only more confused than before.

"You're the fellow they were going to hang in Market Square," he whispered. "The knight. Sir—Sir—Sir Something. Well, it seems you have me at your service, Sir—"

"Croy."

Malden lifted a hand in salute. The knight knocked the hand away with the flat of his sword.

"I apologize for this rude meeting, but I saw no other way to gain your attention," Croy told him. Stranger by the minute, Malden thought. He was not used to armed men treating him with civility. "I wish to ask you but a single question. Will you answer?"

"Under the circumstances, I can hardly refuse," Malden replied.

"I saw you send a message to the villa of Hazoth. And I know someone fitting your description was on Castle Hill the night the tower fell. The night a certain boat was waiting in the river below."

Malden was especially glad then that this knight was no watchman. If Anselm Vry's men had put things together as neatly as this fellow, his neck would already be in a noose. "If you say so, milord."

"You don't deny it. The boat was there to collect you, wasn't it? Cythera's boat. I can see in your eyes it was so. So now I'll ask you—what business have you with Cythera?"

Malden's brow furrowed as he tried to understand what was happening. Was he about to be killed for reasons he would never know? Or would this fool let him go if he answered true?

For some reason, Malden thought he just might.

"I did some work for her, that's all. I'm arranging to receive my payment."

"In the middle of the night? Strange hours to take wages."

"I suppose," Malden said, "that depends on the labor."

Croy's face changed. The smile faded a bit and his eyes widened. "Tell me true, now. What job was it?"

Malden considered his reply carefully. "Sir Croy, I think your interest in milady Cythera is not of an, ah, adversarial nature. To be plain, I think you are her friend."

"More than that, I hope," Croy said.

Malden's heart sagged in his chest. Something he hadn't dared to actually hope for suddenly seemed out of his reach. But more than his feelings were bound to be hurt if he didn't speak quickly. "I will admit to caring for her myself. If this sentiment is one we share, then surely you will understand it would put her at risk if I answered that question? Especially out here, where someone might overhear?"

"I see," Croy said. He lowered his sword so it was no longer pointing at any vital part of Malden's body. "You're right, it's too dangerous to have this talk in public. In that case, let us—"

But Malden didn't hear the rest. He'd found the opening he had sought. As soon as the sword's point dipped, he twisted sideways and bolted for the dark, jogging to one side only far enough to kick the lantern as he went.

Sir Croy called hold again and gave chase, but not for long. Malden had a head start on him, and in the night that was all the advantage the thief required.

# CHAPTER THIRTY-SIX

Knightly interruptions notwithstanding, Malden's preparations were finished long before midnight. He scouted out Godstone Square—a modest plaza deep in the Stink, where the residents were unlikely to open their windows at night—and found the proper spot to lie in wait, then gathered together the tools he needed. This largely amounted to stealing some poor citizen's clothesline and digging an old but still sound basket out of a rubbish pile in an alley. Not the most sophisticated tools, but the simplicity of Malden's plan was its strength.

The Stink at that hour of night was all but deserted. Up on the Golden Slope, across the river in the Royal Ditch, the rich would be up and about, taking their night's entertainment in gambling houses or playing cards or listening to chamber music in their well-lighted apartments. They would be out in the streets in the murk of night, led along the wide avenues by the linkboys who ran through the streets carrying pitch torches. Down here, though, the poor could afford little light after the sun set. Candles were expensive, oil lamps doubly so. The people of the Stink kept out of their dark streets, sleeping early behind thick shutters and locked doors. Only thieves prospered after dark here. Thieves like Malden.

He took his place, then settled in to wait. His body drooped with the need for sleep and his belly was far from full but he'd learned a long time ago how to ignore his muscles and wait in silence for long periods of time.

It was no more than two hours later when Bikker and Cythera approached the square. They came silently, without lights, and walked directly up to the Godstone itself in the middle of the crossroads.

A monolith about fifteen feet tall, inscribed with dread runes that time had weathered to illegibility, it had been a center for the worship of the Bloodgod centuries ago. The first Burgrave had ritually defiled it, however, and the people stopped coming. Too big and too heavy to be carted away, it waited out the years and the rain in mute witness. Even the bloodstains that once washed its lower half had faded away to nothing, and now it served only as a landmark, an unloved boil on the face of an unloved district. Neither Cythera nor Bikker even looked at it as they approached. Their eyes studied the shadows, the corners, the recessed doorways of the houses around them.

They did not think to look up. Malden stirred himself carefully—his limbs were stiff with immobility—and cleared his throat.

His two employers did not flinch. As one they turned their faces upward and looked upon him where he crouched atop the stone. Bikker looked annoyed. Cythera looked merely like she wished to be somewhere else.

He could sympathize. "Did you bring the gold?" he asked.

Bikker's face softened. "You could at least have picked a less public meeting place."

"Certainly. A dark alley, perhaps? Or maybe we could have met at the top of a cliff above the Skrait, so you could just push me in."

"You don't trust us?" Cythera asked. There was no hurt in her tone.

"I don't trust *him*. He killed two just to draw attention." Malden rose to his feet and paced back and forth atop the stone. It was just barely two strides across. "As for you—I can imagine why you took your little boat away. I don't think any of us expected things to turn out this way."

"If you mean we didn't expect you to bungle the job," Bikker growled, "you're right, there."

Malden laughed—though not loudly. "We all survived. I have the thing you want. As long as you have my gold, I think we did just fine."

Cythera reached beneath her cloak and drew forth a bulging sack. It looked heavy in her slim hands, but she showed no sign of effort as she lifted it. "All the same, you'd do well to lie low after this. We drew more scrutiny than we would have liked. And they'll be looking for the object."

"Bah," Bikker said. "They probably think it's buried in the rubble. Come down here, boy, and give it to me. Then we'll leave your gold. Then we'll never see each other again, if you know what's good for you."

"I have a better notion." Malden kicked the basket over the side of the stone so it dropped to the cobbles at their feet. The clothesline tied to its handle had its other end in his hand. "Put the gold in there and I'll raise it up. *Then* I'll throw you your prize."

"Out of reach of my sword, up there," Bikker said. His face showed a kind of grudging admiration. "Of course, you can't stay up there forever. Eventually you'll have to come down, and I can wait a long time."

Malden favored him with a grim smile. If it came to that, he knew he could leap to the wall of the nearest house and be over its roof before the swordsman could climb the God-stone. He didn't say as much.

"Enough," Cythera said, and placed her sack in the basket. Malden hauled it up quickly, before Bikker could grab at it. It was as heavy as he expected—there must be ten pounds of gold in the sack. His heart lurched at the prospect. Opening the sack, he was relieved to see it was not full of stones or bars of lead. Quickly, he counted the money. One and a hundred golden royals! The exact amount he needed. He tied the sack to his back underneath his cloak.

"Many thanks," Malden said. "As for your prize—it's at the bottom of a horse trough two streets to the west. I would have brought it with me, but I couldn't bear its incessant babbling."

"You—You blasted fool," Bikker frothed. "What if some vagrant stumbled upon it and hawked it already to a pawner?"

Malden shifted his shoulders so the gold at his back clinked. "Not my problem anymore."

Bikker cursed and dashed out of the square, shouting for Cythera to stay and watch Malden. When he was gone, Malden slipped easily down the side of the Godstone, using the carved runes as handholds, and bowed deeply before her.

"It's not wise to anger him," she said with a sigh.

"I don't intend to meet him again." Malden turned on his heel to dash away. Something stopped him. He should have known better, especially after meeting Croy, but he couldn't help himself. What if there was a chance? "You, on the other hand—"

"Me? You'd wish to see me again?" she asked.

"I think I made that clear, when last we spoke. If you're amenable."

A strange look crossed her eyes. Her face was too opaque with tattoos for him to read it. "Then perhaps," she said, "I have something you might like to hear. There's another reward. From my master."

"Hazoth?" Malden said, confused. "I want nothing else from him."

"Then take it from me," she said, her voice soft and low. She stepped toward him and smiled. "A kiss. Just one. Don't you find me desirable?"

Malden laughed, but more from uncertainty than the

humor of it. "More than any woman I've known in a long time."

"Perhaps I find you handsome. Perhaps I merely want to show my proper thanks."

Malden's heart raced. The offer certainly held its attractions. Yet it seemed strange she should offer it as coming from Hazoth. What had she meant?

She was very beautiful. Especially by moonlight. White flowers were blooming in the ink just below her left eye. Exotic, and all the more comely for it.

She moved closer, close enough to embrace him.

Malden took a step back. Something was happening here, something he didn't understand. There was one thing he definitely needed to know. "Oh, milady, you've tempted me sore. But I'm not sure my new friend Sir Croy would approve," he said.

"Croy," she said, like a woman waking from troubled dreams. She blinked rapidly and straightened her posture. It was all Malden needed to hear. The offer of a kiss had not been given in good faith. Hazoth must have charmed her into making it—or maybe Sir Croy was testing him for some reason. "Did you say—"

Before she could finish her question, though, Malden was gone. He was really getting quite good at slipping away in the dark.

# CHAPTER THIRTY-SEVEN

An hour later Malden was fast, and finally, asleep.

He did not go home to his room above the waxchandler's, of course. That was for fear that he'd find Bikker waiting there, his nasty sword dripping acid on the floor-boards. Instead he took to sleeping rough, under the Corn-market Bridge, just below Market Square. It was an odd and exposed place to doss. The bridge passed not over a river, but over the very houses of the Golden Slope. It had been built to allow goods to be brought from the Smoke straight to Market Square, without disturbing the wealthy citizens in their mansions. Its span was like a ribbon of stone float-ing over the rooftops, and where Malden perched he had a good view of a hundred chimney pots directly below, each of them trailing a thin stream of smoke. It was like lying on a cloud. It was a strangely exposed location, but its oddity made it ideal—no one would think to look for him there. In his rumpled, dusty cloak he looked the very picture of the broken men who frequented the place. None challenged him as he found a spot between two stone plinths and curled up, his cowl pulled tight around his face for warmth.

Only once, during the night, was he disturbed. In his sleep he felt rude fingers test the fabric of his cloak. His eyes snapped open and he was instantly awake. Should someone steal the gold now, it would be a foul jest, would it not?

His hand was already loosely closed on the hilt of his bodkin. He rolled slightly onto his side and drew it from its sheath as the hand grew more bold and insinuated itself into his clothing. Then he spun about on his hip and brought the knife up where it could be seen.

"Och, m'lud," the beggar who'd been trying to roll him pleaded, filthy hands up and fingers spread wide, "there ain't nothin' needful in that."

"Glad to hear it," Malden said. "Find elsewhere to bed down, or someone less wary to plunder."

The beggar nodded heartily and scurried away. Malden went back to sleep.

When he woke, before he opened his eyes, he reached around behind him and touched the sack of gold at his back. Still there.

He let himself smile broadly and luxuriate in the feeling. A fortune, and though it would be gone shortly, by spending it he would earn the right to replace it.

Today, he thought, will be the best of my life.

Then he opened his eyes. In the morning light the space under the bridge lost much of its charm. It was strewn with refuse and furry with gray, stunted weeds that never got enough sun. The penniless men who lived there lingered long in their slumber, brains still addled by the night's freight of cheap drink. All but one, who had a fire going—it looked like it was made of old table legs—and a pot made from a pikeman's rusty helmet. Whatever stew he was cooking up to break his fast smelled evil and looked worse, so when he offered to share it, Malden politely declined.

Exiting his erstwhile lair, he crawled out on one of the supports of the bridge and then clambered up and over its rail. A drover with a load of dressed stone bound for the palace gazed at him askance, but Malden had never yet been hurt by a nasty look. He fell in with the crowd of people heading down into the Golden Slope—servants and tradesmen and carters of sweetmeats and fuel, honest men up early to get to their work and earn another day's wage.

Malden did not sneer at them, for he pitied them some. They would slave and toil for decades until their backs gave out and their beards grew long, and it would profit them little. They would die as they had lived, beholden to masters who cared not a jot for their welfare. Whereas he himself, who had been spurned by their society as not good enough—well, he had only to drop off his earned fortune, to pour it out dramatically across Cutbill's desk—and then, and then!

And then he would be a full member of the guild. He would be a thief in good standing, with protection from arrest and a dwarf to make his tools for him. He would be, in certain circles, a gentleman of stature. He could begin to make money, real money, for himself. He would buy a fine new cloak, he thought, and rent better rooms. He would drink good wine from now on, instead of weak ale, and eat meat at least one meal a day. His standard of living—and concomitantly, his life expectancy—would improve by great measure, and all manner of things would improve.

And best of all—most important of all—he would be

truly free. A man with money could not be made a slave. He could travel where he liked and count himself safe. He could escape the tawdry past and make his own fortune. His own future.

*What a fine and clever fellow am I. What a wise and cunning scoundrel. My mother would be proud indeed.*

Such feelings put a bounce in his step and he made good time as he wended his way downhill, through the Smoke and the Stink, down to the Ashes. In the charred embers down by Westwall he even began to whistle a jaunty tune.

He saw no sign of the urchin army that guarded Cutbill's hiding hole. All to the good—they must recognize him now, he considered, and kept back out of respect. As well they should! Journeyman thief! Man of station!

He came around the corner of the ruined inn and merrily hailed the three old veteran thieves where they sat on their coffin . . . except they weren't there.

Odd.

Lockjaw, 'Levenfingers, and Loophole never budged from that spot, in his experience. Still, he supposed they must sleep sometime. And it was, by the standards of the larcenous crew, still very early. The sun wasn't even over Castle Hill as yet. Malden shrugged and found the trapdoor that led down into Cutbill's headquarters.

"Bellard? Anyone? It's Malden, and I'm coming down," he said in a forced whisper. He knew from previous visits the strange acoustics of the stairwell leading down, which widened as it descended and thus amplified all sounds that issued from its top. Malden thought it wise to announce his entry into that place, if the old trio could not do it for him.

Yet at the bottom no one waited for him, nor was he challenged by any sentry. The common room was, in fact, empty. Slag had deserted his workbench. No whores were sleeping it off on the divan, and for the very first time no gamblers were throwing dice upon the wall.

It took a moment for Malden to notice what else was different. First off he saw this: the divan was shoved out of its place, its legs having scuffed the stone floor. A booted foot stuck out from behind it. As Malden approached, with dread in his heart, he saw that it was Bellard back there. And Bellard was not down for drink, or white snuff, or even just a late night.

Blood frothed on the bravo's lips. His eyes stared at nothing at all.

"Bellard," Malden said, bending over the body. "Bellard, who did this?" He saw that Bellard was clutching at his stomach, and lifted the dead man's hand away. The wound beneath was a deep gouge that pierced his vitals. Clotted blood lay thick around the injury. It looked like someone had taken an axe to Bellard's middle.

Malden heard something—a door being drawn back, perhaps. A foot scraping on stone. He whirled about and saw, secondly, this: the ancient and historied lock that had always warded Cutbill's door was broken in pieces and lay scattered on the floor. And Cutbill's impregnable door stood slightly ajar.

Malden tried to run. He did not get far. The door slammed open and men with halberds wearing cloaks-of-eyes came boiling out. "Seize him," someone said, "whoever he is." And then a dozen hands were on him and they dragged him inside, into what had been Cutbill's private sanctum.

# CHAPTER THIRTY-EIGHT

The rough hands that dragged Malden inside the door threw him down to land on hands and knees. The butt of a halberd struck him in the back, and someone put a boot on his neck and pushed him down to the floor. His bodkin was wrenched from its sheath and his purse dragged out of his belt. A man of the watch found the sack of gold at his back and tore at it until it burst open and coins bounced and rolled across the rushes that strewed the floor.

"Lady's kneecaps, there's a treasure," someone swore. Malden could see little from where he lay save for boots and the bottom of Cutbill's desk. He could hear the voices of half a dozen men, however, and knew he was hopelessly outnumbered.

"Stolen, do you think?"

"Of course—where are we, but the citadel of crime?"

"Ought to seize it for the city coffers."

"Make an accounting of it, so we can split it later and—"

"Count it. All of it. And then place it here." When this last voice spoke, the watchmen around Malden all came to attention. "Let him up, so I may speak with him," the voice said. The boot on Malden's neck moved away and he scrambled backward to get to his feet. Finally he was able to see what was happening in the office.

The watch lined the walls of the room, the points of their halberds almost scraping the ceiling. In the center of the room Cutbill sat at his ledger, quill pen in his hand—just as Malden remembered him from their last meeting.

Standing next to him was Anselm Vry.

Malden recognized the bailiff of the Free City, as would any citizen of Ness. After the Burgrave, Vry was the human face of the city. As bailiff he not only led the watch but also saw to every administrative detail of city life—enforcing the Burgrave's edicts, seeing that weights and measures were kept scrupulously exact, overseeing the moots of the trade guilds. He was the second most powerful man in the city, and if he were here personally, it could mean only one thing. He knew the crown had been stolen, and he wanted to find it at any cost.

Malden had already seen the price that Bellard had paid.

"Is he one of yours?" Vry asked, staring at Malden.

The question was directed, however, at Cutbill. "One of my thieves? No, of course not," Cutbill answered. He made a notation in his ledger. "Look at the state of his clothing. My fellows can afford to dress themselves."

"And this money? This gold?" Vry demanded.

Cutbill did look up then. He glanced at the stacks of gold coins a watchman was placing on his desk. Then he turned his gaze on Malden and lifted one eyebrow. He was sending Malden a message, which was this: *be circumspect and do not gainsay me.* Malden was wise enough not to acknowledge that he had received the instructions.

Cutbill gestured dismissively with his pen. "The money is mine, yes. This boy is merely here to deliver it. Perhaps before we say anything else, he should be sent on his way."

Vry studied Malden with concentrated disdain. "Very well. Give him his knife back—he's no danger to anyone with that pig-cutter."

"Boy," Cutbill said, "if you leave by the door to my left, you'll find yourself well on your way back to the Stink."

Malden nodded and accepted his bodkin from the watchman holding it. He did not ask why Cutbill was sending him out through the door on the left, when it was the door directly behind Cutbill's desk that led back to the surface. He pushed back the tapestry that hid the specified door and stepped through. Beyond was a tiny room with no other exits—a closet, really, empty of furnishings or ornament.

It did have one defining feature, however. Just to one side of the door, at the height of a man's eyes, a very small hole had been drilled through the wall. Someone looking through that hole could see—and hear—anything that happened in Cutbill's office.

So this was a spy chamber. If Cutbill had sent him here, it was with good reason. Malden placed his eye against the hole and made himself silent.

Back in the office, the bailiff and the guildmaster of thieves were already in close consultation.

"If it was one of your thieves who stole the crown," the bailiff said, "I will hang every one of your crew. You I'll have drawn and dismembered, and your remains scattered across the kingdom. I'll have this place torn down, and your organization—"

"It was not one of mine. Of that I can assure you. Not one of my thieves would think the prize worth the effort. After all, how could they sell the crown once they had it?

No fence in the Free City would accept it, much less pay for it. That means its value for us is nil. You must look elsewhere, milord Vry."

"Perhaps someone else commissioned the theft. Someone who would stand to gain by embarrassing the city."

"But why would one of my thieves take on such a job? Surely they would know how much trouble it would cause for my operation. I do not recruit dullards or fools."

In the closet, Malden winced.

"Enough of this nonsense," Vry fumed. "I can hardly trust you to speak the truth. You'll say anything to save your neck, won't you, Cutbill?"

"I've spoken plainly with you, and told all the truth I know."

"Luckily I need not take you at your word." Vry snapped his fingers and one of his watchmen hurried out of the room. He came back a moment later, leading a robed figure with a heavy wooden mask covering his face.

Malden gasped. Luckily no one heard him.

"A wizard, Vry? You'll put me to the question by magery? Surely not," Cutbill said as the magician was led over toward his lectern. "You'd never break one of your own precious laws."

Vry shrugged. "It's true. No man may be condemned in the law courts by sortilege or divination. Yet this is no law court. As for the point of ethics involved, well . . . needs must when the Bloodgod drives."

Cutbill pursed his lips and put down his quill. "Very well. And how should it be done, hmm?"

The magician brought something out from the folds of his robes. A slab of stone about the size and thickness of a book. One side of it had been ground and polished as smooth as glass. "It is a shewstone," its owner said in a burbling, unnatural voice. "It sees what is hidden, what is placed out of sight. I must unveil to use it properly."

The watchmen stirred uneasily at the thought. Neither Cutbill nor Vry reacted at all. "Do it," Vry said.

The magician reached up and pushed his mask up on top of his head.

Malden's cry of horror was swallowed up in the general chorus.

# CHAPTER THIRTY-NINE

Wizardry was not technically illegal in Skrae. It was not very widely practiced either. It could be highly lucrative. There were stringent laws about summoning demons, and the penalty for doing so was inalterable, swiftly meted out, and one hundred percent fatal. Yet other kinds of magic—divination, the infliction and relief of curses, the brewing of love potions and the like—were permitted, and there were plenty of customers for such a trade. The wealthy people of Ness were always looking for an edge, a way to maintain their station, and they would hardly turn their noses up at even the most disreputable worker of miracles. There were easily a thousand men at work in Ness that day who claimed to do magic, and of that number perhaps two or three dozen who could actually match their claims with results. They were all well compensated for the time they spent learning their art.

Yet they were never so numerous as to form a guild. For every child in the Free City learned one fact about thaumaturgy while still very young, and it was enough to keep most of them from pursuing the occult arts. It was this: *magic always has a price.*

Magicians drew their power from the pit and its infernal inhabitants. By making pacts with demons, they were able to work wonders and marvels beyond human reckoning. Yet in doing so they were exposed to the otherworldly energies of that place of torment, and it changed them.

Vry's diviner must have spent countless hours peering into his shewstone, looking for secrets. Whatever he found could not be worth what he'd paid for the knowledge. The skin of the left side of his face had thickened and callused until it resembled the bark of an oak, but it was as white as death. Even the bones of his skull must have changed, for his left eye had migrated downward until it stared, lidless, from where his cheekbone should have been. At his chin and along the left side of his neck, tendrils of pink flesh hung down like a ghastly beard. He could not close his mouth on that side—which explained his strange voice— and the teeth behind his altered lips were visible: they had become fused together in a pair of bony plates that didn't quite meet.

Had he been born like that, the magician would have been doomed to become a beggar, or perhaps a freak in a traveling fair. It was clear from the untouched right side of his face, however, that he had only come to this favor late in life. It must have happened gradually, over time. Malden wondered—when the man saw the first signs of what was to come, why had he not shattered his stone and given up magic altogether?

Perhaps for some the appeal of secrets was too great. The draw of the mysterious and strange. For some, perhaps, the price was not too steep.

When the watchmen stopped murmuring to one another and most had regained the color in their own faces, the magician looked to Vry with his good right eye. "Tell me what you wish to see. It will be revealed."

Cutbill left his pen lying on his lectern. Even he could not look away.

Anselm Vry turned aside. "Look again, as you did this morning, and see if you can find the crown. It may be in this very room—perhaps if you are closer to it you can see it better."

The magician nodded and bent over his stone. From the spy hole, Malden had a good view of its polished surface, but he saw no change there. Yet the very air of the office seemed to change, to grow thick as heavy fog. There was a whispering of invisible voices in the room and the flames of the oil lamps were stifled as by bad air.

The magician passed his hand over the stone a number of times, never quite touching the polished face, as if he were exhorting it to better seeing. Eventually, though, he shook his head and gave off. "All is as before. It exists, still, but its location is forbidden me. It is like trying to look for a coin at the bottom of a muddy lake. Occasionally a glimmer is perceived, but it wavers and is gone before I can grasp the image. Perhaps if I try again later in the day, when the etheric currents are less brisk and the stars take different stations in their wheels . . ."

Vry grunted in frustration. "Never mind. Do something useful this time, and look into that man's heart," he said, jabbing one finger toward Cutbill. "Find the lies he has recently spoken, and find the truth behind them."

Cutbill's lips compressed into a tight frown, but he did nothing to stop this.

The magician bent over the stone again. He made one quick pass with his hand, then closed his eyes and began to chant. He spoke no words but only moved his lips as alien and ugly sounds came bubbling up from his throat. Then his eyes snapped open and he looked to Vry.

"No lies," he said.

Vry thundered at the man, "What? He has never told a truth in his misbegotten life! Look again!"

"There is no need," the magician said. "I tell you, I saw his heart. He has been completely honest with you. He knows not where the crown is, or who might have it."

"Such a waste, to bend your principles for nothing," Cutbill said. "You should have listened to me, Vry. I have no reason to lie to you, and nothing to gain from doing so."

The magician passed his hand across his stone again. One of the oil lamps guttered out and left the room partly in shadow. "This also is the truth," the magician burbled.

Vry grabbed the stone out of the magician's hands and stared into it himself. "I see nothing here! This man's testimony is meaningless." He threw the stone back at the magician, who caught it as he might a falling baby.

"I say only what I see," the magician insisted. "Not what you want me to see."

"Useless! Get out of here. Go back to the palace and read the Burgravine's fortune for her. That's the only reason I let you live, you mountebank."

The magician hurried out of the room without further protest. One watchman went with him as an escort. Once he was gone the lights came back up and the air began to flow in the room once more.

"There," Cutbill said. "As you see—I am wholly innocent."

# CHAPTER FORTY

**I**'m half of a mind to string you up anyway, just on principle. It might not get the crown back but it would make the city a better place."

Cutbill sighed and turned to the next page of his ledger. "That would be a foolish thing to do. I have long held a special arrangement with—"

"With the Burgrave. Not with me!"

"With the Burgrave," Cutbill agreed. "Who always saw me as a necessary evil. I am allowed to operate for the most part unmolested. In exchange I keep a tight rein on the crime in this city. The wealthier citizens are under my protection and the better districts safe at night. If you remove me and my influence, you'll have a hundred fat merchants to answer to."

Malden stifled a gasp. To think that the mastermind of crime was in league with the very authorities he flouted!

Not for the first time, his admiration for Cutbill's genius was enlarged.

Cutbill entered a figure in his ledger. "The commonest kind of thief will run wild in the streets, and while you'll catch them soon enough, there will always be more to take their place. The system works. You can't afford to kill me."

Anselm Vry grabbed the quill out of Cutbill's hand and snapped it in two. "You'll pay attention when I speak to you. I will find the thief who took the crown. And when I trace him back to you, Cutbill, I will be well justified in turning this place into a charnel pit. If your organization is needed, you can still be replaced!"

"Of course," Cutbill said. He closed his ledger, though he kept one finger between the pages as a way to mark his place. "No man is truly indispensable. Yet it would take time to find someone with my particular gifts, and more time to place him properly where he could be effective. And at this very moment you require my services. In fact, without them all hope is lost."

"How so?" Anselm Vry demanded.

"You need to find the crown. And soon. For the nonce you can say the Burgrave is ill, and that he cannot be seen in public. Yet in seven days he must appear. It will be Lady-mas then, and he must lead the procession. His position as head of the church demands it. He must also be wearing his crown when he does so."

"A replica can be made. No one will know the difference."

Exactly, Malden thought. That was what Bikker had suggested.

"Without being plain, which would be unwise just now as we are not alone," Cutbill said, referring to the watchmen still in the room, "you and I both know that would not work."

Vry scowled but said nothing.

In the spy hole, Malden pursed his lips. He wondered what that could possibly mean. A replica crown seemed a perfect solution—yet Cutbill and Vry both seemed to think it would not do. But why?

"I'm sure you have your watch scouring the city already, searching for the crown high and low. But I guarantee they will not find it. Whoever committed this crime is clearly intelligent enough to keep it out of sight."

"They'll go house-to-house then, looking for it."

"You don't have enough watchmen to carry out even a cursory search in that time. Whereas I—"

"Yes?" Vry demanded.

"—have a network of informants and observers who see everything that happens in this city. If I investigate with the fullness of my powers, I can find the crown, and return it, safely, to the Burgrave."

The bailiff glared at Cutbill with pensive rage.

Cutbill opened his ledger to the place he'd left off.

Then he stood up from his lectern, crossed over to his desk and took up a fresh quill.

With a sharp knife he trimmed the nib. Then he stirred it in his inkwell.

He sat back down at his lectern.

And began to make entries.

Anselm Vry was still staring at him.

Cutbill doesn't make an offer unless he knows what the answer will be, Malden remembered.

"No," Vry said.

Malden had not been expecting that.

The guildmaster of thieves did not react visibly.

"No. Too long, Cutbill, you have clutched this city like a hawk clutching a mouse in its talons. You have the temerity to think you are invulnerable. Well, I will show you better. I will find the crown myself, before Ladymas. I will find whoever is holding it, and I will torture them until they give me your name. And then I will return here, and I will finish you, and all your works. I will *eradicate* you."

Cutbill made another notation in his ledger.

"Did you hear me, you glorified cutpurse?" Vry demanded. A vein stuck out from his forehead. Even in the dim light streaming through the spy hole, Malden could see it pulsing.

"Quite clearly. It sounds as if our business is complete.

Now, if you'll excuse me, I need to get this place cleaned up before the day's receipts start coming in." Cutbill bent over his ledger as if the bailiff had already gone.

Vry fumed a while longer, but then signaled his men and they all trooped out of the office, out through the door to the common room.

## CHAPTER FORTY-ONE

And then Cutbill was alone. For quite a while he continued to make his notations. Then he sighed and pinched the bridge of his nose. "Malden," he said in a clear voice, "the main problem with skulduggery and subterfuge is that all the involved parties must actually know how it is done. For instance, they should know when it is safe to emerge from hiding without being told. Will you come out of there now? I have something to say to you."

Malden's heart fell inside his chest and crashed into his vitals. He opened the spy closet door and stepped out. Cutbill gestured for him to approach.

"I imagine you heard all that," Cutbill said, when Malden stood contrite and fidgety before him. "I imagine you followed most of it. Surely you grasped in just what desperate straits our esteemed bailiff finds himself. And you must have drawn the naturally following conclusion—that he will not be swept under the current alone. You understand, then, how much trouble has found its way to my doorstep."

"Yes," Malden confirmed.

"Someone, it seems, did a very rash thing. They stole the Burgrave's crown out of his tower. I can, of course, understand how a thief would covet it. It must be one of the most valuable things in the city. Yet it has never been stolen before, not in the eight hundred years since it was made. Do you have any idea why?"

"The . . . consequences that would follow from its theft."

"Indeed!" Cutbill said. He scratched another entry in his ledger. "It was my belief that you were a clever sort, and here I have proof. You follow me precisely. May I be certain, then, that you would never do something so foolish, so irretrievably stupid, as to bring down my entire organization? I'm afraid I can't be certain of that at all. I think you've done just such a thing, Malden. I think you've made a very bad blunder."

"I thought—"

"Here," Cutbill said, and tapped at an entry in his ledger, "is receipt of your dues payment. One and a hundred gold royals, paid in full. And here," he said, flipping forward a page, "is an expenditure of one groat." Cutbill dug a half-penny out of his tunic and handed it to Malden.

"What's this for?" Malden asked in a small voice. He stared at the coin in his hand.

"It is the traditional severance fee. When a thief leaves my operation he receives that price."

"I see."

Cutbill made another entry. "It is to be placed in the thief's mouth. After his tongue has been cut out to make room. Then his throat is slit. Normally, Bellard does the honors, but he isn't . . . available today. Would you be so kind as to perform the necessary operations yourself, with that rather silly dagger you carry?"

Malden couldn't breathe. He tried to speak but no words would come. Unable to bear his own weight, he sat down on the edge of Cutbill's desk.

"In your own time, of course," Cutbill said without looking up.

Malden drew his bodkin and held it before him.

He could—he could kill Cutbill, now. He could strike the guildmaster down. There was no one in the common room to come to Cutbill's defense. He could kill the man, and then run—and run—and—

And yet, he didn't do it. Cutbill must have considered the possibility when he ordered him to self-slaughter. There must be good reason for Cutbill not to fear his blow. Perhaps . . . perhaps Cutbill had some defense that was not immediately apparent. A charm against blades. A spell up his sleeves. Or a cunningly hidden archer, ready to pierce him through with an arrow at the first sign of violence.

Yes, that was exactly the sort of thing Cutbill would have. Malden lowered his weapon.

"You," Cutbill said, "have achieved something Vry could never do. You have single-handedly destroyed my organization. All by making one phenomenally poor choice. You chose not to tell me what you were going to steal."

"I—I didn't wish to implicate you, or the guild," Malden protested. "Already that has paid dividends—the shewstone found no lies in your heart. And now Vry has no proof I was working on your behest."

"Proof? Proof is for the rich. When a man of property must be taken to court, and tried by his peers, then proof is required." Cutbill glanced up at Malden for the first time. "When the bailiff comes for me the next time, there will be no trial. He will have my name because he will torture enough people until one of them names me merely to make the pain stop. And then he will do as he promised."

"He only has seven days, though. He won't be able to find the crown in that time."

"Everyone knows that perfectly well. That will not stop Vry from destroying me."

"I know where it is," Malden said. "Right now. Or at least, who has it."

"That would be useful information. Too bad a dead man can't provide it."

"But you could simply tell Vry where it is, and—"

"That would change nothing. No." Cutbill laid down his pen and tilted his head back as if his neck was tired from stooping over the lectern for so long. "That would only speed the process. The only chance, the only possibility of a chance of resolving this in my favor, is if I could somehow recover the crown myself. If I could bring it to the Burgrave before Ladymas. He and I already have an understanding. He could chain Vry like the dog he is. But of course, I can't get the crown, now can I? It is in hands I dare not snatch at."

Malden shook his head. He knew exactly where this was going. Cutbill wanted him to come to the conclusion on his own, however. He, Malden, would have to regain what he had already sold. It would be his only chance to save his life. "Let me do it. Let me go to Ha—"

Cutbill clucked his tongue.

"—to the man who has it," Malden said, glancing at the corners of the room, knowing Cutbill did not wish to hear Hazoth's name spoken aloud, but unsure who might be listening. "I'll buy it back. Or trick him out of it."

"Quite unlikely," Cutbill said.

"Permit me to try," Malden pleaded. What choice did he have?

"Very well," Cutbill said. "Do what you can. Let us be clear, though. Should you fail, I will be killed."

"I know that," Malden said. "I heard—"

"I will be taken to the dungeon, and tortured, and then hanged. Perhaps drawn and quartered. That will take a few days. During that time, while I yet live, I will still be able to contact my remaining thieves. At least a few of them will remain loyal to me. They will ensure one thing: the moment I perish, your throat will be slit from ear to ear. If you fail, Malden, we will both die."

"And if I succeed—you must grant me a reward," Malden said.

"Oh? Must I? Tell me, what is your heart's desire?" Cutbill rejoined.

Malden swallowed the lump in his throat. "My life, of course. And reinstatement in your books."

"I suppose you can't have one without the other. Go, Malden. You don't have much time, so you'd better get started now."

"I promise you I will—"

"Leave me," Cutbill repeated.

Malden fled.

# CHAPTER FORTY-TWO

Sir Croy had been raised to be a knight, to be a champion on the battlefield, a slayer of demons, a devout and pious man. He had been trained from birth to command companies of men-at-arms and ride fiery-tempered warhorses.

That night he was called upon for quite a different kind of duty. His patron, the rich merchant who was hiding him from the law, insisted that he attend a dinner party as a guest of honor. He was to be put on display for the merchant's guests, a symbol to prove the merchant's largesse and power.

It was the only thing the merchant had asked for in way of payment for his kindness. Croy could not say no. Had a legion of demons erupted from a crack in the world at that particular moment, however, he would never have been happier to smell brimstone on the air.

"They say the Burgrave has taken ill—did you hear that, Croy? Mayhap he was hurt when the tower came down."

Croy turned to the woman on his left, who had addressed him. She wore a wimple and a ridiculous pointed hat, perhaps to draw attention away from the unfashionable roundness of her face. He could not remember her name. She was the wife of a rich merchant—a dealer in silks? Or maybe it was furs. He only knew that she had been trying to get his attention all night, and when she spoke to him she ran the toe of her slipper up his calf, under the table. Politeness demanded he ignore it. He saw that her cup was nearly empty and he refilled it from the flagon of good wine that sat before him on the table.

"I haven't been much for the news, of late," he apologized.

"The Burgrave didn't appear at the courts of law today," she went on, as if he'd said nothing. As a dish of roasted larks went past she speared one with her knife and dropped it on her plate. It was the seventh or eighth course—there were dozens more to come, small dishes brought out each as they finished cooking, as was the style at this sort of banquet. When the larks were offered to him next, Croy waved them away. He wasn't hungry. "I was there. There was a very interesting case waiting to be heard—a man had killed his wife. He said she had been inconstant, which normally would have been the end of it, but the witnesses said she was pregnant, which complicates things. I like to go to the courts of law some days. I like to look at all the men in the dock, they're so . . . desperate. So wild. I feel a little thrill whenever they gnash their teeth and demand their innocence."

As she prattled on he nodded politely. He'd been trained in how to attend such meals, and knew which salt cellar to use, and when it was permitted to belch, and how to keep his fingers from getting too greasy. One couldn't be a knight and not be versed in polite manners. He had never enjoyed any meal that took half the day, however, and his legs were falling asleep from sitting in one chair for so long.

And his thoughts, of course, were elsewhere. He kept seeing the face of that thief again, the one he'd followed from the Ladypark up into the Stink. Malden, his name was. Cythera had been waiting for him in her boat, Croy recalled, when he had jumped from the wall of Castle Hill. What possible business could that sort have with Cythera? He needed to find out.

"Sometimes I imagine I'm a magistrate, and as the condemned men kneel before me and ask for clemency, I— Oh. Oh, I do beg your pardon," the merchant's wife said. She had gone quite pale.

"Are you all right?" he asked, his attention dragged back to her at once.

"It's just—here I am going on and on about that man they're going to hang, and you . . . you were just on those gallows yourself. Even now you're a wanted man, in hiding from the watch. Why, at any moment they could come and— and—it's so exciting, I was quite overcome. But I've been tactless. You forgive me, don't you? Please tell me you do."

The doors at the far end of the chamber opened silently

and a face peered through. Croy's hand automatically started to reach for the swords at his back—though of course they were safely locked away up in his rooms. He was getting jumpy. Inaction and worry were making him a bundle of nerves.

"Of course," he said. "Will you take some of this sauce?"

"Mmm, please," she said, and stared deeply into his eyes. "You say you forgive me but I know I've been cruel. Perhaps there is some way to . . . earn your forgiveness?"

A footman in livery came into the room and scanned the table. Moving quietly so as not to disturb the banqueters, he moved around the table and over to where Croy sat. He hemmed and hawed for a while before bending down to whisper in Croy's ear. "Sir Knight, there is—there is a situation."

"Hmm?"

The footman licked his lips in apprehension. "Normally I shouldn't like to interrupt your meal, but—but there is a situation. An uninvited guest, er, that is to say—someone came to the door just now, I would have turned her away, but—"

"Speak freely, man. You're interrupting nothing of importance," Croy told him, keeping his voice low so the merchant's wife wouldn't hear.

"A woman, not a lady, but—but in some state of distress, has come to the door, and begged of me that I find you, and bring you to her. Just say the word, sir, and I'll give her a coin and send her on her way, but there was something about her look that made me think she was no beggar. In fact, I don't think I've ever seen a woman with tattoos on her face before—"

Croy didn't wait for the rest. He jumped up from the table and made a few perfunctory bows before hurrying through the door the footman had left open. He worried he was offending the merchant's wife, and perhaps even his host, but hopefully they would simply think he needed to use the chamber pot.

Cythera waited for him in the receiving hall. He saw at once she had been crying. He rushed toward her and barely remembered in time not to grab her arms as he begged her to tell him what was wrong.

"I didn't know where else to go," she told him. "I know this was a mistake, but—I couldn't stay in that house a moment longer. I had to get out. I've endangered you, now. I'm sure he was watching me when I left—and now he'll know where you are, Croy—I'm so sorry."

"I can take care of myself," he told her. "What happened?"

"I've been punished," she said. She clenched her eyes closed and sagged toward him. She did not touch him, but moved her face quite close to his. "I failed him."

"Hazoth?" Croy demanded.

She nodded.

Croy looked up at the gallery that overhung the hall but saw no eavesdroppers there. He pulled a chair away from the wall for her and she sank readily into it. Kneeling down next to her, he moved his hands over hers, wishing he could be of more comfort. "What do you mean, you failed him?" he asked.

She shook her head bitterly. "You'll think me wicked," she said. "Please . . . please don't think me wicked. Last night—you met a thief in the darkened streets, did you not? He was doing some work for Hazoth. Foul business. I was to meet him, with Bikker, and receive the goods he'd stolen."

"He seemed a good enough sort to me," Croy said. A twinge of something ignoble went through his heart, but he couldn't help himself. "A . . . friend of yours?"

Cythera shook her head. "Oh, he's just a cutpurse. Someone Bikker found—we needed a thief, and—well, that's a long tale. The point is this: Hazoth decided he must die. That he knew too many secrets, and that once we had our prize, we were to kill him. Bikker offered to do it, of course, but Hazoth seemed to find it more amusing if I was to be the instrument of destruction."

"You told him you wouldn't do it, of course."

Cythera turned her face away from him. "Croy, I had no choice. I must obey him. So when the business was complete, I—I asked the thief to kiss me."

Croy's entire body stiffened, but he said nothing.

"You understand, don't you? What that would do? Every curse I've stored up over the last five years would be released at once, into the poor thief's body. He would have been slaughtered in an instant. But he refused me. Lucky for him, he knew your name, and knew the effect it would have on me. He's really very clever for a pickpocket. And then he ran off, and I could not give chase. When I returned and told Hazoth that the thief had escaped, he was furious. He stormed about his library, making books jump off of their shelves, and his eyes glowed with magic. I thought he was going to turn on me and try to blast me with some spell. He has a terrible temper."

"Did he hurt you? You said he punished you—what did he do? Cythera, tell me!" Croy wanted to grab up her hands or pull her into an embrace. He didn't, of course. It would be his death.

"He cannot. His magic is no use against me. He can't even have his guards beat me. And that just made him angrier. So he did the thing I've dreaded for so long. He turned on my mother instead."

"The cur," Croy swore.

"He has her in one of his rooms, trapped inside a magic circle. She has languished there for so long at his pleasure, but never before has he actually taken advantage of her imprisonment. I thought . . . I believed that when this time came, he would use magic against her. That he would wrack her with a curse, or perhaps attack her mind with his mind. But he didn't."

Cythera covered her face with her hands.

"He had her whipped," she said. "With a plain leather bullwhip. Ten strokes across her back until the skin peeled away. And . . . he made me watch." She lowered her hands and stared into his face. "He made me keep count."

Croy stood up to his full height. "Wait here while I fetch my swords. I'll kill him. I swear it, Cythera. I will slay him, and free you and your mother from his bonds, and then—"

"Croy," she said, very softly, but it was enough to quiet him. "Croy, if you go there now, girded as for war, he will destroy you."

"If I die for honor, for love, for fellow feeling—"

"You'll still die. No matter how noble the principle, you can only die for it once. And then you'll be no help to anyone. I do not wish you to get yourself killed for my mother's sake, Croy."

"You can't ask me to listen to this story and do nothing," he insisted.

"No," she said. She straightened the hem of her dress. "No. That isn't why I came here. There is something you can do. Some action you can take that might help me."

"Finally," Croy said, with a sigh. "Tell me all."

# CHAPTER FORTY-THREE

Malden needed a plan, desperately. He needed some stratagem that would see him inside Hazoth's house, where he might find the crown and escape with it to safety. He needed to do a great deal of thinking and hone his wits to a razor's edge.

First, though, he needed to get drunk.

He could tell himself that he was looking for creativity in a cup, that the best plans were based on the kind of daring folly that came to one only when the mind was befuddled and the tongue loosed.

Mostly, though, he just needed to drink until he wasn't afraid.

"Ale," he said, and the barkeep obliged. Malden slid a wedge-shaped farthing across the bar and it disappeared. He did not have many left. He had chosen a particularly filthy tavern in one of the worst parts of the Stink, not for the ambience, but because it was cheap and his funds were small. The place had a few grimy windows made of the bottoms of old glass bottles stuck in plaster. Only a few beams of blue and green and brown light made their way inside. There was a bar made of an old door up on trestles, and behind that a stack of barrels with leaking bungs. There were a few tables but most of the patrons stood and drank from leather tankards and wiped the foam from their beards with their sleeves. A brawl had just been dying down when Malden entered, and one poor fool still lay knocked out on the floor. The serving wench stepped high over him every time she had to pass.

"More," Malden said when he was done with his cup. The barkeep waited until he took another farthing from his purse and laid it on the bar.

The fear of death was nothing new to Malden. At their first meeting Cutbill had threatened him casually enough, and he stood up to the promise of death without quaking in his boots. That had been different, however. The threat was meant as a spur, to make him take the action Cutbill desired. It was understood by all parties that he retained an option, that he had a chance to save himself. That had just been good faith negotiation. There were countless other times over the years he'd been in mortal danger, and every time he'd kept good cheer and found the way through. Even in the Burgrave's palace, when he faced instant death from the traps and the demon, he had known there was a way through if he was clever enough to find it.

Stealing from Hazoth, though, was another matter.

Bikker would slay him the moment he walked through that gate. There was an enchantment over the entire house—he had watched the footpad lifted into the air and held there like a starling impaled on the claws of a cat. There were armed guards all over Hazoth's estate, and no diversion to draw their attention.

Worst of all, should he succeed, and find some route into the sorcerer's inner sanctum—he would then be prey to magic.

No man was wise who flaunted wizardry. Magic was unpredictable at the best of times. Students of the arcane were

more liable to blow themselves up—or drawn down bodily
into the pit by angry demons—than to live long enough
to ply their trade. Those who did succeed in their studies,
however, became *powerful*. They gained access to abilities
normal men could scarce imagine. And Hazoth was one of
the greatest sorcerers of history.

Malden had begun to believe all the stories he'd heard
about the sorcerer. There was the tale of how Hazoth drove
the elves away from southern Skrae by making every tree
for a hundred miles wither and die in a single night. Old
men sometimes spoke of the day Hazoth wiped out an entire
barbarian army almost single-handed, how a simple wave of
his hand rooted the painted berserkers to where they stood
so they could do nothing but rave and curse as the knights of
Skrae cut them down at leisure. The stories of what Hazoth
had done to men who crossed him were too gruesome for
Malden to want to remember.

The sorcerer might place some dread curse on him that
would make the rest of his life a living hell. Hezoth might
make his skin turn inside out. He might boil his stomach
inside his body, so he died shitting out parts of himself over
a course of days. Or he might simply flay the flesh from his
bones with a word and a wave of his hand.

"Another," Malden said, and slapped his money on the
bar. He was starting to feel the liquor in his veins. It wasn't
helping.

For distraction, he turned and studied the low-lifes in the
barroom. Most of the patrons were honest enough folk—
laborers in leather aprons, covered in flour or candle wax
or soot from some forge. They talked loudly to each other
and laughed lustily and stamped their feet when they made
some jest or swore an oath. In the back of the room, near
the hearth, a card game was in progress. The players looked
like the kind of desperate bravos who would cut each others'
throats over a mislaid wager. They were playing in earnest,
though, and were almost silent as they took turns laying
down their trumps. The game they were playing was unknown to Malden, so he wandered over to observe. One of
the players, a mangy fellow with an unkempt beard and a

smear of dirt on his forehead, looked up and growled, but the others insisted he play his hand, and he ignored Malden after that.

The game, it turned out, could not be simpler. The cards were thin pieces of paper with hand-drawn pips on one side and nothing on their backs. They were numbered from one to ten. Each player had a hand of five cards, drawn at random from the deck. He would throw coins into the center of the table based on how high his cards ran, and the others were required to match his wager or forfeit the hand. Then the player would lay down his cards to show the table what he had. If none of the others could beat it, he took all the money. Everyone who had played would draw a new card and the cycle would begin again with the betting.

One of the players had the king's share of the coins before him. Clearly the cards had been running his way. From the way the others glared at him, they must have been wondering how he got so lucky. He did not bother to look their way, instead pausing in his play only to drink from his cup. Bizarrely enough, he had a hollow reed stuck in his tankard, and when he wished to drink would place his lips around its end and suck up ale like water through a hosepipe.

"Are ye playing, lad, or gawkin'? 'Cause there's a tax for gawkin'," the lucky player said. The others guffawed, but Malden's mouth fell open. He had been paying attention to the cards and not the faces of the players, or he would have recognized the man sooner.

"Kemper?" he said. "What are you doing here?"

A ripple of anger went around the table as each player in turn stared wide-eyed at the lucky man.

"Kemper?" the gambler with the dirty face said, rising from his stool. "I've heard of a cove called Kemper. A cheat, they call him."

"Then they lie, don't they?" Kemper told him. "Now sit back down, ye piebald cur."

"I'll not sit at table with a card sharp!"

"Play, or leave, 'tis all the same to me."

"You've been taking my wages all day!" the gambler shouted. "Let me see those damned cards of yours. They must be marked!"

"Sit an' play," Kemper repeated.

Malden jumped back as the gambler grabbed up the table and hurled it aside. Coins and cards went flying as he rushed at Kemper, his belt knife suddenly in his hand. Kemper did not rise from his seat as the gambler thrust the knife again and again into his chest.

There were screams and shouts from every corner of the room, and the barkeep stormed out from his post with a hand spike, but it was already over. The gambler had gone milky white and stared at the knife in his hand. There was no blood on it. He staggered backward, and Malden saw that Kemper was unharmed, sitting with perfect composure on his stool, still holding his cards.

"Clean this up, then," Kemper said to the gambler, "and get back t'playin', a'ready."

The dirty-faced gambler ran gibbering from the barroom. The others eased away from Kemper as if they'd seen a demon jump up and save him from the knife. All but one of the cardsmen, anyway, who bent down to anxiously grab up coins from the floor.

"Leave 'em," Kemper insisted. "They's mine. For me trouble, like."

The greedy gamester nodded and hurried off.

"Ah, lad, yer timin' is not of the best. Yet I'm glad to see ye, I am," Kemper said, and finally rose from his stool. He pushed his cards in his pocket and stepped toward Malden.

"That knife—his aim was deadly serious," Malden said. He wondered if his face showed as much shock as he felt. "Yet there's no drop of blood on you."

Kemper laughed. "Here, shake me hand an' see why." He held out a callused and scarred hand, and Malden reached to take it.

It could not be done, however. Malden's hand passed right through Kemper's as though it weren't there. He felt nothing more than a cold clamminess, as if he'd tried to hold a wisp of fog. He gasped and grabbed at the man's arms and then his hair, unbelieving. He could not touch the man at all. He might as well try to grapple with his own reflection in a mirror.

"You're—a ghost," Malden said.

"A livin' ghost," Kemper agreed. "Which's the saddest contrary I ken."

# CHAPTER FORTY-FOUR

Kemper drew too many stares after that to allow any comfort in the tavern. He gathered up his cards and his drinking reed—and of course the pile of coins scattered across the floor—and the two of them headed out into the streets, bound on a wild carouse. Perhaps just to spite those who glared, Kemper handed Malden his things and walked right through the closed door, which rose more than a few startled gasps. Malden bowed deeply to the astonished patrons and then walked right into the door himself, smacking his face on its wooden boards. Perhaps his three cups of ale had more of an effect than he thought.

Without looking back he opened the door and stepped out into the road. Kemper was waiting for him, whistling random notes that never quite added up to a song.

"It's good to see ye, son, it surely is. 'Tis always a pleasure t'have such company as one can speak plainly to, and not have t'worry 'bout keepin' secrets and bein' circumspect. I'll just have those," Kemper said, and took his things back. The reed and the coins went into his tunic, but he kept the cards in his hand and riffled them as he walked.

"How is it you can hold those cards, when you cannot hold a tankard?" Malden asked. He had already worked out that the reed was necessary as Kemper's hand would pass unheeding through any drinking vessel he tried to pick up.

"Well, now," Kemper said, coming to a stop and lifting his chin like an orator. "The curse on me's a strong 'un, yet a mite imperfect, if ye catch me meaning. If I concentrate hard 'nough on it somewhat, I can grip it. With long practice, I can hold just about anythin'. Like me reed, and me cards, which I've had since afore ye first soiled yer bedclothes in the night. I've mastered sittin' in a chair, and lyin' abed, an' food an' drink are available t'me. Seems the wizard what did this wanted me livin', and not allowed the peace o' death. I've not touched a woman, nor e'en changed me clothes, since the day 'twas done."

"It's a pitiable condition," Malden sympathized.

"Yet not without its consolations, y'know, for a gentleman of fortune like me an' yerself. It's a rare gaol that can hold me, an' I can carry coins, if they're silver. As ye see." He flashed a coin between his fingers and twirled it for Malden.

"Only silver?"

"None as is livin' can say why, I reckon. Yet silver's a metal no magic e'er touches, y'see?"

"I'm not sure I follow," Malden admitted.

The card sharp sighed. "Some virtue o' the metal, some property arcane, or mayhap a fault in the way magic's woven, who knows? Yet 'tis a fact. Silver'll cut through any spell, and no curse works 'gainst it. So even if I'm t'be punished for me sins, still I can clutch silver coins."

"Ah! Hence the silver chains—in the Burgrave's dungeon," Malden recalled. "I wondered why they would use such precious rope to tie you."

"Aye, lad. Only silver can hold me, and most places're too poor to afford so much as a silver bootlace. Ye can imagine the advantages this offers t' a man o' my profession."

"And when you disappeared—I thought you had run up the dungeon stairs, but instead you must have just walked out through the walls." Malden shook his head in wonder. "Yes, I can see how that would be advantageous."

"Yer a smart lad, I can see," Kemper said. "'Tweren't

easy, I don't mind tellin' ye. I had to walk through solid
rock, aye, for what felt like leagues. Never really got a
feelin' for that. Ye're blind as a bat the whole time, and
wond'rin' whether ye'll come out sixty feet up over the
Skrait." The card sharp reeled a bit as he walked—clearly
he'd been drinking himself and wasn't quite sober. "Or, or,
and this'd be worse, that ye'll just keep walkin', goin' deeper
and deeper into the world till ye come out again in the pit
itself, with ugly old Sadu starin' up at ye with them fiery
eyes of his. I always figgered if'n that happened, I give him a
proper salute, like, and walk right past like unto I owned the
place. Confidence, confidence is key in our game. Hold up.
Hold up, lad, I'm goin' to piss."

Malden stood at a corner and waited until the card sharp
was finished. He had to admit a certain curiosity—would
Kemper's water be as immaterial as his body? He thought it
impolite to ask, though.

"How d'you like the look o' this place? Think they'd take
kindly t'gamin' inside?"

Malden looked up and saw that they had come to the
door of another tavern. Such were not infrequently found
in the Stink. He knew this one by its sign, which depicted
an ogre's severed head. "It's where the local priest of the
Lady comes to drink," he said, shaking his head doubtfully.
"Good honest folk come here."

"Me favorite kind," Kemper said with a smile. "Them's
as honest themselves never cease to doubt the honesty o'
their fellows. And if ye know a man don't trust ye, ye know
how to gull him, right enough." He gestured for Malden to
open the door for him.

There was much ale that followed, with Kemper gra-
ciously picking up the bill from his winnings. The night de-
volved from a continuous narrative into a series of isolated
incidents, separated by muddy stretches Malden would not
remember clearly in the morning. There was a lot of singing, he knew, and he was encouraged to add his own voice,
which was untutored. There was a great deal of gambling, at
which Kemper proved more than lucky.

Sometime during the night he confided in Malden his

great secret for winning. "Now y'see these cards, they're
not marked at all, perish the thought," he whispered as
they crossed the river Skrait by the Turnhill Bridge. "'Tis
as I said—if a man doesn't trust ye, ye can take advantage.
They expect me to cheat, y'see. They expect marked cards.
I've seen marked cards afore, so cleverly done you'd think
'twould take a dwarf to find the spots. Yet always, always
some clever fella's goin' to find 'em, for he's lookin' for 'em.
'Tis only a matter o' time afore he sees how it's done. An'
then the jig is up, ain't it! Nay, me secret's simpler. Y'see
how grimy they got, with greasy fingers holdin' 'em these
many years, and general wear. I don't need 'em marked by
now! Ha, lad, smell this."

Malden recoiled as the cursed card sharp shoved the ten
of bells toward his face. He did have to admit it had a certain
aroma of unwashed clothing.

"It's fouled," Malden said.

"Hardly! Smells like me armpit, aye, don't it? An' when
any man holds that card, why, I can smell it 'cross the table.
An' each of 'em's got their own partick-uler odor, don't it?
Why, with me discriminatin' nostrils I can tell ye've got a
high card, or a low. From long use and practice I know these
cards a fair sight better than the back o' my hands, in troth."

"Brilliant, simply brilliant," Malden laughed, for by that
point he'd reached the point where everything seemed admirable, the world was a lovely place, and death was never
farther away.

The night provided all manner of diversions. At one point
they were chased by the watch, but escaped easily—Malden
by ducking into a shadowy alley that was mostly used as a
privy, Kemper by simply walking through a wall.

They were ejected, sometimes by force, from any
number of drinking establishments. On one such occasion it
was because Kemper had grabbed at the buttocks of a passing serving wench. His hand went right through her skirt,
of course, but she felt *something*. Her face had gone quite
white and she dropped her tray and then whirled around in
bitter anger to confront her molester—only to find Malden
sitting alone on a bench, looking innocent. It was all he

could do to stumble his way out of that place—only to find Kemper in the street outside, laughing boisterously. At the first sign of trouble, the card sharp had merely ducked backward through the wall and to safety, leaving Malden to bear the barmaid's wrath.

When he realized what Kemper had done, he could only laugh, and laugh, and laugh.

Then he was sick, over the side of a bridge. Afterward he felt weak and queasy, and Kemper assured him the best cure for what ailed him was more ale. Malden enthusiastically agreed.

The carouse ended only slightly before dawn—but on a sour note. They had wended their way down to the city walls without really meaning to, and Malden came up short when he saw the green common of Parkwall ahead of him. He was right back on Hazoth's doorstep.

"Kemper," Malden said. "Kemper."

"What?"

"The wizard who cursed you, who made you like unto—unto . . . The sorcerer who cursed you, was his name Hazoth?"

Kemper laughed until he wheezed. "Hazoth? Ye think 'twas him, the grandmaster of sorcerers, the auld bastard? Sadu's eight index fingers, save me skin from such a fate! Oh, laddie, nay. Nay, it was but some hedge wizard, in a blighted village a hunnerd miles from here."

"But this hedge—hedge wizard—must have been, you know. Very powerful. To do this to you."

Kemper shook his head violently. "Nay, in comparison, the bugger who got me—that is, compared to yer Hazoth—he was like hawkin' a gob o' spit next t'the ocean." He sat down hard on the grass. "Magic's strong stuff, it is. E'en a mild curse's no joke. Yet what Hazoth could do t' a body, I shudder t'think. Strip the flesh right off o' your bones and make it dance a jig, maybe. Or just crack th'earth open, right at yer feet, and drop ye into the pit like a pebble in a well."

"Oh," Malden said, and threw up again. Partly from strong drink. Mostly from fear.

"Izzat *his* place, then?" Kemper asked.

"This is the place," Malden said, pointing across the grass toward the sorcerer's villa. "The crown must be inside." Over the course of the night he'd told Kemper everything—including the fact that he had no choice but to break in there and steal the crown back. "It's not like he'll just give it to me," he said.

Kemper shuffled his cards with one hand, no mean feat considering how drunk he was. He seemed to think of something then. "Have ye asked?"

Malden blinked and tried to clear his head. He wasn't sure if what Kemper had just said was a stroke of genius or utter folly.

"Bikker would kill me the moment he saw me," he said finally, shaking his head.

"Then ye wait till Bikker's na' a' home," Kemper said. Then he started hiccupping and had to sit down for a while.

"It's too—too dangerous," Malden insisted. "No. I need to break in. But how? There's an invisible wall of magic around the place, not to mention guards and dogs, and—and Bikker, and Cyth—Cythera. I need to sit down, too."

He fell backward onto his fundament on the grass. He was not feeling at all well. He tried to lean on Kemper's shoulder and fell right through him, which made them both laugh so hard they couldn't breathe.

# CHAPTER FORTY-FIVE

It was not difficult to get into the Burgrave's palace, if you did so in the middle of the day and you appeared to have business there. The denizens of the palace consumed vast quantities of food, drink, firewood, and other commodities every day. Carts came in and out through the massive iron gates in the wall of Castle Hill almost constantly. Laborers carrying sacks of flour, rashers of bacon, or hogsheads of lamp oil passed into the palace proper through an entrance in the back, nearest to the kitchens. On this day they had to line up and each wait their turn, as the courtyard was full already with workmen, masons, architects, and stone-breakers overseeing the careful demolition of what remained of the tower. It was a great chaos of people dressed in every imaginable hue and style.

When Croy entered, walking alongside a cart full of grain, he was still stopped by a guard at the gate, but not because he'd been recognized. The harried guard did no more than to assure himself that Croy carried no weapons before sending him through. Though Croy was wanted for escaping the gallows, the guard didn't even glance at his face.

"You're growing complacent, Anselm," Croy chuckled as he headed across the courtyard toward the palace. There were no archers up on the castle walls, and what few watchmen he saw were arguing with the masons atop the ruins of the tower. The masons had set up a huge triangular crane that could lift away the chunks of broken stone, but the watchmen seemed to think they would damage the palace in the process. The masons argued they knew what they were doing and should be left to their work. Meanwhile their laborers stood around idle, leaning on picks and shovels or sharing a jug of wine. A group of apprentices, boys no older than ten, had started kicking a ball around the courtyard while they waited for the argument to finish so they could start work again. Croy took advantage of the chaos, slipped in through the back of the palace and walked right past the castellan. The old dotard was too busy counting bushel baskets full of candles to pay any mind.

Beyond the storerooms lay the servants' quarters, narrow little rooms smaller than the cell Croy had been given at the gaol. Because it was the middle of the day, these chambers were all deserted—the servants were at their work, of course. Croy climbed a spiral staircase at the end of the hall and came out on the second floor, near the Burgrave's chambers. Vry's office was nearby, in case the Burgrave should demand his presence on a moment's notice.

There was a guard at the top of the stairs. Croy was glad in a way to see that—he didn't like to think of such important people being so vulnerable. The guard was dressed in leather jack with iron plates on his shoulders and down his forearms, and he wore a wide-brimmed kettle helmet. Because it was a warm day—Ladymas always brought sunny weather—the guard had removed the padded hood he should have worn under such a helmet. He lowered his halberd across the exit from the stairs and bade Croy to hold. "What's your business?" he asked.

"I have a message for the bailiff," Croy said, trying to sound frightened. A real messenger would be staring at the blade of the halberd, he thought, so he turned his head as if he were looking at it. His eyes, though, never left sight of the guard's hands.

"Give it here, and I'll see he gets it."

"Oh, you want it?" Croy asked. "Very well." He brought out the sap he'd been hiding under his cloak and smacked the guard across the temple. The kettle helmet rang like a bell and the guard grimaced as his eyes fluttered closed. Croy barely managed to catch him before he collapsed to the floor.

Then Croy stopped perfectly still, crouched on the top riser of the stairs with the guard in his arms, and listened. The ringing helmet had made far more noise than he'd liked, and he needed to know if anyone had heard him.

He could hear the workmen outside grumbling about having to wait to offload their wares. He could hear horse hooves clopping on the flagstones of the courtyard. He could hear a guard atop the wall, hailing his fellow across the way, checking that all was well. He did not hear what he'd feared: no cry of alarm, no voice raised inside the palace to ask what that sound was. No one calling for the unconscious guard, to ask if something was the matter.

Very good. Getting the guard back down the stairs was not easy, but Croy had good muscle in his arms and a strong back. He shoved the guard into a verger's room, then stripped him of his armor and tied his hands together behind his back. With a gag in the guard's mouth, he thought he would be safe awhile. He threw his own cloak over the supine form of the guard for modesty's sake, then pulled on the leather jack and put the helmet on his own head. He found the padded hood on the man's belt and drew that on as well. It hid both his blond hair and his square chin.

Then he headed back to the second floor and straight to the door of Anselm Vry's office. He raised the knuckles of one hand to knock, intending to announce that there was a message from the moothall and a reply was expected. That would get Vry to open the door with no fuss.

Yet just before he knocked he stopped and listened a moment—and heard a conversation beyond the door that grasped his attention.

"You must put it on. People expect to see you wearing the robe." That was the voice of Anselm Vry, certainly.

Croy didn't recognize the other voice. It was that of a grown man, but there was a childlike petulance to it—and at the same time a sort of hollowness, as if the owner of the voice was gravely ill, or, for that matter, ghostly.

"You can't make me. You can't make me do anything. I'm free of it!"

"If you won't wear the robe," Vry said, sounding exasperated, "you can't appear in public at all. I'll have you locked up in your room. And then we'll see how free you are."

"I'm free. I'm free! Every night, when they took it away—every night I dreamed. I dreamed of this! And in the morning when they brought it to me again, I wept. You won't—you won't bring it back, will you? Promise!"

"I promise. Now put on the robe. And stop sniveling. It doesn't befit you. After Ladymas things will be different, just dream of that."

*Enough.* Croy had never been a keyhole-listener before. He did not relish gossip, or knowing other people's secrets. He knocked and announced himself firmly. "Message for you, your honor. From the moothall."

"Damnation—what do the shopkeepers want with me now?" Vry said behind the door. Croy heard footsteps approaching and he stepped back to allow the door to open. Vry poked his head out and extended one long-fingered hand. "Give it here, and be gone," he said.

Croy grabbed the hand and hauled the bailiff out into the hallway. Vry started to shout for his guards, but Croy was quick enough to get an arm around his throat and hold him still.

"You've come . . . to murder me, Croy? It doesn't . . . seem your style," Vry managed to gasp out as Croy put pressure on his windpipe.

"I saw no other way to gain audience with you, Anselm. No, I'm here for exactly the reason I said, to deliver a message—though not from the masters of the guilds. Will you listen to me if I release you? I have vital information you require."

"I'll listen," Vry choked. Croy let him go. "I'll listen, then I'll have you arrested. I don't know how you managed to get in here, and I can only wonder how you expect to get back out with your head attached to your neck. What message could be so important that you would risk your life for it?"

"The sorcerer Hazoth has the Burgrave's crown," Croy said.

"What? What are you talking about?"

Croy shook his head. "You needn't pretend. I know everything. And now so do you. The crown is safe, sealed in a leaden coffer in Hazoth's sanctum. What he wants with it I have no idea. Now, I must be going."

"You're right," Vry told him. "This is vital information. I don't suppose you'd tell me how you came by it."

"I'm bound to secrecy," Croy said.

"Of course, of course." Vry nodded in understanding. "Hazoth," he said. He tapped his upper lip. "Can you get the crown away from him, d'you think?"

"By myself? No. But you can marshal troops enough to wrest it from him, certainly?"

"I suppose I can. I owe you my thanks, Croy." Vry clapped him on the shoulder. "I only wish I could pay you back for this debt. But you know that the Burgrave's word is law, and he has ordered your death. What can I do for you, that will not counter his decision? It's not in my power to pardon you, much as I'd like to."

Croy clutched his friend by the forearm. "Just give me a head start. Don't call your guards for five minutes. That will be enough. Oh, and Anselm?"

"Yes?" the bailiff asked.

"You really should take better note of who comes and goes through your gates." Croy smiled broadly and gave the bailiff a deep bow. "I still serve the Burgrave," he said. "My duty was clear."

And yet—the words tasted wrong in Croy's mouth. For in truth it was not for the Burgrave he'd come to the palace. Cythera had told him all about the theft of the crown, and together they'd made this plan. She could not leave Hazoth's service as long as he held her mother prisoner—and while he lived, he would never release her. Croy knew he could not destroy the sorcerer on his own. No matter how strong his arm, no matter how puissant Ghostcutter's blade, he could not match Hazoth's magic.

Yet if it were to come to light that Hazoth was behind the plot to embarrass the Burgrave, well . . . perhaps the wheels of justice could turn in the right direction, just this one time. Anselm Vry would bring every guard and watchman in the city down on Hazoth's house, and they would see just how strong his magic was then.

# CHAPTER FORTY-SIX

It was not Anselm Vry who next approached Hazoth's villa, however.

It was Malden.

He had spent most of the day hiding in the bushes of the Parkwall Common, crouching like a footpad without even a jug of brandy to keep him company. The last thing he wanted after his night carousing with Kemper was more liquor.

It was easy enough to stay still. Every time he moved he felt like his brains sloshed back and forth in his skull. He felt weak and queasy. He was not sure if that was his hangover or only fear.

The gate of Hazoth's villa opened and Bikker came striding out. This was what Malden had been waiting for. The bearded swordsman clanked as he walked—Malden could hear him all the way across the common—and he scratched at one armpit as he headed toward Old Fish Street, the road that led to the wharves on the river Skrait. Malden had no way of knowing what his business there might be, but he didn't care. As long as Bikker did not return for an hour or more.

When Bikker was well out of sight, Malden rose painfully to a standing posture and then walked across the green common, in full view of Hazoth's house. He wanted very badly to turn around and run, or at least to approach in a less conspicuous manner—there were trees all along one edge of the common that would hide him well.

He did not turn away.

At the gate, Hazoth's guards were waiting for him. They stood well inside the fence, and Malden knew from watching them a long time that they would be inside the radius of the spell that protected the place. He offered them no threat and they made no move to challenge him. They leaned on their polearms and just watched him come closer, daring him with their eyes to step through the gate.

There were six of them visible. They wore chain mail and surcoats in the colors of Hazoth's livery: black and scarlet. One of them turned his head and spat as Malden stepped up to the gate.

There was no turning back once he was through.

He stepped over the threshold.

He could perhaps be forgiven for closing his eyes as he

took that fateful step. Yet nothing happened—at first. The forecourt of the villa was covered in crushed gravel, with here and there a dandelion or a sprig of clover poking up through the rocks. The gravel crunched under Malden's leather shoes. He took another step.

And that was when the spell took him. He felt as if he had run at full speed directly into a brick wall. His body tensed at the impact and his bones thrummed, though he could see no barrier before him. It felt like ghostly hands passed over his face and chest, and then something gripped him around the waist.

One of the guards laughed.

Malden did not cry out—he had no breath in his lungs— as the invisible force lifted him bodily off the ground. The grip around his waist and chest held him immobile as invisible fingers rifled through his purse and inside his tunic, as his cloak was lifted and checked for concealed weapons. He had been smart enough to leave his bodkin at home, but the buckle of his belt and the handful of copper coins in his purse grew searing hot for a moment, until he thought they would burn through his clothes. As quickly as it had come, however, that phantom heat dissipated.

The invisible hands lowered him to the ground again— but held him still.

"Good morrow to you," Malden managed to croak out. He caught the eye of one of the guards. "Will you let me speak?"

The guard came over and jabbed him in the chest with the butt of his pikestaff. Hard enough to rattle his sternum. "What business have you here, dog?"

Malden licked his lips. His mouth was still very dry from the night before. "I have a message for Hazoth. One he desperately needs to hear."

The guard smiled broadly. "Tell it to me, and perhaps we'll let you go."

Malden nodded agreeably. "Would that I could. I'm afraid it must be communicated directly to the sorcerer, however. It is information of a . . . delicate nature, and best not spoken aloud where unwanted listeners might hear."

The guard scowled. Yet he walked over to one of his fellows and conferred with him a while. Malden could do naught but wait—the invisible wall still held him pinned. He could not so much as scratch an itch.

The second guard ran into the house. He was gone quite a while. The others moved closer to the gate, weapons at the ready in case Malden had some charm that would free him from the invisible wall.

Not very clever of them, he thought. They should have been watching the fence, looking for some armed force approached from another direction. His own approach could have just been a diversion to hide the advance of a more dangerous force. The fact that he, who had no training in security, could see as much told him something. These were not soldiers, then, but only bravos hired to look menacing, not to effectively guard the villa. *Good to know.*

Not that he could make use of that information if the invisible guardian continued to hold him. It seemed he waited forever, exposed under the sun, unable to move. For a span nothing happened. Eventually, though, the guard returned from the house. He rushed over to his post as if nothing had happened, and Malden wondered if he should be left there, suspended in nothing, until he died of thirst.

But then Cythera stepped out of the doorway.

The hood of her velvet cloak was up, hiding her face in shadows. Her hands were bare, though, and seeing tattooed coils of ivy twisting around her fingers, Malden knew it was her.

She approached him directly, stopping five feet away. He supposed that spot must mark where the barrier ended on the inside—another useful thing to know.

"I am very glad to see you," he said, smiling down upon her. "I'd bow to you, as you deserve, but as you can see, I'm a bit indisposed. If you'd be kind enough to let me down I'd be most obliged."

"You're a fool," she said. "You'll die here."

"I'm desperate," he told her. "If not here, I'll die elsewhere, and just as certain."

She gave him a look of uncertainty. A questioning look.

As if she could not believe he had come here and risked so much. He smiled in return, hiding his true fear. A part of him was woefully glad to see her again, and not just because she was the only one who could get him out of the barrier.

"As you wish," Cythera said.

She lifted her hands in a complicated gesture, her fingers tucked in or stretched outward in weird contortions. She spoke a word that Malden could not hear clearly, even at so close a distance.

The air flexed with magic and he dropped to the ground, falling on his knees and scraping his hands on the gravel. The magic wall was gone. "I offered to bow, and now you see me kneel. You have my thanks, lady."

Cythera did not offer to help him up. Instead she turned on her heel and walked back toward the house. The guards weren't even looking at Malden. He staggered to his feet and then raced after her, through the massive stone doors and into the coolth of a dim portico.

# CHAPTER FORTY-SEVEN

When Malden's eyes adjusted he found himself in a broad marble hall held up by massive columns of braided stone. Light streamed in through tall windows at the far end of the room, which looked out over a garden maze. The glass alone in those windows would be worth ten times what a craftsman up in the Smoke might make in a year. Along the walls stood alabaster statues of ancient scholars and wizards, some of whom he recognized by the things they held or the way they were dressed. There was Antomach the Sage, who had proved the world was round.

He was identifiable by the compass he held before him, his other hand held high with a miniature planet floating above his upturned palm. Malden could not see how it was suspended—perhaps by magery. Another statue depicted the necromancer Vull, a figure of such antiquity no one living now remembered what land he'd hailed from. He was shown here in one of his favorite shapes, that of a massive bear with skeletal human hands. Other statues were draped in cunningly wrought shrouds of stone, or stood nude with wolves curling around their titanic legs.

At the center of the hall a double staircase of worked stone rose gracefully toward a gallery above. Standing next to the stairs on a stone plinth was something that shocked Malden as incongruous—a globe of iron, its surface pitted and mottled with rust. A fine sifting of red powder made a crimson shadow on the floor around it. It must have been fifteen feet across and was as ugly as the sharp end of a crossbow bolt. What it was doing in such elegant surroundings was a mystery.

Cythera's footsteps rang on the floor, which had been polished near unto a mirrored surface. "He's waiting for you through here," she said, and gestured toward a tall doorway in the wall to Malden's right. "Don't anger him by tarrying here while you gawk."

He nodded and let his gaze run over the hall's features one last time before following her.

"Surely you must realize you are unwelcome here," she whispered to him as she opened the door and ushered him inside. "I thought you were smarter than this."

"Think me not clever?" he asked, mocking hurt feelings. "I waited until Bikker went out, did I not? How soon do you expect him back, by the way?"

Her brow furrowed, though it was hard to tell from the tattooed creepers that grew upward from her eyelashes. "Bikker? He shan't be returning."

"Doesn't he live here?" Malden asked. "I thought he was a retainer of the sorcerer, like yourself."

She shook her head. "He's no servant of my master. And I am no retainer." She seemed unwilling to say more.

She brought him into a long hallway lined on one side with doors. More windows pierced the outside wall, their glare cut down by gauzy curtains that hung from the ceiling. Small tables and display cases stood between the windows, holding curios, some that Malden would very much have liked to stop and examine more closely, and others that made him flinch and look away. He saw one case that held a collection of severed human hands, while another was full of what appeared to be giant pearls. A stuffed and lifeless snake lay coiled on one table, holding a carved ball of white jade in its jaws. The purpose of such things—or if they even had a purpose beyond mere ornament—was lost on him.

At the far end of the corridor Cythera opened another door, which led into a library. Despite himself, Malden's jaw fell open once again.

It was a comfortable, snug space, though several times larger than the common room at Cutbill's lair. Sumptuous rugs covered the floor, and a fireplace filled half of one wall. Couches and chairs upholstered in leather stood here and there, where a visitor might choose to sit and read, and an enormous tapestry map of the continent hung from the ceiling showing all the cities, roads, and rivers of Skrae and the Northern Kingdoms in cunning detail. What really astounded Malden about the room, however, was the collection of books.

Books were expensive. They had to be inscribed by hand, then bound in costly hides. Illuminators and engravers were employed in their construction, and since very few people in the kingdom could read, there was a premium on their production. Even the Burgrave might have had only a single shelf of books in his palace, mostly devotional works praising the Lady.

Yet Hazoth had hundreds of books here—perhaps thousands. Far more than Malden could count. Thin folios and massive tomes, miniature librams that would fit in the palm of the hand, grimoires bound in carved wooden covers inlaid with gold and silver and bronze. Books adorned with gemstones, and others with leather covers tooled with a pattern of skulls and bones. Some shelves held loose papers in great sheaves, bound with string, or scrolls and palimpsests wound about ivory rods, or forms of printed matter Malden had never imagined—books built into miniature chests, or folded fans of paper, or books made of pentagonal signatures tied together with ribbon. Books that glowed with their own light, and books that looked like they had scuttled into the shadows at the back of deep shelves, as if afraid of the sun. Opened books sat on lecterns or scriptoria, written in languages and even alphabets he did not recognize. Ink pots of black and red and purple were arranged around one table, and quills from birds far more exotic than the typical goose or crow.

He had a chance to look at only a few of the titles inscribed on the spines of the books nearest to him, but they inflamed his imagination. *A Season Within the Pit, Marloff's Compendium of Diabolic Keys, The Book of The Names of The Dead, The Fraternity of Fame, Wand'ring Formes and Theyr Dispelment.*

"How could he read them all within one lifetime?" Malden breathed.

"He's older than you think," Cythera said.

"Older even than she knows," Hazoth replied.

Malden's feet left the floor in surprise. He whirled around to find the sorcerer taking his ease in one of the leather-bound chairs. He was dressed in a simple black robe and matching hose, with a black veil down over his face. Malden was certain he had not been sitting there a moment ago.

# CHAPTER FORTY-EIGHT

"So you can read, boy? I'm impressed."

Malden lowered his head in humility. "I have that gift," he said. "Milord Hazoth, I beg your pardon for my intrusion. I assure you I would not have come here had I not been in possession of certain information, which—"

"Cythera," Hazoth said, ignoring him, "perhaps things have changed since I was last abroad in the world. It is possible that manners have changed. Is it common these days for peasants to speak before they have been bidden?"

Malden looked up to see Cythera blush beneath the ink on her face. "Malden is no peasant. He is a free man, master. At least as long as he resides within the city's walls."

"Indeed?" Hazoth said, sounding surprised. "And that entitles him to come to my house and disturb my studies?" He rose from his chair and walked across the room to the tapestry map, as if trying to recall to himself where he was. "And if I were to, say, transport him instantaneously to—let us see—to here?" He pointed at a place close to the Western Reach, a region marked on the map as devoted to agriculture and possessing no towns large enough to merit inclusion at the map's scale. "If he were to find himself in the midst of a bean field, on some petty viscount's estate, with no way to return. What would become of him?"

Cythera glanced at Malden and shook her head a tiny fraction of an inch. He was not to speak now, that much was clear.

"He would be arrested for trespass by the reeve of that place," she replied. "Most likely he would be forced to accept an oathbond, and would spend the rest of his life toiling as a common farmhand."

"And then he would be required to pay proper respect when brought before his betters." Hazoth reached under his veil and stroked his chin. "It would require a certain ritual to send him thence, however, and such operations take time. Far quicker, I think, to simply ensure that he does not talk out of turn again." He brought his free hand up in the air and made a complex gesture.

Malden felt as if an iron pincer had gripped his throat. He tried to open his mouth and felt the invisible force constrict until he could barely breathe. It was much like the barrier outside that had held him aloft in the air, but worse—the barrier had been unpleasant, but this was actually painful. He had no doubt that if Hazoth so chose, he could cause the force to squeeze until his windpipe were crushed.

"There," Hazoth said, and moved back to his chair. "Much better. I hadn't finished speaking, boy. I had more to say, and now I can. I was going to say how impressed I was with you. Cythera has spoken quite highly of your abilities as a thief, but that is a subject I find uninteresting. I am far more admiring of your willingness to overcome your—quite natural—fear of anyone more powerful than you. Coming here today was an act of uncommon valor in a lowborn not-quite-peasant such as yourself. And valor is commendable, even in its cruder forms. Rudeness, however, is always unacceptable, and I will not have it in my house. Had you not impressed me so much, I would extinguish your life like that of a rodent I found in my larder, do you understand? But I have chosen to be merciful." He waved his hand. "You may now say, 'Thank you, Magus.'"

The hold on Malden's wind was gone, as if it had never been there.

"Thank you, Magus," he said.

"You are most welcome. There. Not so hard to be polite, is it? You may speak."

"I apologize," Malden said, his heart burning in his chest, "for my rudeness."

"Quite all right. I believe you had a message for me. Say it now."

Malden cleared his throat. "I've come to tell you that you are in danger. Anselm Vry, the bailiff of this city, is searching you out even now. He knows the crown has been stolen, and he intends to recover it regardless of who might be inconvenienced."

"That's all you came to say?"

Malden nodded. The sorcerer had not told him he could speak.

"Very good. It is ever so kind of you to come and tell me this. It shows good business sense as well. You were hired to perform a task and you were paid handsomely. I take it your coming here to offer me warning was all part of the service, hmm? You are acting out of pure altruism, and want nothing further as recompense. Surely you didn't think this would earn you some more coin. After all, the gold I gave you already should last a lifetime for one of such humble aspirations of yourself. That is, if you haven't already drank it all, or spent it on some shiny but worthless bauble. You may speak."

Malden chose his words carefully. "I admit, Magus, that my intentions were not unalloyed with self-interest. Vry intends to torture anyone connected with the theft until they provide the crown's location. I fear he has some way of discovering my involvement, and that he will put me to the ordeal. It had occurred to me that you might be able to offer me some protection from that fate. It would be in our mutual self-interest, as then I could not reveal—"

"You and I have no mutual interests of any sort," Hazoth told him. "Tell me something—you may answer me this— do you know why I wear this veil?"

Malden lowered his eyes. He thought of Anselm Vry's hedge wizard, and what came from peering into his shewstone. "It is my understanding that magic is never free. That power comes from the demons a magician treats with. So as his power grows, his body is twisted and deformed to resemble the creatures of the pit. I assume you wear the veil to hide some disfigurement." An eye out of place, a face turned the texture of tree bark, a beard of writhing flesh . . .

"Oh, very good! And yes, that is the reason for the tradition. I don't suppose your brain is capable of understanding what happens when one siphons power through the flaws in the underpinnings of our fractured cosmos, but you have the gist down pat. Perhaps you will brace yourself to take a look at what is beneath my veil."

Malden's stomach tightened as Hazoth reached up to lift the black crape away from his face. For a sorcerer as powerful as Hazoth, the price of magic must have been exceeding steep. Would the uncovering reveal skin as scaly and shiny as an asp's? Would there be pus, and open sores that never closed, or even wounds so deep the skull would be visible? Would the face look human at all?

Then the veil was rolled back and Malden saw Hazoth's face and he gasped in surprise. For the countenance thus exposed was perfect.

It was the face of a demigod. The cheekbones were high, the limpid blue eyes set perfectly far apart, the nose powerful without being over prominent. The skin was as clear as milk, with no blemish visible anywhere. It was a face of youth, of compassion, of inherent goodness and decency— except for the eyes, which were as hard as iron.

"I wear this veil," Hazoth told Malden, "because if I did not, no one would take me seriously. They would think my power slight, my magic untested. Whereas in fact the opposite is true. When one becomes powerful enough, one is able to shape one's appearance to fit one's fancy. And I am quite powerful indeed. Let Anselm Vry come to my door, as you did. I will welcome him inside, and if he troubles me, I will dispatch him like an obnoxious fly."

# CHAPTER FORTY-NINE

Hazoth rose from his chair and went over to one of his bookshelves. He ran his finger along a number of spines before selecting a slim volume and pulling it free. "It was good of you to come here and give me your warning, boy. However little it was needed. Do you have anything else to say before you leave? You may speak."

Malden bit his lip. Circumspection was everything now. "I can only plead with you then, Magus. Beg, if I must. I'm in a great deal of trouble, trouble I earned in your service. Does that not entitle me to some consideration? It would be a trifle for you to offer me some protection under your roof. If nothing else I could come work for you, in whatever capacity you saw fit."

"A job? You want a job? But you already had one, dear boy. If there were risks involved, you knew them when you took it. Or perhaps you will claim you didn't understand the magnitude of your crime. Well, considering your limited resources, I suppose that's understandable. Come here."

Malden's legs started walking toward the sorcerer before he thought to move them. He'd had every intention of doing as he was bid, but it seemed the sorcerer wanted to compel him anyway. When he was standing only a few feet away—inside knife range, he thought bitterly—his legs stopped and froze in place.

Hazoth gestured with the book he held in his hands. "If I needed a table boy, or someone to muck out my stables, I could have you with a thought. I could render you mindless and servile. Bind you to my service for the remainder of your life, and do it in such a way you would be unutterably happy, thrilled every morning to rise from your pile of straw and spend another day working for me until your fingers bled. If I wanted that, it would already have begun."

Malden swallowed carefully. His heart was racing.

"Such a waste that would be, though. You can read. Do you understand how rare that is? Reading is the difference, the mark, of a being capable of thinking beyond its own petty concerns. It is the one thing that truly separates humanity from the beasts. Somehow you have managed the art, and like a trained dog that can count with its paws, you amuse me. So no, I won't give you a job. Or my protection. But you may have this instead: the greatest treasure I can convey, or at least the greatest that you will be able to comprehend." Hazoth pressed the book into Malden's hands.

It was bound in calf's leather and was duodecimo in size. Gold characters were printed on the spine but in an alphabet Malden did not know.

"Read it at your leisure. I'm sure you'll find it most edifying." Hazoth smiled, revealing a double row of perfect white teeth. "You may thank me."

"Thank you, Magus," Malden said.

"It is nothing. Now. Cythera—perhaps you will see our little friend out. Take him the back way, so no one sees him leave. I have no doubt Vry is already watching this house and saw him enter. Or," Hazoth said, turning his frigid eyes on Malden, "did you not consider that when you came?"

Malden had not been told to speak, so he held his peace.

"Come," Cythera said, and headed toward a door at the far side of the library from which they'd entered. Malden glanced over his shoulder on the way out and saw that Hazoth was no longer in the room.

"A neat trick," he said as she led him down a side corridor. "This vanishing and appearing. You know it as well," he added, remembering how he'd first met her, when she appeared out of thin air on the roof of the university cloister.

"A simple one, once it's mastered. Mostly it is a matter of misdirection. Of moving when no one is looking." She pushed open a wide set of doors and brought him into the villa's dining room. Its walls were of carved oak, and the table could seat sixteen in spacious comfort. The chairs were pushed up against the walls—they were carved of some glossy wood in intricate patterns and looked far too delicate to support the weight of a human being. The table itself was a slab of marble three inches thick. Something about it demanded Malden's attention. When he looked closer, he saw it had no legs. The slab simply floated in the air, perfectly motionless. He couldn't resist the urge to push down on one edge, but the table easily resisted any force he put on it. Cythera sighed in frustration and pointed toward the door. "Leave that be, Malden. You must go now, and quickly, before he changes his mind. He is known to be capricious."

"Oh? You think he'll take his book back?" Malden asked.

"He has decided to let you live for today. I'm worried he'll rethink that choice."

At the back of the dining room was a small preparatory, where food brought in from the kitchens could be arranged on platters before going to table. The preparatory had a single high window that was open to catch the breeze. It didn't look like it could be locked.

"You're concerned for me," Malden said as she opened the doors to the garden. "I'm touched." He blinked in the sudden rush of sunlight when she led him out onto a gravel path.

She turned to face him, her face an impassive mask. "I don't like to see people hurt. It gives me no pleasure. In that way, I am different from him. But don't count on that fellow feeling for too much."

He sketched a simple bow as they hurried along, and made a show of stumbling so that his foot kicked a spray of gravel against the side of the villa with an annoying rattle. They were passing the kitchens, which were housed in their own outbuilding. That way if they caught fire they would not burn the main house.

"Do you find me handsome?" he asked, with a grin on his face.

"I find you brazen. If you think I'm going to swoon over your looks, or give you my kerchief to tie around your lance, you're fishing in the wrong pond."

"Ah—but you smile when you see me. You admire my courage. You like me, I can tell. Well, working for that sort, I can understand why you'd turn your affections toward gutter trash. We're easier on the heart."

She stopped in the middle of the path and turned to face him directly.

"After today, I will never see you again. So it really doesn't matter if I care for you or despise you, does it?"

Malden stretched his hands out at his sides. "Life is long, and the city is not so big. Only a fool says 'ever' or 'never.'"

"Then think me a fool." She moved her hands through the air, and it felt like a cloud passed through Malden's body and was gone. "There. The barrier is down. Go, and do not return."

She held out one arm and pointed toward the gate. But he didn't move. Not until she looked at him, as if to see what was the matter with him and why he didn't flee.

He caught her eye, though she tried to look away. She sighed and rolled her eyes, but he held her gaze until she stared back at him defiantly. Still he looked into her eyes, the only part of her he could see that was not covered in the images of sorcery. He held her gaze until something behind her eyes softened, if only for a moment. Softened, and looked back into his eyes, and did not flinch away.

"Just as I thought," he said. Then he touched his forehead in salute and left without awaiting a reply.

The back garden gate brought him out a hundred yards from the towering Parkwall, which cut off the sun and left him in deep shade. He hurried along the wall's length until the houses surrounding the common swallowed him up again, and only then did he allow himself to relax. As long as he had been in sight of the house he was certain he was still being observed. Once he was in the Stink proper, though, he headed toward a tavern several streets away and immediately headed into a private room in the back. A serving boy brought a flagon of small beer and some sausages when he called for them, then left him alone. Malden sat back in a chair to wait.

It was only a moment before Kemper walked through the wall and sat down next to him. "How went it, lad?"

"Like a charm," Malden told him. "They let me in with barely a question, and Cyth—that is, his servant—showed me half the house without meaning to. I even offered to come and work there, though I was rebuffed."

"A job! Y'asked fer a job!"

"Of course," Malden said. "Think on it—after a day inside those walls, I would have learned more than I can studying it from the outside for a month."

Kemper laughed heartily. "A bolder scalliwag I ne'er yet met. Ye've cased the premises, and him none the wiser, ha ha!"

"He even gave me a book," Malden said, and reached inside his tunic to bring it out. "I can't read the title, but it must be worth a fair handful of silver." He examined the small volume and admired the snug binding, the gilt lettering on the spine. He put a thumb inside the cover and started to open it, intending only to look and see if the contents were in the same alphabet as the title.

"He just gave it t'ye?" Kemper asked, his eyes suddenly suspicious.

"Well, yes," Malden said. "He was so impressed by— Blast!" He dropped the book to the table, where it fell open, facedown. A tiny droplet of blood welled up on his thumb. "I cut myself on the paper," he said. A second drop appeared on his flesh, and he stared at the wound. It didn't look like a paper cut. It looked like a rat bite.

"Lad," Kemper said, jumping away from the table. "Lad!"

The book was crawling across the table. It arched its back—its spine—and pushed itself along the scarred wood with its pages like a slug. It was headed for a sausage on a plate and left a trail of drool or slime behind it as it moved.

"He tried to kill me," Malden exclaimed, jumping out of his chair. "I went in there to give him a friendly warning, and he tried to kill me." He watched the book move for a moment, fascinated by its silent slithering. Then he drew his bodkin and brought the point down hard through the cover of the book. The thing flapped and shook for a moment, then a trickle of black ink ran out from underneath its dead pages.

Kemper stood as far from the table as he could get, and refused to come back.

"It's all right," Malden said. "I think it's dead now."

Kemper shook his head in distaste. "I'm glad I never larnt t'read," he said.

"I'll tell you one thing," Malden said as he cut a slice of the sausage and popped it in his mouth. He kept one eye on the predatory book, not unafraid it would rise again and come for him once more. "Before, I had nothing against the sorcerer. I was only going to break into his house because I had to."

"An' now?" Kemper asked.

"Now I'll be happy to take this bastard down a peg. Kemper, tell me—how did you make out? When the barrier spell came down, did you get inside?"

"Aye, son, aye," Kemper said. "An' none as saw me either. Let me tell ye what I found."

# CHAPTER FIFTY

Kemper had been reluctant to help Malden in his reconnaissance of Hazoth's villa, yet he admitted he owed Malden a significant debt. Had Malden not rescued him from the Burgrave's dungeon, he would have been tortured to death.

Besides—the plan had been half Kemper's idea, or at least it inspired by the card sharp's offhand comment the night of their carouse. Kemper had asked him why he didn't just go in and ask for the crown back. He had, of course, been joking. Yet when Malden sobered up he realized that he did in fact have the perfect cover story to get him inside the sorcerer's house. And casing the place was essential if he was to steal the crown back.

"I can see no other way to resolve my difficulties," he'd told Kemper. "Will you help me?"

"Aye," the intangible scoundrel had said at last. Together they formulated a scheme for it. Kemper could walk through normal walls like a ghost, but the wizardly wall surrounding Hazoth's villa would keep him out as well as if it had been made of solid silver. The wall had to be dropped, however, every time someone came in or out of the grounds.

When it was lowered for him, Kemper would have a chance
to sneak in as well.

After the fact, Malden was deeply glad they had worked
the thing so carefully. The wall didn't just immobilize those
who tried to cross it. It searched him with invisible fingers,
combing through his pockets and his clothes with studied
precision. Had Kemper been caught in that wall even for
a moment, the jig would certainly have been up—Hazoth
would have known the game they were playing and would
have destroyed them both in the time it took him to blink an
eye. It had been a major risk anyway, since they had no way
of knowing just how aware Hazoth was of who was in his
house at a given time. They had proven, Malden decided,
that it was possible to enter the house without immediately
alerting Hazoth to one's presence, and that was a major step
forward in the plot. Something to be grateful for anyway.

"I could tell, o' course, when it came down," Kemper
said, leaning forward to suck drink through his reed. "I
could feel it in me bones, smell it in the air. I knew I must be
quick, so I dashed in through the garden, while the guards
weren't payin' close watch. I think they was watching you
up front, mostly, and I learned long ago how t'keep low and
out o' sight. The door hard by the kitchens was closed, but
'twas no problem for the likes o' me. I slipped through neat
as eel pie and found the stairs what servants use afore the
wall was e'en up agin."

Malden had guessed beforehand—and been proven correct—that what he'd be allowed to see of the interior of the
house would be restricted to the lower floor. In his experience, most rich men kept their offices on the ground floor of
their homes, rather than force their guests to climb stairs.
Thus he had tasked Kemper with exploring what he could of
the upper two floors.

"The second story's about what ye'd expect, plenty
o' bedrooms, a couple o' garderobes, storage fer linens,
clothes, and whatnot. I didn't check much there, seein' I was
bein' careful wi' the time. The third story's where things
get int'restin', though. His own bedchamber's up there,

and ooh, is it grand. Silken sheets and pillers, divans an'
lookin' glasses ever'where. There's chains hangin' from the
ceilin', too, with manacles on 'em, what felt like cold-forged
iron. What you think he gets up t'wi' those, eh? Eh? Maybe
human lasses is too normal for his lot. Maybe he's conjurin'
up suck-you-bye from the pit t'have his way wi'. What you
s'pose that's like, eh? Eh?"

Malden's eyes went wide just with imagining. In the
House of Sighs, the most expensive of the city's whore-
houses, there was a famous fresco of a succubus copulating
with a sleeping man. He had run many errands to the House
of Sighs as a boy, and that image had been impressed firmly
in his youthful mind. He'd never before considered, though,
that succubi might actually exist. Did they have wings, like
in the painting? And horns, and— But enough. "What of the
rest of the floor? Surely there's more than just the one bedchamber. There must be. Did you see the crown?"

"Nay, lad, nay. But I think I mighta seen where it's hid.
There's a study on that story, a mickle space for him to write
letters and do his reckonin's. Then there's a workshop fit
for a dwarf, wi' all manner o' tools and materials waitin' to
be fashioned. There's a room full o' glassware, I ne'er seen
its like, all manner and shape o' tubes and pots and bowls,
some bubblin', some smokin', some full o' what looked like
ghost-stuff. I didn't spend long in there for the smell, which
were like rotten eggs. The biggest room up there's at the
end of a hallway, ain't never used by the folk o' the house.
There's dust on the rugs in there, and the doors is all locked
up tight, and the lock's half rusted. I'm figurin' there's traps
all over that corridor, set for any thief what dares to try for
the big room."

"But what's in this big room?" Malden asked.

"That," Kemper said, "shall remain a mystery, I fear. I
was bein' extra careful in that hall, in case there's such a
trap as could kill a nosy ghost, mind. I was barely inside th'
hall when I heard ye out in the garden, scuffin' up gravel
and chattin' all frien'ly like wi' yer tattooed lady."

"I tried to make as much noise as I could, without causing fuss, and stall as long as possible to give you time to

make your escape," Malden promised. It had been their agreed upon signal that he would make some noise when he was being ejected from the house. Kemper had to exit the place at the same time he did or risk being stuck inside the magical wall when it was brought back up.

"Oh, aye, ye did marv'lous well. I fled down th' stairs and out th' side, where some trees grow right up t'th' fence. Now, trees or fence, it makes no diff'rence fer one o' my proclivities. I was out like a crossbow quarrel and away, e'er ye was finished makin' time. So who's yer leman, huh? Who's this bird, anyroad? Ye've taken a fancy to her?"

Malden blushed. He actually blushed at the thought. "She's fair enough to look at. Not fair as in light of complexion, of course. But underneath all that ink she's a beauty. But—this is silly talk. She's betrothed, I think. Or at least promised."

"Betrothed ain't the same as wed," Kemper said with a leer. He tried to jog Malden's ribs with his elbow, but of course it just went through Malden's flesh like air. He felt his breath turn to ice and coughed out a puff of vapor.

"Betrothed . . . to a fellow with a whacking great sword," Malden clarified. "I don't know that it would work out. She seems to like strapping men with chiseled features. I like women whose paramours can't cut my head off for looking upon them."

"No woman's perfect," Kemper admitted. " 'Course, if'n you was diddlin' her, well, she'd be right useful t' a fella wanted t'break into her house, wouldn't she?" He sucked up a great sip of his drink. "What in the Bloodgod's hairy arse is this? Small beer?"

Malden shrugged. Small beer was what you served children, of course—milk being too useful for making butter and cheese, and water being nowhere in the city so clean you'd give it to any child you liked. "I figured after last night—well, my head's still pounding."

"And th' cure for that's this weak brew?" Kemper shook his head. "Nay, lad, ye've much I can teach ye yet. What we need now's brandy, and great lashings of it. Call the servin' wench. We've a great vict'ry today, let's celebrate it!"

Malden did as he was told, though in truth he didn't feel much like celebrating. He'd seen the inside of Hazoth's house, yes. But what he'd seen had told him his work was cut out for him. Stealing the crown had been hard.

Stealing it back would take a miracle.

# PART III

# The Crew

# INTERLUDE

Cythera prepared Hazoth's dinner that evening—a good haunch of venison and a plate of radishes soaked in milk—and laid it out on a silver tray. She started to walk from the preparatory to the dining room where he normally took his evening meal, alone at that enormous table. He had invisible footmen to serve him, but he didn't trust them to make his dinner—they lacked tongues or noses, and so had no idea how to properly spice meat, he said. Cythera suspected he had another reason for demanding that she cook for him. Perhaps it was yet another of the indignities he liked to heap on her, for—

Light sprang up around her, interrupting her thoughts. She felt her stomach slide sideways while the rest of her shot upward into the air, straight through the ceiling, and suddenly she was standing in Hazoth's inner sanctum, the tray still clutched in her hands.

She did her best not to gasp. It would cost her if she flinched or showed any weakness in his presence. Still, it was always surprising when he transported her like that.

Normally, magic did not affect her at all. The charm on her skin kept her safe from all enchantments and dweomers. Hazoth had explained, however, that the displacement spell he used to move her around his villa did not, in fact, work *on* her. It moved space around her instead, shifting the villa through various dimensions without ever touching her directly. It was one of his favorite tricks, probably because it disoriented her so.

She found herself standing before the rose window, red and blue light streaming across her face. The pattern of glass was a hex of considerable power—it was very good at shielding the sanctum from magical viewing. Cythera had always found it beautiful in its own right, at least until recently.

She allowed herself a momentary glance to the side. She moved only her eyes, and just enough to get a glimpse of the wretched form in the magic circle. Her mother did not lift her head. If Coruth was aware of her presence at all, she made no outward sign. Cythera could only hope that the witch had some other, more subtle sense that let her hear her thoughts.

*Help is coming*, Cythera whispered in her mind. *Croy will not fail us.*

She received no reply.

"Well, don't let it get cold, girl," Hazoth said, behind her.

Cythera turned and forced a smile. Hazoth liked her to be cheerful when she served him. It was difficult to keep her composure when she saw what he was doing, though. On a long worktable he had the body of a minor demon pinned down and cut open. It was little more than an imp, a long-legged batrachian thing with eyes like fire opals. Hazoth had his arms up to the elbows in its viscera. When the imp turned its head to the side to look at her, she nearly dropped the tray.

The demon made a horrible gurgling noise. Cythera forced herself to ignore its obvious suffering.

"It screamed like a natural thing before I disconnected its larynx," Hazoth assured her as she set the tray down on a nearby table, pushing aside a number of arcane instruments to make room. "This is going to take all night. I didn't wish to be distracted by coming down to the dining room, so I decided to sup here."

Cythera did not reply.

"Strange. There's no digestive apparatus at all," Hazoth mused as he pulled his hands free of the vivisection. "They devour their prey, everyone knows that, but they can't draw sustenance from it. Unless they persist simply on the suffering and fear of their victims."

Cythera often wondered if the same could be said of her master. She stood by, motionless, waiting to see if he required anything else.

Hazoth came over to the tray and stared down at it. Then he glanced at his hands, which were still coated in ichor. "Hmm," he said, "I really ought to wash. No time, though." Sneering at the slimy mess, he spoke a word that curdled in the air. Blue flames licked over his wrists and palms, consuming the gore that had coated them. Cythera did not even wince as she felt new vines and flowers blooming in the small of her back.

She watched in silence as Hazoth grabbed up the haunch and started chewing on it. She had a linen napkin tucked up the sleeve of her gown, and she removed it carefully in case he should require it.

"Oh, since you're here—there's something I'm sure you'll want to know. My little trick with the book failed. That rodentine thief of yours is still alive. You know, I'm almost glad. I admit I find him more amusing by the day. Maybe we'll have to bring him here and give him a job after all, hmm?"

It was not a question that required an answer. Cythera held her tongue.

"Of course, it's no great surprise he survived. We already knew he had an animal's uncanny sense for danger. After all, he knew better than to kiss you, didn't he? I really thought I had him there. What man could resist your charms, if he didn't know what the price would be? Perhaps you warned him, though. Perhaps you didn't try hard enough. Even though we both know you *wanted* to kiss him."

Cythera kept her eyes focused straight ahead. She did not allow her cheeks to flush, did not permit herself the slightest reaction. Hazoth only spoke to her like this when he was bored. It was a little game. An amusement. He would say something provocative—perhaps hint at some dark secret relating to her mother, or tell her a story of some perverse sexual encounter he'd had four hundred years ago. If she gasped or even so much as shuddered, he would crow and caper. And then he would punish her.

He had so many different ways to punish her.

"I could tell, when I saw the two of you together. I could hear your heart beating faster. The smell of your breath changed. You want him. You want the little thief to be your plaything, don't you, Cythera? Hmm? I asked you a question, girl."

"As you wish, master. If you wish for me to desire him, then I shall."

Hazoth laughed. "You can't hide it from me. I could taste it in the air, the change that came over you. You were *concerned* for him. *Afraid* of what I would do to him. Just ask me, girl, and I'll bring him here. I'll put a charm on him that will drag him straight to your bedchamber." He tore off a strip of venison with his teeth and chewed noisily. "I'll make him kneel before you. I'll make him burn for you. Just a word, and that can be yours. Of course, you'll destroy him the moment he paws at you with his coarse hands. One rough touch and he'll be torn to pieces. But maybe that would give you pleasure, hmm? Would that make you sigh? Would it make you moan?"

"I serve at your pleasure, master. Not my own."

Hazoth stared at her with his perfect, clear eyes. She knew he was trying to look into her heart, to winkle out her secrets. The charm on her skin made that impossible, but he still tried from time to time. He took an interest in her, certainly. After all, she was all that stood between him and a series of gruesome deaths.

"I think perhaps I'll summon your Sir Croy instead. That jumped-up man-at-arms needs to be taught a lesson one of these days. I think I'll bring him here right now. And then you'll tell him. You'll list all the things you dream of doing with the thief. Sir Croy will have to stand here and listen while you describe all your filthy longings. How does that sound? Do you think he loves you enough to listen to that and forget everything he's heard? Do you think he'd still love you as much after he heard those secrets?"

"If it would amuse you, master—"

He clucked his tongue in distaste. That was the worst part of the game. Even if she did maintain her composure, even if she swallowed her bile and kept her thoughts to herself, it simply angered him.

Sometimes that was worse.

"I could bring them both here, if you liked. I could bring them both to this room, right now, and make them fight over you. I could make them tear each other apart with their bare hands. Would you like that? Would it excite you, child, to see them struggle for your affections? Well? Would it?"

Cythera couldn't help herself. A small sound started deep in her throat, a tiny whimper. When it came out of her mouth it was so soft she thought it must be lost in the noise of Hazoth's chewing.

She was wrong.

"I've got you," he said, and dropped the haunch back on the platter. He wiped his fingers on his robe and came to stand behind her, his meaty breath hot on her ear. "I got through, at last," he whispered. "Both of them, no less! You care for them both!" He nearly giggled in his excitement. "Oh, Cythera, my dear, you'll stretch your heart too thin! I'll summon them both and make them both lust for you, shall I? Make them compete over who gets to deflower you first. Oh, I can see in your eyes how much you don't want that."

"I want nothing but—but—" she stammered.

He waved a greasy hand in dismissal. "Never you mind, Cythera. In point of fact, there's no need to do any of that. In a few days it will be Ladymas. In the confusion of that day, Bikker will hunt them both down and butcher them while the watch is preoccupied."

"Of course, master," she managed. She had regained her composure once she knew he wouldn't follow up on his threats. "May I go now?"

"I suppose," Hazoth said. "I should really return to my studies."

"Thank you, Magus," Cythera said. She waited for him to transport her back to the preparatory.

He began to make the necessary passes in the air with his hands—but then stopped without warning.

It seemed he had one more thing to say.

"I know you hate me, girl," he muttered. "I know you're plotting against me. I know you think Sir Croy is going to come here and save you and your mother. But it's hopeless,

Cythera. No one can help you now. You're mine, and always
will be."

"I—I—"

"I think you need to be reminded of this simple fact."

In the end, there was never any way to avoid the punish-
ments.


# CHAPTER FIFTY-ONE


There were many eyes watching Hazoth's villa the next
day, when Anselm Vry sent his watchmen in to take the
crown back. It was an overcast morning, with a light drizzle
falling from time to time. For Malden and Kemper, who
watched from the north end of the common, it was a miserable way to spend their hours. They had intended to spend
the day studying what could be seen of the villa from afar.
When the watchmen arrived, however, they hid themselves
in the bushes hard by Ladypark and kept out of sight as best
they could.

Kemper shuffled endlessly through his precious cards,
reestablishing the bond he had with them that let him hold
them when another deck would fall through his hands.
Malden had nothing to do but sit and hold the collar of his
cloak tight against his neck, trying to keep the chill rain
from running down his back. Yet he would not have moved
from the spot. Though he could not know for certain, he
believed he knew exactly what the watchmen had come
for. Somehow, it seemed, Vry had learned where the crown
was—and that could be a very bad thing. If Vry found the
crown now, if Hazoth allowed it to be taken, it would be

the end of all his—and Cutbill's—schemes. It would mean death for both of them.

Meanwhile, Croy watched from the house of his wealthy friend, in comfort, with a flagon of wine and a loaf of bread for breakfast. This could be the day he finally freed Cythera from her bonds, he thought. If Vry was successful and found the crown, it would be the end of Hazoth. Cythera and her mother would be freed of Hazoth's enslavement and they could go anywhere they liked. Croy could take Cythera away from him, he could marry her and bring her to his castle. Everything could turn out right.

As for Cythera herself, she watched from inside the villa and perhaps had the best view. Certainly she had the most to gain from this. Hazoth's punishment of the night before had been cruel, and she ached for the sorcerer's comeuppance. She very dearly wished she could just watch and see it play out. However, she was forced to pay attention to her regular duties—seeing to the needs of the villa, arranging for foodstuffs to be delivered, sheets to be changed and washed, silver coins handed out to all Hazoth's retainers and servants, so she was often away from the windows. She did not know what to think, or what this raid could mean. She dared not hope for too much.

None of them would leave—or breathe easily—until it was done.

It seemed to take forever for the watchmen to gather at the southern end of the Ladypark. First came their serjeant, a big fellow in a cloak-of-eyes with a red hem. He brought two porters who set up a tent where he could sit in relatively dry comfort. Next his men arrived, four of them, carrying halberds and watching the sky with doubtful looks. There was a great deal of discussion between the four and their officer, none of it particularly heated.

Only four, Croy mused. Four against a sorcerer. What was Vry thinking?

When the time for discussion was done, the men each took a cup of ale. They leaned on the hafts of their weapons and drank their ration in silence. When the cups were empty, they left the tent and walked across the common. Their boots kicked up crystalline spray from the swampy grass as they marched toward the villa. The serjeant remained in his tent, where it was dry.

"Now ye'll see somewhat, lad," Kemper said with a wicked grin. "This oughta be a bloodbath, and no foolin'."

"You think Hazoth won't even let them in," Malden said.

"More fool if'n he does, eh?" Kemper laughed. "Ooh, it's gonna be good. After what they did t'me, strappin' me up in that donjon. I can still feel the silver bitin' into me wrists an' ankles. Let's see how them cloaks-of-eyes like it, bein' hoisted in the air. Ooh, it's lovely."

Malden could not share the card sharp's vindictive glee. He wasn't sure how this would play out, but he knew if Hazoth killed the watchmen, or even if he just refused them entry to his house, it would only mean more trouble. Vry couldn't leave it at that—he would have to send more watchmen, and more after that, until every armed man in the city was standing outside Hazoth's gate demanding to be let in. That could hardly end well for anyone involved, and it would make it impossible for him to get in and steal the crown back. He didn't know what he should hope for now. He could only watch, and pray for the best.

The four watchmen reached the gate of the villa just before noontime—though only Cythera was aware of the correct time. Hazoth had a mechanical clock on the second floor landing of the villa. Its persistent ticking had always soothed her before, the way it cut the day up into tiny portions, making her hours of bondage easier to digest. Now each tick and each tock were blows against her senses, as all her hopes depended on this next hour.

The watchmen stopped just outside the gate. One of them hallooed the guards and demanded entry in the name of the Burgrave. Cythera alone could hear the response—and alone was astonished by it.

"Well met, fellows. The Magus bids you enter and be welcome," the guard said. He turned and made a signal toward the rose window at the top of the house, and the magical barrier came down, the wet air itself seeming to sigh in relief.

The watchmen filed through the portico and into the great hall. Up on the gallery, Cythera was busy counting the silver—an important job in a sorcerer's house, since any spoon Hazoth ate with could be used against him by a rival wizard. She bent over the cutlery in case anyone (human or invisible) was watching, but listened close to what was said below her.

"I have an official message from the bailiff, which I must present to you, milord," one of the watchmen said. "Then we must ask to search your house."

Hazoth did not sound particularly worried. "Very good, let me hear it."

"It is as follows," the watchman said. He had not been carrying a scroll—most likely he'd memorized the message so he could recite it now.

"Greetings to our good friend Hazoth, much beloved of the Burgrave and of the king his liege. It is with heavy heart that I, Anselm Vry, must send you this deputation today. Certain evidence has been advanced concerning the theft of an item the Burgrave considers the most valuable of all his possessions. This evidence tends to suggest that the item in question may currently be found within the bounds of your property. Under common law I am empowering these men to search the house, outbuildings, and lands of your villa, with all care being taken to minimize the disturbance, and especially any damage, to said property. Your cooperation in this search, my dear Hazoth, will be most gratefully received. Should said item be found upon your land or property, or on your person, or in any way concealed or possessed by your esteemed self, this deputation shall have the power to remove it to safety, and at that time, but not before, criminal charges may be brought against you or any agent in your employ found to have any part in the theft, movement, or concealment of said item. Signed, your servant, Anselm Vry, Bailiff of the Free City of Ness."

The watchman cleared his throat. Apparently he had finished his message.

"I don't see nothin'," Kemper said, sounding annoyed as he peered out through the rain at the distant villa. "No flashes o' light, no hellish smoke boilin' from the windows. No fiery hands clutchin' at the watchmen or demons comin' up through cracks in the soil. You think maybe he just magicked 'em straight into the pit?"

Cythera stepped over to the railing of the gallery and looked down on the scene—watchers be damned.

Croy held his breath.

"Very well," Hazoth said. He lifted one hand and gestured toward the stairs. "Would you like to begin your search in my chambers, or down here in the public areas of the house? And may I offer you something to drink or eat?"

The watchmen looked embarrassed. "We're under orders, Magus, not to take aught from you, not even a cup of small beer, as it might be cursed. Not, uh, not that we would think you would do such a thing."

"Perish the thought," Hazoth said.

"If you'll just stand aside we'll get to things, and leave you in peace as quick as we can."

"Certainly," Hazoth said, and stepped away from the stairs.

The search took much of the afternoon. Cythera was required to assist the watchmen—she held the keys to all the locked rooms, and could open some of the magically sealed doors and cupboards for them. The watchmen seemed surprised by some of the house's more unusual furniture, but never said a word, even when a book in the library jumped off the shelf and fluttered like a fish out of water at their feet. It tried to follow the watchmen as they backed out of the library, as if begging them to take it with them and free it from Hazoth's villa. Cythera knew what the book contained and didn't blame it. Still, she bent to retrieve it, and running one calming thumb along its spine, slotted it back in its place on the shelf.

What's taking so long? Malden wondered as he toyed with the bodkin at his belt.

*They're being thorough, at least*, Croy told himself as he clutched his hands together and leaned forward in his chair.

The last part of the house to be searched was the third floor. The chains in the master bedroom drew the watchmen's attention, and they made a brave try at searching the laboratory, despite the noxious fumes. Other rooms barely drew their notice. By daylight most of the truly dangerous parts of the third floor were subdued and harmless, for which Cythera was glad—she would not have liked to explain some of the things the watchmen would have seen had they come after dark.

When they reached the sealed and locked hallway that led to Hazoth's inner sanctum, they didn't even glance at the door, just kept walking past.

"Here, I can open this for you, though you must be careful inside," Cythera told them. "I believe he disarmed all the traps, but still it would be well if you—"

"Milady?" a watchman said. "There's no door there."

Cythera frowned and pointed out the door again. "This one."

"Don't see nothin'," one of the others said. "Nothin' there."

She studied their faces—especially their eyes—looking for any sign that their minds had been clouded by magic. Hazoth must have enchanted them not to see the door, she thought—and she did not dare to try to break that spell. As for the watchmen, they just stared back at her, blinking occasionally, as if they were bored and wished to return to their work.

# CHAPTER FIFTY-TWO

An hour or so later the watchmen trooped down the stairs to the great hall again, where they apologized to Hazoth for any inconvenience and then took their leave. Hazoth headed back upstairs to return to his studies, telling Cythera along the way that she should return to her normal duties.

As the watchmen stepped back out onto the gravel forecourt of the villa—

—and Croy jumped up, his chair tumbling out behind him—

—and Kemper and Malden leaned forward to get a better view—

—and Cythera clutched a silver serving fork to her chest, bracing herself for she knew not what—

—absolutely nothing happened.

The watchmen were allowed to exit the villa without any further delay. They marched back to the tent, where they reported at some length to their serjeant. Then the porters returned to take down the tent, and all departed together, heading up the Cripplegate Road toward the Stink, and thence back toward Castle Hill.

And still nothing happened.

Hazoth returned to his studies. He did not leave his laboratory for the rest of the day. Cythera went about her duties. Normally she would have been glad for Hazoth's preoccupation. Any time to herself—any time when he wasn't demanding things of her, or torturing her for his amusement—was precious. Now, though, she was more frightened than ever. Hazoth might or might not realize her part in summoning the watchmen, but it didn't matter. When he finished with his day's labors he would want someone to blame for the interruption, someone on whom to take out his anger. What was coming would be terrible, even worse than the punishment of the night before. There was nothing for it, though. All she could do was keep at her work. If her head was slightly bowed, if her hands lingered on the familiar knives and spoons in the silver cabinet as if she were lost in gloomy thoughts, it didn't stop her from finishing the task.

Up by the trees, thoroughly sodden with rain, Malden clucked his tongue in disgust and looked over at Kemper. The intangible card sharp was dry as a bone—the raindrops had passed through him without stop. "I need to get dry,"

Malden announced. "Come, I have a spare cloak back at my rooms. We'll make a fire. And then we need to confer."

"I don't unnerstand it," Kemper said, trailing after Malden as he hurried up the street leading out of Parkwall. "He just let 'em in? Let 'em ransack his spread?"

"They didn't find the crown," Malden told his associate. "That much is certain. If they had they would have dragged Hazoth out of his hole and conveyed him forthwith to the palace dungeon. Or rather, they would have tried. He would not have gone easy."

"Now that, I would've paid t'witness," Kemper chortled.

Malden was thinking out loud. "Vry said he would search every house in the city for the crown. Yet I cannot believe that he would start here without some reason. I would think he would avoid Hazoth's wrath if at all possible. So he must know. He must have some sign that the crown is in there—and yet, his watchmen left without it, and without a fuss." He shook his head. "Perhaps he has another scheme in mind, and this was only a feint. Which only tightens our schedule. We must steal the crown back before he gets it—or all is lost." He shivered inside his wet tunic. "We need to sit somewhere and think hard on this."

"Aye, lad, and sure."

"Perhaps a brandy or two wouldn't hurt."

That seemed to cheer Kemper immensely.

The two thieves were around a corner and gone before they could see the one real consequence of Anselm Vry's raid. In the stables of a rich man's house just across the way from Hazoth's villa, voices were raised and a horse was starting.

"Just be reasonable, friend, it's your death out there!"

Croy turned on his host with flashing eyes. For a second he thought he might strike down the merchant who stood in his way. Then he gripped the man's forearms and leaned close to speak. "Forgive me. You've been so very kind, taking me in like this. I know I've put you in danger just by being here."

"Think nothing of it—but think of yourself now. If you go riding up there in this state of excitement they'll arrest you on the spot."

"Anselm Vry will listen to logic. When I show him I am his only hope, he will give me what I need to finish this," Croy said, and released the man. He grabbed up a saddle from a tack locker and threw it over the back of his host's most hot-blooded stallion. As his host pleaded with him, he cinched the girth tight. He reached back and checked both his swords, making sure they were tied down in their scabbards and wouldn't shake loose. Then he pulled a long felted cape over his back—the teased wool would keep out the rain, and protect his steel from rust. He grabbed the pommel and made to mount, but a hand on his arm stopped him.

"They won't just arrest you," the merchant said, shaking his head. "They'll cut you down like a dog. Once they see your blades, they will not show mercy."

"I will move their hearts with my plea." Croy hoisted himself up over the horse's back and dropped heavily into the saddle. He grabbed up the reins and jerked the stallion's head around so it faced the road.

"You say two different things. Is Vry a man of reason, or a man with a good heart? I've found them to be contraries not often reconciled in a single nature."

Croy shrugged. "One way or another I'll convince him. And if I don't—then maybe I'll die today. But I'll perish in the name of justice."

"Then do me one favor, before you die."

Croy grimaced at the delay, but he nodded. He never failed to pay his debts.

"When you reach the castle gates—dismount. Turn my horse around and give him a good whack on the hindquarters. He knows the way home. If I'm to lose a friend today, I can at least get my best palfrey back."

Croy laughed bitterly and dug in his spurs.

# CHAPTER FIFTY-THREE

Despite the cool day, the palfrey was panting and its flanks were dripping foam by the time Croy thundered up the Cornmarket Bridge and through Market Square. At the main gate to Castle Hill, a guard waved his pikestaff in the air to demand that Croy halt, but the man was wise enough to stand back rather than be trampled as Croy shot through the gate at full gallop and passed into the bailey. Workmen threw down their tools and jumped out of his way as he leapt the pile of broken stone before the tower. He didn't slow the horse until he was right before the main door of the palace, and then only long enough to jump down and send the horse wheeling away, headed back to its master as promised.

For a moment all was stillness in the courtyard. No one dared move, for they did not know why he'd come or what he wanted. If he had sprouted horns and bat wings in that moment, he doubted the watchmen and the guard would be more surprised by his appearance there.

He was thankful for their caution. It gave him a moment—the space of a few breaths—to make his demand.

"Anselm Vry!" he shouted, throwing back the hood of his cloak. He reached back and untied his swords, just in case.

He could hear the palace guards rushing into place behind him, their mail clanking and the butts of their weapons sounding on the flagstones. He did not turn to look at them. "Vry, come out, I would speak with you!"

There was much confusion and raised voices shouted at him, but he could barely hear them. The blood was pounding behind his eyes and the world was tinged with red. If Vry would not come out and speak, then he would go in—and the Lady help any man who stood before him.

But in the moment before he began to cut his way into the palace, Vry appeared, standing on a second floor balcony.

"Sir Croy, this is too much," he said. "I've tried to turn a blind eye, I've tried to earn you mercy with honeyed words, but—"

"Your men—they came and they went. Without—Without *it!*"

Vry looked around at the throng of people in the courtyard and then glared daggers at Croy. "Watch your tongue."

"They searched the right house. They were unopposed. How could they fail? There is only one way. Sorcery."

"The men of which you speak have not yet returned. I have not heard their report. There is no point to this chaos and nothing to discuss."

Vry looked peeved, but he made no order for the guards to attack. For the nonce they held their places, weapons ready. Perhaps none of them wanted to be the first to attack—they knew what Croy was capable of. Once the first of them moved, though, Croy knew the momentum would shift and they would all be upon him.

This was the moment, then. He would make his plea, and Vry must be convinced.

Croy drew Ghostcutter and heard the people around him gasp. Some screamed. He dropped to one knee and held the sword before him, point down to touch the flagstones. He bowed his head before it like a knight standing vigil in a chapel. Like the champion of the kingdom that he was. "Give me every man in the watch. Give me a company of them, at least. I'll tear that house down stone by stone. I'll carve it out of the magician's heart, if that's where he's hiding it."

"I can hardly do as you ask," Vry said.

"Don't take me lightly," Croy insisted.

"Believe me, I don't. If any man could do it, I believe it would be you. But don't you understand? My hands are tied by laws and customs. I'm not a field marshal to make war inside the city walls. I am bound to protect the citizens, not slaughter them based on unproven information and the fervor of *your* belief."

"A crime has been committed! Your city demands justice!"

"I'm afraid that's true," Vry said in icy tones.

Croy stared up at him without understanding.

"I've done all I can for you, Sir Knight. My duty requires this. Croy, you are under arrest. You have violated the terms of your banishment, and by remaining within the walls of the Free City of Ness you have invoked the punishment of death. Guards, take him—alive if you can, dead if you must."

And with that, Anselm Vry turned and went back into the palace.

Croy had failed.

"Drop that steel," someone said from just behind him.

"Get down on the flagstones with your arms spread out."

"Hold where you are or be cut down."

Three of them, then, of immediate concern. Doubtless there would be more behind them. Croy's heart, which had been burning with unquenchable fire a moment before, turned cold and froze over with ice. His brain quieted for the first time in weeks. Every instinct, every reflex he had spent years training and honing, came alive in him.

And he realized—even as he jumped up and spun around to face his foes—the horrible mistake he'd made.

The appeal he'd made would have brought tears to the eye of a general. But Anselm Vry was no warrior. He was a clerk. An administrator. For him the rules, the numbers of life, were everything. It didn't matter what was just or right. Only what was formally *allowed*.

Ghostcutter came around in a broad arc, Croy's hand loose on the hilt. He didn't need fine control for this stroke. The wooden haft of a halberd was cleaved in twain as the iron edge of the sword whistled through the air. A guardsmen's cloak was shortened by several inches. Even as the stroke came around, Croy reached behind him and drew his shorter sword. It fit his left hand just fine.

A halberd point jumped at his face. He parried with the shortsword and metal clanged off metal, not the ring of a hammer on an anvil but the nerve-wracking noise of blade grinding off blade. A pikestaff with a leaf-shaped point came jabbing in low, aimed at his groin. Croy side-stepped the attack, then tipped the pike up and away with Ghostcutter's foible.

The masters-at-arms who taught these guards had convinced them that polearms were superior to swords. That swords couldn't parry halberds and pikes because swords didn't have the reach.

That notion was based on the speed of an average swordsman. For an expert at blades like Croy, who spent every waking moment of his youth practicing ripostes and reprises, lunges and ballestras, the theory fell apart.

Which was not to say he was invulnerable. When a guardsman came up behind him and brought the axe blade of his halberd down toward Croy's unprotected skull, Croy didn't see the blow coming. He only heard it whistling through the air.

So he barely had time to lean back and let the blade slice down in front of him, while the haft of the weapon clouted him across the ear until his head buzzed and rang and his vision swam.

They would encircle him and bind him in a forest of wooden poles, he realized. He could only fight a few of them at a time. No matter how good he was, he couldn't hold off every guard in the castle. In time they would whittle him down, get him with near misses and grazing cuts. If he bled enough he would die, no matter how many men fell with him.

There was a part of him that thought it good. That dying like this, in Cythera's name, was worthy. Had he been a younger man, he might have given in to that death wish, that dream of honor and glory.

But he was older now. He knew what was truly important. If he died here, Cythera would remain a slave forever. As easily as that the bloodlust fled from his veins.

He waited until a polearm came down just before him, its blade cutting deep into one of the soft shale flagstones. Then he put one boot down hard on the polished wooden haft. Swinging Ghostcutter behind him to deflect an attack, he jumped forward and got his other foot on the shoulder of the guardsman before him. The man grunted in pain as Croy levered himself up and over the circle of attackers, jumping free of their ring of death. He came down hard on the pile of broken stone and rolled, tucking his swords in so they wouldn't fly loose from his hands.

Rolling to his feet, he looked around, breath heaving in and out of his lungs. He saw guardsmen everywhere—and more, watchmen streaming in through the gates to aid in the attack. Dozens of men, all of them armed, all wearing coats of mail beneath their tunics and cloaks. Croy had no armor at all.

Someone jabbed at him with the curved blade of a bill-hook. Croy deflected the blow easily with his shortsword with barely a glance. Guards were starting to scramble up the pile of stones to get at him, though. He needed to move.

## CHAPTER FIFTY-FOUR

Ahead of him, at the main gate leading down into Market Square, the guards were lowering the portcullis. The points were halfway to the ground already as they heaved at the winch. If he was going to live through this, he needed to get through there before it closed. Unfortunately there were half a dozen guards in the way.

Croy roared like a lion and charged forward, smacking one man in the face with the flat of Ghostcutter, knocking another off his feet by hitting him in the stomach with the shortsword's pommel. A spear came straight at him, point first, and would have skewered him had he not danced to the side and into the path of another man. The fellow looked terrified as he realized that Croy was inside his reach, his long polearm now a liability instead of an advantage. Croy headbutted him and ducked under the arm of yet another attacker. The point of a halberd dug into his back, but he barely felt it.

The portcullis was right before him then, with no man in the way. It was only a foot and a half from the ground. Croy threw himself forward and rolled underneath, the iron points tearing at his clothes. On the far side he climbed to his feet and stared back through the open grate. More men than he could count were racing toward him, shouting for the gate guards to raise the portcullis again so they could get at him.

He laughed, though not harshly. Then he sheathed his swords and turned to go.

And promptly slipped and fell on his own blood.

He reached behind him and felt the wound on his back. It had felt like nothing—but then, in the heat of battle a man's sense of pain was often skewed. Whether it was a mortal wound or not, he could not tell, but he could tell it was bad.

He had no time to stanch it, however. In a moment the gate would be reopened and all those men would be on his heels. He had to take what little advantage he had, and run while the going was good.

First, though, he had to stand up.

Croy sheathed his swords and got his hands underneath him. The muscles in his back quivered and a faint echo of pain cut through the numbness of battle. His body obeyed his commands, however, and he was able to get his feet beneath him. The oily blood on the cobblestones at his feet nearly made him slip again, but he slid forward and scraped the worst of it off his boots.

Behind him the portcullis groaned as it started to rise again. High above, atop the wall of Castle Hill, guards began to shout, raising the hue and cry. Theoretically that call would summon every able-bodied man into the streets, to help with apprehending Croy. He knew from past experience, however, that most citizens would simply shutter their windows and bar their doors. He had chased down his own share of criminals, in more civic-minded places than the Free City of Ness.

He bolted for Market Square just as archers appeared

atop the wall. As he dodged between a row of produce stalls, an arrow flashed past his cheek and buried itself in a side of beef. Croy ducked low around the front of the butcher's stall as more arrows peppered its tarred wooden roof.

Not even a trained swordsman like Croy could fight off a rain of arrows. Using the stalls as cover, he made a short line for the side of the square, where the custom house and a granary pressed close together. Between them a narrow alley ran down to Prosper Street, a broad avenue full of horses and carts. Squeezing out of the alley, he stared wildly down the street, hoping desperately it would be clear of watchmen. He saw none and dashed downhill. Men screamed and pressed up close to the shops on either side of the street when they saw his wound. It must be grisly indeed.

"Stop him!" someone shouted from behind Croy. He did not pause to look and see who it was. Just before him a cart full of boxes of fresh fish was headed down into the Golden Slope. Croy launched himself into the air and landed hard on his shoulder in a pile of smelts and sardines.

"Who—what . . . ?" The driver of the cart stared at Croy with wide eyes and gaping mouth. As Croy pulled himself up on the side of the cart and tried to think of what to say to the man, the driver shouted in fear and jumped off his bench and into the street. He hit the cobblestones wrong and went rolling away, even as the horses pulled their cart ever onward, leaving him far behind.

"Blast," Croy cursed. He got one leg onto the bench and tried to grab for the reins. The pair of horses must have smelled the blood on him, however, for they whinnied in fear and bolted downhill. He fell tumbling back into the fish, which were flying out the back of the cart and leaving a silver trail on the street behind.

The cart jumped and bounced—it had never been meant to travel at such speed. Croy found it barely possible to get to his feet and climb up onto the bench. The reins were dragging in the street, hanging down between the traces where he couldn't reach them. The horses' hooves were thundering on the cobbles, their iron shoes clanging so loud he could hardly hear himself think.

A boy—an apprentice in some trade, judging by his leather smock—barely jumped away in time before he was trampled. A wagon full of hay blocked half the road ahead, and Croy was certain he would smash against it, but the horses pulling the cart were not so made as to run headlong into that obstacle. They turned at the last possible moment, throwing the cart up on one wheel. Croy fell sideways as the seat under him shifted and nearly fell out of the cart, only holding on with one hand to its side, his feet bouncing and dragging on the cobblestones. He considered just letting go—he would hit the street hard and roll for a ways, but then at least he would be off the runaway vehicle.

But no—that he could not do. Without him on board, the cart would be totally out of control. The horses would run roughshod over anyone who stood in their way. He couldn't live with the notion of someone being hurt because he had to get away from the castle in a hurry. Fighting the pain of his wound and the red haze that filmed his eyes, Croy dragged himself back up onto the cart as both wheels crashed back onto the pavement. Heaving and grunting, he pulled himself into the seat, and looked forward to see where he was headed.

Ahead in the street men and women went racing in a panic to get out of the way of the runaway cart. Croy shouted out to warn them and waved his hands, but the only way he could avoid catastrophe was to get the cart back under control. Wounded as he was, that would take some doing.

Prosper Street ran down the length of the Golden Slope at a steep grade that only added to the horses' headlong speed. It traveled straight as an arrow's flight down into the Smoke, where it lost itself among a maze of byways. If he didn't slow the horses before they reached that district, the cart would surely crash. As the maddened beasts threw themselves downhill, Croy stepped out onto the tongue between them and then threw himself over the back of the left-hand horse, the leader of the team.

"Whoa, whoa, easy there," he said, trying to soothe the animal. He clutched to its mane and did his best not to be bucked off. The horse turned one wild eye to stare at him and bit at the air with its massive teeth. "All's well, be at ease," Croy crooned, but the horse merely redoubled its efforts to shake him free. This was no destrier, bred for war and trained by a horsemaster. It was a simple dray animal that had never known such excitement.

The horse on the right, the wheel horse, perhaps thinking its mate was under attack, nipped at Croy's shoulder. He pulled back to avoid it and nearly fell off.

Clearly the horses had no intention of obeying his commands. By giving them a common enemy to face he had slowed them a trifle, but there was still great danger of a crash. To save his own life he might leap off the horse's back—but at this speed he would hit the cobbles like a catapult stone.

He looked ahead and saw that the horses were only a few seconds from reaching the Smoke. The street there curved around a tanner's yard. It would be impossible for the cart to turn at speed and follow the road.

"You have my apologies, fishmonger," he said to the poor driver of the cart who was about to lose his livelihood. Then he drew his shortsword and sliced through all the traces that held the horses to the cart.

The effect was instantaneous. The wheel horse, riderless, broke for freedom and galloped down a side street. The leader, with Croy on its back, jogged out of harness and took the turn around the tanner's yard at speed. Just behind Croy the cart slammed into a fence of wooden palings and disintegrated, its cargo exploding into the air in a rain of silver mackerel and cod.

The noise only frightened Croy's horse more. It began to stand and balk, and it was more than Croy could do to hold on. His shortsword went clattering into the street and then his left leg got tangled in the harness. Trying to pull it free only unseated him and he was thrown to the ground, with barely enough time to tuck and roll so his neck wasn't broken. He somersaulted out of the way of the horse's flashing hooves and then fell back, beaten, bruised, and exhausted, and watched it run away from him, into the warren of convoluted streets that made up the Smoke.

# CHAPTER FIFTY-FIVE

There was nothing Croy wanted more than to just lie down on the cobbles and rest a moment. His body was wracked with pain and he was still bleeding from the wound in his back. Yet he knew it would be only moments before the watch found him there—he had hardly covered his tracks on the way. He rolled onto his side and put a hand down on the cobbles. His strength was faltering and he could barely sit up.

The wound in his back must be deep. He could not afford to lose any more blood. His shortsword lay in the street next to his outflung hand. He grabbed it up and used it to cut off a wide swath of his cloak. This he tied around his back, as tight as he could bear. It might help, a little. Then again, it might be too late. He had already lost a great deal of blood. He had rarely felt so close to death before. Never had its chill embrace seemed more welcoming, more to be desired.

Yet there was that within him that refused to give up. As tempting as it might be to close his eyes and let slumber take him, his work was not yet done. Cythera and her mother remained enslaved. Hazoth still had the Burgrave's crown. He had to get up. He had to move from this place. He could rest, he promised himself, but only once he found a safe place to lie down. Where that might be, he had little idea.

As long as he lived, though—as long as Cythera needed his help—he had to make the best of what strength he had. And that meant standing up.

He regained his feet. He did not know how he did it— the simple act of putting one foot under him, then the other, made his vision go black and his brain howl in protest until he could not think. His muscles were trained to keep going, though, no matter what occurred. They got him upright and walking.

He struggled with the remains of his tattered cloak, managing to pull it over the hilts of his swords so they didn't show. Down here, armed citizens were rare, and the swords would draw exactly the kind of attention he wanted to avoid. Not that he saw anyone about—or much of anything at all, really.

The air was thick with smoke and fumes, unhealthy vapors rising from the rendering vats in the tanner's yard. Down the street a great pillar of ash and sparks rose from an iron foundry. The Smoke was shrouded in a poisonous miasma at all times—on an overcast day like this its air was as thick as porridge. This foul air and its characteristic stench would flow downhill, into the district of poverty and crime called the Stink. It was the fumes that gave the Stink its name. He headed down a long street with no doors or windows, only blank walls like a great chute. At its end was an open yard where Croy saw two men in a ropewalk, walking backward as they braided together stout cords into rope. One made a joke and the other laughed boisterously. As he staggered past they turned to stare at him. One called out, but Croy couldn't understand what he said—the blood was pounding too loud in his ears.

He passed a cooperage where workers scorched the insides of barrels by swishing spirits of wine around inside them and then setting them alight. Red fireballs leapt from the mouth of each barrel as the lighter ducked down out of the way.

Next door was a brewery, the air around it thick with the smell of fermenting hops and steam off the great malting kettles. Croy started belching as he passed through a thick cloud of vapor. For a moment he could see nothing, the acrid cloud making his eyes water.

When he stumbled out of the cloud, someone put their arm around his shoulders.

"Careful now, friend! I mean you no harm," the stranger cooed as Croy reeled away and tried to draw his shortsword.

He let his hand fall back. "I know you—*urk*—not," Croy said.

"Ah, but I'm your best friend in the world, aren't I? A

fellow like you needs a good friend at a time like this. Here, lean against me, I'm solid enough."

The stranger was a fattish man in a tight jerkin and leather breeches. His eyes were set close together and he had very little in the way of a chin. He was certainly no watchman, nor a palace guard. He had a belt knife but no other visible weapons.

"Don't I have an honest face? Ha ha," the man laughed. "Come with me now, we'll see you safe and warm in a moment. I know a little place right around the corner."

He thinks me drunk, Croy thought. "What kind of place?"

"A sort of temple," the stranger told him. "A little shrine, for the right sort of devotee. Ha ha. It's just up here."

Had he been feeling stronger, Croy might have shaken the man off. He knew what game was being played out here. He lacked the strength to walk away, though. As it was, he had to lean hard on the stranger, but they managed to turn the corner. He had fully expected the man to lead him into an alleyway and there try to slit his throat, but it seemed this little temple was a real place: a tavern, where workers just coming off their shifts were spending the little pay they'd earned that day. It had an open storefront where an alewife poured ladles of watered wine for passersby. Behind her Croy could see a roaring fire and a crowded common room.

It would be good to get out of the mist and dry off, he thought. And perhaps a drink would bolster his flagging body. The laughing stranger hurried him inside and made a hand sign at the taverner, who leaned on a second bar inside. "Here, give me a coin, will you? An offering to the god of the house, call it. Ha ha."

Croy drew a coin from his purse and too late saw that it was silver. It was already in the stranger's hand. "Ooh, pretty, hark the way it shines, hmm? This'll do nicely, ha ha. Come, let us find a place to sit, oh, it's quite crowded out here, isn't it?"

"Private room," Croy rasped. "I need to—sit down."

"Sure you do. Long day's work for men like us, hmm? This way, this way, mind that fellow's feet, he's a real rough customer, wouldn't want to start anything, ha ha, here, here, no, over here, through the door, that's right. Here's a bench for you, and a little table. And, ah! Here comes the priest himself to perform the mass."

"Stow that nonsense, Tyron," the taverner said, backing through the door with a tray in his hands. He set an earthenware bottle of distilled spirit and two goblets on the table, but poured into only one of them. "He's probably so far gone he doesn't understand a word you're saying." He scratched his eyebrow with one filthy nail, then rubbed his thumb across his fingertips. The stranger—Tyron—nodded discreetly. So the taverner was in on the scheme, Croy realized.

Croy leaned forward on the edge of the table. Sitting down was helping, he thought. He hadn't realized how taxing just walking through bad air could be. A little strength trickled back into his arms.

"A bit of this will have you back on your feet, ha ha," Tyron said, and pushed the full goblet toward him. Croy made a show of reaching for it, then knocked it over clumsily so its contents spilled across the table. The liquor had the viscous consistency and milky color of blisswine. Even if it wasn't adulterated with some drug—and Croy was certain it was—it would have put him to sleep before he finished the generous portion. "Oh, clumsy, and that stuff's expensive, ha ha," Tyron japed, "lucky for me it's not my coin. Here, lean back, that's right. Get comfortable. There's no place for you to be, nothing needs doing. Let me loosen your cloak for you, it's catching at your neck." Nimble fingers undid the clasp and the cloak fell away from Croy's shoulders. "And here, this is too tight as well," Tyron said, reaching toward Croy's belt. Instead of opening the buckle, however, he began to pull at the strings of Croy's purse.

Croy lunged forward and knocked Tyron to the floor. The villain wasn't fast enough to dodge out of the way as Croy's shortsword sprang from its scabbard and came around in a

weak swing—all he could manage—that left its point gently
touching Tyron's throat.

"Thief," Croy said. "You thought I was drunk. You were
going to—what's the word—roll me. Weren't you? Take my
money and leave me unconscious in an alley."

"No, friend, you have me all wrong, ha ha," Tyron said,
his eyes very bright.

"Don't lie," Croy said, and leaned forward a fraction of
an inch. It brought the point of his shortsword that much
closer to the man's jugular vein.

"Ha ha, now don't be so hasty, milord," Tyron said, his
eyes roaming around the room. "There's plenty of fellows
outside that door who know me. And none who know you
from the Lady's archpriest, do they?"

"I can cut your throat before you can call for help," Croy
pointed out. "Then I can—I can walk . . . walk out of here,
and none the wiser."

"They know the score," Tyron said. He wasn't laughing
now. "If you leave here without my arm around your shoulders, they'll know something's gone wrong. They'll stop
you before you reach the street."

"That," Croy managed to growl, "will be of little comfort
to you, as you'll be dead back here before I open the door."

"All right. All right. Take your ease," Tyron pleaded.
"Tell me what you want of me, and I'll do it. I swear. Just
take that cutter away from my throat."

A service. The man would perform a service, in exchange for his life. It was like the old stories. Like the tales
of demons bound to grant wishes. But what did he wish for
at this moment? What could possibly help him? He was lost
in the Smoke, away from all friends and aid. Away from
anyone who could ensure his safety. Nor could he count
on his friends anymore. The rich friend who he had been
staying with—the fellow who was kind enough to loan his
horse—would surely turn his back on him now. Before,
Croy had been a figure of fascination, a symbol of the man's
generosity. Now he was a wanted criminal. No, even if his
friend would take him in, Croy knew he would be doing him
a great disservice by going back there. He thought of Murd-

lin, the dwarf envoy. Murdlin had saved him from the gallows once. But he'd also said their account was square, that he had repaid Croy in full. Dwarves never forgot a debt—but they never gave anything on credit either.

Perhaps, though—perhaps he could call not on a friend but on an acquaintance. Someone with whom he shared the slenderest of links, but a link nonetheless. There was one man in the Stink, one man who cared for Cythera, just as he did. One thief. Tyron might even know him—or at least how to reach him.

"You like silver, don't you? Don't you?" Croy demanded.

"Oh, aye, and who doesn't?" Tyron wheedled.

"Do me a service, and earn it, then. I have a message to send. And I think you might know how to deliver it."

# CHAPTER FIFTY-SIX

"It's just as I said, ha ha," Tyron told them. "Look, he's weak as a kitten. Three against one, those are fine odds. We cut his throat while he's sleeping, that makes even better sense. Then we take his silver and dump the body in the Skrait, yes? It'll be out in the ocean to be nibbled by the fishes before anyone even knows he's gone."

Malden shot a glance sideways at Kemper. The intangible sharper kept his face as still as stone, no doubt thinking exactly what he was thinking.

"Keep your voice down," Malden whispered. "If he wakes it'll take more than us to put him to sleep again."

"It don't take three men t'slit some sleepin' bugger's neckpipe," Kemper advised in even lower tones.

"You can't cut me out of this. I know too much, ha ha,"

Tyron said. "I've seen his face. A man of quality like that. A knight, or better, he is. But wounded like this, and so far from Castle Hill. There must be someone—ha ha—looking for him. But not someone, I wager, he wants to be found by. Else why would he have sent for the likes of you two? He's trouble, this one. You think the watch won't want to hear about this?"

On the floor, Sir Croy rolled over on his side with a moan. The hilts of his two swords stuck up at bad angles from his back. Sweat sheened his face and blood stained his clothes. He wasn't going to wake anytime soon.

"I didn't have to cut you in at all," Tyron went on. "I could have just waited till he slept, then taken everything for myself. We do this together, and then maybe you'll speak the right word in the right ear. Maybe I find myself in a new position, ha ha."

Malden knew what the man meant—his measure was already taken. Before agreeing to come with Tyron into the Smoke, he had learned the man's whole life story.

Tyron was not one of Cutbill's thieves. He was not really a thief at all, at least not all the time. Mostly he labored at a redsmith's, working brass into latten with a cloth-covered hammer. It was not pleasant work and it paid barely anything, so Tyron was always happy to supplement his income with a quick bit of thuggery. Rolling drunks, short change confidence games, picking pockets when he could get away with it—any quick and dirty scheme to make an extra bit of coin. He was smart enough to have an arrangement with the tavern's owner. That showed organizational skills—which had promise. He was just the sort of fellow Cutbill might take on as an apprentice, though it was unlikely he'd ever rise much higher. Tyron only knew he wanted the protection that Cutbill's guild could bring him, and that alone had made him actually carry out Croy's bidding.

When Croy had asked Tyron to fetch Malden, Tyron knew enough to contact one of Cutbill's agents. It might have gone no further, though, had Malden not been at Cutbill's lair at the time, conferring with Slag the dwarf. He and Kemper had come at once, with Tyron leading them. No more than two hours had passed since Croy tasked Tyron with his message.

Had it taken any longer, Croy might have been dead before they arrived.

Malden knelt down next to the knight, who was moaning softly now. The swordsman's face was fish-belly white. He must have lost a great deal of blood. It would be child's play to kill him now, but Malden had something else in mind. He carefully opened Croy's purse. He had a lighter touch that Tyron, though most likely it didn't matter. Croy was feeling nothing but pain.

"Here," Malden said, taking out a mixed handful of silver and copper coins. Not a farthing in the bunch. He picked out ninepence and tossed them to Tyron. "There's plenty more here, if you'll do one more errand. Find me a physick. A *discreet* physick. Bring him here and you can have half this purse. Then you're done—you leave and tell no one about this. There must be a dozen silver galleons here. Not bad for a half night's work, is it? Cross me, however, and I'll send my associate after you."

"Him?" Tyron said. "A beggarly card cheat? Why should I fear—"

Kemper lunged at the thug and drove both hands deep into Tyron's chest. Tyron opened his mouth to scream and a stream of icy vapor issued from his mouth.

"Are we agreed?" Malden asked.

They most certainly were.

Tyron returned shortly, leading a man in a robe and a long conical paper mask. Malden peered through the holes in the mask and saw bleary eyes staring back. He paid Tyron and sent him on his way, with a promise to speak well of him to Cutbill.

"You're a trained physick?" Malden asked when Tyron was gone and he could speak plainly with the healer.

"I am." The man removed his mask—meant to protect him from the disease-ridden vapors of the Smoke—and rubbed at his face. He wore a pomander at his belt and stank of flowers and garlic. "I'm a doctor of physick, if you would know. Trained up at the university, under doctors Jacinth and Detwiler, and—"

"Good enough," Kemper said. "But can ye keep yer mouth shut?"

The physick looked from Kemper back to Malden. "I'm usually employed by the workshops in this area. They pay me well to look after men hurt on the job. My employers prefer not to have suits of law brought against them—even in this place there are laws against negligence. So yes, I can be kept quiet. For the right price. Is this the man I'm to treat?" he asked, pointing at Croy.

"D'ye see anyone else who needs ye?" Kemper demanded.

"You might have moved him to a bed, if you cared about his health," the physick replied. "For all I know you're willing to let him die." He dragged Croy up to a sitting position, then pried the knight's mouth open to look at his tongue. He felt for Croy's pulses and put an ear to his chest to listen to his wind. "Has he moved his bowels since he came here? Or passed any water?"

"Ye want to see his piss?" Kemper asked. "What kind o' sick fella are ye?"

The physick clucked his tongue. "I don't expect that your sort knows *anything* of medicine, nor shall I explain myself in detail. But the urine of a man is a great treasury of secrets, to those who know how to read it. I might find traces of extravagant humors in it. There might be blood in it, which would be a very bad sign indeed."

"Tell ye what, buy me a coupla drinks, I'll give ye all the urine ye can stomach," Kemper said with a cackle.

The physick looked like he might jump up and leave on the moment. Malden rushed forward to put a hand on the man's arm. "Forgive him. He's little more than a peasant. Sure a man as worldly and learned as yourself can rise above such petty taunting?"

"I assure you, my interest in his urine is purely professional!"

"Of course it is," Malden said, "and professionals," he

added, taking coins from his purse, "are paid for their services."

It was enough to make the physick return to his labors.

While he worked, Malden stepped aside with Kemper and spoke quietly. "You don't care for medicos, hmm?"

"Oh, was I rude?" Kemper said with mock shame. "Nah, lad, I ne'er liked 'em, e'en back when I were reg'lar flesh. 'Specially not then. They're more like t'kill ye than heal ye, if ye've anythin' worse'n a bruise on yer li'l finger."

Malden shrugged. "True, but if we do nothing, Croy will die. I at least want a chance to talk to him before that. He had something to say to me, and I can't afford not to hear it right now. We only have five more days before . . . before Ladymas. Croy is connected to what we're doing, somehow. I'd like to know how."

"Aye," Kemper said, looking almost contrite. "Yer in the right. Just don't let that butcher near me."

Eventually the physick straightened up and came over to Malden. Leaning close enough that Malden could smell the garlic on the man's breath, he said, "The wound is deep, but it hasn't festered yet. I've bandaged it properly, which is most of what I can do for now. He'll want an electuary of borage root if he takes fever. Watch his stools for any sign of flux. At the first such movement he'll need to be bled. Do not tarry or the poison will take him in hours. If he's hungry, give him foods that bolster the blood. Black pudding, blood sausage, the like."

"Very good. Anything else?" Malden asked.

"You may want to offer a prayer to the Lady. If he does survive through the night, it will be a marvel. If he's to make it through tomorrow, his stars must be with him. If he survives three days—well, I doubt that will happen. He will almost certainly take to fever, convulsions, and black vomit. Now. My fee."

He held out his hand and Malden poured the rest of Croy's silver into it. Malden had never had a problem spending other people's money. "Is this enough to buy silence?"

"It is. Though let me warn you—I'm not the only one who's going to recognize a knight of the realm when I see him. Get him out of sight, and quickly. The bailiff has sent word down from Castle Hill that this man is a wanted outlaw." With that the physick left.

"Did you hear that, Croy? You're an outlaw," Malden said, nudging the knight's foot with his own. "Just like me now. And no better."

Croy moaned and fell over on his side with a crash.

# CHAPTER FIFTY-SEVEN

Croy didn't die in the night. He didn't wake up either.

By mid-morning, with time growing short, Malden resorted to desperate measures. He filled a basin with water and then dumped it over Croy's face. The knight sputtered and coughed and his eyes flicked open. One of his hands reached over his shoulder, looking for a sword that wasn't there.

The wounded man's face hardened. He looked around the room, even sat up a little. "You moved me," he said.

"You're safe. Or perhaps it's better to say—no one knows where you are," Malden told him. Croy was lying on Malden's own bed, in his room above the waxchandler's shop. "That's a good thing, because right now Anselm Vry has his watchmen searching for you in every district of the city. It could become a bad thing, because none of your friends know where to find you. It's up to you, Sir Knight, if you wish to leave this room again."

Croy nodded. He understood. "Who's he?" he asked, looking across the room at Kemper, who was paring his fingernails with the silver edge of Croy's unusual sword. He had trimmed his beard and his hair as well with the blade, for the first time since he'd been cursed. He'd never had access to a silver knife before.

"A friend. My friend," Malden said. "You needn't concern yourself with that right now. You sent a messenger to find me last night. Luckily for you he did. I had a physick look at your wound. He said it will most likely be your death. When he was finished treating you, I brought you here, to get you out of the public eye. So you owe me something, Croy. First off, you owe me an answer. Why did you send for me, of all people in the Free City?"

Croy pushed himself upright in the bed and put his feet down on the floor. Under Malden's thin blanket he was naked. "Is it still raining out?"

Malden sighed. He drew his bodkin and showed it to Croy.

"You can do better than that rat-skinner," the knight told him. "My shortsword should be around here somewhere. I assume you brought it when you moved me. It'll make a cleaner cut, and kill me quicker."

"Smart talk, for one's weak as a kitten just now," Kemper said. "Ye'd be wise to just answer the question, m'lud."

Croy nodded. "You're quite right, good sir. And I fully intend to do so, as soon as Malden stops threatening me with death. I have no fear of it now, so it's hardly useful as a spur. I just wished to make that clear."

Malden sat down on the windowsill and sheathed his knife. He'd seen the way Croy moved when the water hit his face. For a man with a life-threatening wound, he was still fairly quick. He'd heard, too, of what Croy had done up at the castle. A man that dangerous wouldn't go down easily. Perhaps it was time to stop threatening him and start getting actual information out of him, after all. "I'm sure there's something you're afraid of. If I need to, I'll find it. But for now, very well." He sketched a mock bow. "I won't kill you until I have a reason. Tell me first how you even know my name."

Croy scrubbed at his face with his hands. "Cythera told me, of course. She told me that you stole the Burgrave's crown and sold it to Hazoth. Ordinarily that would be a problem. I'm still technically the Burgrave's vassal."

"He banished you to the kingdom of the dwarves. Then when you returned he tried to have you hanged."

Croy lifted his hands in resignation. "He never discharged me from his service. I swore an oath to defend him until my last breath."

"And you still intend to keep it?" Malden asked.

The knight's brow furrowed. "Yes, of course. How could I break that troth and still live with myself? I would die a thousand deaths before I dishonored myself."

Malden stared at the knight. Then he looked to Kemper, who seemed as uncertain as he was. "So you came looking for me—why? To bring me to justice? Did you expect me to turn myself in, to show contrition now that the theft is done?"

"I thought you might know where Hazoth is keeping it. I thought you might know how I can recover it. If you stole something once, you might know how to steal it again."

Kemper started to speak, but Malden held up a hand for silence. He had no reason whatsoever to let Croy know that he was already bent on that very endeavor. "Do you have any idea how dangerous it would be to try? Can you think of any reason I would even consider the job you're talking about?"

"He's askin' how much yer payin'," Kemper suggested.

"I can't give you any money," Croy said. "But you would have the greatest of rewards—knowing you struck a blow for justice." Malden started to laugh, but Croy stopped him by speaking again. "Cythera is a prisoner of the sorcerer Hazoth. As long as he possesses that crown, she will never be free."

"And what, exactly, should that mean to me?"

Croy blinked. "Everything, of course. You've met her. You know she doesn't deserve that fate. When last we met, Malden, I got the sense you cared for her in some way. If I was wrong I've slit my own throat, clearly. But I don't think I was wrong."

"Let me get this straight," Malden said. "You found yourself in the Smoke, all but dead, hunted by the entire city watch. You knew your only way of surviving was to get the crown back from Hazoth. So you sent for me, the thief who stole it, thinking I would help you simply because there's a woman in peril who needs to be rescued."

"Yes," Croy said, as if very glad that Malden finally understood.

"What in the Bloodgod's name are you?" Malden asked finally.

"In the name of the Lady, I am an Ancient Blade," Croy answered.

As if that explained everything.

Well . . . it did answer a few questions. Malden knew the story of the Ancient Blades, seven legendary warriors so called because they wielded sacred swords. Those swords had been made by human hands in a time so long ago the Free City of Ness wasn't even a tower on a hill. The method of their creation was lost in time, but it was said even the dwarves could not create weapons of such power or with such keen edges.

Kemper looked down at the bicolored sword in his hands. Then he carefully set it down on the floor.

"That thing's one of the blades? It doesn't look like much," Malden insisted.

"None of them do. They weren't forged as parade weapons. They were made to do one thing. To fight demons."

# CHAPTER FIFTY-EIGHT

Kemper held the sword as far away from himself as possible.

Malden understood his reticence. Looking at the blade, a strange feeling passed over him. What had been a simple weapon before had taken on new dimensions, now that he understood what it was made for. He remembered the way he'd felt while holding the magicked crown. The voice in his head had the power of command, the ability to rouse men to deeds of foolish valor and great sacrifice. The sword had no such enchantment on it, yet he could almost feel the power contained in its length.

It was old, he knew. Older than he could imagine. It was a fragment of another time, a relic of when the old stories were all true. Malden disbelieved most of what he'd heard of Skrae's ancient history, of the war against the elves, of the forests full of giants and goblins that preyed on the first human settlers. He had discounted such stories as fit only for children and the feeble-minded. Yet here was a thing that had featured in its own share of those stories, and its reality could not be questioned. It was cold metal, and a kind of magic.

Suddenly all the stories seemed real. All those tales of brave knights wading into sorcerous peril, into the very maws of demons—they might actually be true. The seven blades, who stood alone against all the forces of the pit that would corrupt and defile the very world should they ever be set free.

"Demons are rarely seen now," Croy explained. "Thanks in no small part to the seven swords and the men who wielded them. We have almost wiped their kind from the face of the world—them, and the dread sorcerers who summon them here for nefarious purposes. There was a time, though, when they were thick upon the land. When they tore great swaths through Skrae, leaving destruction and madness in their wake. In that time the Blades were created, and without them I have no doubt humanity would have perished. They are that important.

"Any piece of iron," he went on, "is capable of killing a man, or a dwarf, or even an ogre. It just takes a strong arm to wield it. Demons, however, are different. They are native to the pit, where the laws of nature do not apply. Even dwarven steel is little use against them. To make matters worse, this quality that makes them so strong—that they are counter to nature—also makes them horribly dangerous. They were not created to breathe our air, to trod our earth. When they are dragged up out of the pit, they blight the land that receives them. Their evil is like a disease upon the very fabric of reality."

"Fabric o' what?" Kemper asked, but Malden hushed him.

"Some will turn milk sour inside a cow's udders if she so much as looks on them. Some wither crops wherever they pass. And some are capable of destroying our world, just by being here. The one that brought down the Burgrave's tower—"

"It was tiny," Malden said, nodding, "until it was exposed to the air. Then it began to grow, and did not stop."

Croy frowned. "Had it been permitted to continue, it would have grown until it crushed the entire city under its weight. Even then it would not have stopped, until its tentacles could wrap around the world and crush it to rubble."

Malden felt the blood rush out of his face. He had released the thing from its watery prison. If it had not been checked . . .

"Fortunately, Bikker and I were there to stop it."

Malden cried out. "That bastard's an Ancient Blade, too?" he demanded.

"Yes. He wields the sword called Acidtongue. Just as I wield Ghostcutter."

"Then you know him," Malden said.

"Oh, yes. Very well, in fact. He trained me." Croy rose carefully from the bed, walked over to the window and looked out at the rain, which had grown stronger overnight. "The swords are immortal, but the swordsmen are not. As each Ancient Blade ages and grows infirm, he finds a suitable heir to take the sword and the oath that comes with it. It's up to the others to teach this new blade how to fight. It is a sacred duty and not lightly conferred—but only twice has a blade failed to be passed on correctly. Two of the swords, Fangbreaker and Dawnbringer, were stolen from us by barbarians. Where they are now, no civilized man knows."

Croy stared into the middle distance, as if he could find

the lost swords in his own memory. Then he shook his head and continued with his tale.

"When I received Ghostcutter from its previous owner, there were five of us, gallant knights all. We were in service to the king, at his fortress at Helstrow. It was our duty to protect him from any demons his enemies summoned to attack him."

"Why aren't you there now?" Malden asked.

Croy lowered his head as if he were ashamed of the answer. "The king died. He was poisoned by one of his courtiers. His son, the new king, discharged us. He claimed we were bad bodyguards who had failed to protect our master. We tried to explain that our brief was not to protect against poison, but only demonkind. He didn't listen. Demons are rarely seen in this world nowadays. Our sacred work is rarely called for—as vital as it may be, it's difficult to explain to people how important we are when no one has seen a demon at large for nearly fifty years. The new king didn't understand why he should pay us to train endlessly for a threat that never came. He expected us to do other service to earn our keep. The five of us were forced to split up and go out into the world and find new occupation, wherever we could. Bikker brought me here, where we both swore allegiance to the Burgrave."

"That doesn't seem to be working so well," Malden pointed out.

Croy glared at him.

The thief shrugged off the knight's disdain. "I speak nothing but fact. Neither of you works for the Burgrave anymore. Bikker's working for the Burgrave's enemies now. And the Burgrave sentenced you to death."

"I haven't forgotten my oath, all the same. As for Bikker—something changed inside him. With nothing much to do, he grew bored here. There was not enough action to satisfy his bloodlust, and a man like Bikker must fight or he begins to die inside. Everything that was noble and valiant in him perished for lack of use. It was a great tragedy—but I cannot forgive him for what he has become. He broke his promise to the Burgrave and now he sells his services—and Acidtongue's—to the highest bidder. I called him faithless when he left the Burgrave's employ. I insulted his honor." Croy shook his head. "Now he seeks satisfaction for that slight. He will kill me if he catches me."

"What, because you called him a bad name?" Malden asked.

"Sure, son, an' only apologize, an' make it better, like," Kemper suggested.

"It was unforgivable, what I said. Don't you understand? Honor is everything to such as Bikker and myself. An insult like that is a mortal blow." Croy studied Malden and Kemper with a questioning eye. "You don't understand at all. Is it true what they say, then, that there is no honor among thieves?"

"Aye," Kemper said.

"Yes," Malden agreed.

Croy grunted in distaste.

Malden felt the need to explain. "If that's how you define honor, anyway. When you're poor you can't afford to take offense. If I had to kill every man who ever swore an oath in my presence . . . well, Ness wouldn't be so crowded anyway. But I suppose it's different for the nobility. When two men in the Stink come to blows in a tavern, it's assault, and they're both put in the stocks. When a baronet and an earl hack away at each other with their swords, that's a duel, and half the city comes out to cheer."

"I'm sorry you see it that way," Croy said.

And Malden believed him. Looking into the knight's eyes, he was convinced, utterly, that Croy's world really was that simple. That honor meant the difference between life and death. That there were more important things in the world than a full belly and a warm place to sleep.

And of course, in that world damsels in distress *had* to be rescued.

"Where does Cythera come into all this?" Malden asked.

Croy's eyes sparkled at the sound of her name. "It was while working for the Burgrave that I first met her. She and her mother lived in the Golden Slope then. Her mother is a witch, did you know that?"

"She mentioned it," Malden said.

Croy smiled. "Perhaps you think that I mean she is some toothless hag, selling powdered bat wings and working simple hexes on strayed lovers. Nothing could be further from the truth. Witchcraft is simpler than sorcery, but it's cleaner, too. Coruth—Cythera's mother—counted half the best families of Ness amongst her clients. She consulted with the Burgrave on matters magical . . . and once, when she came to the palace, she brought her daughter with her. Cythera. I was enchanted when I first laid eyes on her."

Malden looked away. He could understand only too well.

"We barely exchanged a half dozen words at that first meeting," Croy said. "Yet I knew when first we met that I would love her forever. I asked her to promise she would be mine someday. She wanted to say yes but she knew she was not her own mistress, not so long as Hazoth lays claim to her services. Anyway, she was too young then to make such a weighty decision. Now she has flowered into womanhood."

"Flowered is the right word," Malden said, thinking of her tattoos.

Croy didn't seem to get the joke.

"Never mind. Tell me more of Coruth. How did she end up in Hazoth's thrall?"

"For defying him. About ten years ago she decided to take Cythera away from here—she considered Hazoth to be an ill influence on Cythera's education. She knew Hazoth wouldn't like it. Should Cythera ever get more than a few miles away from him, the link between the two of them will cease to function and he'll be prey to every demon in the pit. Coruth knew he would do anything to keep that link in place. She tried to flee Ness with Cythera anyway. They made it as far as the city gates, but then—then Hazoth worked a spell on Coruth. He forced her to march back to his villa and submit herself to imprisonment in a magic circle. His power was just too great to resist. Cythera was immune to the spell, but for her mother's sake she could only watch in horror as Coruth struggled and writhed, fighting every step."

"Coruth has been locked away in the villa ever since?" Malden asked.

"Should she become free even for an instant, she could wreak a terrible revenge on Hazoth. He'll never let her go willingly, and as long as he has her, he has Cythera, too." Croy laughed. "That's where we come in. Together we'll fight our way into the villa, striking down every man who—"

"Sneak," Malden said.

"What?"

"We aren't going to fight our way in. We're going to steal in during the night and get the crown before Hazoth even knows we're there."

"And free Coruth in the process, yes?" Croy asked. He looked like he didn't like what he was hearing.

"If I can. For Cythera's sake," Malden said.

Croy seemed to take that as a yes. He clapped Malden on the shoulder. "You're a good man, even if you are a thief. For Cythera! You can keep the blasted crown. Once Cythera is free of Hazoth's bondage, she and I can marry. She will bear me a son, and if he is worthy, I will pass Ghostcutter to him when I am too old to lift it."

He strode over to Kemper and took the sword from the card sharp's hands. Kemper didn't try to stop him. The silver edge of the sword was one of the few weapons that could kill him, after all. Croy lifted the sword above his head and made a swooshing pass through the air with it, careful not to break any of Malden's simple possessions.

"In the past, I have been . . . confused. My duty to the Burgrave and my devotion to Cythera were at odds. Now I see, though, that destiny has led me to this pass. By freeing Cythera, I will recover the crown—and keep to both my oaths. My heart is clear."

He seemed lost in a reverie. Malden took the opportunity to whisper to Kemper, "What make you of this story?"

Kemper laughed. "Methinks we've a walkin' fairy tale in this 'un. Never once did I hear such piffle afore. Yet I heard he fought his way out o' Castle Hill 'gainst two dozen men or more. I wouldn't cross him, if'n I was you."

"I'm afraid you're right. Maybe we should have just cut his throat when we had the chance."

"O' course, mayhap there's a way to profit o' this anyway," Kemper pointed out. "There's liable to be some fightin', afore this is all through."

Malden looked over at the knight and the swords he was holding in his hands. "We could use a man who's good with a sword, it's true. This one's wounded, though. He wouldn't last five seconds against Hazoth's guards."

"Mayhap we don't need to tell the guards that he's hurt," Kemper said. "I bet they take one look at 'im and run off."

It was possible, Malden thought. Certainly, having the knight on their crew wouldn't hurt.

While they spoke, Croy pulled on his clothes and put both his swords back in their rightful scabbards. Any idea Malden had possessed of keeping the knight as his prisoner was forgotten. "I've listened to your story, Sir Croy," he said, "and I've decided to help you." Of course, he'd always meant to steal the crown back. Frankly, as he saw it things were the other way around—he would allow the knight to help him. But it didn't hurt if Croy saw it his own way. "Together we'll retrieve the crown, and together we'll save Cythera."

"You're a good man. I knew it when first we met," Croy said, bounding over to grasp Malden by the forearms. "I saw in your eyes that you were a friend of Cythera."

"A . . . friend. Yes," Malden said. "Of course, I will expect some sort of recompense for my trouble."

Croy's face darkened in mid-beam. "I told you, I can't offer you any money."

"No," Malden said, putting an arm around Croy's shoulders. "No, I don't suppose you can. But you do have one other thing that I want."

# CHAPTER FIFTY-NINE

Later that day, Malden climbed up on top of a house in the Stink near the cloth market. Below him lay Woolcomb Square—actually a triangular space where five roads came together—with merchants doing a bustling trade, hanging out bolts of fine loden and broadcloth on high wooden racks. The women who came there to buy grabbed up handfuls of the stuff and rubbed it against their cheeks to test its softness, or tugged hard at it to measure its strength.

In their midst a girl in a tattered kirtle sold ribbon from a tray around her neck, lengths of her wares hanging down like multicolored tongues. The ribbon covered her hands nicely, and Malden watched with professional appreciation as she went up to one goodwife after another and clutched at their skirts, begging them to buy a little something so her family wouldn't starve. When inevitably the female citizens clouted her across the ear to make her give off, she would cry and run away—straight to the dilapidated stall of a button seller who never seemed to make a sale. Her tiny hand would plunge deep into a barrel full of sequins and the button seller would nod in satisfaction. She was good, this urchin, and Malden chuckled because he never saw the coins she stole. She was just that fast.

Behind him Croy clambered up over a gutter and onto the roof. Malden gestured for him to get down, to lie prone on the scorching-hot shingles, just as he had.

"I beg your pardon for taking so long getting up here," Croy said. His face was white as milk. "I fear I'm not fully recovered yet."

"I'm less worried about your speed than your noise," Malden told him in a harsh whisper. "With all the metal you're carrying, you clang and rattle like a cutler's wagon. Do you really need to carry both those swords all the time?"

Croy frowned. "Well, yes. Ghostcutter has a special destiny, and should be saved for high combat, while simple bladework demands my shortsword, which—"

"Spare me," Malden said. He returned to studying the market below. "You're certain Cythera will come here today?"

"Once a month she ventures here from Hazoth's villa to replace worn or stained cloths," Croy told him. "Beyond her duties as a deflector of curses, she serves as the mistress of his household. All the necessities of life are her responsibility, as he cannot be bothered to see to his own arrangements. He spends every day in his laboratory or his sanctum, deeply absorbed in his studies."

"You've been watching his movements, too," Malden said. "Studying him with equal diligence."

"When I returned to the city I think I already knew that eventually I must face him. He will never let her go for any price. She's far too valuable to him—without her, he must suffer the rivalry of every demon in the pit, and be beset by the curses they send his way on a daily basis. No, I must force him to release her, one way or another."

"Well, that's what we're here for."

Croy frowned. "Are you truly sure we must involve her? She's pledged to his service. She might betray us if we let her know what we plan."

He had thought the same thing, of course. Yet he saw no other way. "If we're to have any chance at all," Malden said, "any hope, we need her on our side. If there's a way she can help us that doesn't put her in danger, I'll take it. But this is too important not to try to enlist her aid. Surely she'll want to help us, since we're her only chance, too."

"I pray you're right."

Malden watched with a frown as the ribbon girl's hand was seized by an especially wary shopper. Great sobbing tears and wails granted her no mercy, and the goodwife squeezed her hand until it opened. The ribbon girl held up her empty palm as emblem of her innocence, and the goodwife was forced to release her. The ribbon girl ran off as fast she could, pitching her ribbon tray on a pile of ordure in an alley. The ribbons had been worthless tat, Malden realized, valued only for the cover they gave her real occupation. Now that she was under suspicion it meant nothing to her. Ah, and it was too bad—a good scheme, but now the game was up. Doubtless she'd have another scheme cooked up by tomorrow, though. The button seller did not react at all to her desertion.

There was still no sign of Cythera. Malden shifted his position slightly to get more comfortable on the shingles. It might be a long wait.

"One thing I don't understand. What does Hazoth want with the crown? Does he simply wish to study its enchantment?" he asked.

Croy had no good answer. "It puzzles me as well. Hazoth was a good friend of the first Burgrave, Juring Tarness. They fought together against the elves that once held this place. Hazoth was instrumental to the founding of Ness. In the intervening years he's showed no sign of rebellion— Ness has always been a safe haven for him. He's been protected here, where sorcerers in other cities have been burned at the stake. In return for that protection he's always supported the Burgravate to the best of his powers. A less civic-minded sorcerer would have been run out of the Free City long since—he would have been burned at the stake. Such men rarely live long, and yet Hazoth has persisted through centuries."

"I imagine knowing all that magic helps," Malden pointed out.

"He is a powerful sorcerer. From the tales I've heard, though, he must have changed much over the centuries. In those days, before the Free City had its charter, Juring Tarness was a great general. He defended the kingdom against the elves and then against the dwarves, who had better weapons and impregnable fortresses all through this land. Hazoth turned the tide in that conflict, as the dwarves had no sorcerers of their own and could not resist his magic. Hazoth was hailed as a great hero, and Juring a protector of the realm."

"I saw the campaign banners hanging in his tower room,

when I took the crown," Malden said, thinking hard. "A great leader of men, was he?"

"Juring? Oh, yes. They say his voice had the power to compel. It was not magic, I think, but sheer force of character."

"So anyone he spoke to would be inspired to follow his orders. Interesting." Malden was beginning to put together a few facts, but so far he had no conclusions. He made a mental note to revisit the idea again.

Croy's voice had a note of the highest admiration as he said, "Juring was a born ruler, and yet he served his king faithfully. When he founded the city, he proved—as is not often the case—to be as good a statesman as he was a warrior. The king of that era asked him what reward he would choose for his service. Juring could have had anything—riches, a grand fief, a personal army. Instead he requested freedom for the people of Ness. They had supported him through a long and trying campaign, you see. A time of great suffering for his army. He used his reward to give them perpetual safety from taxes and bondservice. The freedom you now possess is only guaranteed by the charter he asked the king to sign. In fact—"

"Hold," Malden said.

Down in the market, Cythera had arrived. She was dressed in a fine purple velvet cloak and moved listlessly from stall to stall, barely fingering the cloth on display. She was followed by one of Hazoth's retainers, a sallow-faced man with a chain-mail shirt and an axe on his belt. He pushed a barrow to hold her purchases, but his eyes were watching the crowd, perhaps searching every face for sign of threat.

"I hoped she would come alone," Malden said. The plan had been to draw her into some secluded bystreet, and there converse with her in private. It was crucial she not be seen talking with either him or Croy, as word of such a meeting would doubtless get back to Hazoth. "All right," he said. "This will just take a bit of cunning. Follow me down."

The two of them climbed down a drainpipe on the side of the house, out of view of the crowded market. Croy had some trouble on the way down and nearly fell, but he caught himself in time. Malden led him around a corner and back into the market from a different direction. He did not approach Cythera directly, but made sure to cross her path so she saw the two of them.

When they were buried again in the throng of people, Malden whispered to Croy, "Did you note her face when we passed?" He had been careful not to look at her, but he knew Croy would not have been able to resist.

"She saw me," Croy said, but he sounded crestfallen. "Her eyes—they went cold, and she looked away. Malden, she did not even smile at me."

Nor at me, Malden thought, and then chastised himself. Any hope he'd had of catching Cythera's favor—and it had been a forlorn hope, at best—was gone now that Croy was in the picture again. He'd heard the way Croy talked about Cythera, about how they had pledged to marry. Surely he had no chance of competing with a knight of the realm. A man who owned a bloody castle, for Sadu's sake. No, it was for the best if he put those feelings away. Let them die a natural death.

Still. It hurt.

He waved one hand in the air as if to dispel a miasmic vapor. "That's because she's wise enough to be discreet, nothing more. Come. I have a notion of our next move."

## CHAPTER SIXTY

The button seller looked up with a broad smile as Malden approached his stall. "Well met, sir, come, come, take a look here, finest horn—and not just ox horn, no sir, this is made of shavings from a unicorn's famed weaponry. Proof against poison, sir, you'll never need fear bad drink or food again."

Malden frowned. He met the button seller's eye with a meaningful look and then placed his hand on a barrel of sequins. He pushed his fingers through the thin bits of metal, as if he would root around in the bottom of the barrel. The ribbon girl's takings were at its bottom, he was sure. The button seller stared at him with suspicion in his eyes, but only a moment. Next, Malden stepped over to a barrel full of assorted buttons. Many of them were broken and all were worn and discolored.

"You want none of that dross, I assure you," the merchant told him. "Come, look at these. Genuine pearl, from the shells of clams as big as carts. They grow in only one sheltered cove in the far and mysterious Northern Kingdom called the Rifnlatt, and cost a pretty penny to import, but for you sir, well, I like your look, so—"

Malden took a coin from his purse—a tuppence— and dragged it across the surface of the buttons, digging a narrow furrow through them. With two more sweeping curves and a couple more lines he sketched a simple drawing of a heart transfixed with a key.

The button seller stopped talking at once. He reached for the coin and took it from Malden's hand, in the process smoothing out the buttons and obliterating Malden's handiwork. "I'm up to date on my payments," the merchant insisted. "Move on before someone sees us together."

"He—you know of whom I speak—calls on your aid. You'll be rewarded."

The button seller cast a suspicious glance at Croy, who was standing a ways off, trying to look inconspicuous and failing, utterly.

Malden sighed. "He's a mark," he said, a half lie. "I'm running a game on him. But to pull it off I need a distraction. Did you see a woman come through here, wearing a velvet cloak, followed by a bravo with a barrow? If you saw her face you'll remember her, for it was painted from chin to hairline in vines and flowers."

"Aye," the button seller agreed. "I saw her."

"I need the bravo out of the way so I can speak with that woman. The guard doesn't need to be distracted . . . permanently, just for a few minutes. Do you think you can help me?"

"For—For him," the merchant said, meaning Cutbill, "I can."

"My thanks. And his." Malden wandered away from the stall, one hand reaching for a bolt of patterned damask hanging from the next stall over. Croy came running over to join him, and Malden cursed the knight silently. If he didn't need Croy to gain Cythera's favor he would never have come out with him like this.

"It's done," Malden said, and no more.

"When? Where shall it occur?"

"Keep your eyes open," Malden told him.

They moved through the crowd drawing as little attention as possible. Malden stopped at several stalls and even haggled for a moment with a seller of thread, though he had no intention of buying anything. Croy kept staring at the faces passing by, but there was no help for that. Malden made sure they stayed close to wherever Cythera went, but not too close. When the diversion came he was no more than ten yards away.

"Sir, please sir, my sister, she's gone mad with fever, and she's locked me out of our house. Sir, please, I need your help, I need your axe, milord, please, I need you to chop down our door." It was the ribbon girl, though Malden barely recognized her. She had tucked her hair up inside a snood and turned her ragged kirtle inside out to show a different color. Such talent—Malden hoped Cutbill knew what a marvel he had in his employ, and what she was worth. "Sir, please, your help is most needed!"

Hazoth's retainer snarled and kicked at the girl but she was fast enough to avoid being struck. The tale she spun was obviously something she'd come up with on the spot, but the details didn't matter. The retainer shouted for her to leave off, and suddenly every eye in the market was turned in his direction.

It wasn't so much that the marketers were astounded that a grown man would shout at a girl like that, or threaten her with a naked blade. It was hardly likely they'd been moved by her impromptu tale of woe. But entertainment was where you found it in the Free City of Ness—and this looked like it could be diverting indeed.

Not for the first time Malden gave thanks for the prurience of his fellow citizens. Now that they were all distracted, he could move where he liked through the crowd, and no one would see him go. Better yet, they wouldn't see Croy. The big knight was simply impossible to make inconspicuous—unless people had something else to look at.

Most importantly of all, no one was looking at Cythera. She slipped between the shoulders of two burly men who were laughing at the sight of a toughened bravo beset by a street urchin. Instantly Cythera was swallowed up by the crowd.

"There," Malden said, and pointed to a dark alley closest to where Cythera had disappeared. "Go. Now," he said, and clouted Croy on the arm. The knight headed straight for the alley, and Malden worked his way through the crowd in the same direction, though not by such a direct route.

At the mouth of the alley he stopped and looked into its shadows. Cythera and Croy were already there, deep in conversation. Malden took one last look out at the market. The ribbon girl had managed to pull a length of poplin from a bolt and was weaving it through the bravo's legs. She did it so deftly it looked like she'd pulled the cloth by accident, caught it with her flailing hands. Anyone lacking Malden's trained eye would have no idea what she was doing or what fruit it was about to bear.

Hazoth's retainer lifted one mailed hand to swat the girl away but she was already gone—along with his purse. He must have realized that as soon as he returned his hand to his belt, because he cried out that he'd been robbed. He tried to give chase but was tangled in the poplin and fell flat on his face. The owner of the bolt of poplin came storming out of his booth to berate the fallen retainer, and the crowd laughed riotously at this spontaneous farce.

Perfect. Malden reminded himself to ask for the girl's name. She was born to the game, he could tell.

"—solve all our problems with one stroke," Croy was saying, his voice rising in volume. Malden came rushing toward the knight to shut him up. "And it will only cost—"

Cythera did Malden's work for him by interrupting.

"Last night he had her arm broken," she said, speaking over Croy's words. Her voice was ice hanging in the air.

The effect on Croy could not have been more profound if she'd slapped him across the face. "What? I don't understand," he said. He looked like a whipped dog.

"Did you think Hazoth would not hear of your antic at the palace?" Cythera demanded. "Calling on Vry to storm his home. Such a fool! I cannot believe I ever pinned hopes on your star, Croy." She turned away from the knight in disgust. "Hazoth knows about our connection, of course. He believes I set you to this reckless end. I could not convince him otherwise, and when I refused to confess, he sent two of his men with a bar and a piece of rope. They tied her arm double, and then twisted the rope with the bar until I heard the bone snap."

A tear ran down the garden of painted lilies that decorated Cythera's cheek.

"I meant only to—"

"I know what you meant to do! How much do good intentions mean in your world, Croy? In this storybook place you inhabit, where brave knights ride to the rescue of poor helpless women, is there glory in merely wanting to do good? Because in my world—and his," she said, jabbing a finger toward Malden, "what's in your heart means *nothing*. Not when all your best hopes and desires only make things worse."

Malden watched the two of them closely. Croy was like one thunderstruck, unable to speak or move. Cythera was so wracked with care that her skin was ashen under the vines and flowers on her face.

There was no time for this.

"Milady," he said, "we have moments only before your watchdog comes sniffing for you. Think me not heartless."

"No, Malden, I know you care," she said. She took a cloth from her sleeve and dabbed at the tears on her face, though with such gentle and hesitant motions she barely mopped up any of them. "What say you?"

"I am taking an enormous risk by trusting you. I have no way of knowing you will not repeat to Hazoth everything I say. Yet I have no choice but to ask your help. I seek to get the crown back. Once it is in my hands, Anselm Vry will have no choice but to arrest Hazoth, and likely execute him. Your mother will be freed, and you with her. Croy will be so beloved by the Burgrave that his banishment will be lifted, and with it the noose that belongs around his neck."

"And you, Malden? What will you gain? Can I afford your services?"

"I get my heart's desire," he said. He lowered his eyes. "But you need not pay that price. Meet with us tonight if you can. I have a room in the Stink." He described the street where he lived and how to reach it from Parkwall.

"Very well," she said. "At midnight, Hazoth will retire to his bedchamber and be occupied there until dawn. I'll come then."

"My thanks," Malden said. He watched her head back into the square, never once looking back. "Croy—we have to go now. There is no more time."

The knight didn't move. "Her arm?" he asked, his voice very small.

"Come! Or be damned," Malden hissed. "I only needed you to make contact with her. Get yourself killed now, if that's how you'll find your glory. But if you would aid me— if you would aid Cythera further—come. Now."

Eventually, Croy followed where Malden led.

# CHAPTER SIXTY-ONE

Malden spent the day drawing crude maps of the villa, showing all of its entrances and exits that he knew of, and the location of each room he and Kemper had seen. He studied them over and over with a feverish intensity. Endlessly he made corrections to them as he remembered something, as some detail that had previously seemed trivial suddenly offered new possibilities—or new hazards. His hands grew black with charcoal as he drew the maps again and again, then tore them up and made new drafts.

As confounded as he might seem to an outside observer, Malden was in his element. This was what he had been born for, he now knew. There were two kinds of thieves in the world, in his experience. There were those who turned to crime because they wanted money and they didn't want to work for it. Those were the kind of thieves who ended up very quickly swinging from a rope. The other kind were the sort for whom a perfectly planned burglary was a labor of love—a work, in fact, of art. The planning, the considering of angles, the second-guessing of one's own abilities and of one's opponents' motivations, the sudden inspirations that made the impossible seem, at least in theory, possible— these were what drew Malden to his profession, and in a way, he was quite happy poring over his maps.

Then again, perhaps he was just glad that for all of a day no one tried to kill him, or chase him across the rooftops, or threaten him with baneful sorcery. It was a nice change of pace.

The day fled, and night came all too soon. For hours he'd been thinking through every angle of his plan without bothering to rest or even eat. Now he took a pickled fish from a pot and chewed on its cold flesh without even tasting it. "Tomorrow morning," he said, "we'll have four days until Ladymas. I'd like to get this done as quickly as possible. We

don't know what will come in the next few days. Anselm
Vry might have tricks up his sleeve still. Hazoth might be
aware already of our scheming, and be taking steps to forestall us. So it behooves us to get it done soon, rather than
later."

"Agreed, lad, yet ye mustn't rush," Kemper said. He had
his deck of cards in his hands and he was rubbing each one
with his thumb, which he said always brought him good
luck. "That's been the endin' o' more thieves. This'll be
hard enough."

"I know," Malden said. He scratched his head and
thumped the table with his fist. "All right, let's go through
it one more time." He pulled the map of the villa's ground
floor and the garden toward him. "The magic barrier comes
this far, very close to the fence. I'll be here, and you'll be
. . . here," he said, pointing out a spot with his finger. "You
can hide in these bushes. The guards relieve each other at
midnight." It had taken some dedicated spying to learn that
much, but it seemed to happen the same time every night.
Hazoth didn't seem to rely overmuch on his retainers, and
hadn't trained them with military discipline. Malden had
even seen one fall asleep at his post one night. It was too
much to hope that they would all fall asleep at once, though.
"When the night's sentries come out from the barracks,
here, the relieved guards head inside, ready to fall into their
bunks and sleep. It will take some minutes for the fresh
batch to reach their stations. While they're all in front of the
villa, we'll get Cythera to lower the barrier. It will be down
only for a moment, just long enough for us to run up here, to
the preparatory door."

Kemper nodded. "And where'll yer titled friend yonder
be, then?"

Malden looked over at Croy, who was lying on the bed,
staring at the ceiling. He had barely moved from the spot all
day, and then only to pass water. "Him? I'm not counting
on him at all. When we brought him in on this I thought
he'd be useful, but I've seen now he'll never be one of us.
He's wounded and can hardly run, and anyway, he makes
too much noise even when he's trying to be quiet. He did his

part by helping us contact Cythera. Now that's done. Forget him."

"Just the twain o' us, then," Kemper said, sounding doubtful. " 'Tis much work for two, in the time we got."

"I know. We'll just have to be fast. Once we're inside, you'll head to the front hall. There's likely to be a guard inside—I'm counting on it, in fact. You'll make yourself seen and he'll sound the alarm, drawing the rest of the guards inside."

"I must say I like this bit not," Kemper grumbled.

"You have nothing to fear. None of the guards has so much as a silver boot knife that we've seen—and even if they do have some way to hurt you, you can just slip through the wall and be gone before they catch you."

"Mayhap Hazoth's got some charm 'gainst spectral folk," Kemper said, shaking his head. "Some spell or other t'trap me."

"Probably," Malden admitted. "But if he's locked up in his laboratory, or better yet, in his bedchamber—remember those cold-forged iron chains—then he's not likely to come out just because one of the guards thought he saw a ghost. They know nothing of you, remember. It's my face they've all memorized."

"So be it," Kemper said finally. Malden could tell the card sharp was not satisfied, but Kemper owed him—if he hadn't freed Kemper from the Burgrave's dungeon he would be dead now. Besides, Kemper stood to benefit from this caper in more tangible terms. Hazoth had a full set of silver plate and cutlery, which Kemper could carry out of the villa and keep for himself. Malden wanted nothing of the treasures the house contained. He would be satisfied with the reward Croy had promised him. His efforts in the villa would be all about getting the crown back.

Which led to the far more difficult phase of the plan. "It's up to me to reach the third floor undetected. The crown is in the sanctum, at the end of this hall—Cythera told Croy as much. The hallway, we know, is full of traps. I'll have to overcome them somehow." Without knowing what they might be, that was a lot to presuppose. But there was no way around it. "Then I can get into the sanctum, grab the crown, and beat a very hasty retreat. The guards will all be inside looking for you, so when we exit through the garden there'll be none there to stop us. Cythera will lower the barrier once more and we escape, both of us unscathed, me with the crown, you with all the silver you can carry. After that we split up. I'll go to Cutbill and you'll leave the city by means I don't want to know about."

"Aye," Kemper said, and shuffled his cards distractedly. The simple motion of his hands seemed to soothe him. It made Malden want to reach over and grab them away from him, throw them across the room, even tear them up and throw the pieces out the window.

He was under a bit of strain.

There were too many variables. Too many things he couldn't plan for. What if Hazoth took the night off from his studies? What if Cythera betrayed them? What if Anselm Vry was watching them right now, waiting for them to make a move—just so Vry could seize the crown as soon as he brought it out of the house, so that Cutbill couldn't claim to have recovered it?

"This plan will work," he said, trying to convince himself.

"Aye," Kemper replied.

"It's the best plan we've had so far."

"Aye."

"With a little luck—"

He stopped because Cythera was sitting on the sill of his open window.

"With a great deal of luck," she said, "that plan will see you both killed very quickly. That way Hazoth won't be able to torture you. He's very good at that."

It was midnight.

Four days left.

# CHAPTER SIXTY-TWO

"Milady," Malden said, bowing low. "I thank you from the bottom of my heart for coming, as—"

"Obsequiousness does not suit you, Malden," Cythera said. She climbed down from the window and came over to the table where the maps lay. Malden noted that she didn't even glance at Croy. "This plan doesn't either. You've badly underestimated the villa's defenses."

Malden stepped back from the table and let her peruse the maps. After a moment she went to the unlit brazier in the corner (Malden used it only in the wintertime), took out a piece of charcoal and began to sketch in parts of the map that neither Malden nor Kemper had been able to draw.

"I take it you've decided to help us," Malden said when she seemed to be done.

"What choice do I have? If I betray you now, for the sake of peace, I will only be delaying the inevitable. He'll find some excuse to torture my mother regardless of what I do. No, her only hope is your foolish scheme. Which still won't work."

Malden looked down at the additions she'd made to the map. Mostly she had drawn in the rooms on the second floor, which did not concern him overmuch, but she'd added two walls on the third floor he had not known were there—and which would have caused him significant problems when he got inside.

"And . . . how is your mother, if I might ask?" Malden said. "Is she at least safe, for the nonce?"

"You could say that," Cythera told him without looking up. "She turned herself into a tree."

"A what, lass?" Kemper asked.

Cythera looked up then. She had never seen the intangible scoundrel before. Yet she did not demand to know who he was. "A tree. A rowan, of course."

"Of . . . course," Malden said.

"The rowan is sacred to witches and magicians. Its wood is the only proper material for magic wands, and its berries are a potent charm against sorcery. Coruth has not fruited yet, though. She is still a sapling, for she lacks the strength to increase her size through magic. At first I thought she had a cunning plan—that she would grow, as a tree, and eventually her branches would break through the roof of Hazoth's house. In that way she might free herself in, say, fifty or one hundred years from now."

"She expects to be prisoned that long?" Malden asked in surprise.

"She expects," Cythera said, "to be held there forever. Hazoth does not age. As long as she is trapped in a magic circle, neither will she. He will never release her, of course—he draws power from holding her captive, for one thing. The demons he commands delight in her agonies, and make gifts of their magic to him in exchange. For another thing he knows that if she ever does free herself, her first order of business will be to annihilate him utterly."

"Fer revenge," Kemper said, nodding agreeably.

"For justice, call it." Cythera turned to Malden. "It was just an hour ago that I realized another reason why she chose to make herself a tree. That was when I decided I would come here and aid you all I can."

"Oh?" Malden asked.

"Cruel boys break the branches of trees all the time, but trees do not feel pain."

"Ah."

"Hark," Cythera said, "I don't have much time. Hazoth is closeted in his bedchamber but he will emerge before the third hour of the morning. I was able to confuse the guards enough they did not see me go, but I must be back before he calls for me. He always does after consorting with demons. He knows the smell of brimstone nauseates me, you see. He is most subtle in his tortures, is Hazoth."

"You must hate him," Malden said.

Cythera stared at him with burning eyes. As if he could

not comprehend what she felt for the man. He supposed in many ways he couldn't, so he looked away.

"One thing I don't understand," he said. "Forgive me, but—you have so much power bound up in your painted skin. Couldn't you simply . . . I don't know. Strike him? Grab him forcefully. Wouldn't that be enough to destroy him? Surely that would satisfy justice." And save me a great deal of trouble, too, Malden thought.

It was Cythera's turn to avert her gaze. "Not all of his protections are magical," she said, her voice almost a whisper. "But there is a simpler reason. The magical link he has with me would make such a gesture futile. I could release the curses I have stored up against him, yes. But the link would simply send them back to me." She shook her head. "There's no answer there. You must find another way."

"I've been working on a plan," he told her, and showed her the papers on the table. "You heard the gist of it, and said it would fail."

"Yes. Look. Here," she said, and pointed to the map. Her finger was aimed at the great hall on the first floor.

Malden knew exactly what she was pointing out. "The great iron sphere there, by the stairs. I wondered about it, but knew not what it might be."

"It's another power source for Hazoth's wizardry. He has many, and I do not know them all."

"But what is it? It's made of iron. Doesn't iron discomfit demons? I would hardly think they would put their power into such an object."

"Cold-forged iron is their bane," Cythera said. "Iron forged in great heat actually strengthens them. It is why normal iron weapons, and even more so, dwarven steel, don't hurt them. This iron was formed in the heat of the pit itself. But it is not the iron that is magical. It is the pit-thing inside the iron."

"There's a demon in there?" Malden asked.

"Sure, an' it's like a magic circle, which'll hold a fiend, aye, only this 'un's in three d'mensions 'stead o' two," Kemper insisted.

Malden and Cythera both stared at him.

"D'you think me a simpleton?" Kemper asked, looking hurt. "Or mayhap you think me unversed in magics? D'you think one o' my affliction wouldn't learn a thing or two?"

"That's Kemper. He's cursed," Malden explained to Cythera.

"And largely correct," she said, shrugging off her surprise. "Yes, the iron is there to contain the demon. But not because Hazoth fears it getting loose. You see, the demon inside the iron sphere is an embryo, still. It has yet to be born. The iron sphere is not its prison, but its egg."

"It's like a babe in the womb?" Malden asked.

"Yes. But do not be fooled into thinking it weak or helpless. Demons are born fully formed and are quite dangerous the moment they are hatched. Otherwise they would never survive in the pit. Demons have no bonds of affection for one another, not like humans do. Even a mother's love for a child is unknown among them. A she-demon will devour her own brood with glee if she gets the chance."

"That's horrible," Malden said.

"It's just how things are done there. The demons see it as natural. As a result, those demons born weak and mewling like human infants don't live long. The ones that do survive are the ones born already strong. This demon is a perfect example. I've seen full-grown examples of its kind, and they are unstoppable slaughterers. The moment this one emerges from that egg it will be ready to hunt. Even before its proper time it will be a terrible thing to behold. I don't know how close it is to being born, but I know it will be hungry, and it will be ready to kill. Hazoth can release it any time he chooses. If he detects you inside his house, even for an instant, he can force the creature to hatch—and to give chase. It will follow you to the ends of the earth, if it must, and devour you. Do you understand?"

"I think I do," Malden said. His hands were suddenly very cold—his blood had turned to ice.

"You won't be able to fight it. Its claws will be sharper than any steel you bring to bear. Its teeth will rend through solid stone. Even with an Ancient Blade in your posses-

sion—and I doubt Croy will just loan you Ghostcutter—
you would never stand a chance against it in single combat,
Malden. You won't be able to hide from it either. It will be
born blind, but with an exceptionally keen sense of smell.
You could try to douse yourself in perfumes, or cross running water, or any of the stratagems that might drive a dog
from your trail. None of them will work with this creature.
Once it has your scent it will find you. And kill you."

Malden went to the bed and sat down on its edge, careful
not to disturb Croy. "What infernal pact did Hazoth make to
contract such service?" he asked, because asking questions
was much easier than contemplating what a newborn demon
would do to his tender flesh once it had him. "Did he get this
thing from torturing your mother?"

"No. He earned its service the oldest way. By siring it."

"Hold, now," Kemper said.

For the first time Croy sat up in the bed and spoke. "You
can't be saying that—"

Cythera looked down at the maps and met no one's gaze.
"You saw the chains in his bedchamber. I see you've even
drawn them in here on your diagram. That is how he enter-
tains his succubi. The demon in the egg was the fruit of one
such union. It is his child. It is not his first."

# CHAPTER SIXTY-THREE

"But . . . why?" Malden asked. He thought of the mural
of the succubus in the House of Sighs, and he supposed
he could see why a man would find that attractive. Yet he
was reasonably certain that mural had not been painted
from life. And even if it was, it seemed Hazoth's intent was

not to take pleasure from his succubi, but a wholly different end. "Why would anyone . . . want to . . . Why?"

"You wonder what would make a man desire a demon child. You wonder why any human being could compass such a thing. You forget that Hazoth does not think of himself as a human being. He does not consider himself bound by conventional ethics."

"I got that when I met him," Malden agreed.

"A sorcerer like Hazoth lives only for power. He cares not for gold, or love, or any of the things that entice normal men. He wants to expand the scope of his knowledge, and to possess power that others cannot match. He's already capable of things beyond your imagining. Yet for a very long time he's felt like a prisoner."

"Truly? But who could possibly compel him?"

"The Burgrave. And the king. There is a law against what Hazoth does, Malden. There is a penalty, if he's caught, and it's burning at the stake. Everything he does in the average day is probably illegal according to the laws of this land." She looked over into the corner of the room, where Ghost-cutter leaned against one wall. "The Ancient Blades exist to enforce that law."

"Croy told me Hazoth lives in Ness because the Burgrave's ancestor granted him a sort of safe haven here," Malden pointed out.

"Exactly. Now he's trapped here. If Hazoth left Ness he would be under constant suspicion. Croy and his brother knights keep a constant watch on any sorcerer who looks powerful enough to draw a demon up from the pit. They are never allowed a moment's rest until they prove they are faithful to the law. Hazoth couldn't live under that kind of watchful gaze. Eventually he would be caught summoning a demon or doing something else so infernal he would be arrested for it. He would be given a trial, but his sort are never very good at defending themselves in a court of law. He would be found guilty and sentenced to death. After so many centuries of life, to be caught by petty reeves and burned at the stake by peasants would seem utter injustice to him."

"Yet why would he want to travel abroad when here, in

Ness, he could live forever and be unmolested?" Malden asked.

"Can you imagine what it is like, to be called a free man, but only if you agree never to leave a certain place? Can you imagine the irony in that freedom, which requires you to remain always inside what must feel like a prison cell?"

Malden pursed his lips. He could imagine that exactly. He remembered when Cutbill had described his own situation in just the same terms. He had never wanted to feel sympathy for Hazoth. Nor did he now—at least not much— but he had to admit he could see Hazoth's motivations.

"Once his demon child is born, it will protect him from such a fate. He can go where he pleases—do what mischief he pleases—and none can stop him."

Malden stroked his chin. "Croy told me something else as well. About demons. How they're unnatural, and how they distort reality around them. How their power will eventually wreck the world if they're not stopped. There was one in the Burgrave's tower that would have choked the world if it wasn't checked."

"This one is much the same, though its dangers are less obvious," Cythera agreed. "Hazoth knows the risk he's running. He just doesn't care."

"That is troubling," Malden said.

"I meant it to be."

"For right now, though . . . it's also immaterial. You say that once the demon is born it will hound me to my death. Well, that just adds one step to my plan. I'll have to make sure Hazoth never becomes aware of my presence in his house—so he can't birth the demon."

"That'll be a nice bit o' work," Kemper said, "if'n ye can pull it off."

Malden shrugged. He hadn't expected this to be easy. He honestly did not expect to survive the job. Yet that thought was unworthy of being dwelt upon. He had a chance, a beggar's chance, to make this work. That was all he would allow himself to think. "It's better that way, at any rate. Even without the demon Hazoth is perfectly capable of destroying me. This changes nothing."

"There are other concerns as well," Cythera said. She stared deeply into Malden's eyes. For a moment neither of them spoke. What was she looking for? he wondered. For conviction, for self-confidence?

Eventually she closed her eyes. The downward-drooping petals of painted cyclamen blooms made her eyelids white as paper. The flowers began to wilt before she opened her eyes again. "There are the traps, in this hallway."

Malden looked down at the map. "Kemper discovered them, though he couldn't discern their nature. We were hoping you might tell us what they were, and thus allow me to take measures to circumvent them."

"That hope is forlorn," she said. "I have lived in that house most my life, but never have I walked down that hallway. Hazoth doesn't use it himself. When he goes to his sanctum—and on those occasions when he takes me there—he transports himself directly without passing through the intervening space. The hallway is a ruse, meant to confound thieves. The traps, I know, are very real, and quite deadly. They can be disarmed by a simple mechanism inside the sanctum. There is a candle always burning there. To deactivate the traps it must be snuffed. But of course, you need to be inside the sanctum to do so. As I have no access to that room, I cannot do that for you."

Malden nodded. "I expected to have to weather the traps myself. I have proven already—in the palace—that I can master such."

"Indeed. Well, that leaves only two layers of defense we have not discussed. There is the magical barrier that surrounds the house and prevents anyone from entering until they have been passed by the sentries."

"But that's where you come in," Malden said. "You'll lower it for us, when the time comes."

Cythera shook her head. "Had you come to me two days ago that might have been possible. Before Croy made a public spectacle of his desire to slay Hazoth."

On the bed, the knight turned his head away.

"Hazoth," Cythera told Malden, "knows I am connected to Croy. When he heard what happened up on Castle Hill, and what Croy said to Anselm Vry, he took the natural step of ensuring I could no longer lower the barrier. It is done with a certain hand gesture. The gesture can be anything—a sign drawn in the air with one finger, a clap of the hands, it doesn't matter. But you must know it to pass the invisible wall. Hazoth changed the signal and didn't tell me what the new pass sign is."

Malden's heart sunk. "But you escaped tonight."

"The captain of the guards knows the new sign. I was able to convince him to perform it for me—but only when I was not looking. I had to lie to him to get him to do it. I told him that Hazoth required some special incense for a ritual, and that it could not wait until morning. Such a thing has happened before, and the captain believed me. It is not an excuse I can use twice, however. The next time I try, he will become suspicious, and he will ask Hazoth if what I say is true. That would defeat your purpose, I think."

"It would."

Cythera scratched very delicately at one eyebrow. "You will need to give them a reason to lower the barrier."

"I'll find one. Is that all, or have you more bad news for me?"

Cythera smiled without humor. "Only one more item. As I mentioned, Hazoth expects Croy to attack him. He does not fear Croy overmuch—he knows that Croy is more full of bluster than bravado."

The knight cringed on the bed but said nothing.

Cythera glanced his way, then went on. "However, he is taking no chances. If one Ancient Blade is opposed to him, he will align himself with another. Tomorrow I am ordered to go out and find Bikker, and bring him to an audience with Hazoth."

Malden cursed under his breath. "I thought you said Bikker doesn't work for Hazoth."

"He doesn't. I don't know who Bikker's master is, actually. I only know Bikker will definitely come when I call him."

"I don't understand," Malden said.

"Stealing the crown in the first place was Bikker's idea.

Or rather, it was the notion of he who pays Bikker's wage.
Bikker first came to the villa a month ago. He said he represented a wealthy patron who wished to contract for Hazoth's services. Hazoth cannot be bought with coin, but there
are things in this world he covets. One is his privacy. The
king would have him burnt at the stake should he ever learn
the experiments Hazoth performs in his sanctum. So when
Bikker proposed this scheme, Hazoth listened, for Bikker's
employer promised him no one would ever learn what he
was about. Whomever it may be—I have never met the
man, nor learned anything of him—he convinced Hazoth
he could offer his protection in exchange for Hazoth's part
in the plot. It was Bikker's employer who decided a thief
would be found to steal the crown—you know that much, of
course—and then Hazoth would be employed to keep it in
hiding. There really is no safer place for it in the Free City.
The spells on the house prevent any spy from seeing it, and
also any diviner from locating it with magic."

Malden thought of Anselm Vry's hedge wizard, and his
shewstone. It had, as she said, not been able to locate the
crown.

"It would take a small army to besiege the house, and
a more powerful sorcerer than Hazoth—if any exist—to
breach the barrier. If you wanted something of exceptional
value to be kept safe, Hazoth's sanctum is exactly what
you'd need."

"Interesting. I thought Hazoth wanted the crown to study
it. Now I learn he is only an agent for some other player,
who remains unknown. But what, exactly, do they hope to
achieve? Bikker said no one would come looking for
the crown. That the Burgrave would simply have a replica
made, and forget the theft ever happened. We know that was
not the case." And Cutbill had told Anselm Vry that a replica crown would not suffice—but why not? There were so
many questions Malden had no answers for, and imagined
he never might. "What do they want to happen?"

"I am unclear on the specifics," Cythera admitted. "I
do know what they think will happen. The Burgrave will
appear in public on Ladymas, without his crown. Somehow

that will cause the people to riot. Bikker and his employer intend to turn that riot into a full-scale revolt. They mean to whip the people into a frenzy and cause them to overthrow the Burgrave."

"But that would be madness!" Malden said. "The king would revoke the city's charter on the instant. He'd have to, just to restore order. And then every man in Ness would lose his freedom."

"There are many who would benefit from that," Cythera pointed out.

Malden scratched at his chin. His whole skin had begun to itch. He chafed under the yoke of his low birth already. Without the freedom granted by the city's charter, he would be no more master of his own destiny than a farmhand out in the countryside.

He would rather have been confined in the pit, tormented by demons night and day.

"The point of all this," Cythera said, "is that Bikker's employer will not wish the crown to be stolen back. So Bikker will be there when you try. He will be leading Hazoth's guards."

"That's a major problem," Malden admitted. "My plan depended on the guards being sloppy and undisciplined."

"Bikker won't allow that luxury. He'll command them personally."

"And if he should discover me inside the house—"

"I don't know if you should be more afraid of the demon, of Hazoth himself, or of Bikker. Not one of them will let you live."

# CHAPTER SIXTY-FOUR

"I'm afraid I've been of little help, save to make you think this hopeless," Cythera said, straightening the maps on Malden's table. "And now I must go. I do wish you luck—for my mother's sake, at the very least."

"Not for my own?" Malden said. "Don't answer that. Get back safely. If Hazoth realizes what you've done, I can imagine you'll suffer, one way or another."

"Yes," she said. She frowned and looked over at the bed. She sighed deeply, but clearly there was something she had to say to her betrothed before she went. "Croy," she said softly. "Croy, we must—"

The knight jumped to his feet and came over to stand quite close to her. "Cythera, how can I gain your forgiveness? I've caused you nothing but trouble. How can I make this up to you?"

"You owe me nothing, Croy. You made a promise—well, we both made promises, didn't we? But sometimes life gets in the way of promises." She looked away from him. Malden could see how upset she was, but he didn't dare intrude.

Then something odd happened. She met Malden's eye. She looked into his eyes and for a second he thought she was pleading with him to say something. To jump in and save her from the hard thing she was contemplating.

As he had no idea what that might be, he could say nothing.

She sighed again and turned to face Croy.

"I don't want you to get killed," she said to the knight. "And right now, if you try to fight Bikker, that is exactly what will happen. So I want you to tell me that you won't try. That you'll let Malden handle this alone."

Alone? Malden thought. So it's all right if Bikker kills *me*?

"Milady," Croy said, dropping to his knees so hard the

floorboards creaked. "I would die a thousand times in your service—"

"But why? Why would I want that? It would accomplish nothing!"

"But I took a vow to save you and your mother—"

"You and I will have to talk when this is over. If any of us are still alive," she said. "Oh, Croy, don't look at me like that."

The knight dropped his gaze.

"Be of good cheer," she told him. "I don't like seeing you like this. Anyway, perhaps things will work out. Maybe a thief can succeed where a knight failed."

Malden glanced over at Kemper, and they both shook their heads. As much as Malden wished his own troubles gone, he would not have traded places with Croy at that moment.

"I didn't mean that to be cruel," Cythera insisted. She tried to meet Croy's eye but he wouldn't look up at her. "I have not forgotten all you've done for me," she told him. "But you must realize—my mother's safety, and my freedom, mean everything to me."

"And to me," Croy said.

"Then you must free me," she said.

"But that's exactly what I—that is, what Malden and I are trying to do," Croy pointed out.

"An' me, son, don't forget I'm riskin' my neck, too," Kemper insisted.

"And Kemper, too, of course. We're all trying to free you," Croy said.

"No, not from that . . . you infuriating man!" Cythera moved toward the door. "Croy—please. Let me go."

He did look up at her then, with utter confusion on his face. "I would never dream of delaying you."

"Then forgive me already and let me be at peace," she said.

"Forgive you . . . but for what?" Croy asked.

Cythera's face creased in grief. "You don't understand. I can't make you understand. Just tell me you forgive me. Even if you don't know why."

"Of course, then, I forgive you. I forgive you all—there is never anything you could do I would not forgive and forget, on the instant . . ." The knight's voice trailed off. Maybe he was starting to get the point after all.

"I go," Cythera said. "Goodbye. Malden, I'll try and come to see you again the day you make your move. If anything changes before then I'll make sure you know it. I'll have to come to you during the day, when I do my marketing."

"I'll be ready," Malden told her.

Cythera left then. The three men watched her head up the lane toward Turnhill Bridge, which would eventually lead her down to Parkwall. When she was out of sight Croy walked over to the table and slammed it with his fist.

"What did she mean by that? Why would she ask for my forgiveness? What has she ever done to harm me?"

Malden bit his lip and went to sit on the bed. It was late and he just wanted to go to sleep.

"Lad," Kemper said to Croy, sounding sympathetic, "ye've not much experience with women, have ye? I don't mean with yer mother or sisters either. Ye don't seem the type fer whorin', but have ye e'er swived one?" He took his cards from inside his tunic and started shuffling them, rubbing each one with his thumb.

"I've spent most of my life learning how to swing a sword properly. She's not the only woman I've ever . . . cared for, if that's what you mean. There was the dwarf king's daughter. I was her protector, and saved her from a fate worse than death. In reward, she allowed me a single kiss."

Malden couldn't resist asking the question he knew was probably foremost in Kemper's mind as well. "Did she have a beard?"

Croy's face went dark. "No. No, she did not. A bit of a mustache, perhaps. But no more than you'll see on many a human woman's face. And I'll have you know," he insisted, when he saw the two thieves were laughing behind their hands, "she would have given me her body, had I asked. But I had my oath to Cythera to consider."

"Methinks that's not a concern now," Kemper said. He

riffled his cards absentmindedly. "Mayhap ye should go back to yer dwarven princess."

"Speak plainly, damn you," Croy shouted. He was bright red.

"He's saying that Cythera was asking your forgiveness for breaking off her betrothal to you," Malden said.

"She . . . she . . ."

"She didn't want to say it in so many words, because she was afraid of your reaction. She was hoping you would just understand." Malden stared at Kemper. Why did the card sharp have to spell it out for Croy? Now the fool knight would probably spend another day lying abed and staring at the ceiling. Malden supposed if you were rich enough you could afford to be moody. "Enough," he said. "Enough. I'm going to bed. Tomorrow morning I'll need to make a whole new plan. And you," he said, rushing over to Kemper, "quit shuffling those damned cards."

"Here now, boy—"

Malden grabbed the cards out of Kemper's intangible hands and shoved them in his own tunic. "I can't think when you're doing that. Now, to bed, all of us."

He doused the lamp and pulled off his tunic, then got into bed and pulled the blanket up to his chin. He did not, however, get to sleep much that night. Croy made too great a racket with his sobbing tears, and Kemper kept grumbling about his cards.

Enough, enough, enough, Malden thought to himself. Kemper was largely safe from harm, no matter what came. And Croy would be nowhere near the villa when he broke into it. The knight would be useless in any scheme he could imagine.

It was up to him to get the crown back. He could put together a crew but he couldn't truly count on them. He would have to pass the barrier, get through the hallway of traps, and retrieve the crown, all without being detected. He would then need to do that which might be harder, which was to escape with his skin intact.

Even then his troubles might only begin anew. Anselm Vry might be watching him at that very moment, waiting until he recovered the crown before swooping in and taking all credit for himself. Cutbill might have him killed regardless of what happened, just for causing so much trouble in the first place.

And Hazoth would still have his demon, and Bikker would still have his acid-drooling sword. And both of them would have reason to want him dead.

The problems seemed insoluble.

Well, they always had. He had to keep going.

He had to think of something.

Eventually Malden did sleep, despite the companions of his bedchamber. He sank deep and came back only when the first rays of dawn burst in through the gap between the shutters and the window. He opened his eyes, checked that his bodkin was under his pillow where he left it, and only then sat up.

"Good morning," Croy said, smiling down at him.

The knight had never looked happier.

"Hmm," Malden said. He rose and pulled on his tunic, slipped his bodkin into its sheath. Kemper was lying curled in one corner, snoring and farting, dead to the world. Croy, however, was fully dressed and looked like he'd just taken a bath. He had his shortsword out and was polishing it with a cloth.

Malden wondered if the man had gone mad during the night. Maybe Croy was going to kill himself. It was not something he wanted to witness. "You seem recovered from your cares," he said cautiously.

"Oh, yes. Everything is better now," Croy said.

"It is?"

"I had a dream, Malden." He put the sword down and rose to his feet. "No. I tell a lie. It was a vision. I saw Cythera in her bridal veil. I saw myself standing before her, with flowers woven in my hair. And when I woke, I understood. Nothing is broken between us that cannot be repaired. She is merely testing me."

"Is she, now?"

"Indeed. All the stories of knights and dragons and fair maidens go like this. The maiden refuses to accept the knight's troth until he slays the beast. He must prove himself, in combat, before she can truly love him."

"In the stories, you say," Malden went on.

"Yes. So my path is clear. I will earn her love. I will do this by killing Hazoth. A sorcerer is in many ways like a dragon, is he not? I will slay him. And maybe Bikker as well. And anyone else who opposes me."

"Even though she asked you not to," Malden pointed out.

"That," Croy said, with a gleam of insight in his eye, "is the crux of the test. I will free Coruth. And only then will Cythera look on me with favor once more. What do you think?"

"I suppose," Malden said, "that anything is possible."

# CHAPTER SIXTY-FIVE

Malden sent Kemper to keep an eye on Hazoth's villa—discreetly—while he went over to the Ashes to see Cutbill's dwarf, Slag. Croy insisted on coming along. "I must do all in my power to assist you. And when the time comes, it must be my swords that cut the sorcerer down," he said.

"Fine. But for today, you leave them behind," Malden told him.

The knight errant looked at the thief as if he were mad, but Malden stood firm. Eventually Croy did as he was told, unbuckling the swords from his baldric and stashing them beneath the loose floorboards of Malden's room.

"Now," Malden said, "walk from here to the bed and back."

"This is folly," Croy said, but he did it.

Malden listened to the man clank his way across the room as if he were a walking thunder crash. "Are you wearing a mail shirt under your jerkin?" he asked.

"No," Croy said. "What is the point of this?"

Malden studied the man's dress, then made him take off the baldric. The heavy leather sash was covered in buckles and hooks that clinked together when he moved. With the baldric off, Croy made far less noise than he had before—but somehow his swagger still made the floorboards creak and the room shake.

"You are the noisiest man I've ever met," Malden told him. "You'll never make it as a thief."

"But—why in the Lady's name should I want to be one?"

Malden stared at him. "You're trying to steal a crown from a wizard's house. By definition, methinks, that makes you a thief. Or a would-be thief."

"Ah, I see the problem," Croy said, smiling. "No, no, we are not common thieves if we take the crown back from Hazoth. We are liberators. Heroes!"

Malden doubted very much that Hazoth would see it that way. He also wasn't sure how he felt about being called a "common" thief. But he had better things to do than argue. "Walk back this way," he said, and listened closely. "Maybe it's your boots?"

Whatever the source of the clamor, there was no more to be done for it. Together they went out into the street and crossed the Stink, keeping well clear of areas regularly patrolled by the city watch. Should a cloak-of-eyes spot Croy, they would give chase on the instant. Not for the first time, Malden thought of turning the knight over to the authorities just to get him out of the way.

When they reached the Ashes he raised one hand in warning. "Don't jump when you see them. Don't make any quick move. Just stay calm."

"See who?" Croy asked, but he didn't have to wait long to find out.

A boy of no more than eight was standing in the road before them. His face was smeared with ash and he was holding a long shard of broken glass in one hand. He did not speak, of course.

Croy dropped to one knee in the soot. "Why, hello there," he said, and held his hand out toward the boy. There was a piece of crystallized ginger in it.

Where in the Bloodgod's name had he gotten a bit of candy? Malden wondered. Perhaps Croy carried sweets around just in case he ever met a child.

He doubted Croy had ever met a child like this. The boy did not take the ginger. He just stood there watching them, his face impassive. Waiting to see whether he should give the signal that would bring a hundred armed children down on the two of them with murderous intent.

"You know me," Malden told the boy. The boy nodded. "I have business here, with *him*." He tapped his chest above his heart. The boy knew what he meant. "This one," he said, gesturing at Croy, "should not follow me." He mused for a moment. "But I want him in one piece when I return."

The boy shrugged. That was up to Croy and how stupidly the knight acted while he was gone. It was the best answer Malden would get.

"Fair enough." He turned to Croy, who was smiling broadly at the boy and even crossing his eyes to try to make the child laugh. "Croy, he'd rather cut your throat than let you tousle his hair. Just mind yourself while I'm gone. I won't tarry."

He jogged around a corner and into the ruin above Cutbill's lair, where he was quite pleased to see the three oldsters sitting once more on their coffin. "I feared you were driven off by unwelcome visitors, or worse," he said, and clasped Loophole's hand.

"Nay, son, we just scarpered at the first sign of trouble," the old man replied. "That's one of those things you learn how to do if you want to get to be an old thief. I'm glad to see you alive, though. We weren't far away, and when we saw you coming in, we wanted to warn you but there was just no way, not without giving away our own position."

"I understand. It was a close thing but I survived my encounter with the law. Did, ah, did Cutbill tell you anything of what it was about?"

Loophole frowned. "And why would he think to do that? His business is his own. And we don't ask questions, the answers to which might get us in trouble."

"Another sound policy," Malden suggested. Some strange intuition gripped him then—a preternatural sensation that something was deeply wrong. He shot a hand down at his side and grabbed a scrawny arm. 'Levenfingers was trying to lift his purse. Malden laughed with glee. "In this mutable world I am glad to see some things don't change."

"It's good to see you as well, Malden," 'Levenfingers said. Lockjaw just scowled.

"So, have anything big planned?" Loophole asked.

His face was the picture of innocence. Malden shot him a shrewd look, but the oldster simply blinked as if he didn't know anything.

Which told Malden what he needed to know. Cutbill might not have told them what had happened, but Malden knew perfectly well that they had asked the dangerous questions—they had just asked them very discreetly. How much they knew would remain a mystery, but it was next to impossible to keep a secret from these three. "Well, as a matter of fact . . . there's a certain house on the Lady-park Common, a very special house—do you know the one I mean? I shouldn't make it any more plain."

"Then there's only one you *can* mean," 'Levenfingers said with a shiver. "Ooh, I wouldn't want to be in that place in the dark. But good luck to you. No one's ever tumbled that place and lived to tell the tale."

"Even I wouldn't try it," Loophole agreed. "And I'd steal pearls off the queen's throat, were she here now."

Lockjaw mumbled something and then spat into the charred ruins.

Malden and the other two oldsters turned to stare at him.

"I said, 'ware the eye, and that's all I'm saying," Lockjaw snarled. "Now get inside, before someone sees you out here."

"My thanks," Malden told him. Then he headed down

into the lair and was pleased to find that things had returned
to a kind of normalcy. Bellard wasn't there, of course, but
the dice game in the corner was back in swing. More importantly to Malden, Slag was working at his bench, putting
together some kind of collapsible fishing pole.

"It's for taking hats," Slag said, hefting the pole. "You
know the arch under the Royal Ditch bridge? Aye? Windy
fucking place. You crouch up in the supports, in the shadows, and you pluck the hats off the wealthy shits as pass
underneath, and they think the wind took them."

"Brilliant," Malden said.

"It'll fucking do. What do you want now?"

Malden described his needs while the dwarf scowled at
him.

"The climbing gear I have in stock, no problem. This
other thing, though—it'll take a week, maybe more," Slag
told him.

"I can give you no more than three days," Malden told
the dwarf. Even that was pushing things—it meant he would
not be ready until the eve of Ladymas.

"Fine. Now pay me. Gilding metal's not bloody cheap, if
you want it to look right."

"Ah," Malden said. "Well, perhaps I can owe you."

It was commonly believed that dwarves never laughed.
This was perhaps because most people were not so foolish
as to ask them for credit. Slag did laugh at the idea, though
the sound was not like a human laugh. It sounded more like
a squeaky wheel coming free of a rusted axle.

"It really is important," Malden said. "Perhaps there is
some way we—"

"Sod off," Slag said, turning back to his fishing pole.

It seemed to be a day for marvels. Lockjaw had given
away a secret (or part of one), a dwarf had laughed—and
now the door to Cutbill's office swung open and the guildmaster of thieves leaned out.

"I'll pay for the work," Cutbill said.

Malden bowed low toward his master.

"Of course, Malden, you'll pay me back," Cutbill said.

"Of course."

Cutbill shook his head. "At a rather ruinous level of interest."

Malden bowed lower. "Of course," he said again.

His business in the lair done, he headed back to the surface. Perhaps Croy had been filleted by the beggar children, he thought. Or maybe they'd just doused him with lamp oil and set him on fire.

One could hope.

Yet when he returned to where he'd left the knight, he stopped in his tracks and just stared. A score of the vile little children had emerged from their hiding places and gathered around Croy. They sat in the dust, staring up at him with rapt faces.

While Croy told them a story.

". . . the dragon came swooping down," Croy was saying as Malden approached, "with fire in his jaw, ready to roast the king's men in their armor. It was fifty feet from wingtip to wingtip, and its eyes blazed red in the dark as its tail swung out behind it like a pennon flapping in the breeze. And then—"

"It breathed fire and they all died. The end," Malden said.

The children scattered like crows when a boy throws a rock among them. They hurried back into the ruins, worming their way through gaps and crevices too small for an adult to pass through and were gone.

"We have work to do," Malden said. "Come with me."

Croy rose and brushed soot from his breeches. He followed along as Malden headed back into the Stink.

# CHAPTER SIXTY-SIX

"Where are we going?" Croy asked as they headed up Midden Lane, where the city's refuse was gathered and sorted and gleaned for anything of value. The smell was horrible, but Malden knew the watch never came down that road.

"A tavern I know." He stepped in something foul and scraped his leather shoe against the cobblestones. Not that it helped much—in this district the cobbles barely protruded through a thick layer of scum that had hardened into a kind of paving. "There we'll find bravos willing to sign on for coin. I need men who are good with weapons to fight Hazoth's retainers—and Bikker, for that matter."

"I'm going to fight Bikker," Croy pointed out.

"Not on your own—not wounded as you are. Even Cythera could see you had no chance to take him."

"And you think a band of common street toughs can? They won't last a moment against Acidtongue."

"Well, that's what they get paid for. To die for some pointless cause. The place is just up here." Malden lifted his chin and pointed. "They only have to live long enough," he explained, "to convince the guards to lower the magical barrier. If they die once I'm inside, they'll have served their purpose. The coin I give them can go to their mothers, or widows, or orphans, what have you."

Croy shook his head. "No, hold, Malden. I'm quite serious. If you're going to engage Bikker you need more than brave young men with stilettos. I can't allow you to throw away lives just for a diversion."

"It's all I can afford!" Malden turned on the knight. "You need to understand something, Croy. I know you've never wanted for anything in your life. You've never had to want for anything since you were a babe. Any problem that might arise could always be met with a sword stroke or a purse of gold, and so you never had to learn about survival. Down here in the Stink that's all we know. Those children back in the Ashes—they already know more than you ever will. They know when to hold their tongues. And when to cut someone's throat. They know how to stay alive, and they don't count the cost too dear."

"You make them sound like bloodthirsty savages."

"Yes! Because that is what they are. They are perfectly suited to the life they've been handed. I admit it's an ugly life, but it's theirs."

"They just need a little compassion shown them. I always find that's worth more than coin."

"Do you really think a few sweets and a stirring tale of brave hearts will change their plight?" Malden demanded. "They're among the very few people in this city with less of a chance at life than I have. They'll never be anything but beggars. Or thieves if they're lucky. All because their parents died before their time. Tell me where the justice is, there. Tell me why they shouldn't become savages, if that helps them survive."

Croy looked confused for a moment. Then he nodded as if he'd thought up the perfect answer. "There's nothing ignoble about begging," he pointed out, "if that's the station the Lady assigns to you."

"The Lady—" Malden caught himself before he could tell Croy exactly what the Lady could go and do. Knowing Croy, he'd probably take that as blasphemy and burn him at the next convenient stake. "Tell me, Croy," he said instead. "Did the Lady choose me for a thief?"

The look of confusion passed over Croy's face again. "Well, no. Since thievery's a sin in Her eyes. Instead, you should have chosen to enter an honest trade."

"Had I known it was so easy, I would have become a goldsmith," Malden sneered. "You think I didn't try?"

"Not hard enough, apparently."

Malden's blood rushed into his face. How dare this hoddypeak of a knight say such a thing to him. What could Croy possibly know of what had driven him to a life of crime? How dare Croy judge him?

But of course, he knew the answer. In Croy's world the poor were simple, honest folk, too crude in their sensibilities to know anything but how to toil and farm. Knights and lords were there to care for them like kindly parents. To make decisions for them since they were incapable of doing so for themselves.

In Malden's world—the world he'd been seeing ever since Cutbill opened his eyes—people like himself were prisoners, caught inside bars of poverty. And people like Croy were the gaolers who made sure they never got out. The Lady, the goddess Croy worshipped so fervently, was the warden who assigned each inmate to his given cell—and made sure they could never, ever escape.

He wanted to slap the knight across the face, or perhaps just call him names. That, of course, could have been dangerous. Yet he couldn't just let his anger go. Croy had been quietly disapproving of his life ever since they had met. It was time to show Croy what the real world was like. "Come. I wish to show you something."

He didn't have time for this, not really. But the knight had rubbed his nerves raw, and he wanted to rub reality in the fool's face for once. He took him down to the bottom of Midden Lane, where the gleaners labored.

A city the size of Ness generates a mountain of dross every day. Though the citizens never threw out anything that could be cleaned out and reused, still they created junk by the wagonload—after all, wood eventually rots, iron rusts, and eggshells and fish bones are only good for so much. The city's moldy vegetables, broken bottles, and the unusable parts of pig and cow carcasses were collected once a week and piled up in great mounds in Hunnicart Yard. It was a great rotting tower of filth, a palace of decomposition, and the smell rivaled anything the tanner's yards up in the Smoke could generate. The heap of it glistened in the sun, the ugly rainbow sheen of rancid grease.

And on top of it whole families were employed.

The work of the gleaners there was never done. Old men in smocks, matronly women with forearms like pestles, even their scrawny children, all worked the mounds, up to their thighs in ordure, flies thick on their backs as freckles. They dug through the middens with their bare hands, searching for any bit of bone that could be carved into a spoon, any torn and soiled rag that could be shredded for its fibers and used to make paper. There were legends of the gleaners, of the ones who found gold coins in the trash, of the gleaner who pulled a magic spear from the bottom of the pile where it had laid for a thousand years, and used it to slay a giant who threatened the city. If the teller of the tale were leaning over a fire for effect, and trying for maximum realism, he would tell of human bodies found at the bottom of the heaps, still moving feebly and begging for help, and what the gleaners did to make sure the watch never came around asking questions.

A wooden palisade ringed the middens, a high fence hammered together from scrap lumber useful for no other purpose. Dogs barked just inside, ready to attack any intruder, and a guard with a cudgel stood at its gate, overseeing the carts that came down the lane laden with garbage. The guard eyed the thief and the knight warily, as if he expected them to break in and steal all the trash in broad daylight. Probably because sometimes thieves tried just that.

"These people are among the hardest workers in the city," Malden said as Croy stared in horror. "They toil in shifts to make sure nothing is missed. Their bodies are riddled with plague and disease, they eat nothing but thin pottage, and they die years younger than their fellows, because they breathe nothing but foul vapors. They toil in the heat of summer, and when winter comes they shovel the snow off those heaps and sort through the offal wearing fingerless gloves. They don't do this for glory, or honor, or love or justice. They do it so they can eat for one more day."

"That's terrible, Malden," Croy said. "I never knew. Are they slaves that do this work? I thought there were no slaves in Ness."

"There aren't. No one compels them to this life. In fact—the gleaners have a patent from the Burgrave that gives them sole right to do this. If you or I were to wade in there and start looking for treasures in the trash, they would drive us off with clubs and thrown stones. They kill anyone who tries to encroach on their livelihood. Generations of men have worked these heaps—when a father dies, he passes down his writ of patent to his sons, who are glad to have it, for they know they'll be able to feed their children."

"So they have pride in their work," Croy said, lifting his chin. "I find that admirable."

Malden shook his head. "Don't you understand what I'm trying to tell you? There is competition for this. There are people willing to risk their lives to sneak in here in the middle of the night and sort through rusted nails and the guts of slaughtered chickens. Because their own lives are *that much worse*."

Croy was silent for a moment. Then he said, "The Lady gives each of us our lot in life, and her abundance sustains us all. This I believe, and this I live."

Was he quoting from some missal? Malden had never listened to the blandishments of the Lady's priests. Not since he'd realized that Her teachings gave an excuse why rich men should always be rich, and the poor shouldn't try to rise above their stations. Like most in the Stink, whatever religious feeling he possessed was directed toward the Bloodgod, who promised equal justice for all, if only after death.

"You'll never understand, will you? I can't make you see it. Enough. Let us find our bravos and be done. Perhaps you can be of some little use by pointing out which of them are likely to last the longest against Bikker's sword."

Malden hurried away—the prospect of the middens never gave him any joy, nor did he wish to linger in that disease-haunted place.

"Hold," Croy said. "If it's strong arms you need, perhaps I have a better idea."

# CHAPTER SIXTY-SEVEN

The river Skrait was the Free City's lifeblood. It flowed through every district of Ness and was used by every citizen. Where it entered the city in Swampwall it flowed clean and pure, and its water went right into cookpots or horse troughs. As it flowed east it became a dumping ground for refuse too liquid for even the gleaners to cart away. After it bent around Castle Hill it supplied the great manufactories of the Smoke, and then washed away the poisons and the waste products of those workshops. Finally, where it widened out at Eastpool a whole flotilla of fishing boats rode its current out to the sea, some miles off, and then rode it back in the evening, rowing against its flow. Ness owed half its prosperity to the mighty river Skrait, and it had always been counted one of the city's best assets.

Yet for one Burgrave in the city's youth, it must have seemed the city's greatest weakness as well. Where it entered the city on its western end it was open to the world outside. An invading army could send war galleys up the Skrait to attack Castle Hill, or fireships to set the city ablaze. To plug that gap, said erstwhile Burgrave had extended the city wall across the course of the river and forced the Skrait through a pipe no more than ten feet across.

He had not consulted with any dwarven engineers before embarking on this great public work. Had he, they might have told him that narrowing the Skrait where it entered the wall would cause it to flood its banks once it came inside. A wide swath of the lowest section of the city was deluged in the weeks following the pipe's construction, and no one had been able to drain it since.

No man or woman lived in Swampwall anymore. Ferns and tall grasses and willow shrubs had taken over the streets, and only the weathered foundations and a few walls of the old houses remained, sticking up through the shimmering plant life. Here and there a bit of old architecture could be discerned—a listing chimney toppling in slow motion toward a pond, a horse rail sticking up from a pool of mud. As Malden—at Croy's behest—picked his way down the muddy slope into the swamp, he followed the remains of a cobblestone street, the old stones worn as smooth as glass under three inches of stagnant water. There was plenty there to be dragged away and refurbished, yet Swampwall had been left alone far more than the Ashes had. Malden could see why. "This place breathes with fever," he said, sneering as his shoe was sucked down into black goo. "And the flies—Bloodgod take these flies!"

"It's farther down than I thought," Croy said, frowning at the expanse of fen before them. "The last time I was down here I came on horseback. Still, it's just over there."

"What is just over there?" Malden demanded. Croy was pointing to a low point in the swamp, where reeds as tall as houses shimmered in the sun.

"You'll see."

Otters plunked down under the water and crabs scuttled away from their feet as the two men clambered into the muck. It never got past Malden's ankles but clung to him like the hands of dead men in a haunted graveyard. He sloshed noisily through the water and pushed at the reeds with his hands, trying to make a path.

"This is your revenge, isn't it?" he demanded. "You don't like the way I talk to you, as if we were equals. So you bring me down here to remind me I'm the lowest of the low."

"Hardly! I only think—" Croy stopped speaking to pull his boot out of the mud. He had to bend down and get his back into it, and he winced at the pain as his wound grieved him. "I only think that if I told you what we were looking for, you would insist that we run away."

"Ah. So you think I lack courage," Malden said. He drew his bodkin and tried to slash at the reeds but they just bent away from the sharp point. For the first time all day he wished he'd let Croy bring his swords.

"No," Croy said. "No, I've seen you be brave. It's just—well." He pushed a stand of reeds down so Malden could see their destination. "Here we are."

They had arrived at the pipe itself. Its entrance was flush with the Swampwall, which rose up before them toward the sky, its face hidden by generations of creepers. The pipe's bottom was buried in the murk, but it made an arch taller than a man. Sunlight streamed inside its length but only penetrated a few dozen feet before it was lost in perfect gloom.

Malden leaned into the pipe and smelled foul air. Water dripped from the curved ceiling and echoed like drumbeats as it fell into the turbid water below. The bricks that formed the side of the pipe were rotten to the touch and thick with niter.

"In there?" he asked.

"Yes," Croy said. "If he's at home."

"I've heard . . . stories. I think maybe we should run away after all."

Croy strode into the pipe, the sloshing of his steps like thunder crashes. "I thought you might. Come—if you dare."

Malden followed, not wanting to be thought a coward. He was ready to dash back out of the pipe at the first sign of danger, though. Children in the Free City of Ness knew what was inside that pipe, even if the adults claimed it was just a tale. Growing up, he had learned not to believe. Now he wasn't so sure.

Before coming down to Swampwall, Croy had stopped in a chandler's shop and bought a pair of candles still strung together by their wicks. Now he cut them apart with his belt knife and lit one with his tinderbox. The flickering light did little to alleviate the pipe's gloom, but it gave Malden something to follow.

Underfoot, the water was moving at a steady rate, pushing Malden's feet backward as he tried to slog forward. It was hard work just to stand up. If anything, the current grew stronger the farther in they went.

Ahead, the pipe curved to the left and Croy followed, putting one hand against the bricks to steady himself. Malden hauled himself along with both hands and kept up as best

he could. Around the curve they saw that bars had been embedded in the pipe's walls, forming a natural fence against
anyone so foolish as to try to come into the city from the
river beyond. Detritus and bones—animal bones—had built
up into a thick scurf at the base of the grating, so the water
crested as it flowed over and around the debris. It plashed as
it came and made it impossible to hear anything, and it took
a while for Malden to realize that Croy was talking to him.

"—not here, I'm afraid," the knight repeated. "Have to—
back later—"

Malden nodded in agreement and turned to rush out of
the pipe, glad to have an excuse to leave. He hurried around
the curve, the current pushing him along faster than he
could run on his own—and then tripped and fell to all fours
in the water.

His heart thudded painfully in his chest and he couldn't
breathe.

At the exit from the pipe, not more than fifty feet ahead,
a massive figure was silhouetted against the incoming sunlight. Malden could make out few details but he was sure it
was far too big to be human.

# CHAPTER SIXTY-EIGHT

Malden looked to right and left, but there was nowhere
to go. The grating behind him blocked that route of
escape, and the monstrous thing at the mouth of the tunnel
would surely catch him if he tried to run past it. He reached
for his bodkin but didn't dare draw it—what use would it be
against this massive beast?

At his side, Croy peered ahead toward the light, shielding

his eyes with one hand. He said something, but in the roar of the water Malden couldn't hear him at all. The knight lowered his hand, then shouted some kind of strangled war cry—

"Gurrh!"

—and dashed forward, right at the beast, which lifted its arms as if to crush him in a vicious embrace. For the first time Malden saw it was holding something huge, like a tree branch or a stone club.

Pressing himself up against the mineral-stained wall of the tunnel, he closed his eyes, dreading the inevitable crunch as Croy's bones were shattered inside his body. The fool didn't even have his swords.

But the sound he heard next, amplified and distorted by the weird acoustics of the tunnel, was a joyful one. It was the sound of booming laughter and astonishment, the noise of old fellows well met.

Malden opened his eyes and saw the most surprising thing he would encounter that day. Croy and the beast were clasping hands and japing with each other.

"Malden," Croy said, "come out already. Come and meet my old friend, Gurrh."

Malden staggered forward, pushed by the current, and stepped out into the light beyond the pipe's mouth. He got his first good look at the monster and nearly soiled his breeches, even if it was a friend of Croy's.

It stood eight feet tall and had the same general shape as a man, though it was far broader and its muscles were as big as those of a horse. It was covered from crown to sole in coarse black fur, matted with grease, and stinking of death. Only a small patch of skin, from nose to forehead, was exposed, and that was as white as the corpse of a dwarf. Its eyes, while merry, were the size of saucers, and its nose was crooked and bent to one side. On its forehead and around its eyes were inscribed some ancient runes.

The thing it held, which Malden had thought was a club, was in fact the carcass of a river otter missing its head. From the look of the stump, the beast had already gnawed the head off, perhaps by way of breaking its fast.

"Thou," the creature said, with a deep, rasping voice, "art a friend of Sir Croy?" It stuck out its free hand. "Then in the Lady's name thou art well come into my home, gentle. I am called Gurrh; a common sort of calling amongst my clan."

The clan of ogres, Malden thought. This creature, with its honeyed words, was an ogre. There could be no doubt. Tentatively he placed his own hand inside the palm of the giant. The ogre took it carefully and shook it gently.

"But . . . how?" Malden asked.

He might not know many of the details of Skrae's history, but he had the broad outlines down pat. He knew that when his ancestors came over from the Old Empire they found this continent already occupied by the elves and the dwarves. Centuries of warfare had been necessary to clear the land for human habitation—bitter centuries, when the likes of Hazoth scorched whole mountains from the face of the world and dug out broad valleys with their magic, when the seven Ancient Blades were forged to fight the demons that roamed the night. At the end of that hellish time, the elves had found themselves unable to resist the onrushing wave of human might. They made pacts with their own ancestral enemies for aid—the goblins, the trolls, and, most fearsome of all, the ogres. The hairy giants were unstoppable in battle, it was said, their tough hides proof against iron blades and axes. They were able to catch arrows out of the air and throw them back at the archers, or to simply pick up human warriors and pull them to pieces with their bare hands.

He had believed that ogres were gone from the world. They had fought tirelessly, but the elves who commanded them were driven from existence, betrayed by the dwarves they'd once considered their allies. The dwarves had always been practical folk, and knew when to make a treaty with humankind and call it a day. The ogres had been too disorganized to keep fighting on their own. The wizards of that time slaughtered them remorselessly, hunting them down wherever they hid, until none were left. Oh, there were stories of survivals, of individual monsters still roaming the wild parts of the woods, but those were just stories. No one believed them.

"I thought the ogres were as dead as the elves," he said.

"Wherefore hath I survived, when all others like unto this favor hath vanished, as smoke into the air?" Gurrh asked. "When at last the killing was done, when the age of man had come, some few of us did still live. The merciful king Theobalt—may the Lady hold him to her ever-abundant bosom—came unto that wretched scattering and bade us bow at his feet. Many there were who refused, and rose up, and were slaughtered in their turn. Yet not all."

"He swore an oath of loyalty to the crown," Croy explained. "He was given a pardon for all past crimes, under the condition that he would serve the king whenever he was called upon. He took the Lady into his heart and was given a place to live. Here."

"And the Burgrave knows he's here? And hasn't sent pikemen and priests to roust him?" Malden asked. "No offense meant, Sir Ogre," he added, looking up into the giant's face. The ogre smiled, showing a double row of huge peg-shaped teeth.

Croy clapped Malden on the back. "He had a royal pardon. The Burgrave had to respect that. Nor would he evict Gurrh if he could. My friend here does a great service to the city, by keeping the pipe clean and making sure the Skrait flows unchecked into the city. Should any spy or sapper try to come in through the pipe, Gurrh would be here to stop them. He keeps to himself down here in the swamp, living on the wildlife, and shuns human society. Every month or so an envoy is sent down from the palace to check up on him and make sure he has what he needs."

"It must . . ." Malden rethought his words. He had been about to say that it must be difficult, being hated and feared by the people you guarded. He didn't know, however, if the ogre was aware that children told stories of the monster in the pipe and dared each other to see how close they could get before running away. If the ogre didn't know about his own legend already, it would be cruel to enlighten him. "It must be very lonely down here," he said instead.

The ogre shrugged. "I hath the birds to singeth me lullabies, and the trees to whisper their orisons o'er me at night."

Ah, Malden thought. So he has gone mad with the solitude.

"Tell me," Croy said to the thief, "would Gurrh be a useful addition to your crew?"

Malden thought it over. Ogres were notoriously difficult to slay, at least according to the stories. They could shrug off the blows of iron weapons, and only steel had proven capable of piercing their thick hides back in the old days—back when steel was rare as gold was now, before the dwarves started selling it to anyone with enough coin. And Malden had to admit that even Bikker would flinch when facing a rampaging ogre coming toward him with claws a-snatching and teeth a-gnashing.

He looked at Croy and nodded shrewdly.

"Gurrh," Croy said, "the Burgrave has need of you once again."

"Hath he? Certes, an' that pleaseth me, Croy. I serve at his pleasure," Gurrh said, and made a deep bow.

Malden frowned. "You don't want to hear what we're paying?" he asked.

"Thou speak of gold? When milord hath need of me? My arm's his, for the asking, and always shall be. Service hath its own reward."

Definitely crazy, Malden thought. But perhaps—usefully so.

# CHAPTER SIXTY-NINE

A new and much improved plan had begun to come together in Malden's mind. He ran through it time and again, arguing over the finer points with Kemper and looking always for the places where it could go dreadfully wrong. There were far too many of those for his liking, of course. He still did not know who had originally paid to have the crown stolen—Bikker's employer remained mysterious. The plan depended far too much on Hazoth being preoccupied and taking no interest in what happened within his house. And at any time various players—Anselm Vry, the Burgrave, even Cutbill—could decide to move in and put an end to things in whatever way they chose.

Still—if everything went exactly right, and he made no mistakes . . . maybe it could be done.

At all hours he had either Croy or Kemper watching Hazoth's villa, looking for any sign that things had changed inside. From time to time they reported something interesting. Cythera was seen going out to market and carrying on with her usual business, which meant she had not betrayed him to Hazoth (willingly or no). Bikker showed up one afternoon with a haversack over his shoulder and took up residence in the guard barracks. Hazoth never left the house—more's the pity—but at night, ofttimes, strange lights could be seen illuminating the rose window at the front of the villa.

"Like unholy fires blaze in there," Croy said. "They dance and tremble and then are extinguished. None of the guards pay any mind."

Malden knew not what to make of that. Hazoth could be summoning demons until his halls were stuffed with them, for all he knew. Or he could simply be engaged in some esoteric study Malden could never comprehend. He tried not to think of it overmuch, and focused on those things he could control.

The special gear he had tasked Slag with constructing would not be ready until the very day before Ladymas. The job would have to take place that night, which was cutting things very fine. Again, there was nothing he could do about that.

It left him with far too much time to think, however. He spent as many hours as he could going over the plan again and again, rehearsing bits of it with Kemper or taking his own turns watching the villa. But eventually he needed a rest, just a pause to refresh his mind. He headed for one of the few places in the city where he still felt at home: the Lemon Garden, up in the Royal Ditch.

Elody took him in without a word. Perhaps she could see in his eyes how haunted he was by what he was about to do. She led him to her own private rooms and gave him wine to drink and a plate of fresh fruit. "Your generosity is welcome, but I know you can't afford this," he pointed out as he stabbed an apple with his bodkin and brought it to his mouth. "I'll pay you back, I swear."

"Oh, Malden, just having you around is payment enough. You get the girls all excited when you turn up. That makes them frisky and they earn more, so in the end I have a net gain." Elody laughed. "You can have any of them you like, on the house. You just have to ask."

Malden shook his head. "The woman I want isn't here," he said, even though he knew what that would elicit. Elody's face lit up and her eyes glowed as she descended on him, demanding gossip, wanting to know all about this new sweetheart.

"She's not mine," Malden said, a bit glumly. He had come here to cheer himself up but suddenly he was in a foul mood. "Most like she never will be. She was betrothed to a knight, of all things."

"Was?" Elody asked. "But she isn't now?"

"I don't think so—it's all so confusing. I think she might have been trying to tell me something the last time I saw her, but . . . I just don't know. How can I compete with a man like that? He has a *castle*, Elody. A castle."

"Not every woman is so mercenary with her favors as the ladies who raised you," Elody replied. "Some, I hear, would rather have love than money." She looked almost wistful when she said it. "You need to give her what he can't. Is he handsome? Does he have strong arms and golden hair and a noble bearing?"

"Yes, all of those," Malden agreed. "He is a bit dim," he added, though, because he couldn't help himself.

"Then try being clever. It shouldn't be so hard for the likes of you," Elody told him.

"When I'm around her I feel an utter fool. I feel as if I'll never be clever again," Malden confessed.

"Then it must be true love," Elody said, and they laughed together.

She kept him there late that night and plied him with wine. He told her everything—of Cythera's cursed skin, of Croy's pledges and vows. She gave him what advice she could, then sent him home very drunk and a little less fearful. He fell into bed thinking he almost had a chance.

In the morning the early light convinced him otherwise. It was the day before Ladymas. His head was pounding, and he had work to do.

When Slag's things were ready, he went immediately to Cutbill's lair and took possession of them. He tied them up in a bundle and went straight back to his room above the waxchandler's. It was almost noon by the time he arrived. Coming up the stairs he heard voices inside where only Kemper should be, and he opened the door warily, ready to run at the first sign of trouble.

When he saw Cythera inside, sitting at his table, his breath caught in his throat. He nearly *did* run away.

"Kemper, go relieve Croy at his watch," Malden said when he'd divested himself of his gear.

"Lad, it's dull as ditchwater down there. Nothing's like t'happen afore ye get in place."

"Then you shouldn't have any trouble," Malden told him.

Kemper muttered something under his breath. "At least gimme cards back. I miss me little friends."

"Your cards." Malden still had them in his tunic, where they'd laid against his skin for days. "You can have them back when we've got the crown." Their eyes met for one last time, and Malden saw that Kemper was ready. It was important that Cythera didn't know the real reason why Malden had been holding onto the cards. "I don't want to hear you cut off your watch early to find a quick game," he said.

"I ain't stupid, lad," Kemper replied, his chin nodding almost imperceptibly. "I know ye'd have me hide if I did."

Malden nodded and watched his companion leave. When

he was alone with Cythera, he closed the shutter of the window, even though it was a hot day.

"Bikker has the guards complaining," she told him. "He's put them through harsh discipline and punished them severely for any slight change of routine." She shook her head. "He doesn't know what's coming, though. Neither does Hazoth. How are things on your end?"

"Everything's ready and in place," he told her. "As much as it can be. I have completely changed my plans, thanks to your information. We start by sending in our pet ogre to—"

She shook her head. "Don't tell me. If Hazoth questions me, he can make me give up your secrets. Unless I don't have them."

"Very well," Malden said, appreciating her wisdom. "Then let me say only: your mother may be free by morning."

Her eyes flashed with hope. She crossed the room to him, her velvet cloak swishing around her feet. "Malden—thank you," she said. "I know you have your own reasons for doing this. But thank you."

He started to bow but then thought better of it. Instead he held out his hand.

She smiled and held her own just above his palm, a fraction of an inch from touching him. Painted clematis and brier rose twisted around her knuckles. "No—don't," she warned when he leaned over her hand to kiss her fingers. "Please, Malden, for your own sake—"

His lips touched her skin with the gentlest of pressures. Had he only breathed upon her hand she would have felt it more.

"Oh, what are you doing?" she asked, her eyes wide. "Kissing me! Malden, once I tried to kill you with a kiss."

"I've faced less sweet dooms since," he told her. "I'd rather die on your lips than on the point of Bikker's sword."

"You . . . you speak words of love to me."

Malden shrugged. "Are you surprised? I've felt something for you, Cythera, since the first time I met you. Tell me that was just a spell. Some charm your mother cast on you, to make you irresistible to men."

"No," Cythera said.

"Then what I feel is real," he said.

For a moment they only watched each other, like duelists preparing to begin. He knew she felt something as well. She must! Yes, it was complicated. Yes, it was dangerous. But he'd been leading up to this for a very long time.

She took a step back. "One rough kiss would be all it takes to release the magic in my painted skin. It would destroy you."

"I'm not afraid of the curses you've stored up," he said. "A rough kiss would set them off, you say. Yet a gentle kiss is harmless, as we've seen."

She laughed, delighted. "You are quite nimble, aren't you?"

"I could show you just how deft I am," he told her. "If you have an hour before you must return."

"Malden, you dare much."

"Do I offend? Then slap me across the cheek," he told her, daring more.

He touched her wrist with one finger and traced a tattooed creeper that ran up toward her elbow. He kept his fingertip barely in contact with her skin, but enough so. He had lived among whores long enough to gain some basic knowledge of the erotic arts. For instance, he knew that a feather-soft touch on sensitive skin could be more maddening and arousing than a rough caress.

"Croy—" Cythera said, but then closed her mouth as a shudder ran through her body. "Croy—"

"Is not here," he told her. He placed a soft kiss on the inside of her wrist. "How long has it been, Cythera, since you were touched like this?"

"Too long," she said.

"But you remember how it feels, don't you?" It was a careful way of asking an important question.

"Yes," she said. "Before I met Croy, there were . . . others. They were brutes, for the most part. Too quick to take what they wanted, or they were cruel and wanted what I did not wish to part with."

"But what do you want?" Malden asked her. He reached

up and unpinned her hair, letting it fall down across her cheeks.

She sighed. "I don't think any man has ever asked me that question."

"Would you like to sit down? My bed is just over here."

She laughed again, as if she didn't know how to react. "If Croy knew what you were doing, his heart would crack like a badly forged bell."

"Is there any reason why you would tell him?" Malden asked. "I'm no brute, Cythera. Nor am I cruel. You can stop this with a word. But if you remain silent . . . well. The choice is yours."

# CHAPTER SEVENTY

When Croy came in, an hour later, Malden and Cythera were sitting on opposite sides of the room, trying to work out between them who Bikker's mysterious employer might be. There were plenty of likely suspects.

"The king wants the charter revoked," Cythera pointed out. "So he can tax Ness. He must lose thousands of royals every year because of a promise his distant ancestor made to the distant ancestor of our Burgrave."

"He has the motive, I'll grant it," Malden said, "but my money's on Bikker himself."

"What do you mean?"

"I think Bikker invented this phantom employer. I think he knew Hazoth would never take him seriously, or maybe he wanted a scapegoat if everything went wrong. When the city riots, I think he'll present himself as its new ruler. A man with an Ancient Blade could rally the people to his standard—and end the violence. He'd be a hero, and a sure bet to be named as Tarness's successor."

"Is a magic sword all it takes to lead men? Why, then, Croy might be our hidden enemy," Cythera pointed out. She and Malden both stared at Croy as if they'd discovered a dire secret.

Croy stared back as if they'd both gone mad. When they laughed at their little joke, he turned bright red and went to Malden's washstand. "Does it even matter?" Croy asked. He poured water over his hands in the basin and scrubbed at his face. "It's too late to make use of such information. It's almost time to begin. The plan can't be changed now."

"I must go," Cythera said. "You know I cannot aid you once things are in motion," she said, glancing at Malden.

He nodded. "You must act as surprised as anyone. But you'll know it has begun when the ogre appears on your doorstep."

"An ogre," she said. "You mentioned it before. Where in the world did you find one of those?"

"It was Croy's doing, actually," Malden said. "His contribution to the scheme. You should see this creature in calmer times, Cythera. It has the voice of a poet and a soul devoted to the Lady, but it looks a fright—twice as big as a man, covered in dark fur, its face engraved with ancient and baleful runes." He laughed. "It should give the guards a good scare."

"Yes, but maybe not much else," she said, looking concerned. She glanced over at Croy, who didn't meet her gaze. "Malden," she said, "these runes. Do you remember what they looked like?" She took a piece of charcoal and drew on one of his maps. "Were they like this, do you think?"

"Yes, exactly." Malden smiled. "I'm sure they say something menacing, like, 'I am your death' or 'Face me at peril.' "

"Not exactly. It's a curse your ogre wears on his face, but not for his enemies. It's for himself. One of the simpler curses, actually, and very effective. Translated, the words you see here would read: 'An you harm any, thou shalt perish.' "

Malden's eyes went wide. "What's the nature of this curse?"

"It's commonly used on paroled prisoners or creatures who have killed men in the past. If your ogre hurts a human being—even in self-defense—the runes will grow hotter and hotter until they burn right through his skull." She wiped her fingers quite carefully on the hem of her cloak. "I don't know your plan. I don't want to know your plan. But if you were counting on this ogre to fight the guards or Bikker, I only hope you have a contingency up your sleeve."

"Thank you, Cythera," Malden said, between lips pressed together to stifle a shout. She nodded and left his room, headed back toward the villa before she was missed. When she was well gone, Malden slowly turned to face Croy.

"You knew all this, of course," he said, quite carefully.

Croy didn't answer directly. Instead he went to kneel above the loose floorboards where his swords were still hidden.

Malden was faster. He drew his bodkin and had its point at the small of Croy's back before the knight could reach for his weapons.

"The success of my scheme depended on that ogre," Malden said. "There's no time now to find a replacement. Have you betrayed me, Croy?"

"Are you calling me faithless?"

Malden almost concurred. Then he remembered that it was the same word Croy had used to describe Bikker—the word that started a blood feud between the two of them. "I'm asking a question. Did you make some deal with Hazoth, to foil my plans? Or perhaps you work for the same master as Bikker."

"Never," Croy said.

"Then why, exactly, did you not tell me that your ogre was hobbled?"

He watched the muscles in Croy's neck tighten. "I am not a liar, by inclination or by practice," the knight said. "But I was left with no choice."

"Speak plainly!"

Croy sighed. "Don't you understand? If I'm to recover

Cythera's trust, I must earn it. I must be the one who frees her and her mother."

"I've been generous enough to let you play a part, but that's all," Malden pointed out.

"The role you've set for me in your scheme is meaningless. I am to stand as a lookout, and nothing more. How can that show Cythera the depth of my devotion to her? It should be *me* fighting for her freedom. It should be my arm, my sword, that strikes the telling blow. And no other man has a right to fell Bikker. That is my duty, and I will perform it."

"You're wounded," Malden said. He did not allow the point of his bodkin to shift even a fraction of an inch. "Even at the fullness of your strength, you're no match for Bikker. He would have bested you up at the palace if the demon there hadn't diverted his attention. He would have killed you then. Are you so hot to die at his hand now?"

"Love will strengthen my arm," Croy said. "Justice will be my shield."

Malden chuckled, and the point of his knife bobbed up and down, just a hairbreadth. Apparently it was enough.

Croy shifted under Malden too fast to follow. One of his legs kicked out and knocked Malden's feet from under him, and the thief fell backward against the bed. It was all he could do to stop his fall with his free hand, while keeping the bodkin pointed in Croy's direction.

Before he had recovered himself, Croy was looming over him with his shortsword in his hand, the point just under his chin. The blade shone so bright Malden could see his own shocked expression in its surface.

"I may be wounded. I'm still an Ancient Blade. You can mock my ideals all you want, thief. You can't deny my skill."

"I suppose not," Malden said. "Very well. Who am I to deny you your own destruction? You fool. Maybe you've cost us everything by this deception." He wanted to spit in disgust.

"I can slay Bikker. I must!"

"As you wish it. Take the ogre's place. Die, if that's what you want. As long as you survive a minute against the retainers, that's all I need."

"You'll find that even if I'm not as strong as Gurrh, when it comes to swordplay I am matchless. Anyway, you have no choice." Croy lowered his sword. "It's almost time to begin," he said. "There's no time to find a replacement. Not even a band of bravos."

Malden nodded. He was still looking into the sword's blade, meeting his own eyes in reflection. "Yes," he said. "Strong. He's still very strong, even if he can't fight." It was like the sun had just come up in his mind. He saw it now, a way to make this work. "Croy, I've just had an idea that might save both our lives. Can you get word to the ogre and give him new instructions? He may have his uses yet."

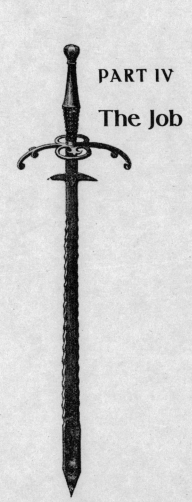

# PART IV

# The Job

# INTERLUDE

Slag the dwarf climbed up into one of Cutbill's chairs and puffed out his cheeks. "That boy Malden doesn't have a fucking chance, does he?"

Cutbill had a great deal of respect for his dwarf. The diminutive craftsmen had a foul mouth, it was true, and a fouler disposition, but his work was immaculate and it allowed Cutbill's thieves to do things that should have been impossible. So he showed the dwarf the signal honor of putting down his pen before he looked up and said, "Probably not."

Slag nodded and scratched at his wild beard. "I just heard from Loophole. He thinks you don't know that he's been asking around, which is just fucking stupid. But he says Anselm Vry is turning half the city arse over eyebrows looking for the—"

Cutbill arched one eyebrow. His office was one of the most secure places in the city, and there should have been no chance of any unwanted ears listening at his doors, but in a world where the bailiff had a wizard with a shewstone at his disposal, no conversation was truly safe.

Slag nodded and held up his hands in apology. "—for the thing," he concluded. "Vry's watchmen are tearing open every damned door in the Stink, as if some poor bastard of a cobbler is hiding it in his privy. You think his wits are buggered? Seems like he's lost his mind with terror."

"Oh, no," Cutbill said. "What he does makes perfect sense. He will fail to find it, of course, but then he can at least show the Burgrave that he made an honest effort. He's looking in the Stink rather than the Golden Slope for the same reason he made no real attempt to recover it from its current location—because he's afraid of the occupants. The rich citizens in their mansions up by Castle Hill would never put up with such outrages. The poor folk living under the Smoke can't afford to be as particular."

"So he won't find it in time, and Malden doesn't stand a chance either."

"I wouldn't say that. I'd say his chances are quite grim. But I picked Malden for a reason, Slag. It wasn't because he showed such ability when he robbed Guthrun Whiteclay. It's because he has a brain in his head. One sees that so rarely in the men who come through my door. If anyone can pull this job off, it's Malden."

"That why you're sitting here, still scratching fucking notes in your fucking book?" Slag asked, gesturing at Cutbill's ledger. "Like any other day. You might be dead tomorrow morning. Shouldn't you be out whoring or drinking yourself sick?"

"I imagine if I am to have my throat cut on the morrow, a bad hangover or a case of the crotch rot would not, in point of fact, improve the experience. But no, I am not working so late because I expect Malden to succeed. I am working in case he does not. This ledger is more than just a record of accounts. It is my life's work. It can never really be done, but I am attempting to make it as complete as possible. It includes a number of instructions that are to be carried out if I do meet my creator in the morning. I called you in here specifically because I need your help with that. Later tonight I want you to vacate the premises well before Anselm Vry and his soldiers arrive. And I want you to take this book with you. There are a number of people who should see it: the Pirate Queen of the Maw Archipelago will be most interested, for one. The Great Chieftain of the barbarians, Mörg the Wise, absolutely must be allowed to read page three hundred and nine if we are to avoid a war with his people."

"Such desperate fuckers as them need to see the guild's records of payments and income?" Slag asked. The gleam in his eye was one of distinct curiosity. Few things could break a dwarf out of his dark moods, but a juicy mystery was near the top of the list. "What's really in there, then?"

"You're free to read it and find out," Cutbill said. He turned the ledger around so it faced Slag. The dwarf made his way across the room and climbed up on Cutbill's desk to see better. Reading along upside down, Cutbill watched as Slag's eye ran down the endless columns of numbers to the spidery glyphs that appeared in the margins of each page. Slag stabbed the coded symbols with one delicate finger.

"Huh. Fucking clever. It's in cipher."

Cutbill favored Slag with a thin smile. "One I'm sure you could break, given enough time."

"That's not why you want me to take the book, though."

Cutbill shook his head. "No. I've chosen you for this task for a very simple reason. When Anselm Vry comes here tomorrow, he will kill every member of the guild he can get his hands on—with one exception. The law will not allow him to kill you." It was true. Any man who turned his hand against a dwarf, so much as to slap him in anger, would forfeit his own life. It was the treaty humanity had made with the dwarves when they allied against the elves at the end of the long-past wars. It was a treaty never broken or ignored, simply because only dwarves knew the secret of making steel, and that made them more valuable to the king than his own subjects. "Furthermore, you are allowed to travel anywhere in the continent you please, and no one can stop you. You are, my friend, the *only* one I can trust with this duty."

"Sure. That's what they always say about the shit jobs." Slag squinted at Cutbill as if the guildmaster of thieves were either an exquisite gem or a worthless piece of paste and he wanted to decide which. "I never had a blasted clue before tonight. But there's more to you than people think, ain't there?"

"On the contrary. I am exactly what I appear to be."

"Oh?"

"I am a man who has very good reason to keep his secrets safe." Cutbill smiled once more. "Now I'll ask you to leave me, if you'll be so kind. I have a great deal to get down before they come for me. Oh, one last thing: if, despite the obvious odds, Malden does succeed somehow—I must ask you to never mention this conversation to him, or anyone else."

"Sure. If that happens, I'll be so surprised I'll probably bust a vein in my skull and forget all about it anyway."

"I do so admire the optimism of your people," Cutbill said.

The dwarf headed for the door. He had work to do of his own. "Ah, sod off, you bigoted bastard," he replied.


# CHAPTER SEVENTY-ONE


It was the night before Ladymas, one of the most important fair days of the year. Though dark had come and the streets were unsafe as ever, still the Free City of Ness bustled with activity. There was much to prepare and make ready before dawn.

In the Ladychapel up in the Spires, the junior priests brought out the giant gold cornucopia that would be the centerpiece of the morning's procession. They polished it with soft cloths until it shone like the sun, even in the light of a single candle. Others started loading it with the hundreds of small cakes and pieces of fruit that would be thrown to the poor as it was carried along. The lesser icons—the rudder, the globe, and the wheel—were touched up with gold paint to hide the chips and scratches where the wood beneath showed through. The senior priests kept vigil at the altar, intoning plainsong prayers and staying on their knees all night before Her sacred image.

In Market Square, vendors fought over the best places to set up their stalls. Most of the disputations were only squalls of words, with the occasional brandishing of a piece of paper as one or another claimed the right to a certain favorable spot. These pieces of paper were of limited utility, however, since most of them had been written by one of Cutbill's expert forgers. The few authentic ones sold for ten times the price, but in the presence of so many counterfeits, they could not be honored either. Occasionally a fistfight broke out, which the few watchmen on hand had trouble breaking up. There was real money to be made at a fair day, after all.

On the Golden Slope, where most houses were already deserted, the last few wealthy citizens supervised their servants as they packed chests full of clothes and food for the next two days. Anyone who could afford to, fled the city during fair days and locked their houses up tight, because it was commonly believed that crowds spread plague. Some of Cutbill's best agents were on the rooftops, making notes.

Down in the Smoke the giant furnaces were banked, a laborious process that was only performed twice a year. The fires that smelted and shaped the Free City's iron had to be throttled down slowly and precisely, lest the forges cool off too rapidly and crack under the stress. Normally the furnaces were kept roaring all through the day and night. The law required that all fires be put out during fair days, however. During the festivities the population of Ness would triple, and should any house catch fire there would be no way to check the conflagration before it spread across town.

In the Stink every shrine of the Bloodgod was holding late services, accepting the small sacrifices of fish and meat the people brought. They lined up for blocks just to leave their scraps and make the proper signs. The poor couldn't afford to displease either god or goddess, and so made a point of placating both in quick succession. At dawn they'd be on their knees in the little chapels of the Lady that dotted their neighborhoods, trying hard to stay awake through the morning prayers.

The watchmen took full advantage of the piety of the poor to break into more of their homes and rummage through their meager belongings. No crown was discovered in these searches, but plenty of copper coins and pieces of cheap jewelry were. It was a holiday for the watch as much as for everyone else.

At every inn the house was full, and travelers were forced to bed down in the stables, or sleep six to a bed in the house, and there was no wine to be had, only new ale and strong beer.

At the Lemon Garden, Elody opened her doors and hung a brass cornucopia over her door, advertising the special rate she gave to pilgrims far from home. She'd brought in extra girls for the increased foot traffic—honest women every other day of the year who wore masks tonight to make a little extra cash, since they could find cheap expiation in the morning for any sins they committed this night.

On the Goshawk Road opposite the northern wall of Castle Hill, the gambling houses closed their doors—but not their tables. The devoted card players and dicers inside kept their voices low in case the watch was listening, but that just drove the stakes higher. Fights broke out there just as in Market Square, but these ended much more quickly. Either the proprietors of the gaming houses ejected the brawlers with due dispatch (if they were of the more common sort), or (in the case of the gentry) helped the combatants make assignations for future duels. To be held only after Ladymas, of course. No nobleman would be so uncouth as to shed blood on the Lady's sacred day.

In the Ashes the beggar children who watched over Cutbill's lair gathered in a burned-down chapel and worshipped their own image of the Lady. It was only a charred piece of an old tavern sign that showed a less-than-divine woman holding a giant ale tankard, but the faith in the children's eyes burned no less bright for it. If anyone needed to court fortune and abundance, it was these urchins.

In the Ladypark a yale bleated as it was brought to bay by a pack of feral dogs. It turned to face them with its wicked swinging horns, but it was severely outmatched. If the yale knew it was sacred to the goddess, it didn't know how to call upon her aid.

In a rarely used chapel on Castle Hill, a certain figure

sat with a bottle of wine and a good book. He would not be sleeping that night—at least until he heard from his fellow cabal members, Bikker and Hazoth. When he was certain the ungrateful thief was dead and Ghostcutter was ready to be passed on to a new owner, then he might relax—but only for a moment, before the real work of the conspiracy began.

All across the city hymns were sung. They could be heard through every window and on every street corner.

Everywhere people made merry, or atoned for sins, or simply enjoyed the warm summer's night.

And on Parkwall Common an ogre walked sedately across the grass and up unto the gates of Hazoth's villa. The guards there challenged him and shouted for him to leave, but he ignored them, and all else. As if he'd found a pleasant place to spend the evening, the ogre sat down on the grass just beyond the gate, and watched the house with his massive, staring eyes. After a while he folded his hands in his lap. He made no attempt to enter, nor gave any sign of violence. Yet a lightning stroke touching the rose window would have elicited less surprise.

# CHAPTER SEVENTY-TWO

At the side of the house, Malden crouched with Kemper beneath a willow bush. He peered through the dark trying to see what was happening. There were torches guttering at the gate, and he could make out the ogre plain enough, but he needed to see how the guards reacted to Gurrh's presence.

"Ye'll know when it's time, lad," Kemper soothed.

"We need to be ready to move at a moment's notice,"

Malden insisted. "Are you prepared? You know what you must do?"

"Aye. Now quit yer jawin'. Look, there. Is yon bastard this Bikker ye're so afeared of?"

"It is," Malden said, grinding his teeth together. The big swordsman was leaning against the side of the villa, scratching at his beard. He did not look well pleased, which was comforting. He kept craning his head around the side of the house to see what the ogre was up to. Which was nothing.

Malden had foreseen this. It was quite possible that Bikker would see through this phase of the plan. The ogre couldn't get through the barrier any more than Malden could. The guards were completely safe inside—and of course, they would be perfectly safe even if the barrier were lowered. Bikker might know the meaning of the runes on the ogre's face and realize he had nothing to fear from the monster.

Yet it would take a man with ice water in his veins not to worry when such a brute showed up on his doorstep for reasons unknown. Bikker was smart, he was disciplined, but Malden was counting on the fact that he had hot blood in him. If Bikker wouldn't respond to the ogre's presence, Gurrh had been told to make him react.

"Now, Gurrh," Malden said, as if the ogre could hear him.

Perhaps he could—who knew what the hearing of an ogre was like? Without apparent provocation, Gurrh rose to his feet and went over to the fence that ringed the villa. He grasped one of the wrought-iron uprights and tore it loose from the crossbeams with a noise like a demon being dragged out of the pit—a groaning, shrieking sound that set Malden's hair on end. The upright came loose with a clang, and suddenly Gurrh was holding what looked very much like a wicked spear.

The ogre, smiling broadly, swept it through the air and brought it clanging along the other uprights of the fence. The noise was rhythmic and intense and impossible to ignore. A guard shouted for the ogre to stop but his voice was lost in the clamor.

It was enough, perhaps. The guards rushed backward, away from the fence, caterwauling in their fear. Just as Malden had hoped, at the side of the house Bikker pushed himself away from the wall and came striding out toward the gate.

"You there," the hairy knight called. "You—beastie. What in the name of all that's perverse do you think you're doing?"

Gurrh shrugged and brought his spear around for another pass. The clanging, banging noise was even louder this time. It was enough to hurt Malden's ears, even so far away. Gurrh seemed to pay no attention to Bikker's demand—he looked for all the world like some mindless brute who had just taken a fancy to making that dreadful racket for his own reasons.

The fact that he was obviously there for some distinct purpose must, Malden hoped, be driving Bikker mad. Bikker might be a ruffian, but he was also a trained soldier, and Malden had learned from Croy that the one thing soldiers hate more in the world is an enemy doing something they don't understand.

"The master of this house doesn't want to be disturbed," Bikker announced. "I don't know your game—though I can guess your owner, I think. Leave now or I'll set my dogs on you."

Gurrh made a third racket, and suddenly Bikker was moving, taking long strides toward the barrier. "Lower this damned thing," he shouted, and the captain of the guard came running forward to salute. "You three—and you, boy, drive this thing off."

The four guards he'd chosen balked at the task, but it didn't take more than a few clouts to get them moving. Bikker must have really put a fear into them, Malden thought. They waited for the captain to make the necessary gesture to lower the barrier, then dashed out through the gates brandishing their polearms. They jabbed and thrusted at the ogre the way a swain pokes at a pig to scare it into motion, but the ogre easily fended off their blows with his spear. One glaive blade got past his defense and scored a hit on his hairy stomach, but Gurrh just laughed. The blade bent and then snapped off its pole.

"Sadu's blood an' balls," Kemper said, astonished.

"All the old stories say how hard it is to slay an ogre, that no normal weapon can cut their furry pelts. Come—this is our time to act. We must be quick."

The thief and the card sharp ran across the grass toward the fence. Malden slipped through between two uprights while Kemper just walked through them. The two of them kept very low as they hurried across the garden. Malden was terrified that Bikker would turn around and see them, but his attention seemed absorbed by the ogre.

This was exactly according to plan. Thanks to Croy's recklessness, Hazoth had come to expect an attack on the house—a direct, frontal attack of the kind a knight would make against a fortress. The ogre appeared to be providing exactly that.

Which was not to say this was going to be easy.

Malden and Kemper slipped around the back of the house. Only one guard remained in the garden, and he was doing his best to see what was happening at the front while not technically deserting his post. Bikker had trained and disciplined these guards into a formidable fighting force, but he'd only had a few days to do it. He could not have completely broken all their bad habits in that time.

The back door of the house, which led into the preparatory room behind the dining chamber, was in deep shadow. There were no torches or other lights back there—they would have served no purpose but to ruin the night vision of the guard. Even better, Malden saw that the high window above the preparatory door was open to catch the night air, as it had been a quite warm day. Perfect.

Kemper walked through the door and disappeared. Malden took a length of rope from around his waist and uncoiled it. It was not very thick, nor even particularly strong, but Slag had dipped one end of it in molten silver—at Cutbill's expense. The silver gave that end some extra weight, so that Malden could toss the end up and through the preparatory window. He let the rope play out, then grasped it tight when he felt it go taut. The other reason for the silver was to allow Kemper to hold it. He braced Malden from inside while the thief climbed up to the preparatory window and through. He clambered down in the darkness and dropped a few feet to the floor. There was just enough light to see Kemper's teeth glinting in the gloom.

Malden pulled the rope through the window and tied it once more around his waist. No point leaving it there where the guard might notice it—he didn't intend to leave the house by this same window.

He felt a clammy coolth pass through his elbow—that was Kemper's touch—and reached inside his tunic to take out Kemper's cards. They were a bit damp with Malden's sweat. He handed them to Kemper, who took them without a word.

Together they made their way through the dining chamber and into a corridor that ran from one end of the villa to the other. Windows along one wall shed enough moonlight to show a hall furnished with small tables, a chest of silver plate, and thick carpets on the floor that would soak up the sound of footfalls.

Kemper gave Malden a silent salute, then started off down the corridor. He paused at one of the tables and on its top laid a card, the two of hearts. Next he stopped at the chest. Its lid creaked as it opened. Malden tensed and prepared himself to run, but a mouse might make as much noise. Kemper slipped the seven of acorns inside the chest and closed it again, this time without a sound.

All correct. Malden parted ways with Kemper then, heading back through the dining room and into a servant's closet. A narrow flight of wooden stairs led up to the second floor from there.

A window pierced the wall by the stairwell, and through it Malden could hear the ogre laughing and Bikker shouting terse orders.

Perfect.

# CHAPTER SEVENTY-THREE

The second floor of the villa was as silent as a tomb. Malden reached the top of the stairs and stepped into a hallway with a single candle burning at its far end. There was just enough light to see the doors on either side. Framed pictures hung on the walls here, and he stole a glance at one, but it made his head hurt so he looked away quickly. It didn't seem possible that the woman in the picture would be able to accommodate the giant insect she'd taken as a lover. He did not intend to waste time resolving how it was done.

Kemper had explored this floor and found little of interest—bedrooms, a garderobe or two, linen closets. Malden made his way down the carpeted hall as noiselessly as possible, ignoring the doors until he saw one begin to open. Instantly he pressed himself against the wall and pulled his hood down over his eyes so they would not shine in the candlelight.

He heard a woman's sigh as the door opened fully, letting pale light out into the hall. The woman's shadow was projected on the wall opposite, and he could see from the silhouette that it was Cythera.

He would gladly have made himself known and spoken with her. She could provide valuable information that would aid him in his skulduggery. On the other hand he had far better reason not to let her see him. If he startled her, she might cry out. At the very least, if she spoke to him, someone else might hear them. He could not afford to take that chance.

So before she stepped out into the hall, he took the great risk of opening the door nearest to him and slipping inside. He did it quickly but without making any noise at all. Luckily it seemed the room he'd entered was empty—an unused bedroom, with the furniture all shoved up against one wall and covered in cloths. He pressed his ear against the keyhole of the door and listened as Cythera stepped out into the hall and walked away. He counted to one hundred in his head before he considered leaving the empty bedroom again.

When he was certain it was safe, he tried the door's latch—and found that it had locked behind him. He wanted to curse but didn't risk the sound. What kind of door locked automatically from the inside? It made very little sense to him. Whoever stayed in this room would be trapped until someone came along and let them out.

He turned and looked again at the furniture against the wall. There was a bed, a clothes press, a basin on a stand, a low stool—all common enough fixtures. Something about the bed looked odd to him, though, and he twitched the cloth back to have a closer look. It was then he saw the manacles bolted to the headboard, and the bloodstains on the straw-filled mattress. He let the cloth go in disgust. Curiosity got the better of him, though, and he lifted the lid of the clothes press.

Inside, instead of the garments he'd expected, he saw trays full of rusted steel implements. He recognized only a few of them—a saw, a hammer, a variety of shears and pincers in various gauges. A great many knives. There was one tool with a watertight leather bulb at one end and a long tube on the other, and something else that resembled a meat hook stretched out long and thin.

He could hardly guess at their purpose, but then something occurred to him. He looked to his left and saw it again as if for the first time. There was one piece of furniture in the room he definitely recognized, from his childhood. The stool. A low three-legged stool about twelve inches high. It was the kind of stool midwives used.

When Malden realized what that meant and where he was, he wanted to close his eyes and just make this all go away. He wanted to jump in the Skrait and drown, because at least then he could die clean.

He was wasting time. He closed the press and pulled the cloth back over the bed exactly as it had been, then went to the door and unwrapped the lock picks hidden in the hilt of his bodkin. The lock on the door was a simple mechanism, easily defeated, and soon he had the door open. Yet as he was stepping back into the hall and closing the door behind him, again a sensation, unbidden and very much unwanted, came to his mind.

Malden had the distinct impression someone was coming up behind him. Was it Cythera, returning from some errand? Or a less welcome intruder? He flattened himself against the wall, knowing his only chance was to hide in the semidarkness of the hall. It was a forlorn hope. The light from the candle was plenty to see by—but his reflexes were such he couldn't help but try to hide.

It turned out not to matter.

The thing coming up behind him wasn't human. It was only roughly man-shaped in outline, and seemed to be made of living smoke. It left misty footprints of condensation on the floor where it walked, but it passed Malden without even turning its head—assuming that lump at its top was some kind of head. It walked right past him and into the stairs and then was gone.

He had no idea what that thing had been. A demon of some manner? A ghost? A spirit of the upper air?

More to the point, had it seen him? Could it see at all? Would it warn Hazoth as to his presence? He couldn't know. He could only hope that by keeping still and not touching the thing, he'd somehow escaped notice.

If that was incorrect, he was sure he would find out very soon.

With a shudder, he stole down the hallway, toward the gallery at its far end.

On that gallery he chanced a quick look down at the enormous sphere of iron by the grand staircase. The egg of the demon. It remained motionless and seemingly quite inert— a thin stream of powdered rust fell from one of its sides, but otherwise it could have been dead inside. That was a good sign, of course—it suggested Hazoth was as of yet unaware of his presence in the house—but he couldn't help but associate it with what he'd seen in the locked bedroom. What he might call the birthing room.

Enough. He was frightened enough without adding to his

load of troubles. A flight of stairs led up from the gallery to the third floor, and his destination. He crept up the risers, keeping close to the banister, where the steps were least likely to creak.

He didn't have much time left, perhaps less than an hour. When Croy and the ogre were both dead, slain by Bikker if no one else (as he was certain they would be), the barrier would be closed again and he'd be trapped. It was crucial that he find the crown and escape before that happened.

# CHAPTER SEVENTY-FOUR

Gurrh made no attempt to fight the guards, but they couldn't harm him either. He fended off most of their attacks with ease, and when one of them did manage to strike him, he either shrugged off the blade or just laughed as if he was being tickled. From his hiding place, Croy watched Bikker get more and more red in the face.

"All of you, get out there," Bikker ordered. The guards rushed forth as the barrier was lowered once more, all except the captain.

"But sir, why aren't you leading the men?" the captain demanded. "Surely your sword would make short work of that thing."

"I can't very well abandon the house, now can I? Did it occur to you that this might be a trick? Do as you're told."

"Yes, sir," the captain said, and hurried out to join his men.

Gurrh grabbed a halberd that came whistling toward his nose and snapped its haft like a twig. He buried the blade end in the grass by his feet. Its owner tried to smash at the

ogre's eyes with the broken length of wood in his hands, but
to no avail.

Two of the guards got around behind the ogre to attack
from the rear, but Gurrh didn't even turn to engage them.
One of them sunk a military fork into the thick matted hair
near Gurrh's spine, but the ogre only rolled his shoulders as
if he were having his back scratched. The other aimed his
pikestaff at Gurrh's left kidney, and this time Gurrh did respond, but only by shifting slightly to one side so the guard
staggered past him with the momentum of his charge.

The flanking maneuver was not without result, however. As Gurrh sidestepped, a guard with a glaive saw his
opportunity and jabbed upward, right past the metal fencepost Gurrh was using to parry. The long curved blade of
the glaive slipped through Gurrh's defense and caromed off
the giant's cheek. A dark line of blood appeared on Gurrh's
preternaturally white skin.

Croy gasped. He'd been convinced that the ogre was invulnerable. He'd never have suggested Gurrh for this job if
he'd thought there was a chance the gentle creature could
be hurt. It was all he could do not to run out of hiding and
rescue Gurrh from his attackers.

Not that the ogre really needed the help. Gurrh grabbed
the glaive away from the retainer and threw it into the dark
grass behind him. Its owner raced after it. The giant blocked
two more attacks, then reached up with his free hand and
patted at the wound on his face.

"Thou hast bloodied me," the ogre said. He seemed more
surprised than angered. He brought his iron spear around
and put a deep notch in the wooden haft of a billhook that
might have touched his chest if its wielder had been faster.
"I thought it not possible."

Croy bit his lip. The ogre's face was his one weak spot—
the one part of his body not covered by the thick protective
hair. This fact was not lost on the retainers. They might be
sell-swords, cheaply come by and poorly trained—but some
of them, at least, were not fools.

Suddenly every attack was aimed at Gurrh's eyes or nose
or mouth. The severed end of a polearm (Gurrh had already

broken off the iron blade) slammed into the ogre's lower lip, and more blood leaked from the white flesh there. A guard with a bow started firing arrows toward Gurrh's eyes, releasing and notching a new arrow as fast as he could. Glaive and halberd blades were jabbed and swung at Gurrh's face with great rapidity, and it was all the ogre could do to keep them from slicing his features to ribbons.

It was time. Croy could wait no longer. He would defend his friend with his own blades. There was no curse stopping him from fighting. Malden's original plan had required him to stay behind as a lookout while Gurrh took on Bikker and his men, but Croy refused to accept that role.

He would show Cythera what he was capable of. That she could trust him—that he could save her, and her mother, if he was just given a chance. Enough skulduggery! Enough thievery! This was work for a real knight.

Croy slipped his shortsword out of its sheath and brought it to a low ready position. He stood up from the bush where he'd been crouching like a footpad. Enough, he thought. Enough skulking, enough lurking.

It was time to fight.

## CHAPTER SEVENTY-FIVE

Croy's wound throbbed as he strode across the grass. It did not pain him, but only sought to remind him that he was not at the full extent of his powers.

He ignored it.

The ogre was beset now, with guards on every side trying to bring him down. They focused their attacks on his vulnerable face, and it was all the ogre could do to protect his eyes. Already he was bleeding from a dozen cuts on his cheeks and forehead.

"Enough," Croy said, loud enough to be heard over the clamor of battle.

His announcement did not have the effect he'd hoped for.

One of the guards looked over and saw him, but the rest maintained their attack on Gurrh. Apparently the guards still thought the ogre was the main danger, even with the presence of an Ancient Blade on the field. Well, Croy thought, he had taught plenty of men to respect the sword he carried and the office it represented. He snarled and lifted the round oak shield he'd strapped across his left forearm. Normally he fought with two swords and no protection, but his left arm wasn't strong enough yet to hold a sword properly so he'd chosen the shield instead. It had an iron boss in its center and a strip of steel around its rim. He'd trained with every manner of shield made by man or dwarf, and he knew exactly what to do with them. Just now, he clanged his shortsword against the boss, making a noise as loud as a ringing bell. "Over here," he shouted.

That got a few more of the guards looking at him. One split off from the group attacking the ogre and jogged over to confront him. He was a big man carrying a military fork, its two long tines sharpened only at their points. A weapon usually meant for bringing down horses on the battlefield or for punching through heavy armor.

Of course, it would pierce Croy's vitals just fine, should he allow its owner an opening.

"Who are you, and what in the Bloodgod's foulest name do you want?" the guard challenged. He brought his fork down and shifted his hands backward on the haft. That put his points close to Croy's chest and kept the guard well outside of sword range.

The knight smiled. "I am Sir Croy, and I serve the Burgrave, the king, and the Lady. I want you to drop that thing and run away. But I don't think you will."

"I think you're right. Get out of here, knight—we have our hands full already."

Croy shook his head. "I can't do that. I want you to know

that I'm sorry about this. But you serve an evil master, and I have much work to do tonight. So I can't offer you any quarter."

The guard's lips curled back and he started to laugh wickedly.

Gurrh screamed then. It was not a pretty noise—it sounded like a lion being brought down by archers. The guard looked over his shoulder to see what was happening.

Croy took the advantage. It wasn't the most honorable thing he'd ever done, but he was hard-pressed. He jammed his shield forward onto the tines of the military fork, hard enough to embed them deep in the oak. Before the guard could respond and pull them free, Croy twisted his left arm around—it hurt, but he had the strength to do it—and wrested the haft of the polearm right out of the guard's hands. Then he hurled himself forward, leading with his right shoulder, and let the shortsword whistle through the air.

Swords *wanted* to cut. They *wanted* to draw blood—it was what they were made to do. Like a horse that when given its head will follow a track rather than traipsing off into brambles and rough ground, the sword cut through the air with very little help from Croy's strength. It connected with the guard's shoulder and bit deep into the meat of his arm. The guard howled and dropped to his knees as blood darkened his sleeve.

It wasn't a killing blow. The guard would heal in time and feel no lasting effects. But it was a painful wound, and it would render him unable to fight with a polearm for the rest of the night.

Croy had promised himself that he would kill these men if he had to. He had steeled himself against the necessity. But this man had barely been paying attention. A killing stroke would have just been unsporting.

A good shake of his left arm—which was starting to pain him—loosened the military fork from his shield. Croy let it clatter on the ground and then lifted his blooded sword high. "Who among you shall be next?" he shouted.

Suddenly all the guards were staring at him.

# CHAPTER SEVENTY-SIX

Malden crept down a hallway that ran the length of the third floor, looking for the locked door that would lead to Hazoth's sanctum. He could afford to be a little noisier now, since the hallway itself was far from silent.

Visitors to the house would never be allowed up here, he knew. Because this was where the villa got *strange*. The floating dining room table, the living books, the man of smoke he'd seen downstairs had all been miraculous, even wonderful. But up here was where Hazoth's real magic was done.

The door to the laboratory was open, and Malden could hear foul ichors and mysterious fluids bubbling and oozing inside. A greenish light leaked out of that room, and the air before its door shimmered as if something inside were enormously hot—though when Malden passed it, he felt a chill and unwholesome breeze. The next room down the corridor concealed a kind of bestiary, judging from the mournful howling and frightened whimpering he heard. What manner of beasts were trapped within, whether ordinary animals to be experimented upon or exotic creatures kept as curiosities, he could not guess. He was not so foolish as to open the door just to find out.

A third door seemed to breathe in as he passed it, then exhale as he watched. As if the door itself was alive. He could see a dim, shimmering light coming from the crack between the bottom of the door and the floorboards. The light was the dark red of pitfire. Malden couldn't help himself. He reached for the doorknob, thinking to throw open the door and see what lay beyond.

Just then, however, the door exhaled again—and filled the air before him with the stench of brimstone. He withdrew his hand quickly.

It couldn't be, could it? This must be some kind of sorcerous joke. There was no way even a man like Hazoth would have a door in his house that led directly to the pit itself. What if someone opened that door by mistake?

But then—no one who was allowed up here would ever make that mistake. Not unless Hazoth wanted them to.

Malden kept moving. He passed another door and heard a very different kind of sound—no less plaintive—coming from within. Someone was weeping in there, though not someone human. The sounds were unnatural and unnerving, rising now and then to a crescendo of wailing that never came from any human throat. Lower, and harder to hear, was a rhythmic grunting that did sound human. It would seem Hazoth was . . . entertaining in there.

An urge to throw open the bedchamber door and see what a succubus really looked like gripped Malden, but he was able to fight it back down. It would be his doom, for one thing—to surprise Hazoth like that would be the very definition of folly. For another, judging by the sounds she made, he was willing to guess the succubus looked nothing like the toothsome painting on the wall of the House of Sighs.

A few steps farther and he came to a quite ordinary door that proved to be locked when he tried its latch. This must be the door Kemper had described for him, he decided. The door that opened on the trapped corridor. Beyond lay the sorcerer's unholy sanctum—and the crown.

To this point Malden's trespassing had gone without significant setbacks. Beyond this door the real game would begin, he knew. He wished for the thousandth time he could guess what lay beyond. Kemper hadn't dared risk it, and Cythera had been unable to tell him anything. He would be wholly reliant on his own wits.

Glancing up and down the corridor to make sure Cythera wasn't about to walk up behind him, he knelt on a rug before the door. He unwrapped his tools from the hilt of his bodkin and laid them out carefully beside him. Then he took a small dark lantern from his belt, and carefully lit the tiny candle inside. The tin lantern let no light at all escape until he slid open a hatch on its side. The beam thus released was just wide enough to shine into a keyhole. He needed that light to determine which of his rakes and picks would open the lock.

Yet when he looked into the lock, he recoiled in fright.

There were teeth in there.

Not metal spikes filed to points. Not the teeth of cog wheels. These teeth were the color of ivory and they glistened with saliva. Malden had no doubt that if he placed a finger inside the keyhole, those teeth would strip his flesh to the bone.

There was no tongue in there that he could see. He did not think the mouth in the keyhole would scream if he tried to pick the lock. He inserted a long thin hook to test this hypothesis—he was ready to run and find some other way to the crown if it made any sound at all—but the only result was that the teeth bit down hard on his hook, and snapped it off an inch from where Malden's fingers clutched it.

Blast. That hook had not come cheap. Yet it could be replaced. He selected a much stronger tool, a torsion wrench, and slipped it into the lock. The teeth bit at it but Malden jerked it away in time—then shoved it in past the teeth when they opened up again. They closed on the iron tool and worried at it, but lacked the strength to chew right through it.

Good enough. He fitted a stout rake inside the lock and felt for tumblers. They were there, just beyond the teeth, but they felt wrong. Less like the precisely crafted cylinders he was used to, and more like the ribbed flesh on the roof of a dog's mouth. Malden pushed down his squeamishness and tickled the pins until they started to slide back. He put some tension on the wrench and it started to turn.

Instantly the teeth began to gnash and chew at his tools with great fervor. A thin trickle of drool leaked from the lock and spilled down the outer surface of the door. Malden grimaced and rubbed the rake back and forth across the tumblers. It was no time for delicate work. One by one the tumblers slid back and the wrench turned all the way around. The dead bolt slammed open and the door creaked slightly as it opened an inch or two. Malden felt the pressure on his wrench and rake slacken, and he chanced another look into the lock. There were no teeth in there anymore—just a simple mechanical lock, something any dwarf could make in an afternoon.

Yet when he inspected his tools, he saw dents and scratches all over them. The teeth had been real. Now they were not. He wrapped his tools back up and stepped into the hall of traps beyond, having no time to consider the nature of magic or the dubious humor of those who practiced it.

# CHAPTER SEVENTY-SEVEN

Gurrh dropped to one knee. The iron fencepost he'd been wielding clanged on the ground as he clutched at his left eye with both furry hands. The captain of the guards shouted an order and his troops moved back, giving the archer room to draw a perfect bead on the ogre's face.

The archer held his arrow and did not fire.

Four of the guards rushed to take position around Croy, boxing him neatly. They made no immediate move to attack, but kept their weapons up and ready. As soon as the captain gave the order they could lunge forward in concert and skewer Croy as neatly as a bird on a spit.

It seemed the captain wanted to parley first.

In some ways that was a bad sign. It meant the captain—or more likely Bikker—knew of Croy's reputation, and that he'd survived against far greater odds up at the palace. Of course, then he'd had the option of running away. That wasn't possible here.

Croy stood to his position, his shortsword pointed at the ground but held away from his body so if he needed to bring it up he would be ready to sweep it in a broad arc. As the captain approached, he breathed deeply and readied himself to move.

"Your beast is strong," the captain said, "but he has no belly for a fight. He hasn't so much as scratched one of us. I think you may have picked the wrong partner."

Croy nodded at the man in way of salute. "He's served his purpose. Half your men are disarmed, or carrying pieces of kindling that used to be weapons."

"But half of them are not. And we have plenty of spare weapons inside the fence. You look like you're ready to take us all on by yourself, Sir Croy. I'd know why, before I order your death."

The wound in Croy's back pulsed angrily. His body didn't like being held so immobile. "I've come for the Burgrave's crown. Thieves hid it here. If your master will give it up, I will leave you in peace. I'm not here to kill anyone, if I don't have to."

"I'd prefer to avoid it myself. The city watch will be here soon, I have no doubt. Half the city must have heard us fighting down here. When they do arrive, I don't want to have to explain what a dead ogre—and a dead knight—are doing on my lawn. I don't know anything about a crown. But if you leave right now, I'll let you take your pet away with you. This can just . . . stop." The captain stared in frustration at Croy. He knew very well it wouldn't end that way. "Surely, Sir Croy, this is the best you can hope for!"

"I won't leave without the crown," Croy insisted.

The captain raised his hands in disgust. Then he turned on his heel and threw a hand gesture toward the archer.

The bowstring twanged, and the arrow shot through the air too quickly for human eyes to follow. It was headed straight at Gurrh's uninjured eye. Simultaneously, the four guards around Croy stepped forward in perfectly drilled unison and lunged with their halberds and glaives.

Gurrh snatched the arrow out of the air a split fraction of a second before it pierced his eye. He snapped it in half between his fingers.

Even Croy's senses, heightened by the thrill of combat and the onrushing specter of his own demise, could not

follow everything that happened next. Luckily, he didn't
need to see or hear everything. He had run through this
exact scenario a thousand times, back when he was training to become an Ancient Blade. His fencing master—
Bikker—had known this day would come, when he was
trapped in an unwinnable contest. He had trained Croy to
be ready for it.

In such a situation there was only one course of action
that could be countenanced. You defended against every
attack that time allowed—and you minimized the damage
done by those attacks you could not avoid.

Croy's shield took a glaive blade in a glancing blow that
sent the weapon up and away. His shortsword parried the
axe blade of a halberd, the two weapons grinding together
until the halberd was mired in the shortsword's quillions.
Croy threw his hips to one side, and a third attack—this one
from behind—just grazed his side.

The fourth hit home, and six inches of iron buried themselves in his side.

Croy gasped in pain, but he knew the blow had missed
his kidney. Which meant he would not die from the wound.
At least not right away. That meant he still had some time.
Time to counterattack.

The glaive his shield had deflected was pointed up in the
air. The man who wielded it was changing his grasp on the
haft, trying to bring it back under his control. Croy put his
head down and rushed toward the man, while twisting his
right hand around to free his shortsword from the halberd
that fouled it.

He felt the sword slip free, but it was his shield that
smashed the face of the glaive-bearer. That man went
down with a grunt. Croy swung around and suddenly he
was facing three opponents head on, rather than being surrounded by them.

A halberd red with Croy's own blood came swinging at
his face. He slapped that attack away with the shortsword's
foible, then swung his shield around to block a glaive blow
that came sweeping up at him from the ground. He no
longer saw the men who held the weapons—he was too busy

watching the movement of the halberd points and axe blades and the curved, glinting cutting edge of the glaive.

A halberd drove point first toward his left leg. Croy brought the shield down and the point slammed into the oak, piercing it so he saw the point come through the inner side of the shield. Ignoring the pain in his back he threw his left arm wide, pulling the halberd out of the guard's hands. He pressed his attack and brought the shortsword around to slice at the front of the disarmed man, cutting his tunic open and drawing a line of blood across his chest. The guard twisted to one side and fell away.

That left him with two opponents, both of whom stood with their weapons across their bodies in defensive positions. Croy pointed at one, then the other, with his shortsword.

"How much does Hazoth pay you?" he asked.

"Not enough," one of them answered. He threw his halberd on the ground and ran. The other was not long behind him—though he took his glaive with him.

# CHAPTER SEVENTY-EIGHT

Malden stepped through the doorway and into the trapped corridor, careful to test his footing before he put his weight on the floor. It did not give way. He closed the cover of the hand lamp and closed his eyes tightly, then opened them wide again to adjust them to the darkness. He had expected some small amount of light in the corridor—surely at least a little would spill in from under the door or through the keyhole. Yet his eyes swam with the complete absence of light.

Well, almost complete.

The hallway was pitch-dark save for a blot of orange light high off in the distance. His eyes couldn't seem to adapt to the gloom otherwise. He pulled back the hatch of his dark lantern, trying to see anything at all. A pale glow emanated from the lamp, but only for a moment before the candle inside the lantern sputtered and died.

Malden cursed silently and reached into his tunic to find his tinderbox. Before he could reach it, though, the distant orange light flared up and he looked toward it. What had been a shapeless glow was now a fiery orb with a black center, surrounded by a burning ring of gold. It looked a great deal like the eyeball of some enormous monster.

It looked at him. It looked into him. It looked through him. And then madness swept through him like a wind howling out of the pit.

Malden staggered and clenched his eyes shut. He dropped the dark lantern but didn't hear it fall. He clutched at his head with his hands.

*'Ware the eye*, Lockjaw had said. And nothing more. What had the old thief known? Had Lockjaw broken into this villa once and fallen afoul of the same trap? Or had he only heard tale of it from someone else? Malden had realized long ago that Lockjaw's silence didn't only serve to guard his secrets. It made other people feel it was safe to tell him their own. Lockjaw was a great treasure trove of gossip. Yet if only he'd been a bit less stingy with it this time . . . well. What hadn't Lockjaw told him?

Malden shook himself as if he were cold, though in truth he felt like he'd been singed by a firestorm. He opened his eyes, but shielded them with one hand so he wouldn't meet the gaze of that hellish thing again.

He needn't have bothered. The eye was gone. So was the darkness.

He was standing in a corridor perhaps twenty-five feet long. Tall windows stood every ten feet or so down its length, and moonlight spilled in to form pools of silver on the wooden floor. Between each patch of light lay impenetrable shadows. It was as if the hall were one column of a game board with alternating spaces of light and dark.

He turned around and saw that the door he'd come through was gone. The wall there was smooth plaster and wood.

A corridor lined with windows, letting in moonlight—he knew this place. He'd been here before. It was the same corridor he'd crossed to reach the tower room where the crown slept, guarded by its tentacled horror. It was the twin of the moonlit corridor from the palace. A place of traps that he had bested through his skills, and this its perfect double, as if a team of dwarves had worked at copying that hallway down to the placement of each dust mote, the angle of every beam of light. It was as if he'd been transported bodily back to the palace, back to the place of his greatest success—and worst blunder—as a thief. He could almost believe that this was exactly what had happened.

Except—it couldn't be. That hallway had been severely damaged in the demon's magical enlargement. That hallway probably didn't even exist anymore. Surely the Burgrave had no reason to rebuild it exactly as it had been. Which meant he was still in Hazoth's house. Yet there was no way such a hallway could exist in the villa, in this particular location.

There could be no windows in this hallway. The trapped hallway in Hazoth's villa was surrounded on both sides by thick-walled chambers. There was no way the moon could come into this place.

So the moonlight, at least, was an illusion. A phantasm conjured by Hazoth's sorcery. And yet—why did it look so maddeningly like the corridor in the palace? Why would the magician choose to make this place the replica of a corridor that only a handful of people had ever seen? It made no sense.

At least he knew the secret of the hallway. The shadows between the pools of moonlight would hide pressure plates that caused spring-loaded spears to shoot down and impale anyone foolish enough to step on them. The final patch of moonlight would have a collapsing floor, which opened on a shaft that led to the Burgrave's dungeon, or its fell equivalent in the villa. Or—would it? Malden reviewed the plan of the villa in his head. The hallway lay at the center of the third floor. Below it was the gallery that overlooked the grand hall on the ground floor. So the shaft at the end of this hall would drop an unwitting thief onto the iron sphere.

Perhaps there were other differences, too. Perhaps that was the point.

Ah.

*'Ware the eye*. Malden thought he understood a little now. The eye had seen into his mind, and made this place from his memories. That was the only explanation for how it could look so exactly the same. It was a subtle spell, and a shrewd one. It could have made him think he was standing in a field of flowers, or at the bottom of the ocean, or in the pit itself. But he would have known instantly that those were illusions. The eye knew he expected to find a hallway full of traps—so it provided one. The illusion was so complete, and so convincing—the color of the moonlight was a wan silver, the air smelled of old stone and the clean air of Castle Hill. If he had not known better, he might have thought that the disorientation he felt was simply his eyes adjusting to the moonlight. He might have believed utterly in the hallway before him. Without Lockjaw's warning, he probably would have thought all those things. The old man might just have saved his life.

The hallway was based on his memory of the place. There was no reason it would play fair with those recollections. He looked around him for his dark lantern but could not find it. Perhaps it was still there but the illusion concealed it.

In a pouch at his belt he had three of Slag's most reliable creations. Leaden balls, wrapped in leather to keep them from clinking together. He drew one out of the pouch and hefted its weight, then tossed it down the hallway. It landed in a patch of moonlight with a dull thud, then rolled into the darkness beyond where he couldn't see it. If this hallway obeyed the rules that Malden remembered, a trio of brass spears should drop downward from the ceiling like a portcullis and impale the ball in place.

Except that wasn't what happened at all.

Instead the darkness opened wide, and enormous white teeth flashed in stray moonlight. The teeth crashed to-

gether on the ball and shredded it. Then the teeth flew open
again. A tongue as thick as Malden's arm, forked at its end,
flopped out of the mouth/pit and licked at the floor around
the teeth like a hungry dog searching for a stray morsel of
food. When it found nothing, it flicked back inside the teeth,
which closed together and disappeared until only darkness
remained on the floor.

Malden thought of the teeth inside the lock he'd just
picked, which had chewed at his rake and wrench. Those
teeth had disappeared as soon as the lock opened, but they'd
left very real marks on his tools. So whether this set of
teeth—many, many times larger—were illusory or not, they
would certainly make short work of him should he fall into
their grasp.

He didn't like the look of that tongue either. If he jumped
over the dark sections of the hallway floor—a tactic that had
worked admirably in the palace—could he be sure the maw
wouldn't open anyway? That tongue could grab him out of
the air and pull him into its teeth before he reached the next
spot of light.

This was going to take some care and thought. He knew
he didn't have a lot of time left. He would have to be quick
about this. But if he was too quick, it would be his doom.

He wanted to see just how close he could get to the maw
in the floor without causing it to open. Keeping near the
wall by the windows where the light was best, he walked out
into the first patch of moonlight. He watched the darkness
beyond quite closely, looking for any sign that it was aware
of him. Thus, when his feet started sinking into the floor, he
thought only that he was walking on a thick carpet.

He didn't notice that the moonlit floor was not solid, but
as yielding and viscous as porridge, until it had already
sucked him in up to the ankles.

# CHAPTER SEVENTY-NINE

The floor did not ripple or shimmer like liquid. It looked as solid and flat as stone. Yet it sucked him downward, little by little, and Malden could feel its substance filling his shoes and sticking to the hairs on his legs.

He tried to pull his left foot free of the floor and found only that this threw him off balance—his right foot had nothing to brace against. He kicked and flailed, but that only sped his descent until the floor sucked hungrily at his knees. He started to fall backward, and knew that if he didn't stop himself he would be sucked down into the floor until his face was covered, until the silvery moonlight stuff filled his nose and mouth and he drowned.

Up and down the hallway the patches of darkness between the pools of moonlight came alive, toothy maws opening and quivering with laughter while long tongues snaked and licked at the air. The hallway was mocking him.

Malden refused to let a patch of floor think him a figure of fun. He had no real honor, as he'd told Croy, and he'd never let pride get in the way of a job before. But no gods-damned inanimate object was going to laugh at him and get away with it.

Desperate for anything to hold onto, his hands shot out and his fingers latched onto the sill of the window. He was embedded in the floor up to his waist, but he could hold himself up if he used all the strength in his arms. That strength was not, unfortunately, enough to haul him free.

He was stuck facing the window. He looked out through the glass and saw the palace grounds—the wall of Castle Hill no more than a hundred yards away, the moon high in the sky. A thin finger of cloud was nearly bisecting the full moon. As he watched, though, Malden saw that it never moved. The stars around the moon never twinkled.

This was all an illusion. The moon, the viscous floor,

the mouths that gibbered and guffawed. All created by that orange eye he'd seen in the darkness. It could affect him—it could kill him, he was certain—but none of it was real.

Heaving, pulling with all his might, he managed to lift himself a few inches. Enough to get his right elbow up onto the windowsill. He braced himself there, resting most of his weight against the wall. Then he released the fingers of his left hand from their death-grip on the sill. He nearly fell back into the liquid moonlight, but just managed to keep steady. The window, he saw, was made up of a dozen long panes of glass leaded into a frame of solid wood. He reached up with his left hand and bashed at the closest pane. It did not shatter (for which he was somewhat glad—he'd worried the breaking glass would shred the flesh of his hand), but instead splashed away from him, as fluid as the floor. He reached through the opening he'd made and felt the air outside. Except it wasn't really air. It felt the same as when he tried to shake Kemper's hand. Cold and clammy, a nothingness that could not exist according to his other senses. His mind could not accept that absence and thus made of it a presence, gave it texture and sensation where none existed.

For all the misery and misfortune he'd experienced since agreeing to steal the crown, Malden was grateful then for the education those misadventures had given him. Most thieves, he knew, avoided magic and the supernatural like the pox, and for good reason. A common man no matter how deft or agile had little chance against even the simplest wizardry. But he was a fast learner, and because he'd had no choice, he learned something of magic in the last week or so. He learned it operated by rules. Not—by definition—the same rules the natural world obeyed. Magic was a perversion of those fundamental laws. Yet like any perversion, it must mirror the original, if only in a distorted fashion. Magic was never just arbitrary, though it could seem that way. There had to be an inherent logic to it, a set of boundaries beyond which it would not pass. Light and glass might act like liquids here, but they would always act like liquids. Solid objects here seemed as strong as steel. For the nonce, at least, he thought he had the hallway's measure.

He reached up through that wet nothingness and grabbed at the wooden frame that held the panes of glass in place. Another pane splashed and dripped away from his touch and his hand closed on the wood, which thankfully was as solid as it looked. More so—it felt as solid as iron in his palm. He thought it might hold his weight.

Thus anchored, he carefully brought his right hand up to grab at the frame as well. He pulled himself up the frame as if climbing a ladder. Little by little his legs came free of the floor. The moonlight did not stick to them or hang in droplets from his breeches, nor did the moonlight shift or flow as he pulled free of it.

In time he climbed up onto the frame of the window altogether, and got his feet up on the sill so he could stand there and let his legs take his weight. Then he looked down.

The floor below him looked as solid as ever. The mouths in the shadows had shut themselves again and showed only darkness. The hall was exactly as it had been when he first entered it. He had progressed about six feet down its length.

Well. That was something. He also had the measure of the place now. He knew its rules—at least some of them.

The next patch of moonlight was ten feet away. He needed to cross over a maw of darkness to get there, and when he arrived he would have to deal with its floor trying to swallow him whole. He thought he might know a way to handle that. Taking the rope from around his waist—the same one he and Kemper had used to get inside the villa, with its end dipped in silver—he tied it to the highest part of the window frame. He gave the rope a couple hard tugs until he was sure it would not come unknotted when he put his weight on it. Then, holding to its silver end, he leapt back to the featureless wall behind him, where the door had been when he came in. The floor there was solid and did not have teeth. It was perhaps the only patch of ground he could stand on safely in the entire hallway.

He rubbed his palms on his breeches to wipe the sweat away, then tied the silver end of the rope around his wrist. Getting a good running start, he dashed forward to the patch of liquid moonlight and then jumped up onto the rope.

It swung him far out over the moonlit floor and up over the darkness beyond.

Beneath him teeth snapped at the air and a long pink tongue shot out to grab him the way a frog seizes a fly. Malden pulled his legs up and tucked them against his chest, and the tongue barely tickled him as he passed.

The end of his arc came fast and he crashed against the second window. The glass there made no sound as it splashed away from him. He was able to grab the frame with one hand before anything more than his toes had sunk into the moonlight beneath him. He scrambled up onto the windowsill halfway down the corridor.

It had worked.

Malden let himself gasp for breath for a while. The hard part was still ahead of him. He had another patch of moonlight—and another wizardly mouth—to cross before he reached the end of the hallway. His rope was still tied to the window behind him. When he recovered his wind, he wrapped one leg through the bars of the window frame and took a strong grip on the rope. With all his strength, he heaved.

The window frame creaked and groaned where the rope was tied to it. The sound was enormous in the otherwise silent hall, but Malden was past caring about making too much noise. He pulled and grunted and sweated as the muscles in his back burned—but then the rope came free, dragging a broken piece of window frame with it. The knotted end fell toward a patch of moonlight, but Malden hauled it in before it could get fouled.

Untying the knot with shaking fingers, he picked broken bits of window frame out of the rope and made another knot, tying the rope to the top of the second, unbroken frame. It would be difficult to repeat his swing from before—he had no room to get a running start this time—but if he failed, he would die.

Malden refused to fail. He kicked off hard from the windowsill and swung for the next window. He didn't get as far out or travel as fast as the previous time, but he made it far enough to get the toes of one foot on the sill of the third and last window. Beneath him a toothy mouth bit and chewed at the wind of his passage, but it couldn't touch him and its long tongue couldn't reach him.

He repeated his trick again—pulling his rope free, tying it off, swinging desperately as the corridor tried to devour him—and suddenly he was at the end of the trapped corridor. He reached down tentatively with one foot and found the floor there was solid. Leaping down, he found himself face-to-face with a statuette of the Bloodgod—just like the one he'd seen in the palace, save one difference. Its eyes were glowing orange.

He ignored their stare as he pushed down on the statue's hinged arm, the one that held the arrow. In the palace, that triggered a section of floor to pivot and transport him into the tower room. Here it had a different effect.

The hallway went black—instantly. Malden's senses reeled, and when he could see again he found the hallway lit well by burning cressets. It was the same length and width as before, but largely featureless now. Just a stretch of unadorned hall with no windows. A normal door stood at either end.

The illusion was gone.

Above Malden, on the wall above the door to the sanctum, was a glowing orange eye mounted in a brass plate. It stared down at him for a moment, burning with hatred. Then brass lids closed over it and it went dark.

The door before him was unlocked. He opened it carefully, then stepped inside Hazoth's sanctum. Now nothing stood between him and the crown.

# CHAPTER EIGHTY

Croy took a step forward and nearly collapsed. The wound in his side was deep and bleeding freely. The wound in his back had reopened, and though it was only oozing blood, the muscles there were painfully stiff and the wound sent jolts of agony through his body every time he moved.

He took another step. It cost him.

The five remaining guards watched him with awe. Two of them had dropped their polearms and looked ready to run away. The rest weren't moving. Their captain kept glancing back at the villa, as if he expected reinforcements to arrive at any moment.

If they rushed him now, Croy knew he was doomed. He could not fend them all off, and Gurrh couldn't help him. The ogre was wounded himself and kept blinking blood out of his eyes.

Croy took another step. Sometimes courage was what mattered, not the strength of your arm. He'd learned that lesson countless times. Courage.

Even if it was empty bravado.

There was an element of showmanship in swordfighting. Bikker had taught him that. A battle of arms was often really a battle of wills, and sometimes brag counted more than bravery. A man with a savage grin on his face could look more dangerous than one with a sword in his hand. He was wounded, exhausted, and ready to slump to his knees. If he showed any sign of weakness at this point—and Lady, how he wanted to just wipe his brow or take a deep breath— he would be finished, and the guards would fall on him in a pile. But if he could just put on a brave face and keep standing, just maybe he still had a chance.

He lifted his shortsword, which was clotted with gore. Brought it up as far as his arm could reach and clanged it against the side of his shield.

"Which of you is next?" he demanded. His voice was hoarse with fatigue but he could still shout.

The two guards who had already divested themselves of their weapons ran off across the grassy common, into the night. Another started shouting for the barrier to be lowered. He ran toward the gate of the villa, but when he passed through was caught up by the magical barrier and lifted into the air. He struggled in vain as his polearm was ripped out of his hands by invisible claws and thrown away.

"He's bleeding," the captain said, then wiped at his mouth with one hand. "He's injured. Look at him! He can barely walk!"

The two remaining guards looked to each other. Then they dropped their weapons and fell to their knees. One of them started praying to the Lady for deliverance. The captain clouted him across the ear, and he fell over on his side.

"What's wrong with you curs?" the captain demanded. "He's just one man! I don't care if he's the king's own champion, one man can't stand against us all. Not if we fight together!" He grabbed at the arms of his charges, trying to drag them forward through sheer willpower.

Croy felt a burgeoning respect for the man grow in his breast. Had things been otherwise, if he had fought beside the captain on some battlefield, he might have called the fellow a hero. If he could avoid it, he very much wanted to keep this man alive, if only for the sake of honor.

But that meant convincing him to shirk his duty, now.

"They don't want to die," Croy said. He pointed his sword at the captain. "Do you? Do you feel such loyalty to the sorcerer that you'll die for him?"

The captain tried to sneer. He failed. "I think I'm more than a match for one bleeding fool," he said. But even he didn't sound convinced.

Gurrh reached down and helped one of the kneeling guards to his feet. The man screamed and ran off. Apparently that didn't violate the terms of the ogre's curse. The other guard, the devout one, crawled away as if too terrified to run.

"Come no further, Sir Croy," the captain said. He looked

toward the villa, where the trapped guard still writhed in the grip of the magical barrier. "Bikker!" the captain shouted. "Bikker! You are needed!"

"Bikker's a faithless coward," Croy said. He took another step toward the captain. He lifted his sword and made his shield ring. "If he was going to help you, he would be here already."

The captain brought his halberd up. Swung it around so the point faced Croy.

Croy stepped closer. Close enough. He brought the short-sword around in a wide arc. The forte of the blade caught the point of the halberd and knocked it away. The captain had no strength in his arms and couldn't hold his weapon still. Its iron fittings rattled as it shook in his hands. That happened to men in the extremes of fear, Croy knew. Their muscles turned to water.

"Hold that thing properly," Croy said to him. "There's no honor in slaying a man who can't fight back."

The captain bit his lip and closed his eyes for a moment. "If you kill me, what do you gain? The barrier is still up. Even your fancy sword won't bring it down."

"No," Croy said, "that's true. But you can lower it with a gesture, can't you?"

The captain stared.

"Lower the barrier," Croy said, "and then walk away from here."

"My lord and master has tasked me to stop you," the captain said.

"I serve your true lord, the Burgrave. I do the Lady's work here. In every man's life a moment comes when he must choose to serve good, or to do evil. What choice will you make? What profit will evil bring you?"

The captain closed his eyes again. It would be effortless to step forward and strike him down, Croy thought. It would be the easiest thing in the world.

The captain raised his hands in the air. He made a complicated gesture with one hand bent in half, the fingers of the others splayed.

The night air on the common fluttered, as if a great flock

of birds had all lifted into the air at the same time. The barrier was down. The guard who'd been trapped by it fell to the gravel with a thud and lay still.

"Thank you," Croy said, turning to look the captain in the eye. But the man was already gone. His halberd lay abandoned on the grass.

Croy breathed deeply. He was badly hurt, and he knew it. But now the barrier was down. His path was clear.

"Hold," Gurrh said. Croy whirled to face the ogre. It was a bad idea, as it aggravated his wounds. For a moment he could see only blood, and his breath caught in his throat.

"Into that place, goest thou must. But not yet," Gurrh told him. The ogre had torn the tunic off one of the fallen guards. He ripped it into bandages and stanched Croy's wounds. "Now, thou art ready."

Croy grinned. There was less humor in his smile than he would have liked, but at least it didn't hurt to move his mouth. "Thank you, Gurrh. You know what you must do now, don't you?"

"I do," the ogre said. He walked over to a point about twenty yards before the gate of the villa and sat down once more in the grass, to wait.

Croy strode up to the gate and hesitated only a moment before walking through. On the far side the gravel crunched under his boots. The main door of the villa stood before him. He started toward it, walking as fast as he could.

But of course he would not be allowed to enter the house, not yet.

Bikker was leaning against the side of the building. His arms were folded across his massive chest. Croy could see the cowl of a chain-mail hauberk emerging from inside his tunic. The big swordsman's face glowed with ruddy health.

"Croy," Bikker said, and stepped away from the wall. "Might I have a moment of your time?"

# CHAPTER EIGHTY-ONE

Hazoth's sanctum was a long room with high vaulted ceilings shrouded in darkness. As Malden entered, the only light came from the rose window at its far end, a massive round piece of stained glass that cast long ribbons of red and blue illumination across the floor. After the gloom of the corridor and its dark illusions, it was almost enough light for him to see clearly by—he almost welcomed the eerily hued light that streamed into the room. Peering forward, he sought what he'd come for, though he wasn't sure what it would look like.

Vague shapes of furniture and magical equipment were all around him. Every corner of the place was cluttered with gear and apparatus, and he was careful not to step forward until he was sure he wouldn't trip over something baleful or disgusting. Once he'd taken a few strides, he began to make out more distinct shapes. He could vaguely see the silhouette of a tree in the middle of the room, its branches raised high like the beseeching arms of a woman in distress.

That must be the witch Coruth. Cythera's mother, who had transformed herself into the shape of a rowan tree, to avoid torture at the hands of the sorcerer.

Malden took a step toward the tree—and the room erupted in light.

Red fire leapt up all around him, from braziers and cressets and dozens of candelabra on high stands. The flames danced wickedly—these were no normal flames, but tongues of fire summoned straight from the pit. They lit up every detail of the room but gave the place a ruddy cast that made everything look stained with blood.

The walls of the room were lined with bookshelves—he had thought Hazoth's library on the first floor impressive, but here there must be ten times as many books, scrolls, palimpsests, and fragments of stone tablets. Standing before the bookshelves were worktables covered in magical implements: athames, compasses and calibers, goblets, wands, styli of bitumen, silver chains, bundles of herbs tied together, ready to be cast into the magical flames. Incense burned from a dozen censers. The mummified body of a lizard with a long, toothy snout hung in chains from the ceiling.

On one of the tables stood a glass dome on a carved wooden trivet. Inside the dome a thing perhaps nine inches tall scratched at the glass with tiny pincers. Its face was almost human but its body was . . . not. Malden chose not to study its form too carefully. Looking away, he saw that on another table stood a bowl full of what looked like quicksilver. When he walked past it, its substance stretched upward until a cluster of argent eyes stared at him, mounted on a thin stalk of liquid substance. It made no attempt to molest him, so he showed it the same respect. A third table held the body of a small demon, pinned to the boards with long iron needles, its lights and guts exposed to the air. The demon's seven eyes blinked and quivered, and Malden knew it was still alive. He shuddered as it beseeched him with its alien gaze, begging him to free it. For all of its alien form, he might have done just that if he hadn't known better, and if not for far more pressing errands waiting him. He looked away again and scanned more of the room.

Skulls inscribed with tiny writing sat in a heap. Charts of the heavens, with the constellations picked out in gold, lay half unrolled on the floor. A thing like a clock made of brass lay in pieces across one table. Its numbered face did not measure time in any fashion Malden recognized.

A scholar of the arcane might spend a lifetime cataloging all the oddments in the room. Malden had so little time he barely bothered to glance at the assembled paraphernalia. He moved quickly to the magic circle in the center of the room, where Coruth stood imprisoned. The circle was merely a diagram in chalk inscribed on the floor, a double circle with runes and sigils drawn between its concentric lines. It looked like a child's scrawl on a pavement, not like an inescapable prison for a powerful witch. Then again, Coruth's appearance was deceiving as well.

In the red light she looked far less like a woman and more like a normal tree, though she lacked foliage even now in the height of summer. There was a vague suggestion of a face in the bark of the rowan, but it did not open eyes or whisper secrets to Malden as he approached. If he had not known otherwise, he would have thought it a perfectly natural tree. It was strange, perhaps, that its roots were driven into the wooden floorboards of the room, or that they spread to fill the circle to its full extent but never edged outside the chalk lines inscribed on the floor.

Far more important, and thus absorbing all of his attention, was the leaden coffer half tangled in those roots. It was a simple box traced with a few simple runes, four feet long and two feet high and wide. It had been sealed with great heat so that its lid was fused closed.

Malden knelt down just outside the magic circle and reached tentatively toward the coffer. He knew he had to free Coruth, but the crown was in there! He could almost hear it speaking inside his head, and it demanded to be released. His fingertips passed over the outermost chalk mark of the circle and—

—he pulled his hand back instantly. He had expected the circle to burn him, or perhaps to grab him and hold him like the magical barrier outside. Instead, it only deflected him. He felt no resistance, suffered no pain. His hand was merely repelled, gently, without apparent force. Just enough that he could not have overcome the resistance no matter how hard he tried. He could tell it would be physically impossible for him to reach across the circle and touch the coffer.

There must be some way to break the circle. There had to be some tool for that in this room, some combination of herbs that, when burned together in a flame, would release the circle's captives.

Before he could find them, however, the red flames that lit the room jumped high, and burned a furious white so bright they overwhelmed his vision and blinded him completely.

# CHAPTER EIGHTY-TWO

Bikker made no move to draw Acidtongue from its glass-lined scabbard. Croy left his own swords in their sheaths. There was an etiquette to these things. When two swordsmen met in single combat, the resultant duel was known as a conversation. Typically it began with exactly that—a verbal back and forth, designed to test the will of the opponents. Such contests could often be resolved long before the first sword was drawn. Croy knew better than to think he could drive off Bikker the way he had frightened the guards or reasoned with their captain. No, it would never be that easy—for Bikker knew about bravado as well. Yet he could score some points against the man with a clever quip or a daring taunt. He might infuriate his hirsute opposite number and goad him into an ill-timed attack. He might chip away at Bikker's confidence, and convince him to spend more effort on defense and thereby avoid a devastating attack. Or he might simply gain some honor by calling Bikker the cur that he was.

"Hello, old friend," Croy said. "I don't suppose you've come around and regained your honor, have you? Care to apologize to me, offer a prayer to the Lady, and be on your way?"

Bikker laughed. "Oh, and is it that easy for a dog to change his spots? I suppose I should make some act of contrition as well. Some penance for my evil ways. Yes, I suppose I *could* give in to your outmoded notions of honor and chivalry. Or I could just kill you—crush you like a gnat that buzzes in my ear, and then go back to my debauchery. Like any sane man living in the real world would do."

Croy smiled, though it pained him. "You know, in some strange way it's good to see you again. It takes me back to better days. You remember, back when you were young and you were at your best."

"I'd like to say it's good to see you, too. Except that you don't look well, Croy," Bikker said, frowning as if this saddened him. "How much blood is left in you?"

"Enough yet to boil, old friend," Croy said. Enough to keep me standing for perhaps a moment or two longer, he hoped. "Enough to best a dozen men, just now."

Bikker nodded in respectful appreciation. "Yes, you certainly showed those dogs how a real man fights. By feint and bluff, mostly."

Croy bowed low. "Perhaps I've been taking lessons from the master of deception," he said. "You taught me much of that style."

"Just as I taught you how to hold that piece of iron you call a sword." Bikker took a step toward Croy. "Tell me. Why are you here? For Cythera, truly? I daresay right now she could fight better than her champion."

"I've come for the crown you stole. The one you paid to have stolen, rather, at the behest of the man who holds your leash."

Bikker shrugged. "Perhaps. Perhaps that's why you came. But you must know you won't leave here with it. I think you came for another reason, though. I think you came to apologize and beg my mercy. To make amends for the time you impugned my honor."

"Do you mean when I called you faithless, because you sell your sword to any man with a purse?" Croy laughed. "A gross insult indeed. Though how, may I ask, did I besmirch your honor—when I spoke nothing but the truth? You were sworn to defend the Burgrave, just as I was. Now you've received a better offer and you work for the man who would unseat my lord."

Bikker's face darkened with rage. "Wake up, Croy. Put away your dreams, your naive ideals. We are Ancient Blades! The Burgrave doesn't deserve our service."

"It isn't a question of merit. It's a question of loyalty. Of duty. You may call those things fancies, but I will not. I believe in them and I will fight to prove it."

"When you die by my sword, what will that prove?"

"That honor is immortal," Croy replied.

Bikker's hand went to his scabbard, and Acidtongue leapt free. Its pitted and corroded surface glinted wet in the moonlight. A droplet of acid formed on its tip and fell to the ground, where it smoked and bubbled. "Draw your sword," the big swordsman said. He held Acidtongue almost straight out at his side.

Croy bowed his head. He uttered a short prayer to the Lady, that She might strengthen his arm in Her service. Then he reached behind him and drew his shortsword, bringing it down over his shoulder to point directly at Bikker. Ghost-cutter remained safely in its sheath.

"You bastard," Bikker said. "Draw your real sword."

"Ghostcutter is for killing demons," Croy said, "or worthy opponents. You are neither, only a churl whose blood will befoul even this length of simple steel."

It was a harsh insult indeed, but it had the desired effect. Bikker's wrath bubbled over and he slashed wildly with Acidtongue, bringing the blade up high and then driving it down toward Croy's quillions.

That might have been enough—that one blow could have carved right through the dwarven steel of the shortsword and had enough momentum left to drive Acidtongue right through Croy's body. It could have been the stroke that killed the knight.

But he still had his shield on his left arm. He brought it up high and took the blow hard on his forearm. The acid-wet blade burned through the oak shield and cut through its iron boss as easily as it cut through the air, but Croy rolled his arm under the cut and sent Acidtongue driving down into the grass and dirt between his feet.

Bikker leapt backward, pulling his blade free and out of range of a counterattack. He laughed maniacally. "Very good, Croy. *Very* good." The rage drained out of his counte-nance. Had it been a ruse? It had looked real enough. "You might survive five minutes if you keep fighting defensively. Will that be long enough?"

"Long enough for what?" Croy asked.

"For your friend Malden to reach the crown. After all, the real reason you're here is to distract me, isn't it? To keep me out of the house while your pet thief robs the place."

Croy could not help but let his face show his surprise. How could Bikker know that?

"You didn't think we would leave the crown unguarded, did you? How very foolish of Malden. Hazoth is a *sorcerer.* He has many ways of watching what goes on inside his own house. He knows that Malden is in there right now, and he knows what Malden is trying to do. Ah! There, look!"

Bikker pointed up at the rose window on the third floor of the house. Multicolored light burst from inside the glass.

"Hazoth is greeting his uninvited house guest even as we speak," Bikker announced.

"No," Croy breathed. "No." It could not be. If Hazoth caught Malden red-handed and killed him as a trespasser, then who would retrieve the crown? Who would free Coruth, and by so doing, Cythera?

"No!" Croy shouted again, and ran at Bikker, his short-sword flashing up and around for a desperate cut.

# CHAPTER EIGHTY-THREE

Malden scrubbed at his eyes with the balls of his thumbs, trying to clear away the burning smears of light that flickered in his skull. His eyesight returned very slowly—whatever caused that flash of light had been strong enough to blind him. He could only hope it wasn't permanent.

His hearing was unaffected. He could sense there were

other people in the sanctum now. He could hear them walking around him. And he could hear someone applauding.

"Very impressive indeed. I thought it was a clever trick that a gutter ape had learned to read! Now I see that animal cunning can evolve to handle basic problem-solving as well, given an adequate stimulus. Though of course, I should not be surprised. Last summer we had a mole that burrowed into the garden, coming through the barrier from underneath the ground, where I never thought to extend it. Vermin will always find a way."

"Good evening, Magus," Malden said, because the voice belonged to Hazoth. Fear washed down his back like a spill of icy water, but he tried to keep his voice level.

"Did I say you could speak? No. Still. You're a bold rodent, aren't you? Courage is admirable, even in lower orders of life. So I'll forgive that breach of manners. I'll forgive your insolence, if only once." Hazoth strode over to stand before Malden, who was hunched over, still rubbing at his eyes. He could see nothing in detail, just vague shapes and shadows.

"You bested the Eye of Klaproth," Hazoth said, as if he couldn't quite believe it. "I wonder—did you somehow see through its illusions, or is it simply that your simple mind was incapable of providing the imagery it works with? Either way, your primitive brain has served you quite well. You might have actually succeeded—I was preoccupied, and I might have remained ignorant of your presence if Cythera hadn't warned me."

"Wh-What . . . ?" Malden managed to ask.

*Cythera?*

"Even a fool of Sir Croy's caliber would not think he could cut his way into my house, not with the magical barrier in place. It was a noisy diversion you had him make out front, but I could not figure out why he was doing it. So I summoned Cythera and demanded she tell me everything. Every detail of your ambitious little plan. And she did, without much hesitation."

Cythera had betrayed him? Malden could scarcely credit

it. She had so much to lose—but then he supposed Hazoth
had ways enough to get information from her. He moved
one hand down toward his belt, inching it toward the hilt of
his bodkin.

But . . . no. He could barely see. Striking out blindly now
would be foolish. He fought down his immediate reaction,
the rage at being discovered, the terror of what was to come
next. It wasn't useful to him. He could deal with it later, if he
lived through this.

"Interesting. Look, look at this, Cythera. You can see
his thoughts as they grow ever so slowly in his head. Watch
his hands, and his mouth. They give him away. Fascinating,
really."

Malden held his tongue.

"You're a rodent, my friend, and nothing more. A ver-
minous little animal. Yet you do amuse me, after a fashion.
I thank you for bringing a bit of excitement to my tedious
routine. Here. You shall have a reward—I will return to you
your eyesight."

Instantly Malden's eyes cleared. He blinked a few times
and then looked around him. The room had changed little.
The flames burned a healthier hue now, and the light was
better so he could make out more of the sanctum's contents,
though he saw little to recommend the improvement. Hazoth
was exactly as Malden remembered him, though now he
was wearing a nightshirt and a fitted leather skullcap.

Cythera stood behind him, her eyes downcast. She looked
as lovely as ever, even if Malden knew she'd betrayed him.
She met his gaze and mouthed an apology, though she did
not speak out loud. She looked so piteous, so sympathetic,
that he wondered if he could summon up real anger at her
betrayal.

He found he could not.

She had pinned her hopes to Croy's star and been disappointed. She had hoped Malden could help her, and that
appeared to have failed, too. Her life—and that of her
mother—were bound in unholy union with Hazoth, and she
could not free herself. She needed help so she had turned
to anyone she could get, even a poor thief like him. He'd

done his best, and she had helped him to the full extent of her ability. But they had both known it was a long shot. A suicide mission. No, he could not blame her now. Had she maintained her innocence, if she'd held her tongue, Hazoth would have taken out his rage on Coruth.

Malden knew Cythera would never let that happen, if she had any choice at all.

He glanced over at Coruth and the leaden box that held the crown. They were unchanged.

"Quite safe," Hazoth said. He walked over to the magic circle and bent to inspect the chalk lines on the floorboards. While he was thus busy, Malden looked over at Cythera, trying to think of what signal to send her.

All he could do was shrug.

Cythera turned her gaze on the tree that was her mother. A single tear rolled down her painted cheek. Malden's heart went out to her. She must have dared to hope when she saw how close he had come to rescuing Coruth. The plan had gone so smoothly, and now . . . Well. Things had changed.

He longed to speak to her. To reassure her, perhaps, though what words he would use to do so escaped him. Hazoth had not given him permission to speak anyway, so he kept silent. He tried to communicate with Cythera using just his eyes, but she would no longer look at him.

"One thing," Hazoth said, rising to his feet again, "escapes me. I would like to have an answer before I decide what to do with you, little rodent."

He came back over to Malden and stared down at him with unquiet eyes.

"What you are doing here is quite clear. You came to steal back that which you were paid for," Hazoth said. "Why you would do so is no mystery. I imagine you think that if you can recover the item you will be able to bargain for your life with those who seek it. A logical conclusion, though there is one fallacy in your reasoning. The players in this game outstrip you in power and in intellect. They would be glad to have the thing back, certainly. But they would not let you live once they had it. Don't you see? You've learned too much. An animal in possession of a secret is a dangerous animal. They would slaughter you even more readily than I."

Malden bit his lip.

"You may speak," Hazoth told him. "In fact, I insist. Tell me who sent you, and what they want from the crown?"

Malden frowned. "Surely you know the answer. The Burgrave wants what was stolen from him. He will be embarrassed if he appears tomorrow in the Ladymas procession without his crown."

Hazoth smiled. "The Burgrave? Do you mean Ommen Tarness? I really don't think he was the one who employed you." He laughed at the thought. "No, not Ommen."

"Why should he not?" Malden asked.

"Because Ommen Tarness is an idiot," Hazoth answered.

# CHAPTER EIGHTY-FOUR

"A fool, perhaps, but—"

Hazoth's face clouded with anger. "I did not say you could speak!" he thundered.

Inside Malden's chest his heart stopped beating. Pain lanced through his limbs and he dropped to the floor in a quivering heap. He could not draw breath, could not move, and every sound in the room was a distant echo—

—and then he recovered. He sat up carefully, unsure if he was still alive or had passed into the afterlife.

Hazoth went on as if nothing had occurred. "I do not use that word as a casual insult. Ommen Tarness is mentally an infant. He has been since he was thirteen years old, when his father died and he became the Burgrave—his brains stopped growing, even as his body developed. He can barely feed himself. I understand that getting him dressed each morning is a tiresome chore—he doesn't like to wear state clothing, and throws fits of tantrums when the castellan tries to put a robe over his shoulders."

Malden frowned in confusion. He'd seen Ommen Tarness in public many times, and the man had always struck him as highly intelligent and composed.

"Ommen's father, Holger Tarness, was the same. And Holger's father, and his father's father—the line of Tarness is corrupted in the blood. There hasn't been one of them that could wipe his nose properly in centuries," Hazoth said. "It really isn't proper to call Ommen the Burgrave at all. He is like a horse that carries a rider, and that rider is the true Burgrave. Who is currently sealed into yon leaden box."

Malden turned to stare at the coffer tangled in the rowan tree's roots.

"Tell me, rodent. Are you bright enough to know who I speak of? You may answer me, if you think you've worked it out."

Malden considered the puzzle carefully. "I think perhaps I can work out your meaning. I have enough clues to piece together now. The crown spoke to me, when I held it. It possessed an air of command, as if it was accustomed to people accepting its orders without question." He shook his head. He could still remember how it called to him—and how desperately hard it had been to ignore its commands. It wanted him to place it on his own head. He thought he understood now exactly how foolish that would have been.

He considered his second point. "Further, I saw the chamber where it resided when not in use, and that room was full of campaign banners and the trophies of war. Mementos of a military man, placed where no one would normally see them. Yet clearly they were treasured by someone. There is only one man I can think of who fits the bill."

He nodded to himself. "Finally, I know that no other crown will serve Ommen Tarness. Bikker initially suggested that when the crown was stolen, the Burgrave could simply have a replica made and that he would not even come looking for the original, for fear of embarrassment should its theft be discovered. Since then, however, certain . . . others have told me that only this one will do. That it cannot be so simply replaced. But why not? No one ever heard the crown speak, except for me and presumably Ommen Tarness. A nonspeaking replica would be accepted by the people without question. So it must be that Ommen requires the crown to function as Burgrave."

He met Hazoth's gaze directly. "Based on these elements, I believe I have a conclusion. Are you saying that Juring Tarness lives on, eight hundred years after his supposed death, imprisoned inside his own crown?"

Hazoth's eyes flashed with excitement. "Wonderful! You have it precisely. Juring Tarness, the first Burgrave, who founded the Free City of Ness. The general who handed his king a country, and asked for a cesspool as reward. Yes! But you have one subtle detail wrong. It is not Juring who is imprisoned by the crown—it is Ommen."

Malden thought he understood the distinction, but he said nothing rather than risk Hazoth's displeasure with his rudeness.

"Juring and I were fast friends, eight centuries ago. He came to me one night at the end of his life and begged me for my aid. He had a son at that time, an heir who would take up his crown and his title when he died. Sadly, the boy was a wastrel—all his energies were given over to petty entertainments, wine, and whoring. Anyone could see the son would never be a fit ruler. Juring loved his city and worried what would happen to it when his son took power. He had built a fiefdom for himself and ruled it ably. Perhaps his people thought him just and wise. Perhaps they only obeyed him because they knew what he was capable of when angered. His son could not command such respect. More importantly, the boy was incapable of holding onto money. He was a gambler and a drunkard, and Juring knew that if he was given free rein, he would bankrupt the city in a year. The king at that time feared Juring enough to stay out of his business, but once Juring was gone, the king would surely see the son's weakness. One way or another it would end with the city's charter being revoked, and everything that Juring had worked for would be lost."

Hazoth's eyes grew bright as he remembered the long-lost past. Malden was not so foolish as to think the wizard distracted enough to give him any chance of escape. "When he came to me, Juring was at the end of his tether. He could see no solution. If only there was a way for his wisdom to survive his death, some method by which he could continue to advise his son—and to command him, should it come to that . . . He thought perhaps I knew a way to help. I considered the problem from all angles, and eventually I found the answer."

Hazoth grinned. "Juring's body was fragile, like all human flesh. It would perish and decay. His mind, however, could live on, through cunning applications of magics known only to me. It needed something to hold it, however—his mortal brains would rot away, so his consciousness had to be imbued into a vessel that time could not corrode . . . something of gold, which unlike other metals does not rust or tarnish or turn to verdigris. Gold has other qualities that make it ideal for such an enchantment as well—but you would not understand if I listed them. The object in question must also be something that his son would not like to part with. The crown was the obvious choice.

"Juring wanted the crown to speak with his voice, even after his death, and I made it so. Every time the son placed the crown on his head, he heard his father's voice whispering in his ear. He could no longer enjoy his carousing and his ruinous wagers. When he consorted with low company or dealt poorly with his subjects, he was plagued by terrible headaches and by a need to atone. He could only ever be at rest when he was ruling the city with the judicious pragmatism of his father, and so he grew to be a very capable Burgrave. When he grew old, he worried very much what would become of the city under his own son, who was capricious and cruel. But the crown served Juring's grandson well, and his great-grandson, and so on."

Hazoth shrugged. "Even I, however, have difficulty understanding how magic changes over time. It is an unpredictable force even in the short term, and I did not know that the enchantment on the crown would only grow stronger with every passing year. The soul in the crown maintained Juring's brilliance, but its hold on those who wore it made them weaker. The brain is like a muscle of the body. If it does not get proper exercise, it atrophies and eventually dies. Each successive Burgrave was a bigger fool than his father had been. Juring, inside the crown, had to exert more and more control over them, and more and more often had to block out their own misbegotten thoughts and replace them with his own. His character, his intelligence, was imposed on them more frequently, and they suffered for it. Now they can barely speak or count on their fingers without his consultations." The sneer on the sorcerer's face showed how little pity he had for the House of Tarness.

"For a very long time there has been only one Burgrave in this city, and that has been Juring Tarness. It is an unnatural situation, and one some people would like to see changed. Juring was my good friend, and I have always been pleased that he, like myself, survived when so many of our contemporaries grew old and died. But now, perhaps, it is time for new blood to rule this place."

"You betrayed him," Malden said, forgetting himself.

Hazoth seemed not to notice this rudeness. "You speak of loyalty? The man I knew has been corrupted by eight hundred years of stealing someone else's body. He was never meant to live that long. No man was meant to live in that fashion. The enchantment I placed on that crown was meant to last for one generation only. Say instead I am fixing a mistake I made when I was young and foolish."

Malden stared at the sorcerer. He could scarcely credit what he'd heard.

Yet . . . the crown had spoken to him. And he did not doubt it had used Juring Tarness's voice when it did so.

It must be as Hazoth had described. And yet, that meant—

He was not allowed to finish his thought.

"I think the crown will remain here, with me," Hazoth said. "I considered letting you have it. Letting you take it and go free—just to see what would happen. I have a theory, you see. I have a theory that the blood of the Tarness line doesn't matter. That Juring could control anyone who wore the crown. And I am certain you lack the power of will necessary to resist its entreaties. It would convince you somehow to place it on your own head eventually. I wondered if Juring could take some mortal clay—even such a pitiful specimen as yourself—and over time mold it into the stuff of a great leader. I do believe he could. In a span of a few years, I think, you might become king of Skrae."

He looked down on Malden with laughing eyes.

"Imagine that, hmm? A whoreson made into a king. How amusing!"

The sorcerer laughed wildly then, his tongue flapping in his mouth as he gibbered and cackled. It was not a laugh of sanity.

Malden shivered, but not simply because of Hazoth's lapse of lucidity. He considered what would have become of him if he had put on the crown, as he'd wanted to so badly. He didn't doubt that Juring would have given him power in return, knowledge and advice and courage. But he would have been enslaved by it. His greatest fear, that he should lose that little shred of freedom he possessed, would have been realized.

His heart thundered in his ears. It had been a close thing. He barely heard Hazoth when the wizard spoke again.

"But when I tell this tale out loud, I am reminded exactly why I chose to be part of this scheme in the first place. I can't afford to let you become king, you see. Nor can I afford to let the Tarness family—ha ha ha—tell me what to do. I can't afford to have any rivals. No powers must remain that might conscribe me. Do you understand? I think, in fact, you might. How astonishing! How clever! And so tragic, now. No, I'm sorry, rodent. You can't have your prize. And you can't leave my house. Not alive, at any rate."

Hazoth lifted one hand, the third and fourth fingers tucked into the palm, the others outstretched. He began to lift his arm high over his head.

"Malden!" Cythera shouted. "Cover your eyes!"

Malden did exactly as he was told. He also grabbed the hilt of his bodkin and got ready to draw.

# CHAPTER EIGHTY-FIVE

Drops of acid hit Croy's arm and seared right through his leather jerkin. He shouted as the acid burned through his skin as well. Pain lanced up to his spine, while his lungs heaved against the stink of sulfur in the air. Croy couldn't help but cough as the fumes seared his throat and eyes.

It was the sign of weakness he had put off as long as he could. He'd finally broken. Bikker took it for exactly what it was—a call to attack, which he executed with a flurry of devastating blows, one after another. Croy managed to parry them, but not without cost. He had to stagger backward, away from the fight, and wince as the pain threatened to overcome him. He forced his eyes to stay open, to keep watching, to keep assessing the situation.

His shield was reduced to a few sticks of sizzling oak held together by a melting boss. Far worse, the shortsword was etched and notched each time it parried Acidtongue's attacks. Croy could feel his sword growing weaker and less stable with each passing moment.

The weapon was still in better shape than the man, though, and that was the real problem. Already weakened by multiple wounds and loss of blood, Croy's endurance was reaching its end very quickly. Just lifting his sword arm took a great effort and he was gasping for breath. Sweat rolled down into his eyes and he could taste the salt when it trickled across his lips. Proper swordsmanship was as much about the legs as the arms—he could hear Bikker's voice in

his head from back when the bigger swordsman had taught
him how to fight. *You need to* move *when a sword comes at
your face,* boy, lunge *forward with your knee when you riposte,* dance *if you want to stay alive.* His legs felt like they
were made of solid wood. He could barely get his feet off
the ground without falling over.

A sweeping blow came at his injured side, Acidtongue
spitting as it burned through the air. Croy barely brought
the shortsword down to counter. Acidtongue flew back to
recover from the parry and then whistled over Bikker's head
as he brought his corroded sword up for a high slice. Croy
shoved the fuming remnants of his shield up into the blow
but lacked the strength to hold it back completely. Using
Acidtongue like a club, Bikker knocked the shield into
Croy's teeth. Croy's entire skull rattled and he felt his brains
slosh back and forth.

So tired.

Parry. He tried a riposte but found the shortsword tangled in Acidtongue's withdrawal.

His body was failing him.

Parry. Step back, away from the lunge, one foot behind
the other to make his body a narrower target. Acidtongue
jabbed past his face, and he batted it away like a cat batting
at a piece of string—and just as effectually.

He was going to collapse.

Yielding parry—catching Acidtongue just before it cut
his throat, taking Acidtongue's foible with the shortsword's
forte. A classic parry perfectly executed, which should have
given him an ideal chance to counterattack. By the time he
saw the opportunity, however, Bikker was dancing away.

Croy knew he was doomed.

Acidtongue came rushing toward his shield. It might be a
feint, which he should ignore. He lacked the strength to turn
into the rush. Acidtongue picked apart the shield, scattering its pieces. Croy's left was suddenly exposed and unde-
fended. Bikker howled in joy and twisted around, whipping
Acidtongue about and building to a slash that would cut
open Croy's belly and spill his guts on the ground.

One last shred of strength remained in Croy's body. He

used it up stabbing downward with the shortsword, driving
its point into the ground to make a wall against Acidtongue's
slash. The shortsword wobbled, good dwarven steel pushed
past its limits of flexibility. Acidtongue cut through it like
a ribbon. Fragments of steel flew everywhere, one of them
cutting through the skin of Croy's cheek. The sword that
remained was nothing but a hilt with a jagged inch or two of
blade sticking out of it. He dropped the hilt, then closed his
eyes and sank down on one knee.

He couldn't lift his head. His neck was perfectly exposed.
Acidtongue could cut through flesh without resistance when
it was hot and singing with battlelust. One cut and Bikker
could take his head off.

Croy couldn't lift it. He was just too tired.

Cythera, he thought, I love you. I am so sorry.

The blow didn't come.

Croy opened his eyes but still couldn't move. He looked
down at the grass beneath him. It looked very soft, and he
thought it would be nice to fall, face forward, into its green
embrace. One shard of his broken sword lay on the ground
there, etched but still shining with polish.

Bikker still hadn't killed him. What was he waiting for?

"Look at me, Croy."

Slowly, painfully, Croy lifted his head and met his foe's
eyes. Bikker's face was wild, his eyes mad. Froth flecked
his lips.

"Good," Bikker said. "That's taken care of. Draw Ghostcutter. Playtime is over. Now we'll fight like men."

# CHAPTER EIGHTY-SIX

Malden kept his eyes shut until he was sure the hellish light of sorcery had drained from the room. His hand clenched tight at the hilt of his bodkin, and he started to draw it, careful not to make a sound.

When the glare faded from the inside of his eyelids, he opened his eyes again and saw Hazoth still before him. Something had changed, something he noticed only in his peripheral vision, but he focused entirely on the sorcerer. Hazoth was breathing heavily and his hands were down by his sides. Malden bent his legs like springs and then jumped, thrusting the bodkin before him so it would cut right through the sorcerer's belly and come out the other side.

He fully expected Hazoth to turn and glare at him, eyes blazing with some spell that would tear his flesh from his bones. Or perhaps Hazoth would simply vanish before he could reach him. Instead he caught the magician completely off guard. He felt the point of the bodkin part the fibers of the sorcerer's nightshirt, felt it sink into the hated flesh, felt it scrape on bone. He pushed and shoved with all his might until it broke free from the sorcerer's back. He did not feel hot blood pour over his hand, but that surprised him less than the look on Hazoth's face.

The sorcerer simply looked disappointed.

Malden fell backward, pulling the bodkin free. He stared down at the length of iron in his hand and saw no blood on it, nor ichor nor living fire nor any of the things he supposed might flow through a sorcerer's veins. He looked up and saw the hole he'd cut through the nightshirt . . . but the flesh underneath wasn't even scarred.

"A violent response to a threatening stimulus. The hallmark of an unenlightened being. Rodent, you have surprised me so many times tonight—now you prove that there is a limit to what a primitive creature can do with cunning. Ah, well. I suppose even the most advanced of the species must eventually revert to rodentlike behavior. Oh, and now look at what you've gone and done."

Cythera cried out. Malden looked over at her and saw her staring at the palm of her left hand. The ink there looked like it was boiling. Flowers bloomed and their petals fell away, driven up her arm by a howling wind entirely contained within her skin. Vines circled around her wrist so tight they looked like they would constrict her pulse. On her face a hundred snowdrops wilted, while roses erupted in blossom across her shoulders, their thorns gleaming with painted poison.

It would seem the link that bound Cythera to Hazoth wasn't just for inimical magic. It could absorb physical damage as well.

"Cythera!" Malden shouted. "No—please, forgive me, I didn't know—"

"It's . . . all right, Malden," she said, straightening up. "It doesn't pain me. It just startles me a bit when it happens, that's all."

Hazoth looked from one of them to the other. Then he clucked his tongue and faced Malden again. "You interested me, briefly. That's why I've let you live for so long. But not for your animal passions, rodent. For the way you seemed to exceed the limitations of your upbringing. But now I see you've only been so clever, so brave, for one thing—that prize Cythera keeps between her legs." He shook his head sadly. "Pathetic. I'm afraid that attacking me was the last mistake I can permit you."

Malden's blood curdled in his veins. He knew he'd never been closer to death than this exact moment. His brains turned over in his head, desperately trying to imagine what to do next. He could think of only one thing: obfuscate. Stall for time. "I beg to disagree," he said. His mouth was so dry he had trouble forming the words. Hazoth had not given him leave to speak, but he knew it no longer mattered. Silence at that moment would have been his death warrant.

"What's that, rodent?"

"You suggest that my logic was faulty in some way. That I made an irrational decision by attacking you. I would say instead that my information was merely incomplete. I did not try to stab you before, when you caught me. I did not try to do so when your back was turned. I waited until your magic had drained you and distracted your attention to the point where an attack might logically succeed. You see, I thought very carefully before I struck that blow."

Hazoth looked upward, as if consulting a higher power. "Almost clever," he said. "There is one flaw, however. One place where your logic falls apart."

"Yes?" Malden asked, in the tone of a scholar asking for a gloss on a particularly thorny text.

"You," Hazoth said, "are the human equivalent of a cockroach. I am a being of extraordinary power. You should have recognized that someone like you could never, under any circumstances, harm me. The intelligent thing to do in this situation would have been to curl up and die. It would at least have saved you from what comes next."

Hazoth walked a few yards away from Malden and looked up again.

For the first time, Malden saw what had changed. When the sorcerer had cast his spell, Malden did not know what effect it might have. Now he understood. He had been transported from one place to another, without traversing the intervening distance. He was no longer in the sanctum.

Hazoth had delivered the three of them to his grand hall. They stood in the shadow of the iron egg.

"Now, I'll ask again. Who sent you here?"

Malden looked away. "I came on my own—this was all my plan," he insisted. Why implicate Cutbill? It wouldn't save his own life, and it would only make trouble for the guildmaster of thieves. If he could spare Cutbill that, then perhaps he could earn a little something with his death. "I need the crown or Anselm Vry is going to kill me."

Magic buzzed through the air toward Malden like an angry insect. An invisible stinger jabbed him in the chest, causing a bright blossom of pain to stretch its petals all the way around his rib cage.

"Impossible," Hazoth said. "You lack the will for something like this."

"I . . . swear," Malden said as the pain radiated outward, toward his extremities. Red blood stained his vision. "It was wholly . . . my own . . . notion . . . I—"

"It was Croy!" Cythera shouted. "Croy paid him to help me!"

The pain left Malden as quickly as it had come. He dropped to the marble floor, still writhing with the memory of it.

Hazoth turned to face Cythera. "Truly? I suppose I can believe that." Hazoth looked almost disappointed. "I had thought I might discover the name of my fellow schemer. Hmm. But yes—yes, Croy would be foolish enough. Very well."

He shrugged and came over to where Malden had curled up on the floor.

"So. We have reached the end of our experiment. The subject has failed to justify the hypothesis. There remains nothing to say," Hazoth said. "And there are other matters that require my attention. There is a knight errant on my lawn, brawling with the hired help. I think I need to go boil him in his own blood."

"Croy," Cythera said, one hand to her mouth. "No—you can't . . ."

Hazoth looked over at her. "You know perfectly well that I *can*," he said. "And now, by telling me he was behind this intrusion, you've given me every reason to do so immediately."

She went pale beneath her tattoos. "I meant—I meant to say—you may not," she said. "I won't allow it, Father."

Malden's eyes went wide.

"Father?" he said aloud. "He's your—"

"I did not say you could speak!" Hazoth screamed, and Malden's voice was lost.

It didn't matter. His own thoughts were louder than anything he might have said.

*The demon is his child*, she had said. *It is not his first.*

He had assumed she meant he'd sired other demons.

*Not all of his protections are magical*, she had said.

He'd assumed that meant the very human retainers he

kept to guard his gate. But perhaps she'd meant, instead, that he had a hold on her that was more complex than a mere contract of employment. She had betrayed him, Malden, and now he knew why.

In truth, he had never trusted her completely. Even when he'd kissed her, he half expected her to destroy him with her stockpile of curses. He had made sure she only knew half of his scheme. Now he understood that he could not expect her aid any longer. That she was not going to rescue him at the last minute.

He had, in a way, expected this.

It still hurt. It still cut him to the core.

"I will do as I please," Hazoth said, as cool as an autumn day. "As for you, rodent, I'm afraid you have to die. I know your simple brain will have trouble accepting this fact. You'll think there must be some way you can defeat me, no matter how desperate it may seem. I can assure you you're wrong. Please try to think of it philosophically. You had, what, a few decades left to live anyway? Eyeblinks, compared to my life span. The tragedy of your death will last as long as it takes a single tear to roll down Cythera's cheek."

"Very well," Malden said, thinking, Not quite yet. "And how shall I die? Are you going to curse me to death, or open up a crack in the earth and send me down to the pit?"

"Wasteful, and quite beneath me," Hazoth said. "I'm going to give your existence a purpose, albeit a small one. I'm going to feed you to my son." He reached up and slapped the iron egg with the flat of his palm. It rang like a bell.

And then it began to crack.

# CHAPTER EIGHTY-SEVEN

"Glorious! When it is finally born, there will be no power in this world that can stand against me," Hazoth said.

Red lines of infernal fire appeared on the surface of the iron sphere as a cascade of rust fell to the floor. The egg rocked slightly on its stand as the demon inside hammered again and again at its shell, trying to break out.

"The Ancient Blades will stop you," Malden insisted, more for his own benefit than to intimidate Hazoth. "They know how to slay demons."

"Luckily for me I have one of their number on my side," Hazoth pointed out. "Bikker will gladly slay all his old comrades, if I pay him well enough. It's important, rodent, to consider every angle of a problem. That's where you failed. You made a clever try of things, but you just didn't think them through *deeply* enough."

"And you have? This is madness," Malden said. "To release a demon on the world . . ." He thought of the beast that nearly killed him in the palace tower. Unless it was kept wet it grew at a furious rate and would never stop. "It is a creature not natural to this world," Malden said. "What will it do, once released? Will it eat every man and woman in the city? Or will it burn us all with hellfire?"

"Nothing so dramatic," Hazoth said. "Perhaps, when he is fully grown, he will have the power to do as you say. But my son is not ready to be born. When he emerges he will know nothing but pain—and there is only one way to quench that agony. He must devour the first living thing he encounters. Please, don't get any foolish notions. Cythera and I will be perfectly safe, as the demon will know his own blood. But he will swallow you whole, and that will give him strength to return to his egg and resume his gestation."

A thin shard of iron slid free from the shell and clattered to the floor. Red light shot out of the gap thus made.

"He will not rest until he has devoured you," Hazoth went on. "Night and day he will chase you. He could follow your trail for hundreds of miles, even if you do manage to escape this room. I don't think there's any reason why Cythera should have to watch you die. She seems quite taken with you. So I'll leave you to your fate."

Malden shrank back from the egg as it rattled and shook and more shards of iron fell away. "Hazoth!" he shouted. "You said that after eight hundred years, magic had corrupted the Burgrave, yes?"

The sorcerer frowned. "I suppose."

"What of the enchantments on your own self? After so many centuries, what have they done to your soul?"

Hazoth lifted his hand in the gesture that would transport him and Cythera out of the room. "An interesting question, but one that seems quite moot. You'll never learn the answer, I'm afraid."

Malden threw his arm across his eyes as light burst all around him. When it faded he was alone in the great hall.

Though not for long.

The egg continued to hatch as he watched, horrified. For a moment he couldn't move, so transfixed was he by the spectacle of the demon's birth. Then the thing inside the egg howled in utter pain, and he found his feet once more.

Many doors led away from the great hall. The obvious choice was the massive portal that opened onto the front lawn. If he could get out there he could get a head start before the demon came in pursuit.

That would, of course, only delay his doom. Besides, he had another scheme in mind.

He hurried to a door on one side wall, between two statues. It was the door that led eventually to the library, the same way he'd been taken on his first visit to the house. The door was locked but the mechanism was quite simple and perfectly ordinary. Malden hurriedly unwrapped his picks and wrenches from the hilt of his bodkin.

Behind him a clawed hand emerged from the egg and stretched raw flesh in the cold air. The demon started hauling itself out of its prison.

Hands shaking in fear, Malden stared at the rakes and hooks he held. Then he dropped them and kicked at the door until the flimsy lock shattered. When the door swung free he turned and glanced once more at the cracking egg, for a spare fraction of a moment.

What he saw made him yelp in terror.

# CHAPTER EIGHTY-EIGHT

Bikker was sweating. He wiped his brow with the back of one hand.

That was the extent of what Croy's best efforts to kill him had achieved. His tunic was cut in a number of places, but that only showed that the mail shirt he wore underneath it was unbroken. Croy's arm hadn't been strong enough to pierce the chain mail, even with the good dwarven steel of the shortsword.

"Get up," Bikker spat. "Come, now. I trained you to put up a better fight than this."

It was all Croy could do to keep his eyes open.

"Damn you, a good stiff breeze could kill you right now," Bikker insisted. His voice was not so hard as his words. "Croy, you don't have a chance. I could have cut you down a dozen times just now. Don't you want to live? Don't you want to win?"

Somehow Croy managed to find a little breath, which he used for forming words. "I've already won, Bikker. I kept my faith. I kept to my beliefs. You can slay me now, certainly. Doing so won't make you more of a man."

"And letting you live will?" Bikker snarled.

"No. There's nothing you can do to regain your honor. I understand that now. I had hoped to heal the wound on your soul. But it's too late."

Bikker growled then, or perhaps he shouted. It was an inchoate, wordless noise that came out of him as he clawed at the air with his free hand. He stamped his foot in rage. And then, little by little, he regained his composure. He came back to Croy and stood over him and looked down on him with something approaching calm.

"Draw Ghostcutter. Do me the honor of dying on your feet. Come!" Bikker seized Croy roughly under the armpits and hauled him upright. He held Croy there until the knight had his feet underneath him. He could stand, if he braced himself perfectly. But he couldn't lift his arms. The mere effort of standing took all his wind.

"This is folly," Bikker said. "You should learn from it, Croy. *Sir* Croy. You need to be woken up from your dreams of nobility and honor. Did I not teach you that even a mighty lord dies the same way as a humble villein? Apparently you weren't paying attention that day. A shame—if I kill you now you'll never learn. You'll go and sit by the Lady's side still thinking that heroes bleed a different color than the rest of us."

"I kept my faith," Croy whispered. "I lived that dream. I do not fear death."

A mischievous light crept into Bikker's eyes. "Interesting. Because it absolutely terrifies me. That's why I trained so hard, learned to be so strong. Because I knew that the only thing standing between me and the pit is my right arm and whatever iron I hold. But perhaps—perhaps there is something more to life."

"Yes."

"Perhaps," Bikker went on, "it's all true. All those pathetic slogans and vows of sacrifice you made, perhaps they mean something after all. Shall we see?"

"What do you mean?"

Bikker leaned very close until his face was only inches from Croy's. "Let's perform an experiment, like Hazoth in his laboratory. You'll be my test subject. I'll give you a simple choice and we'll see how much you believe your own fancies. Hmm?"

Croy was too tired to reply.

"I'll make you a promise. You can go free, and I won't chase you. After all, killing a weakling like you isn't going to be any fun. I'll let you live the rest of your life unmolested. All you have to do is turn around and walk away from me, without another word."

Croy frowned. This seemed unlikely.

"There is one proviso, however," Bikker said. "You must leave Ghostcutter here."

He looked very satisfied with himself for having devised this bargain. Croy's lips drew back from his teeth and he snarled.

"'My sword is my soul,'" he quoted. "You taught me that."

"Exactly," Bikker said. "So choose. Give up your soul, or forfeit your life."

He said no more.

Croy shook his head, disbelieving. Bikker was an Ancient Blade, same as himself. How could he make such an infernal demand? It was counter to everything Croy had ever believed, everything he'd ever learned. A Blade died with his sword in his hand, or only after passing it on to someone who could make better use of it in the endless war against demonkind. That was the law of their existence. The most important rule of their order.

But of course, that was the point. Croy had called Bikker a faithless coward. That oath only meant something if Croy could prove he, himself, was otherwise. If he accepted the bargain, he would make his insult meaningless. But he would live.

Croy could never accept such a fate. Except—

If he died now, he would never see Cythera again. She and her mother would remain in bondage under Hazoth's rule, forever. If he surrendered now, there would be another chance. Someday. Another possibility of rescue.

Croy made his choice. He lifted an arm that felt like a bar

of lead and placed his hand around Ghostcutter's hilt. Inch by inch he began to draw it from its scabbard.

# CHAPTER EIGHTY-NINE

The demon howled in agony, and Malden had to hang on to the door frame not to be knocked down. It was a hideous thing to look upon, but he could only imagine its pain. It—Malden could not bring himself to think of the thing as a "he"—must have experienced every instant of its new life as an eternity of suffering.

As Hazoth had said, it was not ready to be born. It had no skin on its stringy muscles and it oozed pus every time it stretched. Steam lifted from its back in great white coils, and where its feet touched the marble floor, the stone grew slick with its blood. In shape it was not unlike a horribly deformed hound, though it had seven legs—none of them the same length or shape. Sprouting from its shoulders on long thick necks were a row of human skulls with wicked fanged jaws. The eye sockets were filled with wet red membranes that throbbed and sucked at the air. Malden assumed that was how it scented, and that this was the only sense it possessed.

When it screamed, the sound issued not from the clacking jaws of the skulls but from a gaping mouth in its chest filled with round half-formed teeth.

It pawed at the floor, stumbling like a newborn foal. Every footfall made the entire house shake. Its skull heads wove through the air at the end of the clumsy necks, and its nostrils squeezed shut, then shot open again. One by one the skulls turned to point directly at Malden. How it could smell anything through the thick reek of brimstone in the air was an open question, but he had no doubt it was quite aware of him.

Malden shrank back as far as he could, yet it was as if he were transfixed, so horrified by the thing's appearance he couldn't move.

The demon took a tottering step forward, its multitude of claws clacking on the floor.

Time to run.

The paralysis of horror left him in a rush of blood to his legs. Malden slammed the door behind him, only to hear it splinter and crack as the demon rammed its way through. By that point he was well down the hall beyond, nearly at the door of the library. The demon squeezed into the hallway and came galloping toward him, no longer so awkward or graceless. It was fast—far faster than he was—and it would be on him in a second if he didn't move. He flung himself at the door to the library and, thank the Bloodgod, it flew open.

Inside the library he leapt over a divan just as the demon smashed through the doorway, shattering the door frame with its odd number of shoulders. It reared up and swung two of its legs through the air, an instant away from crushing Malden beneath one foot that looked like a hoof and another like the paw of a wolf.

Malden threw his arms across his face, knowing that if the thing struck him even once, it would be his end. He rolled back and away from the beast as it came lurching forward—

—and then stopped in mid-attack.

Kemper, I hope you made it this far, Malden thought. He'd given the card sharp strict instructions to include the library on his itinerary as he made his way around the house, but Malden also knew that if there had been any danger of being caught, Kemper might have cut his circuit short.

Yet now the demon sniffed and sucked at the air, and its skull heads craned around the room, searching something out. Malden edged away slowly, crawling backward on his hands so as not to make any noise, in case the thing had ears hidden somewhere on its body.

One of the skull heads fixated on a particular glass-fronted bookcase. It brought a second head around to sniff as well, as if making sure it had the right scent. Then it threw all of its considerable mass at the case, pulverizing the glass, sending the books flying, smashing through the thick wooden shelves. It savaged the case with its jaws and its huge wet mouth, striking again and again with its claws and hooves and talons until it battered through the wall behind the case as well.

A lone playing card, the six of acorns, floated out of the wreckage and drifted to the floor. The demon stamped on it, tore it to shreds with its teeth, and swallowed the bits of paper that remained.

By the time it was finished, Malden had already broken for the next door, and the next hallway.

# CHAPTER NINETY

Croy gritted his teeth.

For my lord the Burgrave, he thought. For honor. For the code of the Ancient Blades. For the sake of my immortal soul.

*For Cythera.*

Every fiber of his being was in agreement. He would not surrender his sword. He would not turn and walk away. If he died in the next moment, he would die as he had lived. The sacrifice was acceptable.

But he didn't intend to die.

As he drew Ghostcutter free of its scabbard, warmth flowed down his arm. His heart was giving up the last of its strength, all in the service of one final battle.

Bikker smiled, as if this was exactly what he wanted. "You'll fall quickly enough. But you'll die on your feet," he said. "Do you see what honor is, now? Honor is something that exists between men like us. Strong men! The weak of this world, the peasants, the little people—they know nothing of it."

Croy thought of Malden and Kemper affirming that there was no honor among thieves. Maybe Bikker was right.

But—no. Malden had risked everything to help Cythera. Malden had gone into Hazoth's villa, uncertain of what he could achieve, but willing to try.

"You were wrong earlier," Croy said.

"What? What are you prattling about?" Bikker demanded.

"Earlier. You said I thought my blood was a different color from yours. You were wrong."

"I think you're feverish, Croy. Your wounds would certainly warrant it. Speak clearly, man, or just be quiet and let us finish what we've started."

"I don't think I bleed a different color than you," Croy said. "Blood is the same in every man's veins. But there is something in me you can't match."

He thought back to when Bikker had trained him, to one day in particular. They'd been going through postures for hours, Croy learning every way there was to hold a sword. They'd practiced hundreds of parries, thousands of lunges. Bikker called a halt when neither of them could see for the sweat in their eyes. Then, when Croy put Ghostcutter away for the day, Bikker picked up a wooden practice sword and knocked him into a pigpen with one solid whack to the back of his knees.

"Fencing is something gentle folk do," Bikker had said. "You can train a lifetime to master it. But never forget—anyone, even a peasant, can bring you down with a single, solid blow. It only takes one cut to kill a man."

So now he faced Bikker with Ghostcutter gripped in both hands, the point aimed directly at Bikker's heart. Bikker took his own stance, with Acidtongue at an angle across the front of his body.

If he was focused and committed enough, Croy thought, he might strike one more blow before his body gave out completely. He would have to make it the one that brought Bikker down.

The two of them nodded at each other in way of salute.

And then they began.

# CHAPTER NINETY-ONE

Malden hurried down the long corridor at the back of the villa that opened on the dining room and its pre-paratory. The door there would provide another chance to escape into the night—but he wasn't done yet.

Behind him the prematurely born demon howled and raged and clawed at the walls. An ornamental table stood in the hallway, a delicate piece of turned rosewood. The nine of bells lay on its surface like a calling card.

With a cry of rage the demon smashed the table to flinders, then beat at the wall and floor where the table had been with an unquenchable will and a strength a hundred times greater than a man's. The card was obliterated, but still the demon smashed and clawed until the plaster wall exploded in a cloud of white dust and the wattles behind it burst like matchwood. Malden hurried down the hall, breathing heavily now. Surely it wouldn't take much longer.

Behind him he could hear the demon clawing at the walls, pulling down timbers from the ceiling. The house shook and danced, and he was nearly thrown from his feet with every step. The demon was taking the place to pieces in its search for him.

Half the house was in ruins now, torn apart by the beast

as it sought out his scent. It must be horribly confused, he thought, because it smelled him everywhere—everywhere Kemper had left one of his cards.

Cythera had told him that the demon hunted by smell alone, and that it could follow its prey's scent through any obstacle or diversion. It made him think of someone else who worked miracles with his nose—Kemper, the card sharp, whose cards were not visibly marked but who knew the stink of every one of them so well that when he dealt them, they might as well have been faceup.

With all that in mind, for the past three days Malden had carried those cards inside his tunic, through all manner of exertions. He had rubbed them on his armpits and his groin, on the sweaty back of his neck, on any part of his body that might imbue them with his smell. He had not lacked for exudation—fear made him sweat copiously.

When he gave them back to Kemper, the card sharp was most displeased. Malden had ruined them for gaming by changing the invisible markings Kemper knew so well. But for the purposes of this scheme, the card sharp had been willing to make the sacrifice. While Malden worked his way into the sanctum, Kemper had moved around the house as only an intangible man could, walking through walls and locked doors, keeping out of sight, and placing his cards here and there, one under a fine mahogany dressing table, one in a closet full of crockery and plates.

The cards served the purpose of slowing the demon down. It had to investigate each card, and its method of investigation was to destroy whatever it smelled. The time it took the demon to smash Hazoth's finest furniture was all the time Malden needed to get a head start on it and keep clear of its jaws.

Hopefully, the cards would serve another purpose.

Malden had known it would be impossible to steal the crown back without alerting Hazoth to his presence. The man was a sorcerer, after all, and this was his own house. After hundreds of years in it he must know its every nook and cranny better than Kemper knew his cards. So Malden's scheme to retake the crown had been constructed, by necessity, around the knowledge that eventually he would have to face the demon.

Malden turned in a doorway and looked down a long hall lit only by a single cresset. Halfway down the hall the demon roared as it pulverized a linen press, searching destructively for the card Kemper must have hidden at its bottom. Shreds of cloth and fibers of the best linen floated in the air as the demon beat and flailed at the walls with its mismatched legs.

Malden stepped through the door and slammed it behind him. He was no longer worried about making any noise. Especially when the house had begun to creak and moan all around him. He could hear its columns and its boards shifting on foundations that had stood for as long as there was a city around it. The wood was strained by the damage the demon did to its walls. Malden pricked up his ears as he heard a series of popping noises like thunder cracks. Nails giving way above his head, one after the other, bursting from the beams and rafters they held together.

It was time to flee, definitely. Behind him the demon raged and threw itself at the door he'd closed, desperate to get at him, needing to devour him so it could return to its egg and resume its long sleep. The wall around the door shook and split, as a wide crack opened in the plaster and went racing toward the ceiling.

Get out now, Malden thought, and raced toward a solarium at the far end of the house. A door there stood between him and the garden. It was locked, and far too sturdy to knock down with his shoulder. He cursed as he reached for his bodkin and the tools woven into its grip. He needn't have bothered, though. Before he could get his first pick free, the entire house leaned over to one side, the walls and ceiling seeming to career right toward where he stood. The door before him, warped out of its frame, went spinning off into the night.

Behind him the demon crashed into the solarium. Its skull heads circled around in the air, its red nostrils pulsing. Malden ran through where the door had been and out into cool night air, the demon hard on his heels. It got one of its skull heads and two of its legs through the doorway before the second and third floors of the house collapsed all at once on its back.

The noise was beyond imagining, like the earth opening wide to suck the entire city down into the pit. Debris was everywhere, tumbling and arcing through the air, entire rafter beams dancing end over end across the Ladypark Common. A rolling cloud of plaster dust hit Malden like a tidal wave and he was knocked down by the shock wave. A piece of glass jagged as a knife blade cut across his forehead, and blood made red tracks through the dust that covered his face.

Choking and heaving for breath, he got back to his feet and surveyed the destruction. It looked like a storm had loosed every lightning bolt in its quiver at the house, all at once. The villa had become a chaotic hell of rubble and wreckage, with barely two boards still standing attached to one another. In the mess, a few small fires burned, while dozens of small animals, freed from their cages in the ruin, burst into flight or went howling away on long legs or only crawled or slithered out of the cataclysm.

Malden could hardly believe his eyes. This had been his plan all along, of course, but even so—the damage was immeasurable. The destruction utterly complete.

He started to dust himself off, but stopped when he saw something moving inside the debris. A massive board was heaved clear and then a snowdrift of plaster went sliding into a cavity in the heap. A pink, raw arm reached up from inside and hauled at a crossbeam that was still mostly intact. Little by little the demon pulled itself clear of the remains of the house. Its skull heads lifted clear of the wreckage and its mouth began to howl once more.

"Bloodgod take my eyes," Malden cursed.

The demon had survived.

# CHAPTER NINETY-TWO

A minute earlier, outside:

Bikker took a step toward Croy's left, but did not advance.

Croy stood where he was. Ghostcutter's point tracked Bikker as he moved. Croy had lived with the sword so long it took no effort at all to keep it pointed at the bearded swordsman.

This would all be over in a moment.

One strike—and Acidtongue would carve Croy like a chicken. The vitriol on its blade would sear through his flesh and he would be undone.

One thrust—and Ghostcutter would drive through Bikker's shirt of chain, pierce his vitals, and leave him gasping in his own blood. Assuming Croy had enough strength left to complete the stroke.

"Are you ready?" Bikker asked.

"There is no such thing as readiness," Croy said. "One fights, and lives, or one prepares, and one dies. You taught me that."

"Do you regret it has come to this?" Bikker asked.

"Yes."

Bikker sighed. "As do I, to be honest. Shall we count to three, and then strike?"

"One," Croy said.

"Two," Bikker responded.

"Three," they said together.

Acidtongue whirled through the air, coming down hard and fast from Croy's left, his weak side. Croy tried to lean out of the way but knew he wouldn't be fast enough. Ghostcutter shifted in his hand and came upward to parry. The two blades met with an awful grinding, sizzling noise. Acid bit into Ghostcutter's silver edge and notched the iron underneath. Bikker pushed forward suddenly and Croy went sprawling, his left hand out to catch him as he fell.

Not enough, not nearly enough—Croy had wasted his one cut—it was the end—in a moment Bikker would remise, following through on the stroke Croy had parried, bringing the blow home, and—

—Ghostcutter broke free of the engagement, ringing clear of Acidtongue. The acid had made the blades slick and unlocked them. Croy turned at the waist as he fell, trying to catch himself before he fell on his back, and Ghostcutter whistled through the air in a tight arc. Croy used every bit of control he had over the weapon and brought it low and inside Bikker's guard. Busy gaining leverage for his remise, Bikker had his arms up, and that left his side unprotected.

Ghostcutter was a heavy blade. Its own momentum sliced through the chain-mail shirt over Bikker's hip and deep into the flesh beneath. It didn't stop until it had sliced halfway through Bikker's spine.

Bikker gasped and took a step backward, and Ghostcutter came free of his midsection as easily as it was pulled from its own scabbard.

"Sadu take you," Bikker shouted, and lifted Acidtongue again for another stroke. He lunged forward, but before he was halfway to Croy he stumbled and blood came vomiting out of his mouth.

Acidtongue dropped to the grass. It was dry by the time it landed—it secreted vitriol only when held by a strong arm. Bikker dropped to his knees beside it and then fell face forward into the earth.

Croy crawled toward his old teacher and rolled the man over on his back. Bikker's face was congested with blood and his eyes weren't focusing. His mouth moved but the words that came out were inaudible whispers. Croy bent his ear over Bikker's lips to hear what he said.

"When you find an heir for my sword," Bikker told him, his voice no louder than the breeze that ruffled the grass, "teach him that stroke. It's a good one."

Croy closed his friend's eyelids, and wept.

He was not given time to grieve, however.

The grass was blown back by a flash of light more bright than the sun at midday. Hazoth and Cythera were suddenly standing over him. He looked up into her eyes but didn't like what he saw there.

She might have spoken—but just then, behind Croy, the villa fell in on itself with a mammoth crash.

# CHAPTER NINETY-THREE

"Croy! Croy!" Malden called, racing around the side of the house where the debris was not so thick. He jumped onto a fallen rafter beam and leapt into a drift of plaster dust that billowed up around him like a cloud. He managed to sidestep a pile of broken glass but still came down hard on a plank of wood that shifted under him and sent him sprawling forward.

Behind him the demon's skull heads bit at the air. It was almost upon him.

"Croy! Kill it!" he screamed as he came around to the front of the house, where the rose window had fallen in a million shards of colored glass.

He took in the scene in an instant, though he liked little of it. Bikker looked dead, which was a good thing, and Croy was still holding his sword. The knight was sitting down in the grass, however, with his knees up to his chest, and he looked as pale as a sheet. Had the two fools killed each other?

Cythera and Hazoth were there, too. Both of them were staring at the pile of rubble that had been their home. They seemed too paralyzed by surprise to react.

"Demon!" Malden shouted, his feet slapping against the grass. "Croy!"

He raced up to the knight and then jumped over Croy's head. The demon was right behind him, snatching at his heels with one clawed foot.

Ghostcutter was pointed at the sky, suddenly. Croy did not rise, or call out a threat, or even shift from where he sat, but his sword pointed upward. The demon couldn't see it, having no eyes, and as the blade bit into its belly, at first it seemed not even to notice.

Then the cold iron blade pierced it through, and the point came out through the demon's back. It fell on Croy hard enough to crush any man, and scratched at the ground with every one of its mismatched legs, but it couldn't seem to get free.

Cythera shouted for Croy, but the knight was completely covered by the demon's body. If he heard her, he could make no reply.

"Malden, he was already gravely wounded—if we don't get him out of there soon he'll smother," she said, beseeching the thief.

Malden started to shrug. What could he do? His bodkin was useless against the thing. He was no Ancient Blade to fight a demon. But then—

He saw Acidtongue on the ground next to Bikker's body. Like Ghostcutter, it was made for fighting demons. Malden grabbed it and found that he could barely lift it. He'd never used a sword in his life and realized instantly that it wasn't just a matter of swinging it around like a stick.

But then drops of vitriol appeared along the blade's length like sweat. Grabbing the hilt with both hands, Malden rushed toward the demon, holding the sword straight out from his body. He jabbed it into the demon's back and leaned on the pommel until it sank deep into the demon's vitals.

The skull heads reared up and screamed at the stars as the demon redoubled its thrashing. Malden let go of the sword's hilt then and staggered back, trying to get clear of its flailing legs.

Eventually it died, and lay still. Its flesh fumed and lique-fied until its bones stuck up through its raw musculature. Its claws curled and withered like paper in a fire. Soon it was no more than wisps of foul-smelling smoke and a pool of vile liquid. Underneath its remains, Croy struggled to pull Ghostcutter free of the infernal thing's rib cage.

Malden stared at the beast in utter incomprehension. He couldn't believe what he had just done. He had killed a demon. He—the puny thief, who had never even cut a human being before—had killed. Of course, it had been pinned and immobile, and— But he had killed it—

Malden started to whoop in joy. But then an invisible hand grasped his heart and began to squeeze.

"My son . . . my house," Hazoth said. "You destroyed my house."

Malden dropped to the ground, unable to move a muscle. The sorcerer leaned over him.

"I was going to allow you a quick death, rodent," the sorcerer said. "No more."

# CHAPTER NINETY-FOUR

Malden rolled on the ground, his body coming to pieces from the inside out. Pain gripped him like iron tongs as Hazoth twisted one hand in the air, and his guts tied themselves in knots. He could barely see anything—his vision had turned the bright red of arterial blood.

Then it cleared, just enough for him to look up into Hazoth's face. "I want you to see me while you suffer," the sorcerer told him. "I want you to feel everything. The pain I'm about to inflict on you would normally drive a rodent unconscious. It might even kill one outright. Your primitive brain would rather die than live through this agony. But I won't let it. You are going to suffer for what you've done to me. And I know more than anyone about what suffering means."

Malden gasped for breath, but every ounce of air he inhaled felt like he was swallowing knives. His arms curled around his chest, constricted by pain, but still he could see the magician staring down into his eyes.

So he could see it very clearly when a red blotch appeared on Hazoth's cheek and burst through the skin as an ugly boil.

It was such a surprise he almost forgot the pain. Almost.

"Your spells are . . . slipping," he wheezed.

"You know nothing of magic. Save your breath for the screams you are about to utter," Hazoth told him.

Yet even as the wizard spoke, pimples erupted near his hairline. Hazoth reached up to feel the bumpy skin there and something miraculous happened.

The expression on his face changed. He started to show real fear. He even cried out as one of his eyes grew thick with cataracts.

On the ground, Malden wanted to laugh. He wanted to crow for joy. The pain he'd felt disappeared as Hazoth reared back and clutched at his ear, which had begun to drip blood. "What is this?" Hazoth demanded. He turned to stare at Cythera.

"The link between us is fading, Father," she said. The vines and flowers on her face writhed and bloomed wildly. "He did it. The thief did it—Coruth must be free. When the house came down it must have broken your magic circle. She has undone the connection she once made between you and I." Cythera looked like she could hardly believe it herself. As if she didn't dare believe what was happening.

But it was real. The curses Hazoth had avoided so long, the inimical magics cast on him by the demons of the pit in revenge for all he'd done to them, were getting through. Instead of being deposited on Cythera's skin as painted flowers, they were appearing on his own skin as blossoms of blood and corruption.

"Damn that woman," Hazoth said, his voice thick with phlegm. He shook himself and spoke a few words in some ancient language. Instantly, the sores on his face stopped weeping and closed again, until his countenance was as unblemished as before. "She's weak, though. Too weak to resist. I'll find her and prison her again."

"No, I don't think you will," Cythera said.

Then she grabbed him by the arms and mashed her lips against his cheek in a brutal kiss. "Farewell, Father."

Hazoth's eyes went wide. Green sparks lit up his hair and his chest.

On Cythera's left hand an oleander flower curled up and withered. A vine retracted around her wrist, shrinking back on itself.

"Malden," Cythera said, quite calmly, "you should go now."

The thief scrambled to his feet and ran. Behind him he heard Hazoth start to scream as the skin of his back split open and demonic arms reached out to grasp at him with shredding claws.

Every curse Cythera had stored on her skin for decades came loose at once, and they lashed out at Hazoth with interest. As the magician's protective spells came apart, the demons he had exploited and enslaved sensed the release down in the pit, and sought every crack and crevice in the universe through which they could reach his side, intent on having their vengeance before the curses could undo Hazoth entirely. The people who lived on Ladypark Common closed their shutters and hid under their beds, but could not escape for the next three hours the screams of a dying sorcerer and the bellowing rage of the Bloodgod's children, denied this prize for so long. They took their time destroying Hazoth. They savored it.

# CHAPTER NINETY-FIVE

Witchly light filled the sky over the common, and the gruesome sounds of Hazoth's demise made the air shiver. Malden did not look back over his shoulder, as much as he might have enjoyed watching Hazoth meet his sticky end. He had places to go yet tonight, things to achieve, or all could still be lost.

He could see his path easily in the weird illumination as he broke for the streets beyond the common, intending to lose himself in that maze and make good his escape.

He was not to be so lucky.

Ahead of him on the Cripplegate Road, a score of men in cloaks-of-eyes were waiting with weapons in hand. They moved quickly to cut off any avenue of escape, circling around him should he even think to return to the ruined villa. When Malden was completely surrounded, one of them came forward and held out an empty hand. "Give it over, thief," he said.

"I beg your pardon?" Malden tried.

"We know you've got a dagger at your belt. Give it over or I'll run you through and take it from you."

Malden stared at the man with pure hatred. But there was nothing he could do. He drew the bodkin from his belt and handed it over. "I'll want that back, now."

With a chuckle, the watchman tossed the knife over the wall of the Ladypark.

Malden's heart sank. The message was clear. He wasn't going to need the knife anymore. He would not be given another chance to use it.

The rank of watchmen parted and someone came through the gap. Anselm Vry—with an expression of annoyance on his face.

"You really couldn't do it with less fuss?" he asked.

Malden blinked in feigned incomprehension. "Do what,

milord? I was only walking on the common, something I often do at night. I find it calms my mind. I'm not sure what's going on over there," he said, pointing at the green fire dancing on the other side of the common, "but I think you should definitely go investigate."

Vry sneered at him. "What's that on your belt, then?" he asked.

Malden patted his belt as if he couldn't guess what the bailiff meant. Then he said, "Oh!" and unbuckled his belt to remove it. "You mean this." The belt had been threaded through the golden crown he'd hidden under his cloak. He handed it over to Vry, who snatched it away from him.

The bailiff closed his eyes and held the crown up in both hands. His eyes snapped open for a moment and he stared at Malden, but then looked away and nodded. "Yes, of course, milord," he said, as if talking to the crown, not to Malden. "You," he said, to one of his watchmen. "The bag." A velvet sack was brought forth and the crown placed carefully inside. "Very good, thief," Vry said.

Malden bowed low. "So, may I inquire if there is a reward? I prefer it in gold, but will take silver if I must."

"I'll count it out in steel," Vry said with a short, nasty laugh. "You—kill him. Then form a detail and carry his body to the Skrait. Make sure you weigh it down so no one ever finds it."

A watchman with a halberd came lunging forward, but Malden had expected this and was already moving. He scurried up the wall of the Ladypark and dropped into a stand of bushes on the far side. There, he lay still and held his breath.

A half dozen faces appeared over the top of the wall, including Vry's. They peered into the darkness for a long minute before withdrawing:

"It makes no difference. Let panthers and wolves fight over him now," Vry said. "If he lives through the night, we'll just find him in the morning."

And with that they left.

Malden stayed still for a while longer, and then, when he was sure no one was watching, he got up and started looking for his bodkin.

# CHAPTER NINETY-SIX

"Lay easy," Cythera said. She held Croy's hand tight. His other hand still clutched the hilt of Ghostcutter. He looked at the blade and saw a bad notch in its silver edge, a wound it had taken when it blocked Acidtongue's attack. He wondered if a dwarf could repair that damage, or if he should leave it there forever, in memory of Bikker.

"It's over," Cythera said again. "Hazoth is dead."

"Hazoth?" Croy said, confused. "No, it's Bikker, that's—that's Bikker there. I killed him. It had to be done. In the end I think maybe I was getting through to him, but—but it had to be done." He struggled to sit up, and she pushed him back to the grass. He could not resist her hands.

Her hands! She had touched him, and not been very gentle about it. But that could only mean one thing. He looked to her with wild eyes. Her face was . . . was unpainted. The curses that had ornamented her skin were gone. All of them.

She was even more beautiful than he remembered. Her skin was clear and fair, her eyes dark pools of calm and wisdom. Her slender arms were unadorned by so much as a painted leaf.

She was free.

"Over there," she said, and pointed at a pillar of what looked like charred wood standing in the grass a dozen feet away. As Croy watched, it collapsed in on itself, like a log burned down to charcoal and ashes. "That's all that's left of my father."

"What of your mother?" Croy asked.

"I am here as well, but in far better condition." Coruth was suddenly standing at Croy's feet, looking down on him.

She was exactly the way he remembered her. Wild and unkempt hair the color of new-forged iron. A nose as thin and sharp as a halberd blade, and eyes that saw everything. She wore no pleasant countenance, but for that she could hardly be blamed. She'd spent the last ten years imprisoned in a magic circle. Of late she'd been a tree. Now she wore a simple black robe and had one arm in a makeshift sling, but he knew that if the kings and queens of the world could see her, they would bow their heads in respect. There was an aura around Coruth that anyone could sense, an aura of power.

"I will heal your body," she said. "That shall be your reward. For the thief, perhaps, there will be something more."

"I thank you," Croy said.

Coruth looked away and nodded. Then she turned herself into a flock of blackbirds and flew away, chattering to herself with many voices.

"She'll be back for you, don't worry," Cythera told the knight. "And I'll stay until she returns."

He reached out his left hand and she took it again.

Together they sat and watched the ruined house. Its fallen timbers smoldered and settled through the night, with occasional rumblings and groans, and now and then a loud report as a broken rafter collapsed or another piece of glass snapped under pressure. The wreckage was full of sharp barbs and unstable piles of masonry, leavened with heaps of broken glass that would shred any foot that tried to walk through them. Occasionally a bolt of green or red or blue discharged as some arcane energy was loosed from long confinement.

The ruin did not look safe at all, but that didn't mean it was left undisturbed.

The first figure to crawl over the pile was that of Kemper. The intangible man cackled and clanked as he picked through the fallen house. His tunic was stuffed full of silver: knives, spoons, plates and dishes, actual coins, buckles, fittings and ornaments. The house had been a treasure trove of the stuff, and he was given the right to first pickings. When he finally left, barely able to walk for all the silver he'd stuffed into his clothes or carried in his straining arms, he was carrying a fortune.

The next visitors to the fallen house were the beggar

children of the Ashes. Tipped off by Malden, they arrived early and made quick work of sorting through the wreckage. They carried away books and tapestries and valuable pieces of unbroken glass. They carried off magic wands and shards of rusted iron that someone would buy. They took the bits of gold they found, some melted in the fires, some still in the shape of broken jewelry and dented goblets. Malden had told Croy that a rousing story of bravery would not change the children's lives, and the knight thought the thief was just being apathetic, that he did not care for their welfare. He saw now that Malden had arranged for this—he must have given the children notice of what was to come. The quality of life the children enjoyed would be enlarged tenfold overnight, and Croy was glad. One of the children, a little girl in a dress made of an old sack, came over and stared at him for a while. He smiled at her, and she pressed a tiny treasure into his hand. A single glass bead, blue in color, quite valueless, but pretty. He thanked her with all the courtly politesse he could muster before she shrugged and ran away.

Nearer to dawn the dwarf Slag arrived with a team of four horses and a massive wagon. He stared out into the darkness with alert eyes while a crew of human workers made their way through the wreckage with pry bars and block and tackle. It was not easy, but they were able to shift the half of the demon's egg that remained unshattered. Rolling it on its side, they managed to get it into the wagon, and Slag hauled it away before anyone could see. What he wanted with several tons worth of pit-forged iron Croy could not imagine, but he was certain the dwarf would make good use of it.

Others came, people Croy did not know. The news must have spread quickly that Hazoth had fallen and his treasures were up for grabs. Footpads, rogues, and bravos combed through the wreckage and took away what they desired— loot and weaponry, mostly. A papermaker and his apprentices came and carried off great sheaves of scorched and torn paper and cloth, which they would pulp down for raw materials. Half of the chandler's guild came and took all the broken glass away, and sawyers took those beams and wattles that had not already been ground to sawdust in the collapse. Just before dawn gleaners from the Stink came and carted away that which no one else deemed valuable.

It seemed impossible that anything would remain, yet one last looter did come. Gurrh the ogre, who had been sitting on the grass outside the gates the whole time, rose at dawn and made his way into the ruin. He picked through the debris until he found a leaden coffer, still sealed and barely dented. He tucked it under his armpit and then headed west, toward Swampwall and his home.

All according to plan.

As the sun came up, Cythera and Croy greeted it together, alone again. "It's Ladymas," Croy said, and Cythera kissed his cheek. "We prevailed," he said, because he couldn't quite believe it. "We won."

Meanwhile, inside the Ladypark a wolf snarled and snapped at the air. Behind it a dozen more circled, waiting their turn to attack. Malden held his hands out toward the beast, trying to calm it. He wished it didn't look so hungry. He wished he'd kept Acidtongue as a prize, so he wouldn't have to rely on his laughable bodkin. He wished so many people didn't want him dead. He wished he knew better how to fight.

He wished he could go home and go to sleep.

Instead it looked like his short career as a thief was going to end with him being devoured by a pack of wolves. All this for nothing, he thought.

The wolf took a step forward, its paw patting at the ground as if it were afraid of something, afraid to lunge. A hundred birds cawed and squawked behind Malden then, and he nearly jumped out of his own skin.

Then an old woman in a dark robe stepped around him. She held one hand down low where the wolf could sniff at it. The animal licked her palm, then laid down in the grass and rested its head.

"I think I know you," Malden said to his rescuer. "I've seen you before."

"Yes," the woman agreed.

"Of course, at the time your complexion was more . . . barky." He put his bodkin away. "You're free, then. It worked."

"Yes."

"So . . . it's over," Malden said, because he devoutly wished that could be true.

"No," she said.

"No," he repeated. "No, I don't suppose it is. Not quite yet."


# CHAPTER NINETY-SEVEN


Market Square was thick with crowds, people of every station and profession crammed together into the wide cobblestoned space, with cheers and prayers going up from every lip, with banners unfurled from every high place and gold or brass or tin cornucopias pinned to every hat and tunic. Since dawn the priests of the Lady had been out ministering to the faithful, leading long liturgical plainsongs and invoking the Lady's blessings on the people, the city, and the king. They had to pick their way with care through streets so crammed with people there was no room to move freely. The citizens of Ness and all the pilgrims who had come for this holiest of days were all abroad, moving back and forth across the city as best they could, paying visits to each other or simply walking, taking in the fine weather while they uttered their prayers and thanks. In a riot of color and noise they praised the Lady.

It was the kind of crowd that could move mountains if it chose. It was the kind of crowd that could, with the slightest push, be inspired to riot. To tear up the city in its excitement.

A little wrath, a little shocked surprise, and the whole Free City of Ness could erupt like a burst dam.

The throng gathered thickest and most fervent directly outside the Ladychapel, the great spired and vaulted church where the day's grand procession would begin. The massive wooden doors were still closed, but men of the watch had to form a double cordon outside to keep the faithful from rushing in and seeing the icons before their proper time. With quarterstaffs and ropes they pushed the crowds back again and again. A few young devotees tried to climb up the heavily carved exterior of the chapel but were knocked down with long poles.

One climber, however, had the brilliant idea to ascend the back of the chapel, where the guards weren't watching. Of course, he was not one of the faithful overcome by religious zeal. He didn't want to fall prostrate before the Lady's altar, nor did he wish to break in and steal the cakes and sweetmeats loaded in the giant golden cornucopia inside either.

Malden clutched at a gargoyle and hoisted himself up to one of the clerestory windows high on the side of the church. The window had been cranked open to let in some air—this close to midsummer, it was already hot just two hours past dawn—so he slipped inside and hid himself in the holy images mounted around the chapel dome.

The acoustics of that place were such, and his senses so sharpened by nervous dread, that he could see and hear everything that took place in the nave below. A red velvet carpet had been unrolled from the altar all the way to the massive doors. Anselm Vry was down there, dressed in a cloak of state. It had the repeating eye motif of a watchman's cloak, but was brocaded with silver wire. It looked very heavy. The Burgrave was there as well in full regalia, though his head was bare. They stood surrounded by a clutch of green-robed priests who prayed and wafted holy smoke around the Burgrave, while young acolytes went about lighting hundreds of candles and dozens of censers until the icons shone like the sun.

"I said, leave us!" Vry shouted.

"Milord bailiff," one of the priests insisted, "this is a holy precinct, and your authority here is—"

Vry established that authority by drawing a long dagger and pointing it at the priest's face. "The Burgrave is not well. I must administer his physic before the procession begins, and I will not have you watch me do so," he said.

The priest had turned deathly pale when the knife came out. Now he nodded and gestured at his fellows and the acolytes. They streamed out of the nave quickly enough.

When Vry and the Burgrave were alone, the bailiff sheathed his dagger and then turned to look at the Burgrave with disdain. Ommen Tarness was weeping softly, a horrible sound well-amplified by the dome of the chapel. Up on his perch, Malden peered down with unsympathetic interest.

"I don't want to wear it," Ommen said, his voice thick with snot. "I won't! I'm free, finally free. Anselm, I feel . . . smarter today. I feel like—like I'm waking up from a very long nap, and I'm still groggy, but I feel—"

Vry slapped the Burgrave hard across the face. Then he drew the crown from inside his silver cloak-of-eyes. "We discussed this. You will put on the crown. You will go out there and make your speech. I have an archer standing ready to cut you down if you start to babble. When you're done speaking the words I gave you, I will emerge and announce that you have been ill and are no longer fit to serve as Burgrave. Then I will take you away from all this, and you'll never have to wear the crown again."

"You . . . promise?" the Burgrave asked. He sounded like a naive child being promised a candy if he was good during a court ceremony. "Never again?"

"Just this one last time. And anyway, this isn't the crown you're afraid of. This one doesn't talk." He lowered it over Ommen's head, and the Burgrave bit his lip and mewled but didn't stop him.

Ommen squeezed his eyes tight as the crown made contact with his scalp. After a moment, though, he opened his eyes wide in surprise. "You're right! It's lost its power. I'm still—still me!"

Vry smiled without humor. His expression changed drastically, however, when the crown lifted off Ommen Tarness's head and started to float away.

Up in the dome, Malden reeled in his line. He held the hat-fishing pole that Slag had made, the one the dwarf meant to be used under the arch of the Royal Ditch. The line strained under the weight of the crown, but Malden brought it up quickly and soon held the crown in his hand. Or rather, the false crown. Slag had made it as well, out of lead coated in gilding metal. It looked very much like the real crown, and had been polished until it shone like gold, but under close scrutiny the cheapness of its manufacture was obvious. Malden had carried it with him throughout his sojourn into Hazoth's villa. He had known that Vry would show up at the last minute and seize the crown, so he made sure he had something to give the bailiff.

"You! Up there! Thief!" Anselm Vry shouted, peering up into the dome. "That's a funny jape you've made. Now give the damned thing back."

"Or what, Anselm? You'll have me killed?" Malden spoke at a normal conversational tone, but the dome amplified his voice until he was sure Vry could hear him. "If I give it back, will you let me live?"

"Give it back! Give it back! I like this one, it's not as heavy," Ommen cried.

Vry silenced him with another slap. "Thief, let's be reasonable. We both know I can't let you live. I can kill you now, though, quickly and almost painlessly. We can spare you the agony of torture and the embarrassment of being drawn and quartered in public. Surely you'd rather avoid that."

Malden laughed. "Perhaps you'd be willing to fight for it. Of course, that's not your style. All your men are outside. You even sent the priests away. You'd have to face me alone."

"That's not going to happen. I am curious to know, however, what you thought you could achieve here."

"I'm going to save my life, and Cutbill's as well."

"So you think you can escape," Vry said. "I suppose

it's possible. You could flee across the rooftops, while my men would have to push through the crowds to give chase. I'll grant you might make it as far as the city's walls. What would you do then? You're no landowner. Once outside the gates, you would become a simple villein. A peasant. Little more than a slave. You would save your life but lose your freedom. I know your type, thief. You don't want to spend the rest of your days laboring on a farm."

"Hardly. All right, Vry. I'll make you a deal. I think you'll find it a bargain." Malden swung the crown back out on the end of its line and started to lower it again. "I only wish to assuage my curiosity. Answer a few questions truthfully, and we'll end this."

Vry looked around him, as if to make sure no priests were hiding in the corners of the chapel, listening. "Very well."

Malden unreeled a bit of line. The crown descended a dozen feet, then stopped with a jerk. He must be careful, he thought, not to let the line snap. "You were Bikker's employer, weren't you? The theft of the crown was your idea from the beginning."

Vry's face clouded with rage. "I'll admit nothing under this duress, you—"

He stopped talking when Malden started reeling the line in again.

"Yes," Vry said, balling his fists in anger. "Yes, it was me."

Malden paid out a dozen more feet of line. "But not you alone. You formed a conspiracy of three to make this happen. I'm impressed, honestly. The chance of such a plot working out is inversely proportionate to how many people know of its existence. You did all this—you may still bring a city to its knees!—with only three people. You promised Hazoth safety for his services. You hired Bikker because as an Ancient Blade he was likely to notice there were more demons about than usual, and he might feel the need to stop you and Hazoth. When Croy returned to town you must have been very worried."

"Sir Croy? Indeed. The Ancient Blades don't have any

more demons to fight, so they wander the land righting wrongs and helping people." Vry sneered at the thought. "They're always poking their noses in where they don't belong, and since Croy technically outranks me in the peerage, I had to find a way to neutralize him. Juring always had a soft spot for that fool. It took real cunning on my part to have him banished—and then to force the Burgrave's hand on his return, to enforce the penalty of execution."

"And when that didn't work out—when Croy got away— you came up with another scheme. You played him like a fish on a line, pretending to do everything in your power to find the crown. But Croy is a simple man and he doesn't suspect treachery until it's proven to him. I myself was nearly fooled by your performance in Cutbill's lair. It seemed you really *wanted* to find the crown. Even when you sent your men to Hazoth's home and had them search the place—even when they left empty-handed, we both thought you were just an overly officious bureaucrat. That you were hampered by rules and laws, and thus ineffectual. You've played this game well. I wasn't entirely sure until I handed you the false crown last night. You acted as if it was talking to you— though we both know it was false. That was when I became certain. You didn't want the crown back. Even while you made a good show of looking for it, in fact you were making sure nobody could get to it."

"Very clever of you. Yes," Vry admitted. "You have the gist of it."

"I am still not certain why you did it, though," Malden said. He lowered the crown farther. "What benefit will come to you? When Ommen walks out there and makes a fool of himself before the entire city—the repercussions will be dire. The people will realize they're being ruled by a fool, and they won't stand for it. They'll riot in the streets— especially when you spur them on."

"No one likes being hoodwinked," Vry said when Malden paused. "The people of Ness have so much freedom, they love to gripe and grumble about the slightest stricture. If I show them their master is a half-wit, they'll refuse to obey even his just laws. And when the violence does not stop, when the gutters run red with blood, the king will know that the Burgrave is incapable of running the city. He will surely revoke the city's charter. Every man in Ness will lose his freedom."

Malden shrugged. "Every man who does not own property," he said, and let out more line. "Such as yourself." The crown was barely six feet above the head of the Burgrave now. "But the free men of Ness are its heart's blood. Their labor creates wealth. That was Juring Tarness's brilliant idea—and it worked. It worked for eight hundred years. Free men will work to make something of themselves. What do you stand to gain when they are enslaved?"

"Power, obviously." Anselm Vry reached up his hands to snatch at the crown. Malden jerked it away from him. Sighing deeply, Vry said, "You don't understand anything. When the charter is revoked, this city will be plunged into chaos. The only force for law and order inside the walls will be me, and my men of the watch. It will be up to us to keep the city from erupting into mutiny. And when we do—when we suppress revolt, and reestablish the king's rule here—how grateful do you think he'll be? He will need someone to rule the city then. Obviously, he will choose me."

"Thousands may die," Malden said. "Shops will shut down, entire guilds will go out of business. The city you inherit will be half dead."

"But it will be mine. To rule as I see fit—by fire and iron. No longer will I be constrained by the laws of the charter. No longer need I answer to the moothall and the guildmasters who control it. It will all be mine, and mine alone. The first year will be hard. There will be little money coming in and people will starve, yes. The second year they will pay me any price I ask for bread. They will accept much higher rates of taxation, in exchange for their lives. It's a long game I'm playing. But in the end I am guaranteed to win."

"I can see the appeal," Malden said. "And I salute you."

"Oh?"

"You're far more crooked than any thief I know. You have my respect. Very well. Here's what you wanted." With a flick of his wrist, Malden sent the crown dancing through the air to come to rest on Ommen's head. He cut the line that held it and collapsed his pole. "I wish you much joy of it."

And then he laughed.

"Watchmen! Priests! Get in here now," Vry shouted. Doors around the nave flew open and the summoned ones came flooding in.

Ommen Tarness straightened up, his posture improving instantly. "Hold," he said, and everyone froze. There was something in his voice that commanded attention—and imposed his will on every listener. "I have heard enough," he said.

Or rather, Juring Tarness said it.

# CHAPTER NINETY-EIGHT

Earlier—just at dawn—Gurrh the ogre had brought the leaden coffer to Swampwall, his home for so many years. He laid it down in the soft soil and then started bashing at it with his massive, hairy fists.

Eventually it came open. The true crown was inside, just as expected.

Malden had been there to see it emerge. Coruth the witch flew him through the air so he would not be late. He thanked Gurrh, who bowed deeply and then returned to his pipe. Then Malden approached the crown, his hands shaking it a little. He lifted it carefully and heard its voice begin to command him. Before he could be overcome, before it could make him put it on his own head, he shoved it into a burlap sack and slung it over his shoulder. Still, it continued to speak to him, made imprecations and promises and outright threats—until Malden explained to it what he had planned. Then at last, thankfully, the crown became quiet.

Later, when Malden drew the false crown to the dome of the chapel with Slag's fishing pole, it was a simple matter to switch it with the true crown—the crown he had lowered once more onto Ommen's head.

The transformation in the Burgrave was instantaneous. Juring Tarness resumed his control of his imbecilic descendant, and heard everything that was said within the chapel.

"You would depose me, Anselm?" Juring asked then. He looked down at the bailiff. Standing straight, he was many inches taller than his servant. "You would go to such lengths to take what is mine?"

"Milord," Vry said, bowing low. "This was a tale, only, a fabrication spun to appease the thief when—"

"No more lies," the Burgrave shouted. The priests and watchmen around him all drew back. Juring drew a jeweled dagger from his belt. It was one of his symbols of office, mostly for ornament's sake. The blade was kept sharp, though, to represent the keen insight the Burgrave brought to his office. "Kneel," he said.

Vry turned to face his watchmen. "The Burgrave is ensorcelled!" he cried. "Seize him—we must perform an exorcism at once. You, high priest, fetch the appropriate vestments and the holy thurible and—"

"I said, kneel," the Burgrave said again. Neither watchmen nor priests moved from where they stood.

Vry tried to run. The Burgrave grabbed the back of his cloak and pushed him to the ground. Then he grabbed the bailiff's hair and pulled his head back. "No more lies," he said again. Then he pried the man's jaw open and cut out his tongue.

Anselm Vry gasped and choked on his own blood. The noises he made were horrible. Even Malden flinched.

"Now," Juring Tarness said when it was done, "someone bring me a rag. I don't want this traitor's blood on my hands when I lead the joyous procession of Ladymas. You, watchman—take this fool away. Lock him in my dungeon. We'll give him a trial and see how well he speaks in his defense now. Then we'll find some way to execute him more horrible than any we've tried before. Maybe we'll force him to eat his own entrails. To swallow his own excrement, as it were."

The captain of the watchmen did as he was told, with a bow, a salute, and no words at all. The priests cleaned the Burgrave's hands and wiped off his dagger. While it was done, the Burgrave looked up into the dome.

"As for you, thief. Go and tell your master Cutbill that I would speak with him. Eventually. I have a long day ahead of me."

Malden supposed that it was too much to expect thanks. He climbed back out the window in the dome and hurried away across the rooftops of the Spires.

# CHAPTER NINETY-NINE

Coruth, her own arm fully healed now, muttered to herself as she mixed herbs together in a stone mortar, then ground them together with a copper pestle. She sang a little song as she painted the resulting foul concoction across Croy's broken ribs and the acid wounds on his arms. Whenever he tried to speak, she shushed him severely. Throughout it all, Cythera sat by his side, smiling, her face unbesmirched by sorcery. Her eyes glittered with mischief to see him almost naked in the bed, only his nethers hidden by a cloth.

If you had to lie abed for weeks and heal what should have been mortal injuries, Malden supposed you could pick few finer places to do it. Croy had been moved just across the Ladypark Common to the house of his friend, the rich merchant. There was no secrecy about the move, and had the Burgrave wished to seize Croy (for violating the terms of his banishment, if nothing else), little resistance would have been offered. Yet in the six days since Ladymas, no one showed up at the door with a writ of arrest.

It was possible that the Burgrave was only afraid this would displease Coruth. With Hazoth gone, the witch was now the most powerful user of magic in the Free City. Already old clients and new were showing up daily to ask if they might consult with her, but she refused all comers. She had much to do, she said, and once Croy was healed, there would be quite a reckoning of accounts. More than one powerful personage in the city had begun making discreet inquiries, looking to hire any magicians capable of deflecting curses.

When the witch finished her ministrations for the day, she went to the window and flew off as a flock of blackbirds again. No one knew where she went, and there was no way to follow her. Even Cythera could only shrug when asked. "Perhaps she goes to fetch medicinal herbs. Or maybe to spy on the city, and learn how it has changed in her absence. She has never kept counsel with me, even before Hazoth imprisoned her."

"Milady," Malden said, "you'll forgive me if I say you have a strange family."

Cythera smiled knowingly. "We can't all come from noble lineages full of great heroes and comely ladies," she said, glancing at Croy.

The knight was too busy to notice what she said. He was scrawling something on a parchment with a quill pen. "Here, Malden. Your prize. As promised."

The thief took the paper he offered and studied it. When Croy had first come to him, looking for his help in freeing Cythera and Coruth, Malden's first instinct had been to sweat the knight for gold. Then it occurred to him that Croy had something else in his possession, something of infinitely more use to him. The scrap of paper in his hand was what he had asked for in lieu of money. It was a grant of land, in the amount of one eighth part of an acre, in the northern part of the kingdom near the fortress of Helstrow. A very small piece of Croy's ancestral lands. It named Malden as its new owner.

"Is it a pleasant spot?" Malden asked now.

"A rocky field, completely useless for cultivation. It overlooks a dismal bog, and in the summer it is swarmed with flies. May you find much happiness there."

Malden laughed out loud, long and heartily. "Maybe I'll never see it. It matters not. Croy, for this—for everything. I thank you."

Cythera looked confused. "What would a thief want with a desolate patch of ground, not even large enough to put a house on?"

"Freedom," Malden said. "With this parchment, I am a man of property. It makes me a landowner—with the full rights thereunto pertaining. I can go anywhere now. I can leave the city walls and not be enslaved. Here in Ness I can go to the moothall whenever I choose, and stand before the masters of all the guilds, and demand my right to speak. I could even go to Helstrow and request an audience with the king."

"Do you want to do any of those things?"

"No!" Malden laughed. "None of them. But the power to do them—the right to do them—means I am no more a prisoner in the place where I was born. It means I'm free! I imagine you can appreciate that."

"Oh, yes," Cythera said, her eyes far away.

Malden kissed the paper. "My heart's desire. One of them, anyway."

Cythera favored him with a warning smile. Then she looked down at Croy's scarred leg. "You should rest," she told the knight. "Mother says if you don't sleep twice as much as normal, the treatments will be inefficacious."

"You are my lady, and I obey your command," the knight said. He closed his eyes and in moments began to snore.

Malden shook his head. "Like an infant, he sleeps."

"He believes that he has done a man's work," Cythera whispered. "He sleeps like the just. Come with me, Malden. I wish to speak with you."

The two of them headed out onto the room's balcony. It looked out over the remains of Hazoth's villa. There wasn't much left but a pile of ashes and a few scraps of useless lumber—the people of Ness had taken away everything of value, and their definition of value was quite broad.

"Tell me," Cythera said when they were alone, "what reward has Kemper claimed?"

"I had Slag make him a new deck of cards," Malden said.

She frowned. "But with his curse—the only way he could even hold the old deck was because it was so immured with his own essence. He had possessed those cards so long they had become parcel with his being."

Malden nodded. "Aye. So the new deck had to be special. They're made out of pure silver, beaten thin and etched with vitriol for the pips. They're probably worth more than most of the stakes he plays for, but he can hold them easily, and even slip them up his sleeves or down his tunic."

Cythera smiled. "And Gurrh, the ogre? What price did he charge you?"

"None at all. He wished only to serve the Burgrave. If every man had the nobility of that ogre in his heart, we would all live in Croy's world."

Cythera leaned out over the balcony. "Then it seems we all have been repaid for our trouble, and each of us came out of this nightmare better than when we began, and all unscathed."

"All but one," Malden said, his brow furrowing. "I did something, Cythera, that I am not proud of. I took away a man's freedom. It's the greatest sin I know."

"You mean Ommen Tarness?" she asked. "He was a simpleton. And anyway—you saved his life. Had he appeared before the procession in his natural state, Vry would have had him killed afterward."

"I know," Malden said. That wasn't the point, though. In the last moments before the crown was returned, Ommen had said something that struck Malden to the core. He was getting smarter, he claimed. The imbecility was wearing off. He had not been born mindless—only the crown stole his wits, and without it he was becoming himself again.

And he had stopped that process before it could properly begin.

But that was his burden to bear. He decided not to share it with Cythera.

After all, there was one other thing to discuss.

"Come away with me," he said without warning.

She turned around very fast as he put an arm around her waist. He leaned forward and kissed her. Hard.

"I don't have to stay here anymore," he said. "I can travel the world. Come with me, and be my wife."

Cythera glanced into the room, toward where Croy lay in bed.

"Forget him. You broke off your betrothal already."

"Not in so many words."

Malden grimaced. "I was the one who freed your mother. Not him."

"And you think that means I must marry you now?" she asked. "That's how the stories end, isn't it? The hero slays the dragon, and the damsel throws herself into his embrace. Who lives in old stories now, Malden? Isn't that something you always despised about Croy? This is the real world."

"And here, now, I love you," he told her.

She closed her eyes and breathed deeply, and for a moment he thought she would say it in return. Then she leaned her head against his chest. "Malden, you're a thief. A man of property now, but still—a thief. You must understand—you have to understand—that people in the real world do what they must to survive. To make their lives better."

"And that means you will stay with him," Malden said.

"You have a strip of land unfit for human habitation. He has a castle. Servants and retainers. A title. My children will have all those things, too. Do you understand why that matters? Look at my life. Look what my parents gave me. Can you accept that I would do anything not to pass on that inheritance?"

Malden let her go. He strode to the far end of the balcony and looked uphill, toward the palace. All around him the city lay in its unalterable tiers, with the poorest people at the bottom and the rich up top. So it would ever be.

She started to go back inside, to the sickroom. He stopped her by calling her name.

"Do you love him?" he asked.

"What a silly question," she said, and then went inside.

# CHAPTER ONE HUNDRED

Cutbill made a single notation in his ledger, then crossed out two lines. "There," he said. "You are now a journeyman in the guild, with all rights and privileges of that rank." He glanced over the edge of his book at Malden. "There is, of course, the question of the money you owe Slag. And I expect you to start earning right away, to keep my good favor."

And that was it. No thanks, no reward. Fair enough, Malden thought. He'd expected nothing more from Cutbill. He had caused a great deal of trouble for the man, but now he'd repaired the damage. They were even.

And he was in the guild. Croy's deed had made him a man of property, and now he was a man of profession. He could start earning money for himself, having ransomed his place in Cutbill's organization. He was beholden to no one, his own master. He was truly free.

"You may go," Cutbill said. Then he held up one hand, rescinding that. He looked to one corner of the room, where a tapestry was shimmying as if blown by a wind Malden did not feel. "Wait. Use that door, over there."

Malden looked at the indicated door and frowned a question, but Cutbill offered no explanation. Malden stepped through the door and closed it behind him. Beyond lay the spy room, where one could observe what happened inside Cutbill's office without being seen.

Malden bent his eye to the spy hole and watched as a tall man wrapped in a plain brown cloak walked over to Cutbill's desk. The newcomer sat down behind the desk as if he owned the place, then pulled back his hood.

It was the Burgrave. He wore his golden crown and his eyes were very sharp. What was he doing there, unaccompanied?

"Milord," Cutbill said.

The Burgrave was silent for a while. Then he said, "It seems I am once again in your debt. I don't like owing you things, thief."

"Then allow me to say that the debt is all mine," Cutbill responded. "You permit me to exist, and to carry out my operations. If those operations are occasionally to your benefit, I consider it my honor to serve so great a man."

"Honeyed words never sound right in your mouth." The Burgrave got up from the desk and stormed around the room. "I never doubted Anselm Vry. I always thought he was a clerk, and nothing more. Someone gifted with moving numbers around on a page, but wholly incapable of treachery."

"You make him sound like me, milord," Cutbill suggested. He continued to work at his notations.

"Hardly. You—I've never trusted you. But you saved me from a rather unpleasant fate, and you'll have a reward."

"Many thanks. Tell me, milord, have you decided what to do with the two heroes of the day? I speak of Sir Croy and of Malden."

The Burgrave shrugged. "Croy proved his loyalty well enough. I don't suppose I'll make an issue of him. I'll leave his banishment intact but not enforce it. That way, if he crosses me again I'll have legal standing to hang him. Who is Malden?"

In the spy room, Malden cringed. He rather wished Cutbill hadn't used his name at all—it could only lead to trouble.

"The thief who stole the crown. And returned it. One of mine, though he was not acting under my orders in the first instance."

"Oh," the Burgrave said. "Well, he'll have to be killed, of course."

Malden nearly cried out.

"He knows my secret. I can't have that."

"Indeed." Cutbill made another notation. "Understandable. Though . . ."

"What is it?"

Cutbill looked up from his ledger. "You said you would grant me a reward."

"Yes, yes. Gold, jewels, what will you have? It can't be anything official, of course. Nothing on paper."

"Malden's life. Spare it."

Malden's jaw fell open.

"Oh, come now! What do you care about one thief? You have dozens. Many more circumspect ones, at that. This one nearly got you killed."

"But he didn't. He proved far cleverer than he should have been."

The Burgrave let out a curt laugh. "Enough reason I'd think you'd want him dead. Don't tell me you're getting sentimental, Cutbill. I admit, I'd like to let him live myself, but reality is often unfair. You know that all too well."

"Do not mistake me. I don't ask out of a sense of justice. I have none. I ask because he could be an excellent earner, if I keep him under my thumb. He could make me quite a bit of money in the long run."

The Burgrave studied Cutbill shrewdly. "You'll keep him quiet?"

"I'll sew his mouth shut if he threatens to speak out of turn."

"Very well, then." Then the Burgrave left the room, shaking his head in disbelief. He headed through the door that led back up to the Stink.

When he was gone, Malden stepped out of the spy room.

"I don't know what to say," he said, staring at Cutbill in gratitude.

"Say only that I won't regret this," Cutbill told him. "Now. You may go. Don't come back until you have some money for me."

Malden nodded and headed out, into the city that was his home.

If you enjoyed DEN OF THIEVES,
don't miss the next adventures
by
DAVID CHANDLER
available now
wherever books are sold

# A THIEF IN THE NIGHT

# HONOR AMONG THIEVES

# A THIEF IN THE NIGHT

## PROLOGUE

In a place of stone walls, attended by his acolytes and warriors, the Hieromagus knelt in the dawn rays of the red subterranean sun. Both sorcerer and priest, he wore a simple garment decorated with jangling bells. The sound of them was meant to draw him back to the real world, to the present, but for now he silenced them. For now, he needed to remember.

The ancestors spoke to him. For those long lost, forgetting was a kind of death. They pulled desperately at him, trying to draw him into memories of ancient forests, of a time before the first humans came to this continent. Before his people were destroyed, driven away, forgotten. He saw their great battles, saw the works of magic they created. Saw the small, tender moments they shared and the guilt and shame they tried to put behind them. He saw kings, and queens, and simple folk in well-patched clothing. He saw Aethlinga, who had been a queen—the seventy-ninth of her dynasty—but who had become something more. A seer. A diviner. Back then, in the depths of time, she had become the first Hieromagus. Just as he was to be the last.

His body twitched, his eyelids in constant motion as if he were dreaming. A serving girl mopped his forehead with a piece of sponge. He tried to wave her away, but lost in reverie as he could only raise a few fingers a fraction of an inch.

*"I came as soon as I saw the sails. I knew you would want to see this with your own eyes," the hunter said. Together the two of them climbed to the top of a forested ridge that overlooked the southern sea. One tree, an ancient*

*rowan, stood taller than the rest. Aethlinga was old and frail but still she climbed the branches for a better look.*

*Out at sea the ships stood motionless on the curling waves, their sails furled now, their railings thick with refugees. Less desperate than they might have been. They had reached their destination. Down on the shore boats were landing, long, narrow wooden boats crammed with men. Hairy, unwashed, their lips cracked and cratered with scurvy. Their faces gaunt and grim after their long voyage.*

*Iron weapons in their hands.*

"What are they?" the hunter asked. "They look a bit like ogres, but . . . what are they? What do they want?"

The Hieromagus's lips moved, eight hundred years further on. "They want land. A place to make a new start. What are they? They are our death."

It was very difficult to tell, inside the memory, where the Hieromagus ended and Aethlinga began. He had seen this particular vision so many times. Remembered it, for simply to recall was a sacred rite. This was the history of his people. The thing that could never be forgotten.

*Later, when the first skirmish was over and the men from the boats lay bleeding and cold on the sand—but others on the ships still stood out on the waves, watching—Aethlinga went to a private grove deep in the forest. A place where the ancestors wove through the tree branches, whispering always. She had her own sacred memories to recall.*

*But now she turned her face to a pool of water, a simple looking glass. She looked into her own eyes. Formed her own memory.* "I know you will see this," *she said, and she spoke a name.*

She spoke the true and secret name of the last Hieromagus. This memory was for him.

"I need you to remember. Not the past this time, but the future. Look forward and find what is to come. I have glimpsed it as well, and you know I would not ask this, were it not utterly necessary."

The body of the Hieromagus, so far away now, convulsed

and shook. The serving girl drew back in fear that he would lash out and destroy her. It had happened before.

Some memories were less pleasant than others, and this was the worst of all.

Except—this one was not a memory at all. Instead it was foresight. For one like the Hieromagus, who saw past and future all at once, the distinction had little meaning.

Looking forward he saw the knight. He saw the painted woman. He saw the thief. As he had so many times before. Always before he could put their images out of his head. Tell himself it would be many years before they arrived.

Now they crowded in on him as if they were shouting in his ears. He could no longer push them back, nor did he seek to. He only endeavored to separate them, to let them each speak in turn.

*"Some demons are smaller than others," the woman said, and it was her, though the images were gone from her skin she was the same one, and then a twisted hand crashed across her cheek, knocking her to the ground.*

Her, the Hieromagus thought—her—it was the one he sought, but in the wrong time—she was cut loose from him still, but so close, so—

*A man with the features of a priest, but the eyes of a murderer. This one only smiled, and did not speak. This one showed only the teeth of a predatory animal.*

He dared not look on that one too long, even in memory.

*Two knights with the same name, one dissembling, not a knight at all. He was something else entirely, something hated, and yet he was the key to liberation. A draft of burdock root, certain oils most precious, blisswine. An elfin queen throwing herself across a bed in the attitude of a whore.*

Closer now—closer, but fragmented. The Hieromagus beat feebly at the floor with his fists, trying to force the memories—the forebodings—into proper shape. Into an order he could understand. He must see the path. He must choose for his people.

*Three swords, deadly swords. Something worse, some-*

*thing far worse, a weapon of incredible potential. Two men pushing a barrel up an incline of stone.*

Yes. Yes, he had it—

*A flash of light. A burst of energy, searing and brilliant. Molten stone flowing down a corridor.*

There, that was the future he sought. The one he'd glimpsed so many times, only to turn away in fear. The one he'd convinced himself was still a long way off.

This time he must watch the images all the way through. See it all.

*"Malden!" the painted woman called out to her lover, desperate, watching him walk toward utter and certain death. The sword in his hand would be of no help.*

So close now. After so long. So many years of dreading what was to come. Of trying desperately to find a way to forestall it. When it could never be prevented.

*The human knight leaned down over them, his face warped by hatred. Spittle flew from his lips as he barked at the bronze-clad warriors. "You're going to die. Every last one of you will die! It's less than what you deserve for what you did to Cythera!"*

The hatred—the death that was coming—the tumult—

*"He knew," the painted woman said. Her voice thick with loss, with dread at the sacrifices that had been made. "The Hieromagus had seen the future. He saw this, all of this. He knew that what he'd seen could not be changed. That this was the only way for his people to survive."*

The eyes of the Hieromagus opened like window shutters being thrown back.

"No!" he screamed.

No.

*He saw the dead laid out in heaps before him. He saw himself, the Hieromagus saw through his own eyes, crawling over a pile of bodies, his feet treading on the faces of the ones he loved.*

No . . . not like that. It couldn't come to that, to so drastic a turn. And yet . . .

It would. It must.

The painted woman was correct. What was foreseen

could not be changed. And there was only one way forward, now. No turning, no detour was possible, though the way was choked with death and destruction.

He opened his mouth to speak. It was hard, so very hard to get the words out. He felt so very far away.

"They're coming," he said, and the warriors and acolytes stirred, traded terrified glances. Grasped hands in hope. "Very soon now, they will return for us."

Much muttering, much grave discussion followed in that place where the underground sun burned red. Yet the Hieromagus heard none of it, for his memory was not yet done. There was more to see.

*Back in the sacred grove, Aethlinga watched the visions with him. Her face, so slender and beautiful, was deformed by fear and the sorrow for what was to come. For what was to come to him.*

*"Be strong," she said. "I know what we ask of you. There is no justice in it—but you were born to perform this task. This bitter cup is yours to sip alone. I am sorry."*

# CHAPTER ONE

A thin crescent of moon lit up the rooftops of the Free City of Ness, glinting on the bells up high in the Spires, whitewashing the thatched roofs of the Stink. The furnaces of the blacksmiths in the Smoke roared all night, but the rest of the city was asleep—or at least tucked away in candle-lit rooms with closed shutters.

It was the time of night when even the gambling houses started to close down, when the brothels shut their doors. It was the time when honest men and women retreated to their beds, to get the sleep they needed for another long day of work on the morrow. Of all the city's vast workforce, only a handful remained at their labors. The city's watchmen, of course, patrolled the streets all night long.

And, of course, there were thieves about.

Malden moved quickly, running along the ridges of the rooftops, hurrying to make a clandestine appointment. He made as little noise as a squirrel dashing along, and he was careful not to let himself be seen from the street level. For all that he made excellent time as he leapt from one rooftop to another, following routes he'd learned through years of practice, knowing without needing to look where he should put his feet, and where a roof had grown too soft to take his weight. He danced among the Spires, swinging from stone carvings, launching himself across narrow alleys. His route led him around the broad open space of Market Square, then downhill across the tops of the mansions in the Golden Slope. He was very close to his destination when, through the sole of his leather shoe, he felt a shingle crack and start to fall away.

Malden froze instantly in place, careful to keep his weight on the broken shingle as the rest of his body swayed with momentum. He checked himself, then bent low, his fingers grabbing at the broken shingle before it could fall into the street below and make a noise. Very carefully, he laid the pieces of the shingle in a downspout, then dashed forward again. It was very nearly midnight.

He reached his destination and clung to a smoking chimney pot, his body low against the shingles to minimize his silhouette. He had arrived. His eyes, well adapted to the dark, scanned the sides of the houses around him, looking for any sign of movement. He spied a rat scuttering through an alley twenty feet below. He saw bats circling a church belfry two blocks away. And then he found what he was looking for.

Across the street three men dressed in black were climbing a drainpipe on the side of a half-timbered mansion. When the one on top reached a mullioned window on the second floor, he wrapped his hand in a rag and then punched in the glass.

It made enough noise to scare cats in the alley below. Malden winced in sympathy. Had he ever been that noisy? He knew, from long experience, what the three thieves must be feeling. The blood would be pounding in their veins. Their heartbeats would be the loudest sounds they could hear. The thing they were about to do could get them all hanged, following the barest formality of a trial.

The one on top—the leader, he must be—reached inside the window and slipped open its catch. He opened the casements wide, then disappeared into the dark house. The other two followed close on his heels.

Malden shifted his position carefully, to make sure his legs wouldn't cramp while he waited. He had to give them time to do the job right. He watched as a light appeared in the next window over, then as it moved, bobbing and darting, through the house. The thieves took their time about their work, perhaps because they wanted to make sure to get everything.

Grunting with impatience, Malden wished they would hurry up. Down in the street a man of the watch was coming this way. He wore a cloak woven with a pattern of eyes, and carried a lantern held high on the end of his polearm. The watchman barely glanced at the houses on either side of him, but if he should catch sight of that candle moving stealthily through an otherwise dark house, he might grow suspicious.

Malden would have been smart enough to bring a dark lantern with a shield over its light, and shone its beam only when absolutely necessary. Of course, Malden would have been in and out of the house already. And he wouldn't have required two accomplices to burgle a house that size.

The thieves were lucky—the watchman saw nothing. He walked on past without so much as a glance at the mansion. When he was sure the man was out of earshot, Malden carefully stood up, then took a few steps backward to get a running start. With one quick bound he leapt across the alley and onto the roof of the darkened mansion.

The thieves were on the ground floor. Most like, they heard nothing as Malden landed, as soft as a pigeon settling on the roof. He lowered himself over the edge and placed his feet carefully on the open windowsill, then slid inside, as easy as that.

He took a moment to glance around him and study his new surroundings. He was in a bedroom, perhaps the chamber of the master of the house. The bed had a brocade canopy hung above it to keep insects from pestering its occupants. The floor was strewn with rushes scented with a faint perfume. Against one wall stood a pair of wooden chairs and a washbasin. Underneath the bed Malden found a dry chamber pot.

Malden could hear the thieves moving about on the ground floor. How smart were they, he wondered? He needed to make a judgment. If they were at all clever, they would leave the same way they came. Leave as little sign of forced entry as they could. If they were fools they would exit by the kitchen door on the ground floor. An easier method of escape, perhaps, but it would put them in full view of the windows of four other houses—and thus, potentially, any number of eyewitnesses.

No, Malden thought. This bunch wouldn't be that stupid. Cutbill—the master of the guild of thieves in Ness, and Malden's master—kept his eye open always for real talent in the criminal professions. Cutbill had singled these men out, of all the freelance thieves in the City, as Malden's next assignment. And Cutbill never sent Malden on such a mission if he didn't have good reason.

So they would leave through the upstairs window. Which meant Malden had to wait a little longer. He swept his cloak back to uncover the bodkin in its sheath at his hip. Then he reached into a long wooden case he kept strapped to his thigh and drew out three slender darts. He was very, very careful not to touch their tips.

"Make haste, make haste," one of the thieves hissed from the stairs. Another grumbled out some profanity. There was the old familiar clink of metal objects bouncing in a sack. And then the first of them stepped into the bedroom, eyes peeled, watching the shadows just in case.

He did not think to look down, and so he stepped right

into the chamber pot, which Malden had placed before the doorway.

"Son of a whore," the thief howled, as he tripped forward into the room and went sprawling past Malden where he lay on the bed. The other two rushed into the room after their fellow. One held the candle high, while the other had a wicked long knife in his hand. All three of them held bulging sacks.

"What is it?" the one with the candle demanded. His face was yellow in the guttering light and his eyes were very shiny. The one with the knife was quicker, and spied Malden even as he sat up in the bed.

"We're tumbled!" he cried, and rushed forward with the knife.

Malden flicked his wrist and a dart went into the knifesman's chest, just above his heart. As the candle holder turned to look, Malden pitched his second dart and caught him in the neck.

The one who had stumbled on the chamber pot managed to get back to his feet just as Malden readied his third dart. The thief began to cry out in fear just as Malden made his cast. The dart hit him in the tongue and he went silent.

The three thieves turned to look at one another, knowing the jig was up. One by one their faces fell. And then they slumped to the floorboards with a treble thump.

When he was sure they were all down, Malden stepped out of the bed and went to look in their sacks, to see what shiny presents they'd brought him.

# HONOR AMONG THIEVES

## PROLOGUE

The Free City of Ness was known around the world as a hotbed of thievery, and one man alone was responsible for that reputation. Cutbill, master of that city's guild of thieves, controlled almost every aspect of clandestine commerce within its walls—from extortion to pickpocketing, from blackmail to shoplifting he oversaw a great empire of crime. His fingers were in far more pies than anyone even realized, and his ambitions far greater than simple acquisition of wealth—and far broader-reaching than the affairs of just one city. His interests lay in every corner of the globe and his spies were everywhere.

As a result he received a fair volume of mail every day.

In his office under the streets of Ness he went through this pile of correspondence with the aid of only one assistant. Lockjaw, an elderly thief with a legendary reputation was always there when Cutbill opened his letters. There were two reasons why Lockjaw held this privileged responsibility—for one, Lockjaw was famous for his discretion. He'd received his sobriquet for the fact he never revealed a secret. The other reason was that he'd never learned to read.

It was Lockjaw's duty to receive the correspondence, usually from messengers who stuck around only long enough to get paid, and to comment on each message as Cutbill told him its contents. If Lockjaw wondered why such a clever man wanted his untutored opinion, he never asked.

"Interesting," Cutbill said, holding a piece of parchment up to the light. "This is from the dwarven kingdom. It seems they've invented a new machine up there. Some kind of winepress that churns out books instead of vintage."

The old thief scowled. "That right? Do they come out soaking wet?"

"I imagine that would be a defect in the process," Cutbill agreed. "Still. If it works, it could produce books at a fraction of the cost a copyist charges now."

"Bad news, then," Lockjaw said.

"Oh?"

"Books is expensive," the thief explained. "There's good money in stealing 'em. If they go cheap all of a sudden we'd be out of a profitable racket."

Cutbill nodded and put the letter aside, taking up another. "It'll probably come to nothing, this book press." He slit open the letter in his hand with a knife and scanned its contents. "News from our friend in the north. It looks like Maelfing will be at war with Skilfing by next summer. Over fishing rights, of course."

"That lot in the northern kingdoms is always fighting about something," Lockjaw pointed out. "You'd figure they'd have sorted everything out by now."

"The king of Skrae certainly hopes they never do," Cutbill told him. "As long as they keep at each other's throats, our northern border will remain secure. Pass me that packet, will you?"

The letter in question was written on a scroll of vellum wrapped in thin leather. Cutbill broke its seal and spread it out across his desk, peering at it from only a few inches away. "This is from our man in the high pass of the Whitewall Mountains."

"What could possibly happen in a desolated place like that?" Lockjaw asked.

"Nothing, nothing at all," Cutbill said. He looked up at the thief. "I pay my man there to make sure it stays that way. He read some more, and opened his mouth to make another comment—and then closed it again, his teeth clicking together. "Oh," he said.

Lockjaw held his peace and waited to hear what Cutbill had found.

The master of the guild of thieves, however, was unforthcoming. He rolled the scroll back up and shoved the whole thing in a charcoal brazier used to keep the office warm. Soon the scroll had caught flame and in a moment it was nothing but ashes.

Lockjaw raised an eyebrow, but said nothing.

Whatever was on that scroll clearly wasn't meant to be shared, even with Cutbill's most trusted associate. Which meant it had to be pretty important, Lockjaw figured. More so than who was stealing from whom or where the bodies were buried.

Cutbill went over to his ledger—the master account of all his dealings, and one of the most secret books on the continent. It contained every detail of all the crime that took place in Ness, as well as many things no one had ever heard of outside of this room. He opened it to a page near the back, then laid his knife across one of the pages, perhaps to keep it from fluttering out of place. Lockjaw noticed that this page was different from the others. Those were filled with columns of neat figures, endless rows of numbers. This page only held a single block of text, like a short message.

"Old man," Cutbill said, then, "could you do me a favor and pour me a cup of wine? My throat feels suddenly raw."

Cutbill had never asked for such a thing before. The man had enough enemies in the world that he made a point of always pouring his own wine—or having someone taste it before him. Lockjaw wondered what had changed, but he shrugged and did as he was told. He was getting paid for his time. He went to a table over by the door and poured a generous cup, then turned around again to hand it to his boss.

Except Cutbill wasn't there anymore.

That in itself wasn't so surprising. There were dozens of secret passages in Cutbill's lair, and only the guildmaster knew them all or where they led. Nor was it surprising that Cutbill would leave the room so abruptly. Cautious to a nicety, he always kept his movements secret.

No, what was surprising was that he didn't come back.

He had effectively vanished from the face of the world.

Day after day Lockjaw—and the rest of Ness's thieves—

waited for his return. No sign of him was found, nor any message received. Cutbill's operation began to falter in his absence—thieves stopped paying their dues to the guild, citizens under Cutbill's protection were suddenly vulnerable to theft, what coin did come in piled up uncounted and was spent on frivolous expenditures. Half of these excesses were committed in the belief that Cutbill, who had always run a tight ship, would be so offended he would have to come back just to put things in order.

But Cutbill left no trace, wherever he'd traveled.

It was quite a while before anyone thought to check the ledger, and the message Cutbill had so carefully marked.

# CHAPTER ONE

On the far side of the Whitewall mountains, in the grasslands of the barbarians, in the mead tent of the Great Chieftain, fires raged and drink was passed from hand to hand, yet not a word was spoken. The gathered housemen of the Great Chieftain were too busy to gossip and sing as was their wont, too busy watching two men compete at an ancient ritual. Massive they were, as big as bears, and their muscles stood out from their arms and legs like the wood of dryland trees. They stood either side of a pit of blazing coals, each clutching hard to one end of a panther's hide. On one side, Torki, the champion of the Great Chieftain, victor of a thousand such contests. On the other side stood Mörget, whose lips were pulled back in a manic grin, the lower half of his face painted red in the traditional colors of a berserker, though he was a full chieftain now, leader of many clans.

Heaving, straining, gasping for breath in the fumes of the coals, the two struggled, each trying to pull the other into the coals. Every man and woman in the longhouse, every berserker and reaver of the Great Chieftain, every wife and thrall of the gathered warriors, watched in hushed expectation, each of them alone with their private thoughts, their desperate hopes.

There was only one who dared to speak freely, for such was always his right. Hurlind, the Great Chieftain's scold, was full of wine and laughter. "You're slipping, Mörg's Get! Pull as you might, he's dragging you. Why not let go, and save yourself from the fire? This is not a game for striplings!"

"Silence," Mörget hissed, from between clenched teeth.

Yet his grin was faltering, for it was true. Torki's grasp on the panther hide was like the grip of great tree roots on the earth. His arms were locked at the elbows and with the full power of his body, trained and toughened by the hard life of the steppes, he was pulling as inexorably as the ocean tide. Mörget slid toward the coals a fraction of an inch at a time, no matter how he dug his toes into the grit on the floor.

At the mead bench closest to the fire a reaver of the Great Chieftain placed a sack of gold on the table and nudged his neighbor, a chieftain of great honor. He pointed at Torki and the chieftain nodded, then put his own money next to the reaver's—though as he did so he glanced slyly at the Great Chieftain in his place of honor at the far end of the table. Perhaps he worried that his overlord might take it askance—after all, Mörget was the Great Chieftain's son.

The Great Chieftain did not see the wager, however. His eyes never moved from the contest. Mörg, the man who had made a nation of these people, the man who had seen every land in the world and plundered every coast, father of multitudes, slayer of dragons, Mörg the Great was ancient by the reckoning of the east. Forty-five winters had ground at his bones. Only a little silver ran through the gold of his wild beard, however, and no sign of dotage showed in his glinting eyes. He reached without looking for a haunch of roasted meat. Tearing a generous piece free, he held it down toward the mangy dog at his feet. The dog always ate first. It roused itself from sleep just long enough to swallow the gobbet. When it was done, Mörg fed himself, grease slicking down his chin and the front of his fur robes.

A great deal relied on which combatant let go of the hide first. The destiny of the entire eastern people, the lives of countless warriors were at stake—and a debt of honor nearly two centuries old. No onlooker could have said which of the warriors, his son or his champion, Mörg favored.

Torki never made a sound. He did not appear to move at all—he might have been a marble statue. He had the marks of a reaver, black crosses tattooed on the shaved skin behind his ears. One for every season of pillaging he'd undertaken in the hills to the north. Enough crosses that they ran down the back of his neck. Not a drop of sweat had showed yet on his brow.

Mörget shifted his stance a hair's breadth and was nearly pulled into the fire. His teeth gnashed at the air as he fought to regain his posture.

Nearby, his sister, herself a chieftess of many clans, stood ready with a flagon of wine mulled with sweet ale. Mörgain, as was widely known, hated her brother—had done since infancy. No matter how hard she fought to prove herself, no matter what glory she won in battle, Mörget had always overshadowed her accomplishments. Letting him win this contest now would be bitter as ashes in her mouth. Nor did she need to play the passive spectator here. She could end it in a moment by splashing wine across the boards at Mörget's feet. He would be unable to hold his ground on the slippery boards, and Torki would win for a certainty.

"Sister," Mörget howled, "set down that wine. Do you not thirst for western blood, instead?"

Mörg raised one eyebrow, perhaps very much interested in learning the answer to that question.

The chieftess laughed bitterly, and spat between Mörget's feet. But then she hurled her flagon at the wall, where it burst harmlessly, well clear of the contest. "I've tasted blood. I'd rather have the westerners alive, as my thralls."

"And you shall, as many of them as you desire," Mörget told her, his words bitten off before they left his mouth.

"And steel? Will you give me dwarven steel, better than the iron my warriors wear now?"

"All that they can carry! Now, aid me!"

"I shall," Mörgain said. "I'll pray for your success!"

That was enough to break the general silence, though only long enough for the gathered warriors to laugh up-roariously and slap each other on the back. The shadow of a smile even crossed Torki's lips. In the east the clans had a saying: *pray with your back turned, so that at least your enemies won't see your weakness*. The clans worshipped only Death, and beseeching Her aid was rarely a good idea.

"Did you hear that, Torki?" Hurlind the scold asked. "The Mother of us all pulls against you now. Better redouble your grip!"

The champion's lips split open to show his teeth. It was the first sign of emotion he'd given since the contest began.

And yet it was like some witch's spell had been broken. Perhaps Death—or some darker fate—did smile on Mörget then. For suddenly his arms flexed as if he'd found some strength he'd forgotten he had. He leaned back, putting his weight into the pull.

Torki's smile melted all at once. His left foot shifted an inch on the boards. It was not necessarily a fatal slip. Given a moment's grace he could have recovered, locking his knees and reinforcing his strength.

Yet Mörget did not give him that moment. Everyone knew that Mörget, for all his size and strength, was faster than a wildcat. He seized the opportunity and hauled Torki toward him until the balance was broken and the champion toppled, sprawling face first on the coals. Torki screamed as the fire bit into his skin.

# LEGENDS OF THE RIFTWAR

## HONORED ENEMY ▶ 978-0-06-079284-8

by Raymond E. Feist & William R. Forstchen

In the frozen northlands of the embattled realm of Midkemia, Dennis Hartraft's Marauders must band together with their bitter enemy, the Tsurani, to battle *moredhel*, a migrating horde of deadly dark elves.

## MURDER IN LAMUT ▶ 978-0-06-079291-6

by Raymond E. Feist & Joel Rosenberg

For twenty years the mercenaries Durine, Kethol, and Pirojil have fought other people's battles, defeating numerous deadly enemies. Now the Three Swords find themselves trapped by a winter's storm inside a castle teeming with ambitious, plotting lords and ladies, and it falls on the mercenaries to solve a series of cold-blooded murders.

## JIMMY THE HAND ▶ 978-0-06-079299-2

by Raymond E. Feist & S.M. Stirling

Forced to flee the only home he's ever known, Jimmy the Hand, boy thief of Krondor finds himself among the rural villagers of Land's End. But Land's End is home to a dark, dangerous presence even the local smugglers don't recognize. And suddenly Jimmy's youthful bravado is leading him into the maw of chaos . . . and, quite possibly, his doom.